MARY BERRY
Desserts

MARY BERRY

Desserts

Created and Produced by
CARROLL & BROWN LTD
20 Lonsdale Road
London NW6 6RD

CARROLL & BROWN LTD
Editorial Director Jeni Wright
Art Director Denise Brown
Designers Wendy Rogers, Sally Powell, Joanna Pocock
Cover Designer Nadine Kruger

First published as *Mary Berry's Desserts and Confections*
in Great Britain in 1991 by Dorling Kindersley Limited
80 Strand, London WC2R 0RL
Penguin Group (UK)

This edition published in 2013
First published as *Mary Berry Desserts* in 2008

A CIP catalogue record for this book is available from the British Library

ISBN 978-1-4093-3867-3

Reproduced by Colourscan, Singapore
Printed and bound by Hung Hing, China

LONDON, NEW YORK,
MELBOURNE, MUNICH AND DELHI
www.dk.com

CONTENTS

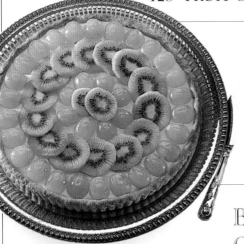

FOREWORD

What's for pudding? A question so often in our minds. This is a collection of good-looking, good-tasting recipes that I hope will answer just that question.

Whether you are planning a grand finale to a special meal, seeking new ways to serve old family favourites, choosing for a coffee morning or bridge tea, or wanting to tempt the young with snacks when they come home from school, in this book you will find a wide range of fabulous choices.

Included in my collection are wonderful variations on perennials like Lemon Meringue Pie, Apple Pie, Brandy Snaps and Crêpes Suzette, or if you are interested in mastering the classics like Apple Strudel and Crème Brûlée, you will discover how easy they are to prepare using the recipes in this book. However, if simple dishes are your choice, try a Peach, Raspberry or Kiwi Fruit Fool or Cherries en Gelée. If, like me, you delight in hearing 'Mmm!' and 'Ooh!' as you serve dessert, Chocolate Truffle Cake and Swiss Chocolate Torte won't disappoint, and I will guarantee that the Swan Cream Puffs and Meringue Mushrooms will please children from six to ninety-six.

I happen to believe that desserts can be good for you as well as just plain good. They can add heartiness to a light menu and lighten a substantial one. Desserts can supply nutritional foods, such as milk, fruit or grain products, which may be missing from the rest of the day's meals. Even if you, or members of your family, are watching your waistlines, you can enjoy desserts in thinner slices or smaller servings, and still conform to healthy eating guidelines.

Full-colour photographs of every recipe show you what to expect, and step-by-step instructions, many of them illustrated, guide you through each technique in preparation. To make great desserts more glorious, there are dozens of garnishes, decorations and serving tips to help you make every dish as pleasing to the eye as it is to the palate.

All the hard work that the designers and editors at Carroll & Brown have expended on my behalf shows clearly in this book. A *very* special 'thank you' goes to Jeni Wright, the project editor, who spent many hours working with me on perfecting the collection. All that remains is for me to wish you 'Bon Appétit', with the hope that this dessert collection gives you as much pleasure to prepare and enjoy, as it did for me to put it together.

Mary Berry

SPECIAL DESSERTS

SPECIAL DESSERTS

In this chapter are desserts that call for a show-off setting – your prettiest glass bowls to reveal textures, and dainty china plates and dishes to enhance colours. Mousses, soufflés, custards and creams are generally soft and smooth, easy to serve and to eat, and stunningly varied in colour and flavour. Many, like Tiramisù, take their shape from the dish in which they are served; others, like Zuccotto, from the mould in which they were placed to set or to firm up. Jewel-toned fresh fruit desserts can put the taste of summer on your table any time, thanks to the year-round availability of many familiar fruits, and add exotic new varieties to the list of dessert possibilities. Rounding out this chapter are tender crêpes and blinis, and meringue desserts as appealing as Meringue Mushrooms and as elegant as Strawberry and Almond Dacquoise.

CONTENTS

MOUSSES AND SOUFFLÉS

Light, fluffy mousses and soufflés – made from fruit, chocolate, nuts and cream – are right for any occasion, from everyday meals for family and friends to special events when you want to impress. And, because cold mousses can be made ahead, they're perfect for entertaining.

REAL CHOCOLATE MOUSSE

 8-10 servings
Can be made day before and kept in refrigerator

4 egg yolks

450 ml/ ¾ pint milk

60 g/2 oz caster sugar

1 tablespoon powdered gelatine

225 g/8 oz plain chocolate, chopped

450 ml/ ¾ pint double or whipping cream

Whipped cream and finely chopped pistachios (see right) to decorate

1 In large non-stick saucepan, beat egg yolks, milk and sugar until blended. Evenly sprinkle gelatine over mixture; leave to stand for 5 minutes to soften gelatine slightly. Stir in chopped chocolate.

2 Cook over low heat, stirring frequently with wooden spoon, for about 15 minutes or until gelatine dissolves completely, chocolate melts and mixture thickens and coats the spoon well (do not boil or mixture will curdle).

3 Pour mixture into bowl; cover and refrigerate until mixture mounds slightly when dropped from a spoon, about 1½ hours, stirring occasionally.

4 In medium bowl, whip double or whipping cream until stiff peaks form. With rubber spatula or wire whisk, fold whipped cream into chocolate mixture.

5 Pour mousse into 8-10 individual soufflé dishes or 1 large serving bowl; cover and refrigerate for 4 hours or until mousse is set.

6 Before serving, decorate mousse with whipped cream and finely chopped pistachios.

Piping whipped cream:
using piping bag with medium star tube, pipe whipped cream in shell shape at edge of each chocolate mousse.

Chopping pistachios:
with sharp knife, on cutting board, finely chop shelled pistachios. Use to sprinkle over whipped cream and chocolate mousse.

Chopped pistachios and whipped cream add flavour as well as colour to this wickedly rich chocolate mousse

RASPBERRY LAYERED MOUSSE

8 servings
Can be made day
before and kept in
refrigeraor

450 g/1 lb frozen raspberries

175-225 g/6-8 oz caster
sugar

2 tablespoons powdered
gelatine

2 eggs

300 ml/ ½ pint milk

600 ml/1 pint double or
whipping cream

14 ginger nut biscuits,
crushed (about
150 g/5 oz)

*Raspberries and mint
leaves to decorate*

1 Sprinkle raspberries
with half of the sugar;
set aside to thaw.

2 Place sieve over non-
stick saucepan. With
back of spoon, press and
scrape raspberries and
juice through sieve to
purée; discard pips.

3 Sprinkle half of the
gelatine over rasp-
berry purée in saucepan;
leave to stand for 5 min-
utes in order to allow
gelatine to soften slightly.

4 Over medium heat,
cook raspberry
mixture until gelatine
dissolves completely,
stirring frequently.

5 Pour into bowl, cover
and refrigerate until
mixture mounds slightly
when dropped from a
spoon, about 1 ½ hours,
stirring occasionally.

6 Meanwhile, in
another non-stick
saucepan, beat eggs, milk
and half of the remaining
sugar until blended.
Evenly sprinkle remaining
gelatine over mixture;
leave to stand for 5 min-
utes in order to soften
gelatine slightly.

7 Cook gelatine mixture
over low heat, stirring
frequently, for 10 minutes
or until gelatine dissolves
completely and mixture
coats a spoon well (do not
boil or it will curdle).

8 Pour into bowl, cover
and refrigerate until
mixture mounds slightly
when dropped from a
spoon, about 1 ½ hours,
stirring occasionally.

9 About 10 minutes
before gelatine
mixtures are ready, in
large bowl, whip double
or whipping cream with
remaining sugar until stiff
peaks form.

10 With rubber
spatula or wire
whisk, gently fold half of
the whipped cream into
each of the gelatine
mixtures.

11 In large serving
bowl, layer half of
the biscuits, then custard
cream, rest of biscuits,
then raspberry cream.
Cover and refrigerate
until set, about 3 hours.

TO SERVE
*Decorate mousse with
raspberries and mint
leaves.*

*The different
layers of Raspberry
Layered Mousse
can be seen if the dessert
is made in a glass bowl*

MARBLED MOUSSE CAKE

 8 servings

Can be made day before and kept in refrigerator

---

60 g/2 oz plain chocolate, broken into pieces

450 ml/ ¾ pint milk

3 egg yolks

200 g/7 oz caster sugar

2 tablespoons powdered gelatine

1 teaspoon vanilla essence

600 ml/1 pint double or whipping cream

200 g/7 oz plain chocolate flavour cake covering

---

1 Place pieces of plain chocolate in bowl over pan of gently simmering water and heat, stirring frequently, until melted and smooth; remove pan from heat.

2 In large non-stick saucepan, blend milk, egg yolks and 150 g/5 oz sugar. Evenly sprinkle gelatine over mixture; leave to stand for 5 minutes to soften gelatine slightly. Cook over low heat, stirring often, for about 15 minutes or until gelatine dissolves completely and mixture coats a spoon well (do not boil or mixture will curdle).

3 Pour half of the egg yolk mixture into small bowl; add melted chocolate. With wire whisk, beat just until blended. Into remaining egg yolk mixture, stir vanilla essence.

4 Cover and refrigerate both mixtures until they mound slightly when dropped from a spoon, 20-25 minutes, stirring occasionally.

5 In large bowl, whip double or whipping cream with remaining caster sugar until stiff peaks form.

6 With rubber spatula or wire whisk, gently fold half of the whipped cream into each chilled egg yolk mixture.

7 Alternately spoon chocolate and vanilla mousse mixtures into 23 cm/9 inch springform cake tin. Swirl mixtures together with a palette knife, to create a pretty marbled design. Cover and refrigerate for 4 hours or until set.

8 Meanwhile, cut sheet of non-stick baking parchment into 30 x 18.5 cm/12 x 7 ½ inch rectangle; place on baking sheet. Melt 150 g/5 oz chocolate cake covering in a bowl over a pan of gently simmering water, stirring frequently.

9 Spread melted cake covering over paper rectangle (see Box, right); refrigerate until firm.

10 Cut chocolate rectangle into strips (see Box, right); peel off paper. Place chocolate strips on baking sheet; refrigerate.

11 Make chocolate curls: with heat of hands, slightly soften remaining chocolate cake covering. Draw blade of vegetable peeler along smooth surface of chocolate to make wide chocolate curls Place curls on plate; refrigerate.

12 Remove chocolate strips from refrigerator; leave to stand for 5 minutes to soften. Remove side of springform tin; place mousse cake on cake stand or plate. Cover side with chocolate strips (see Box, below).

13 With cocktail stick, gently pile chocolate curls in centre of mousse cake.

MAKING CHOCOLATE FRAME

 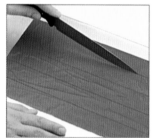

Spreading melted chocolate: with palette knife, quickly spread warm melted chocolate over non-stick baking parchment rectangle to cover evenly; refrigerate until firm, about 30 minutes.

Cutting chocolate into strips: with sharp knife, cut chocolate rectangle lengthways into five 4 cm/1 ½ inch wide strips.

Cake covering is used for making this chocolate 'frame' because it moulds easily to the shape of the mousse

Covering side of cake: place chocolate strips one at a time round cake. Press each strip gently with palette knife to fit shape of mousse, overlapping slightly.

Chocolate 'frame' is made by carefully shaping strips of chocolate round mousse, overlapping them so that frame is made up of more than one layer

For this dramatic presentation, glacé cherries are placed at regular intervals round top edge of mousse cake and grated chocolate is sprinkled round edge of plate

EASY CHOCOLATE ALMOND MOUSSE

4-6 servings

Can be made day before and kept in refrigerator

---

300 ml/ ½ pint double or whipping cream

---

1 tablespoon powdered gelatine

---

175 g/6 oz plain chocolate, broken into pieces

---

4 ice cubes

---

175 ml/6 fl oz milk

---

60 g/2 oz caster sugar

¾ teaspoon almond essence

Whipped cream and toasted flaked almonds (see Box, right) to decorate

TOASTING FLAKED ALMONDS
In frying pan or saucepan over medium heat, cook small quantity of almonds until golden, stirring frequently with wooden spatula.

Leave almonds to cool before using.

1 Pour half of the double or whipping cream into non-stick saucepan. Evenly sprinkle gelatine over cream; leave to soften for 5 minutes.

2 Cook over medium heat until tiny bubbles form round edge of pan and gelatine dissolves completely, stirring frequently.

3 Pour hot mixture into blender or food processor with knife blade attached; add chocolate pieces. Cover and blend until chocolate melts.

4 Add ice cubes to chocolate mixture.

5 Add milk, sugar, almond essence and remaining double or whipping cream; blend until smooth.

6 Pour mixture into 4-6 glasses or bowls; cover and refrigerate for 4 hours or until set.

7 Decorate each mousse with whipped cream and top with toasted flaked almonds.

HOT BANANA SOUFFLÉS

4 servings
Allow 30 minutes preparation time

3 medium-sized bananas (about 450 g/1 lb)

2 teaspoons lemon juice

4 egg whites

25 g/ ¾ oz icing sugar plus extra for sprinkling

1 Preheat oven to 230°C/450°F/gas 8.

2 Brush inside of four 300 ml/ ½ pint soufflé dishes lightly with oil.

3 Peel and slice bananas; place slices in bowl, add lemon juice and mash well with fork.

4 In large bowl, with electric mixer on full speed, beat egg whites until soft peaks form; gradually sift in 25 g/ ¾ oz icing sugar, beating until sugar completely dissolves and whites stand in stiff peaks.

5 With rubber spatula or wire whisk, gently fold beaten egg whites into banana mixture, one-third at a time.

6 Spoon mixture into soufflé dishes; set dishes in baking tray for easier handling.

7 Bake for 15 minutes or until soufflés are puffed and browned.

> **TO SERVE**
> *When soufflés are done, remove from oven; sift tops lightly with icing sugar and serve immediately.*

Hot soufflés look so good when they come out of the oven, puffed and high like these. Don't delay when serving!

ORANGE LIQUEUR SOUFFLÉ

6 servings
Allow 2 hours preparation and cooking time

60 g/2 oz butter

50 g/1 ⅔ oz plain flour

350 ml/12 fl oz milk

45 g/1 ½ oz caster sugar, plus extra for sprinkling

4 egg yolks

5 tablespoons orange liqueur

1 tablespoon grated orange zest

6 egg whites

Icing sugar for sprinkling

Whipped cream for serving (flavoured with orange liqueur or orange juice if liked)

1 In large non-stick saucepan over low heat, melt butter; stir in flour until blended. Gradually stir in milk; cook, stirring constantly, until mixture boils and thickens; boil for 1 minute.

2 Remove saucepan from heat. With wire whisk, beat caster sugar into milk mixture. Rapidly beat in egg yolks all at once until well mixed. Cool mixture to lukewarm, stirring occasionally. Stir in orange liqueur and grated orange zest.

3 Brush inside of 1.2 litre/2 pint soufflé dish with butter; sprinkle lightly with caster sugar.

If you sprinkle inside of buttered soufflé dish with caster sugar it will melt during baking and soufflé will not stick to dish

4 Preheat oven to 190°C/375°F/gas 5. In large bowl, with electric mixer on full speed, beat egg whites until stiff peaks form. With rubber spatula or wire whisk, gently fold beaten egg whites, one-third at a time, into egg yolk mixture.

5 Spoon mixture into prepared dish. With back of metal spoon, about 2.5 cm/1 inch from edge, make 4 cm /1½ inch deep indentation all round in soufflé mixture (centre will rise slightly higher than edge, making top hat effect when soufflé is done).

Making indentation in soufflé mixture for top hat effect

6 Bake soufflé for 30-35 minutes until knife inserted under top hat comes out clean.

7 When soufflé is done, remove from oven and sprinkle top lightly with sifted icing sugar; serve immediately. Hand whipped cream in bowl to spoon on to each serving, if you like.

The 'top hat' effect of this baked soufflé is created by making an indentation with a spoon in soufflé mixture before cooking

SUCCESSFUL SWEET SOUFFLÉS

Hot sweet soufflés consist of a thick sauce of butter, flour, milk, sugar, egg yolks and flavourings folded with stiffly beaten egg whites. For success every time, follow these simple guidelines.

• Always cook butter and flour first, to get rid of the raw taste of uncooked flour. When adding milk, take care to do it very gradually.

• Boil milk mixture for 1 minute so that smooth sauce is formed.

• Beat in egg yolks vigorously with pan off the heat.

• Fold egg whites gently into sauce, taking care not to stir whites.

• Bake soufflé on rack slightly below centre of oven so that mixture itself is centred and has sufficient room to rise.

• Do not open oven door before end of baking time; cold air could cause soufflé to fall.

FRESH APPLE SOUFFLÉ

4 servings
Allow about 1 hour preparation and cooking time

3 medium-sized cooking apples (about 450 g/1 lb)

45 g/1 ½ oz caster sugar

½ teaspoon almond essence

5 egg whites

Icing sugar for sprinkling

1 Peel apples; cut into quarters; with sharp knife, remove cores.

2 Cut apples into bite-sized chunks. In large saucepan over high heat, heat apples and *4 tablespoons water* to boiling. Reduce heat to low; cover and simmer for 8-10 minutes, stirring occasionally, until apples are tender. Stir in caster sugar and almond essence. Pour apple mixture into bowl; set aside to cool.

3 Preheat oven to 230°C/450°F/gas 8. In large bowl, with electric mixer on full speed, beat egg whites until stiff peaks form.

4 With rubber spatula or wire whisk, gently fold egg whites into cooled apple mixture until evenly incorporated.

5 Spoon mixture into 1.5 litre/2 ½ pint soufflé dish. Bake for 15 minutes or until soufflé is puffy and lightly browned. Remove soufflé from oven; sift icing sugar lightly over top and serve immediately.

Although not strictly speaking a soufflé, this simple, low-calorie dessert of apples, sugar and egg whites has a similar light and fluffy texture

CUSTARDS AND CREAMS

Velvety smooth, soft and pleasing, custards and creams are easy and quick to make. Most can be prepared ahead, making them excellent for menus in which other dishes require last-minute attention. Fruit Fools are the exception; they must be made just before serving, but preparation takes only about 20 minutes. In these pages you will find desserts ranging from simple family favourites like Crème Caramel to sophisticated party desserts like Zuccotto.

AMERICAN CREAM POTS

6 servings
Can be made day before (up to end of step 6) and kept in refrigerator

4 eggs

600 ml/1 pint milk

45 g/1 ½ oz caster sugar

1 teaspoon vanilla essence

6 tablespoons maple syrup

1 x 315 g/11 oz can mandarin orange segments, drained, to decorate

1 In large jug or bowl, with wire whisk, beat eggs, milk, sugar and vanilla essence until well blended.

2 Pour milk mixture into six 175 ml/6 fl oz mousse pots.

3 Arrange mousse pots in 30 cm/12 inch frying pan; fill pan with water to come halfway up sides of pots. Cover pan.

4 Over medium heat, heat water in pan to boiling point.

5 Simmer custards about 10 minutes or until beginning to set around edges. Remove pan from heat, then leave custards to stand in covered pan for 15 minutes until fully set.

6 Remove pots of custard from pan; refrigerate until well chilled, about 2 hours. If not serving immediately, cover each chilled dessert tightly and refrigerate.

7 Just before serving, pour 1 tablespoon maple syrup on top of each pot of custard.

8 To serve, top each custard with mandarin orange segments.

Maple syrup and canned mandarins are a quick and clever 'American' way to dress up a simple egg custard

CHOCOLATE CUPS

 8 servings

Allow about 2 hours preparation and chilling time

175 g/6 oz plain chocolate flavour cake covering, broken into pieces

300 ml/ ½ pint double or whipping cream

1 x 400 g/400 ml can Devon custard

Few drops of orange food colouring (optional)

1 large banana

Cocoa powder

1 Place paper cake cases in each of eight 6 cm/2 ½ inch holes in deep bun tin.

2 In small bowl set over saucepan of gently simmering water, gently heat chocolate cake covering, stirring frequently, until melted and smooth.

3 Starting from top rim of each paper case, carefully drizzle melted chocolate cake covering, 1 teaspoon at a time, down inside of case. About 3-4 teaspoons of melted chocolate will line each paper case.

4 If necessary, spread chocolate over inside of case with back of teaspoon.

5 Refrigerate until firm, about 30 minutes. With cool hands, remove 1 cake case at a time from refrigerator; gently but quickly peel paper case from each one, leaving chocolate cup.

6 Place empty chocolate cups on chilled dessert platter and refrigerate.

7 In small bowl, whip double or whipping cream until stiff peaks form.

8 With rubber spatula or wire whisk, fold whipped cream into custard until blended. Add food colouring, if used.

9 Slice banana and divide equally between cups. Spoon filling into cups. Refrigerate for at least 30 minutes or until filling is well chilled.

> *TO SERVE*
> *Lightly sprinkle cocoa through small sieve over creamy filling in Chocolate Cups.*

Beneath this creamy custard is a surprise filling of sliced banana

CRÈME CARAMEL

6 servings
Can be made day
before and kept in
refrigerator

120 g/4 oz granulated
   sugar

5 eggs

60 g/2 oz caster sugar

Few drops of vanilla essence

750 ml/1 ¼ pints milk

Cracked Caramel (page
   253), Cape gooseberries
   or lime julienne and
   citrus fruit segments to
   decorate

1 Preheat oven to
   150°C/300°F/gas 2.
Put granulated sugar and
4 tablespoons water in heavy
saucepan and dissolve over
low heat. Bring to the boil;
boil, without stirring,
until syrup is pale
golden brown.
Remove from
heat and quickly
pour into 6 small
ramekins, or oval-
or heart-shaped
moulds.

2 Mix the eggs, caster
   sugar and vanilla
essence together in a large
bowl.

3 Warm milk in sauce-
   pan over low heat
until it is hand hot, then
pour it on to egg mixture,
stirring constantly.

4 Brush butter on sides
   of ramekins or moulds
above caramel. Strain
custard into ramekins or
moulds and place in a
roasting tin. Pour in hot
water to come halfway up
sides of ramekins or
moulds.

5 Bake in oven for
   about 45-60 minutes
until set. Remove from
oven and leave to cool,
then refrigerate until set
and well chilled, at least
12 hours or overnight.

6 Just before serving,
   loosen custards from
ramekins or moulds with
small knife. Turn each
custard out on to a chilled
dessert plate, letting syrup
drip over custard and
down sides. Add decora-
tion of your choice.

Cracked Caramel

**Cracked Caramel
Decoration:** *with end of
rolling pin, carefully crack
hardened caramel into small
pieces.*

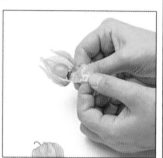

**Cape Gooseberry Decora-
tion** *(also called physalis and
Chinese lantern): carefully
peel back inedible husk to
resemble flower petals.*

Lime Julienne Decoration:
*with vegetable peeler, remove
zest from lime, leaving
bitter white pith behind.
Cut zest into fine strips.*

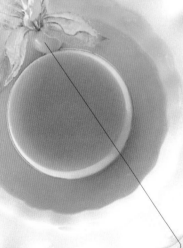

Cape
Gooseberry

Lime
Julienne

CRÈME BRÛLÉE

6 servings
Can be made day
before up to end
of step 3

Crème Brûlée

| 600 ml/1 pint single cream |
| 4 eggs |
| 60 g/2 oz caster sugar |
| ½ teaspoon vanilla essence |
| 45 g/1 ½ oz demerara sugar |

To serve

| Cut-up fresh fruits (strawberries, pineapple and banana) |
| Canned mandarin-orange segments |
| Fresh mint sprigs |

1 Preheat oven to 150°C/300°F/gas 2.

2 Blend cream, eggs, caster sugar and vanilla in large bowl. Pour into baking dish.

3 Stand dish in roasting tin containing 2.5 cm/1 inch hot water; bake in oven for about 1 hour or until just firm. Leave to cool, then refrigerate for at least 4 hours.

4 About 1 hour before serving, preheat grill to high. Work demerara sugar through sieve over chilled cream mixture.

5 Brown under a hot grill for 3-4 minutes until sugar has melted. The melted sugar will form a crisp crust over custard. If crust is done too early, the sugar will become soft and lose its crisp texture. Leave to cool.

6 To serve, arrange some sliced fruit in centre of Crème Brûlée with mint sprigs. Serve remaining fruit separately.

To serve Crème Brûlée, tap top with metal spoon to crack crust and reveal creamy custard underneath

Working demerara sugar through sieve so it will be free of lumps; it should then brown evenly under the grill

BRÛLÉE TOPPING

If your grill isn't very efficient and you find it difficult to get an even layer of brûlée on the top of the custard cream, instead of sprinkling demerara sugar over the top of the custard and browning it under the grill, try this alternative method.

Caramel Topping

Make a caramel as you would for crème caramel: put *90 g /3 oz granulated sugar* and *3 tablespoons water* in a heavy saucepan and heat gently until the sugar has dissolved. Bring to the boil and boil, without stirring, until the syrup is pale golden brown. Remove from the heat and quickly pour over the top of the chilled custard cream; syrup will turn instantly into a hard caramel. Chill in the refrigerator for 3-4 hours to soften caramel a little.

BURGUNDY CREAM

6 servings
Allow 2 ½ hours preparation and chilling time

500 ml/16 fl oz red grape juice

100 g/3 ½ oz caster sugar

3 tablespoons arrowroot, dissolved in 4 tablespoons water

250 ml/8 fl oz red Burgundy wine

Custard Cream (see Box, right)

1 In large saucepan, mix red grape juice, caster sugar and arrowroot dissolved in water. Cook over medium heat, stirring constantly, until mixture begins to thicken and comes to the boil, about 5 minutes.

2 Add wine and cook for 5 minutes longer, stirring constantly.

3 Pour wine mixture into 6 wine glasses or dessert bowls; cover and refrigerate until well chilled, about 2 hours.

4 Meanwhile, prepare Custard Cream and refrigerate it.

TO SERVE
Top each serving with a few spoonfuls of Custard Cream.

CUSTARD CREAM
To make custard cream, in medium non-stick saucepan, combine *400 ml/14 fl oz single cream, 3 tablespoons caster sugar, 1 tablespoon cornflour* and *1 egg yolk.* Cook over medium-low heat, stirring constantly, until mixture coats a spoon well, about 15 minutes (do not allow mixture to boil otherwise it will curdle).

Remove custard from heat. Stir in *½ teaspoon vanilla essence;* pour into bowl. To keep skin from forming on top of custard as it cools, press dampened grease-proof paper directly on to surface.

'CHEAT' BUTTERSCOTCH SQUARES

Makes 15 squares
Allow 5 ½ hours
preparation and
chilling time

120 g/4 oz slivered
almonds

150 g/5 oz plain flour

120 g/4 oz butter or
margarine

100 g/3 ½ oz icing sugar,
sifted

225 g/8 oz full-fat soft
cheese, softened

450 ml/ ¾ pint double or
whipping cream

2 x 69 g/2.4 oz packets
butterscotch-flavour
dessert whip

450 ml/ ¾ pint milk

*Made from a packet mix,
whipped cream and soft
cheese, these butterscotch
squares are unbelievably
yummy*

*Each square is
sprinkled with toasted
chopped almonds*

1 With sharp knife, finely chop two-thirds of slivered almonds; coarsely chop remaining slivered almonds into two or three pieces to use as decoration.

*Mixing ingredients
for shortbread base
with fingertips until
crumbly*

2 Preheat oven to 180°C/350°F/gas 4.

3 In medium bowl, with fingers, mix flour, butter or margarine, finely chopped almonds and 30 g/1 oz icing sugar until crumbly.

4 With fingers, press mixture firmly into 33 x 23 cm/13 x 9 inch baking dish.

5 Bake shortbread base for 15-20 minutes until golden brown. Cool in dish on wire rack.

6 While shortbread is cooling, in same bowl with spoon, beat soft cheese and 60 g/2 oz icing sugar until light and fluffy.

7 In medium bowl, whip double or whipping cream until stiff peaks form.

8 With rubber spatula, fold one-third of the cream into soft cheese and icing sugar mixture; spread over shortbread base. Reserve remaining whipped cream.

9 In large bowl, with wire whisk, prepare dessert whip according to packet instructions, but prepare both packets together and use only 450 ml/ ¾ pint milk in total. Spread dessert whip over soft cheese layer.

10 Fold remaining icing sugar into reserved whipped cream; spread over dessert whip. Refrigerate until firm, about 4 hours.

11 Toast coarsely chopped almonds until golden; cool. Cut dessert into 15 squares, remove from dish, then sprinkle with almonds.

DECORATING WITH SAUCES

There's more to serving a sauce than just spooning it over a pudding. It can be made into an eye-catching decoration that's quick and surprisingly easy to do; all that's needed is a bit of imagination coupled with a steady hand.

Fruit purées, bottled fruit and chocolate syrups, custard, cream and sweet sauces can all be used effectively. The decoration on Black Cherry and White Chocolate Trifle (page 32), for example, is a delicate 'feathering' of raspberry jam on snowy whipped cream. Simple bottled chocolate syrup piped on to custard is all that's needed to decorate Cherries en Gelée (page 50) so attractively.

The designs on these two pages should help to get you started. Each combines two different ingredients of contrasting colour yet compatible flavour. Choose from a wide variety of ingredients – colourful fruit sauces and purées, glistening jams and jellies, rich dark chocolate, golden custard.

Cream Wisps
Spoon raspberry purée on to plate. With small writing tube, pipe dots of double cream in a circle 2.5 cm/1 inch in from edge of purée. Draw tip of knife or skewer through 1 edge of each dot to form the shape of a wisp. Use to frame scoops of ice creams and sorbets.

Chocolate Spider Web
Spoon lightly whipped cream on to plate. With small writing tube, pipe 2 concentric circles of chocolate syrup or melted and cooled chocolate on to cream. With tip of knife or skewer, quickly draw lines in spoke fashion; alternate direction of each spoke, first from centre to edge, then from edge to centre. Use as a decoration for moulded desserts and individual portions of cakes and tarts.

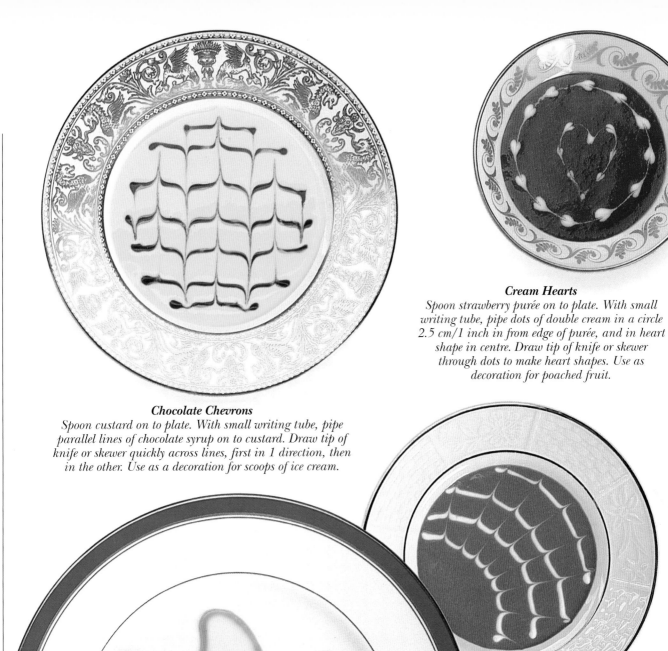

Cream Hearts

Spoon strawberry purée on to plate. With small writing tube, pipe dots of double cream in a circle 2.5 cm/1 inch in from edge of purée, and in heart shape in centre. Draw tip of knife or skewer through dots to make heart shapes. Use as decoration for poached fruit.

Chocolate Chevrons

Spoon custard on to plate. With small writing tube, pipe parallel lines of chocolate syrup on to custard. Draw tip of knife or skewer quickly across lines, first in 1 direction, then in the other. Use as a decoration for scoops of ice cream.

Cream Sunburst

Spoon chocolate custard on to plate. With small writing tube, pipe semi-circular lines of double cream at regular intervals. Starting at smallest circle, draw tip of knife or skewer across lines, towards edge of plate. Use as a decoration for individual portions of sweet pies and tarts.

On Raspberry Pond

With small writing tube, pipe free-form decorative shape of seedless raspberry jam on to plate. Carefully spoon in double or whipping cream to fill shape. If you like, add fruit and mint leaves. Use as a decoration for fresh fruit and fruit salads.

ZUCCOTTO (FLORENTINE CREAM CAKE)

This delicious dessert comes from Italy, where it is traditionally made in a special pumpkin-shaped mould (zuccotto means 'little pumpkin' in Italian). Here *a large glass mixing bowl is used, and it works just as well as a special zuccotto mould, giving an equally good shape, as you can see in the photograph.*

Turned out upside-down, this luscious dinner party dessert looks pumpkin-shaped, which is why the Italians call it 'zuccotto', or 'little pumpkin'

4 Beat melted chocolate into butter and sugar mixture with remaining liqueur until smooth, thick and creamy.

5 In small bowl, whip 300 ml/ ½ pint double cream with 2 teaspoons coffee essence until stiff peaks form. Fold in grated chocolate.

6 Cover cake triangles in bowl with whipped cream mixture.

Covering cake in bowl with whipped cream mixture

8-10 servings
Can be made day before and kept in refrigerator

1 Madeira cake, measuring about 23 x 12.5 cm/ 9 x 5 inches

6 tablespoons almond liqueur

135 g/4 ½ oz plain chocolate

120 g/4 oz icing sugar, sifted

60 g/2 oz butter, softened

450 ml/ ¾ pint double cream

4 teaspoons coffee essence

2 tablespoons slivered almonds, chopped

30 g/1 oz caster sugar

1 Line medium-sized bowl with cling film. Cut Madeira cake into 1 cm/ ½ inch thick slices; cut each slice diagonally in half to make 2 triangles.

2 Sprinkle 3 tablespoons almond liqueur on triangles of cake. Line bowl with triangles; reserve remaining triangles.

3 Break 90 g/3 oz chocolate into pieces and melt in bowl over pan of gently simmering water. Coarsely grate remaining chocolate. In bowl, beat icing sugar and softened butter until creamy.

7 Spoon chocolate and almond liqueur mixture into centre of dessert and smooth top.

8 Neatly cover top of dessert with remaining cake triangles.

9 Cover bowl and refrigerate for at least 4 hours.

10 Meanwhile, in small saucepan over medium heat, cook chopped slivered almonds until golden, stirring frequently; cool.

11 In small bowl, whip remaining double cream with caster sugar and remaining 2 teaspoons coffee essence until soft peaks form.

12 Turn dessert out on to chilled platter; discard cling film. Cover dessert with whipped cream; sprinkle toasted chopped almonds on top.

DECORATIVE FINISHES FOR ZUCCOTTO

You can decorate the Zuccotto very simply, with toasted chopped almonds as in the main photograph (page 26), or you can sift cocoa powder or icing sugar over the top for an equally attractive finish. Another more decorative idea, which echoes the almond and coffee flavours of the Zuccotto, is this Daisy Design, and it only takes a few extra minutes to do.

Daisy Design
A simple daisy made from blanched or toasted almonds and chocolate 'coffee beans' is quick and effective to make: gently press 'coffee bean' into whipped cream icing for centre of daisy, then press slivered almonds round sweet for petals. If you like, make 1 large daisy centred on top of Zuccotto, or several small daisies placed round sides.

Toasted slivered almond

Slivered blanched almond

Chocolate 'coffee bean'

TO SERVE
Cut Zuccotto into slices and arrange on dessert plates to reveal different layers inside.

STRAWBERRY ORANGE CHARLOTTE

8 servings
Can be made day before and kept in refrigerator

2 tablespoons powdered gelatine

175 ml/6 fl oz orange juice

4 egg yolks

350 ml/12 fl oz milk

1 x 400 g/14 oz can sweetened condensed milk

225 g/8 oz frozen strawberries

60 g/2 oz caster sugar

4 tablespoons strawberry jam

4 tablespoons orange liqueur

25 g/ ¾ oz cornflour

2 x 100 g/3 ½ oz packets sponge fingers (boudoir biscuits)

450 ml/ ¾ pint double or whipping cream

1 tablespoon icing sugar

Strawberries to decorate

1 In non-stick saucepan, sprinkle gelatine over orange juice; leave to stand for 5 minutes. Cook over medium heat until gelatine dissolves, stirring often.

2 In medium bowl, with wire whisk, beat egg yolks, milk and condensed milk until blended. Beat egg yolk mixture gradually into gelatine mixture. Cook over medium-low heat, stirring constantly, until mixture thickens and coats a spoon well, about 15 minutes (do not boil or it will curdle).

3 Pour custard mixture into large bowl; cover and refrigerate until mixture mounds slightly when dropped from a spoon, about 1 ½ hours, stirring occasionally.

4 Meanwhile, sprinkle strawberries with caster sugar; thaw. In food processor or blender, blend strawberries and their juice with jam until smooth.

5 Pour mixture into medium saucepan; stir in liqueur, cornflour and 4 tablespoons water. Cook over medium-high heat, stirring constantly, until mixture boils and becomes thick; boil for 1 minute. Remove from heat.

6 Line bottom and sides of 23 cm/9 inch springform cake tin with sponge fingers.

7 If necessary, trim sponge fingers to fit tin so they will line bottom and stand upright round sides. Brush sponge fingers on bottom of tin with 4 tablespoons strawberry mixture (see Box, below). Cover tin tightly; set aside. Pour remaining strawberry mixture into bowl; allow to cool, stirring mixture occasionally.

8 In small bowl, whip 350 ml/12 fl oz double or whipping cream until stiff peaks form. With rubber spatula or wire whisk, fold whipped cream into custard mixture.

9 Spoon half of the custard mixture over sponge fingers in bottom of springform tin. Spoon 150 ml/ ¼ pint of strawberry mixture over custard layer. Add remaining custard mixture (see Box, below). Drop heaping spoonfuls of remaining strawberry mixture on top of custard. Using palette knife, swirl mixtures together to create a marbled design (see Box, below). Refrigerate until firm, at least 4 hours or overnight.

10 When ready to serve, carefully remove side of springform tin from charlotte; place charlotte on cake plate or stand. In small bowl, whip remaining double or whipping cream with sifted icing sugar until stiff peaks form. Spoon into piping bag with medium star tube; pipe in pretty design round top edge of charlotte. Cut strawberries in half and use to decorate charlotte attractively.

MAKING MARBLED DESIGN

Brushing sponge fingers on bottom of tin: evenly spread 4 tablespoons strawberry mixture over sponge fingers.

Adding custard mixture: over second layer of strawberry mixture, spoon remaining custard mixture.

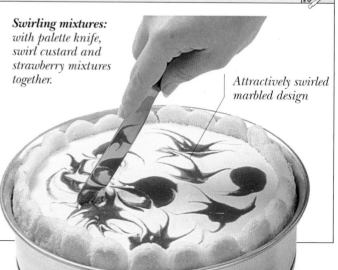

Swirling mixtures: with palette knife, swirl custard and strawberry mixtures together.

Attractively swirled marbled design

Strawberry Orange Charlotte looks very pretty with a satin ribbon tied round its middle

TIRAMISÙ

🍴 10 servings

⏱ Can be made day before and kept in refrigerator

---

450 g/1 lb mascarpone cheese (see Box, below right)

---

75 g/2 ½ oz icing sugar, sifted

---

125 ml/4 fl oz coffee liqueur

---

90 g/3 oz plain chocolate, grated

---

450 ml/ ¾ pint double or whipping cream

---

2 teaspoons coffee essence

---

18 sponge fingers (boudoir biscuits)

1 In large bowl, with wire whisk or fork, beat mascarpone cheese, 60 g/2 oz icing sugar, 3 tablespoons coffee liqueur and two-thirds of grated chocolate. (Set aside remaining chocolate for top of dessert.)

Large rosettes of whipped cream look good piped round edge of dish and sprinkled with grated chocolate

2 In small bowl, whip 300 ml/½ pint double or whipping cream until stiff peaks form. With rubber spatula or wire whisk, fold cream into cheese mixture.

3 In small bowl, stir coffee essence, remaining coffee liqueur and *2 tablespoons water.*

4 Place 4 sponge fingers in bottom of large glass bowl; brush with 2 tablespoons of coffee essence mixture. Spoon one-third of cheese mixture over sponge fingers. Repeat with sponge fingers, coffee essence mixture and cheese mixture to make 2 more layers. Top with remaining sponge fingers, gently pressing them into cheese mixture. Brush sponge fingers with remaining coffee essence mixture. Sprinkle remaining grated chocolate over dessert, reserving 1 tablespoon for decoration.

5 In small bowl, whip remaining cream with remaining icing sugar until stiff peaks form.

Sweetened mascarpone cheese, cream and coffee liqueur are layered with coffee-soaked sponge fingers in this heady Italian dessert

---

TO SERVE
Serve Tiramisù well chilled in a glass serving bowl so that its different layers can be seen.

---

6 Spoon whipped cream into piping bag with large star tube. Pipe large rosettes on top of dessert.

7 Sprinkle reserved grated chocolate over whipped cream rosettes. Leave dessert in refrigerator until chilled and flavours are blended (this will take at least 4 hours).

MASCARPONE CHEESE

Mascarpone, a fresh, double-cream cheese, is one of the great Italian cheeses available in cheese shops, delicatessens and many supermarkets.
It is buttery-smooth in texture and slightly nutty or tangy in flavour. As well as being used in recipes, it is superb with fresh seasonal fruit or fruit purées.

Mascarpone Cheese Substitute

If mascarpone cheese is not available when making Tiramisù, substitute *450 g/1 lb full-fat soft cheese, softened*; in step 1, in large bowl, with electric mixer or hand whisk, beat soft cheese and *3 table-spoons milk* until mixture is smooth and fluffy. Increase amount of icing sugar for cheese mixture to 80 g/2 ¾ oz; beat in with coffee liqueur, then stir in grated chocolate until evenly blended.

RASPBERRY ORANGE TRIFLE

8-10 servings

Can be made day before and kept in refrigerator

1 x 300 g/10 oz Madeira cake

2 tablespoons orange liqueur

2 tablespoons orange juice

450 ml/ ¾ pint double cream

225 g/8 oz fresh or frozen (thawed and drained) raspberries

350 g/12 oz seedless raspberry jam

2 x 400 g/400 ml cans Devon custard

2 teaspoons orange-flower water

1 large orange

1 tablespoon powdered gelatine

60 g/2 oz plain chocolate, broken into pieces

Raspberries and lemon leaves to decorate

1 Cut cake horizontally into 3 layers; brush cut sides with liqueur mixed with orange juice.

2 Whip two-thirds of cream; fold in raspberries.

3 Spread bottom layer of Madeira cake with 1-2 tablespoons raspberry jam; top with middle layer. Spread 3 tablespoons jam over middle layer.

4 Replace top of Madeira cake. Slice layered cake crossways into 12 slices.

5 In large bowl, mix custard and orange-flower water. Grate zest from orange and add to custard mixture; reserve orange for decoration.

6 In small bowl, sprinkle gelatine over 5 tablespoons water; leave to stand for 5 minutes to soften gelatine. Stand bowl in pan of gently simmering water and heat gently until gelatine completely dissolves. Cool slightly, then fold into custard mixture.

7 In small bowl over pan of gently simmering water, heat chocolate, stirring frequently, until melted and smooth; remove from heat.

8 Into large glass bowl, pour one-third of the custard. Drizzle with half of the raspberry jam, then pour over another third of the custard. Drizzle with half of the melted chocolate.

9 Carefully arrange some of the layered Madeira cake slices round side of bowl.

10 Cut remaining Madeira cake slices into chunks and layer in bowl; drizzle with remaining chocolate, then spoon raspberry and cream mixture over top.

11 Pour remaining custard mixture over to cover cake. Spoon remaining raspberry jam over to cover custard.

12 Cover bowl and refrigerate until well chilled, about 4 hours.

13 Whip remaining cream until stiff peaks form; use to pipe swirls on top of trifle. With knife, remove any remaining zest and white membrane from orange and cut out segments. Decorate trifle with orange segments, raspberries and lemon leaves.

BLACK CHERRY AND WHITE CHOCOLATE TRIFLE

Give your dinner table a festive look when you serve this stunning trifle for dessert. No-one will be able to resist its luscious layers of fruit, custard, cream and sponge.

Made ahead of time and kept in the refrigerator, its delicious flavour improves, so it's the perfect dessert for easy yet luxurious entertaining.

 8 servings
Can be made day before and kept in refrigerator

White Chocolate Custard (see Box, page 33)

350 g/12 oz trifle sponges

1 x 397 g/14 oz can black cherry fruit filling for pies, flans and desserts

5 tablespoons kirsch

450 ml/ ¾ pint double or whipping cream

30 g/1 oz icing sugar, sifted

About 2 tablespoons seedless raspberry jam

Chopped pistachio nuts to decorate

1 Prepare White Chocolate Custard; refrigerate until cool, about 1 hour.

2 Cut trifle sponges into 2 cm/ ¾ inch chunks. In small bowl, stir black cherry fruit filling and kirsch until evenly combined.

3 In large glass serving bowl, place half of the trifle sponge chunks.

4 Spoon half of the cherry fruit filling mixture over sponge.

5 Top fruit filling mixture with half of the White Chocolate Custard. Repeat layering with sponge, fruit filling mixture and custard. Cover and refrigerate for at least 4 hours.

6 In small bowl, whip double or whipping cream with icing sugar until stiff peaks form. Reserve about one-third of the whipped cream; spread remaining cream over trifle.

7 Warm raspberry jam in small pan until just melted, then spoon into small piping bag with small writing tube (alternatively use paper piping bag with tip cut to make 3 mm/ ⅛ inch hole) and decorate top of trifle (see Box, below).

8 Spoon reserved whipped cream into piping bag with large star tube. Pipe round edge of trifle (see Box, below). Decorate with pistachios.

 DECORATING TOP OF TRIFLE

Filling piping bag: *into small piping bag with small writing tube, spoon raspberry jam*

Piping parallel lines: *on whipped cream on trifle, pipe raspberry jam in parallel lines, about 1 cm/ ½ inch apart*

Making feather design: *draw tip of knife across lines at 1 cm/ ½ inch intervals, alternating first in one direction and then in the other*

Piping cream: *using piping bag with large star tube, pipe reserved whipped cream decoratively round edge of trifle*

WHITE CHOCOLATE CUSTARD

In large non-stick saucepan, combine *100 g/3 ½ oz caster sugar* and *30 g/1 oz cornflour*; slowly stir in *1 litre/1 ¾ pints milk* until smooth. Cook over medium heat, stirring constantly, until mixture boils and thickens; boil for 1 minute. Remove saucepan from heat. In cup, with fork, beat *4 egg yolks*; stir in about 150 ml/¼ pint hot milk mixture. Slowly pour egg mixture back into milk mixture, stirring rapidly to prevent lumping; cook over medium-low heat, stirring constantly, until mixture thickens and coats a spoon well. Remove saucepan from heat. Stir in *175 g/6 oz white chocolate, broken into pieces*, until chocolate melts and mixture is smooth. In order to prevent skin from forming as custard cools, press dampened greaseproof paper directly on to surface of hot custard.

Piped and feathered raspberry jam looks most effective on top of snowy white whipped cream

With its festive colours, this pretty trifle would make a fitting finale for a Christmas meal

BUTTERMILK BAVARIAN WITH PEACH SAUCE

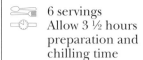

6 servings
Allow 3 ½ hours preparation and chilling time

750 ml/1 ¼ pints buttermilk

75 g/2 ½ oz caster sugar

2 tablespoons powdered gelatine

3 tablespoons lemon juice

1 teaspoon grated lemon zest

150 ml/ ¼ pint double or whipping cream

1 x 822 g/1 lb 13 oz can peach slices in syrup

2 teaspoons cornflour

Shredded lemon zest to decorate

1 In non-stick saucepan, stir 350 ml/12 fl oz buttermilk with sugar until blended. Evenly sprinkle gelatine over buttermilk mixture; leave to stand for 5 minutes to soften gelatine slightly.

If you use a deep fluted mould to set the Bavarian in, it will look extra good when it is turned out for serving

2 Cook over medium heat, stirring frequently, until gelatine dissolves completely. Remove saucepan from heat. Into buttermilk mixture, stir lemon juice, lemon zest and remaining buttermilk.

3 Cover and chill until buttermilk and lemon mixture mounds slightly when dropped from a spoon, about 45 minutes, stirring occasionally.

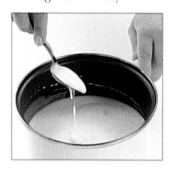

4 In small bowl, whip double or whipping cream until stiff peaks form.

5 In large bowl, with electric mixer on medium speed, beat chilled buttermilk and lemon mixture until foamy, about 30 seconds.

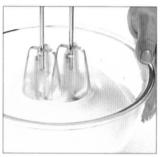

The sprinkling of shredded lemon zest on top of the Bavarian echoes the lemon flavour in the dessert itself

6 Add whipped cream to buttermilk and lemon mixture; beat until mixture is smooth and creamy, about 30 seconds.

7 Pour mixture into 1.5 litre/2 ½ pint mould; cover and refrigerate until dessert is firm, about 2 hours.

8 Meanwhile, prepare peach sauce: into small saucepan, drain syrup from peaches; set peaches aside. Into peach syrup, stir cornflour; cook over medium heat until mixture thickens and boils, stirring constantly; boil for 1 minute. Gently stir in peaches. Cover sauce and refrigerate.

TO SERVE
Turn Bavarian out on to chilled platter. Arrange peaches on top and round bottom. Spoon sauce over; decorate with shredded lemon zest.

FRUIT FOOLS

4 servings (each flavour)
Allow about 20 minutes preparation for each flavour

PEACH

3 medium-sized ripe peaches

30 g/1 oz caster sugar

300 ml/ ½ pint double or whipping cream

⅛ teaspoon almond essence

Mint leaves to decorate

1 Peel, halve and stone peaches. Reserve 1 peach half for decoration. Cut remaining peaches into chunks.

2 In food processor or blender at medium speed, blend peach chunks and sugar together until smooth.

3 In small bowl, whip double or whipping cream together with almond essence until stiff peaks form.

4 With rubber spatula or wire whisk, fold almond-flavoured whipped cream into peach purée.

> *TO SERVE*
> *Spoon mixture into parfait glasses or dessert dishes; decorate with reserved fruits and mint leaves.*

RASPBERRY

225 g/8 oz frozen raspberries

60 g/2 oz caster sugar

300 ml/ ½ pint double or whipping cream

⅛ teaspoon almond essence

Raspberries and mint leaves to decorate

1 Sprinkle raspberries with sugar; set aside to thaw. Over large bowl, with back of spoon, press and scrape thawed raspberries with their juice firmly against medium-mesh sieve to purée; discard pips left in sieve.

2 In small bowl, whip double or whipping cream together with almond essence until stiff peaks form.

3 With rubber spatula or wire whisk, fold almond-flavoured whipped cream into raspberry purée.

KIWI FRUIT

3 large kiwi fruit

30 g/1 oz caster sugar

300 ml/ ½ pint double or whipping cream

⅛ teaspoon vanilla essence

Mint leaves to decorate

1 Peel kiwi fruit. Cut 1 kiwi fruit crossways in half. Reserve 1 half for decoration. Cut remaining kiwi fruit into chunks.

2 In food processor or blender at medium speed, blend kiwi fruit chunks and sugar together until smooth.

3 In small bowl, whip double or whipping cream together with vanilla essence until stiff peaks form.

4 With rubber spatula or wire whisk, fold vanilla-flavoured whipped cream into kiwi fruit purée.

Raspberry Fool

Peach Fool

Kiwi Fruit Fool

CHOCOLATE BOX WITH BERRIES AND CREAM

This spectacular, luscious-looking dessert is simple to make when you follow the easy step-by-step directions below, yet your guests cannot fail to be impressed with your apparently expert skills. And the striking combination of rich dark chocolate with the lightness of the fresh strawberries and cream gives an opulent appearance which makes this dessert the perfect choice for any special occasion or celebration.

6 servings

Can be made day before (up to end of step 6) and kept in refrigerator

175 g/6 oz plain chocolate flavour cake covering, broken into pieces

30 g/1 oz cocoa powder

175 g/6 oz full-fat soft cheese, softened

60 g/2 oz butter, softened

175 g/6 oz icing sugar, sifted

2 tablespoons milk

450 ml/ ¾ pint double or whipping cream

700 g/1 ½ lb strawberries

Mint leaves to decorate

1 Turn 23 cm/9 inch square baking tin upside down; mould foil over outside of tin to make a smooth box shape. Turn right way up and remove tin; place foil box inside tin and press out any wrinkles so chocolate box will come away from foil smoothly.

2 In small bowl over pan of gently simmering water, heat pieces of plain chocolate cake covering, stirring frequently, until melted and smooth.

3 Pour melted chocolate into foil-lined tin and swirl round sides and bottom, keeping edges as even as possible (see Box, below). Refrigerate for 1 minute, then swirl chocolate round inside of tin a second time, to reinforce sides of chocolate box. Refrigerate until firm, about 30 minutes.

4 Meanwhile, prepare filling: dissolve cocoa powder in *2-3 tablespoons boiling water*. In large bowl, with electric mixer, beat soft cheese and butter until smooth (do not use margarine or filling will be too soft to cut). Add icing sugar, cocoa and milk; beat until light and fluffy.

5 In small bowl, whip 350 ml/12 fl oz double or whipping cream until stiff peaks form. With rubber spatula or wire whisk, fold whipped cream into soft cheese mixture.

6 Remove chocolate box in foil from tin (see Box, below), then gently peel foil from sides and base. Place chocolate box on platter. Spread soft cheese filling evenly in chocolate box. Refrigerate until filling is well chilled and firm, about 2 hours.

7 In small bowl, whip remaining double or whipping cream until stiff peaks form. Spoon into piping bag fitted with large star tube.

8 Pipe whipped cream in 2.5 cm/1 inch wide border on filling inside chocolate box. Cut larger strawberries in half and arrange over entire top of soft cheese filling. Decorate top of dessert with mint leaves. Serve remaining strawberries with dessert.

MAKING CHOCOLATE BOX

Pouring chocolate: slowly pour warm melted chocolate into foil-lined baking tin

Swirling chocolate: gently tilt tin from side to side so chocolate swirls round sides and bottom

Removing chocolate box: carefully lift foil to remove chocolate box from tin

The combination of strawberries with long stalks and fresh mint leaves makes this sensational dessert look colourful and stunning

MERINGUES

Light and delicate, crisp and sweet, meringue serves as the case for a classic Pavlova, makes layers for gâteaux such as dacquoise, and becomes tiny shells to hold fillings of cream, fruit and frozen mixtures. Meringue can also be shaped into mushrooms, to make stunning petits fours, while small meringues, spooned or piped into dollops like whipped cream, can top puddings or decorate cakes and gâteaux – bake them as for Miniature Meringue Shells (page 40).

PAVLOVA

 8 servings
Can be made day before (up to end of step 4) and kept in cool place

3 egg whites

175 g/6 oz caster sugar

1 teaspoon vinegar

1 teaspoon cornflour

5 kiwi fruit

300 ml/ ½ pint double or whipping cream

1 Place a sheet of non-stick baking parchment on a baking sheet and mark a 20 cm/8 inch circle on it, using plate or cake tin as guide.

> **TO SERVE**
> *Spoon two-thirds of cream into meringue; reserve few kiwi fruit slices; arrange remainder on cream. Top with remaining cream and reserved kiwi fruit.*

2 Preheat oven to 150°C/300°F/gas 2. In large bowl, with electric mixer on full speed, beat egg whites until soft peaks form. Gradually sprinkle in sugar, 1 tablespoon at a time, beating well after each addition. Blend vinegar with cornflour and whisk into egg whites with last spoonful of sugar.

3 Spread meringue on circle on baking parchment, building sides up higher than centre. Put in centre of oven, reduce heat to 140°C/275°F/gas 1 and bake for 1 hour or until pale cream in colour.

4 Turn oven off and leave Pavlova to cool completely in oven. When cool, carefully remove from baking sheet and place on serving plate.

OTHER FRUIT TOPPINGS

Although kiwi fruit remains the classic topping for Pavlova, other fruits can be used instead. Combine any or all of the following fruits with kiwi fruit, or use them on their own.

- Halved strawberries.
- Peeled and sliced peaches or nectarines.
- Peeled and cubed papaya (pawpaw).
- Pineapple chunks.

5 With sharp knife, peel off skin and thinly slice kiwi fruit.

6 In small bowl, whip double or whipping cream until stiff peaks form.

Softly whipped cream

Thinly sliced kiwi fruit

Mouthwatering 'marshmallow' meringue

DATE AND WALNUT DACQUOISE

8 servings
Can be made day
before and kept in
refrigerator

120 g/4 oz walnut pieces

150 g/5 oz stoned dates

5 egg whites

225 g/8 oz caster sugar

25 g/¾ oz cocoa powder

Mocha Butter Cream (see
Box, above right)

Icing sugar for sprinkling

1 Set aside a few walnut
pieces and a few dates
to use for decoration later.
Coarsely chop remaining
walnuts and cut remaining
dates into 1 cm/½ inch
pieces.

2 In large frying pan
over medium heat,
toast chopped walnuts
until golden brown,
stirring occasionally;
remove pan from heat.

3 Line 2 baking sheets
with non-stick baking
parchment or foil. Using
23 cm/9 inch round plate
or cake tin as guide, mark
1 circle on baking
parchment on each baking
sheet; set aside.

4 In large bowl, with
electric mixer on full
speed, beat egg whites
until soft peaks form.
Gradually sprinkle in
caster sugar, 1 tablespoon
at a time, beating well after
each addition until sugar
dissolves completely and
egg whites stand in stiff,
glossy peaks.

*Meringue layers made with
chopped dates, walnuts and
cocoa are sandwiched together
with a rich mocha-flavoured
butter cream*

5 Preheat oven to
180°C/350°F/gas 4.
In small bowl, with spoon,
mix chopped dates with
about 4 tablespoons
meringue mixture to
separate pieces. With
rubber spatula, gently fold
cocoa, date mixture and
toasted chopped walnuts
into remaining meringue
mixture.

6 Inside each circle on
baking parchment,
spoon half of the
meringue mixture; with
palette knife, evenly
spread meringue to cover
entire circle. Place baking
sheets with meringue on
2 oven racks; bake for
15 minutes. Switch baking
sheets between racks so
meringue browns evenly;
bake for 15 minutes longer
or until meringue layers
are crisp on the outside,
but still soft and chewy on
the inside.

MOCHA BUTTER CREAM

In large bowl, with electric mixer, beat *450 g/1 lb icing
sugar, sifted, 90 g/3 oz butter, softened, 45 g/1 ½ oz cocoa
powder* and *5 tablespoons hot black coffee* until blended.
Beat until butter cream has an easy spreading consistency, adding more coffee if necessary.

7 Cool meringues on
baking sheets on wire
racks for 10 minutes. With
palette knife, carefully
loosen meringues from
baking sheets and transfer
them to wire racks to cool
completely. (If not assembling dessert immediately,
meringue layers can be
stored, covered, for 1 day.)

8 When meringues are
cool, prepare Mocha
Butter Cream.

*Walnut and date topping –
a clue to what is inside this
luscious meringue gâteau*

9 To assemble cake:
place 1 meringue
layer, flat side up, on cake
plate. Cover evenly with
Mocha Butter Cream;
spread to 1 cm/ ½ inch of
edge. Top with second
meringue layer, flat side
down; press down gently.
Cover; refrigerate until
filling is firm.

TO SERVE
*Sift icing sugar over
dacquoise; decorate with
reserved walnuts and
dates. While firm, cut
into wedges, then leave to
soften for 5 minutes.*

MERINGUE SHAPES

MERINGUE SHELLS

6 shells
Can be made day before and kept in refrigerator

3 egg whites
175 g/6 oz caster sugar

1 Preheat oven to 140°C/275°F/gas 1.

2 Line large baking sheet with non-stick baking parchment or foil.

3 In large bowl, with electric mixer on full speed, beat egg whites until soft peaks form.

4 Add sugar to egg whites 1 tablespoon at a time, beating well after each addition until egg whites stand in stiff, glossy peaks.

5 Spoon meringue into large piping bag fitted with medium star tube. Pipe meringue into six 10 cm/4 inch rounds, about 2.5 cm/1 inch apart, on lined baking sheet.

6 Pipe remaining meringue in decorative star border round edge of each meringue round.

7 Bake meringues for 45 minutes. Turn oven off; leave meringues in oven for 45 minutes longer to dry completely.

8 Cool meringues on baking sheet on wire rack for 10 minutes. With palette knife, carefully loosen and remove meringues from baking sheet to wire rack and leave to cool completely.

9 If not using meringues immediately, store in tightly covered container.

MINIATURE MERINGUE SHELLS
Prepare meringue as for Meringue Shells (above), up to end of step 4. With medium writing tube, pipe into thirty 4 cm/1½ inch rounds on baking sheet lined with non-stick baking parchment. With teaspoon, shape into nests. Bake in oven for 30 minutes. Turn oven off; leave in oven for 30 minutes longer. Cool as above in step 8. Yield: 30 miniature shells.

MERINGUE MUSHROOMS

1 Preheat oven to 95°C/200°F/gas ¼. Line large baking sheet with non-stick baking parchment or foil. Prepare meringue as in Meringue Shells (left).

2 With large writing tube, pipe meringue on to baking sheet in 24 mounds, 4 cm/1 ½ inches in diameter, to resemble mushroom caps.

3 Pipe remaining meringue upright on to baking sheet in twenty-four 3 cm/1 ¼ inch lengths, to resemble stalks.

4 Bake for 1¾ hours. Turn oven off; leave meringues in oven for 30 minutes longer. Cool completely on baking sheet on wire rack.

5 Break *60 g/ 2 oz plain chocolate* into pieces, melt in small bowl over saucepan of gently simmering water, stirring frequently; cool slightly.

6 With tip of small knife, cut small hole in centre of underside of mushroom cap. Place a little melted chocolate in hole; spread underside of cap with chocolate.

7 Carefully insert pointed end of stalk into chocolate-filled hole in centre of underside of mushroom cap.

8 Repeat with remaining caps and stalks. Leave chocolate to dry and set, about 1 hour. Store in tightly covered container. Before serving, sift *cocoa powder* lightly over tops. Yield: 24 mushrooms.

Meringue Shells filled with ice cream or whipped cream, topped with a variety of different coloured fresh fruits, make glorious table centrepieces

Miniature Meringue Shells and Meringue Mushrooms make mouthwatering bite-sized petits fours

STRAWBERRY AND ALMOND DACQUOISE

8 servings
Can be made day before (up to end of step 12) and kept in refrigerator

60 g/2 oz slivered almonds

6 egg whites

225 g/8 oz caster sugar

600 g/1 ¼ lb strawberries

Chocolate Butter Cream (see Box, below)

450 ml/ ¾ pint double or whipping cream

1 In frying pan over medium heat, toast almonds until golden, stirring frequently; cool. In food processor or blender, blend almonds until finely ground; set aside.

2 Line 2 large baking sheets with non-stick baking parchment or foil. Using 20 cm/8 inch round plate or cake tin as guide, mark 2 circles on each lined baking sheet.

3 Preheat oven to 140°C/275°F/gas 1. In large bowl, with electric mixer on full speed, beat egg whites until soft peaks form. Gradually sprinkle in sugar, 1 tablespoon at a time, beating well after each addition until whites stand in stiff, glossy peaks.

4 Into meringue mixture, with wire whisk or rubber spatula, carefully fold ground toasted almonds.

5 Spoon one-quarter of mixture inside each circle on baking parchment or foil; with palette knife, evenly spread meringue to cover entire circle.

6 Place baking sheets with meringue on 2 oven racks; bake for 30 minutes. Switch baking sheets between racks so meringue browns evenly; bake for 30 minutes longer or until golden.

7 Cool meringues on baking sheets on wire racks for 10 minutes. With fish slice, loosen meringues from baking sheets and transfer them to wire racks; cool completely.

8 Hull and thinly slice 150 g/5 oz strawberries. Prepare Chocolate Butter Cream.

9 Place 1 meringue layer on serving plate; spread with one-third of butter cream; top with one-third of sliced strawberries. Make 2 more layers and top with last meringue layer (see Box, right).

10 In medium bowl, whip double or whipping cream until stiff peaks form. Spoon about one-third of whipped cream into piping bag with large star tube; set aside.

11 Spread remaining whipped cream on top and side of gâteau. With cream in piping bag, decorate top edge.

12 Chill dacquoise in refrigerator for 4 hours to soften meringue layers slightly so that they are easier to cut.

13 Cut 16 slices from remaining strawberries; press into cream on side of cake.

14 Top cake with remaining strawberries, hulled and cut in half.

ASSEMBLING THE DACQUOISE

Spreading top layer of butter cream: *with palette knife, evenly spread third layer of butter cream over third meringue layer.*

Topping with strawberries: *arrange remaining sliced strawberries over Chocolate Butter Cream.*

Topping with meringue: *place fourth meringue layer on top to complete.*

CHOCOLATE BUTTER CREAM
In large bowl, with electric mixer, beat *450 g/1 lb icing sugar, sifted, 90 g/3 oz butter, softened, 3 tablespoons milk or single cream,* and *45 g/1 ½ oz cocoa powder* until smooth. Add more milk, if necessary, until butter cream has an easy spreading consistency.

TO SERVE
After dacquoise has been spread with whipped cream, use a 4-pronged fork to make attractive vertical lines all round side; decorate with strawberry slices just before serving.

PANCAKES AND CRÊPES

Pancakes can be folded, rolled or stacked, with or without a filling, to make a different dessert every time you serve them, or they can be enjoyed just as they are, with, a simple sprinkling of caster sugar and a squeeze of lemon. One side is always browner than the other, so have the pale side up when you fold or roll the pancakes, so that the browner, more attractive side is visible.

FREEZING PANCAKES

Pancakes can be prepared and frozen up to 2 months ahead. After stacking pancakes, interleaving them with non-stick baking parchment, allow to cool, then wrap stack tightly in foil; label and freeze. Use within 2 months. To thaw, allow to stand, wrapped, at room temperature for about 2 hours.

PANCAKES

8-10 pancakes

120 g/4 oz plain flour

1 egg, beaten

300 ml/ ½ pint milk and water mixed

1 tablespoon salad oil

Oil for frying

2 With pastry brush, brush bottom of 17.5 cm/7 inch pancake pan and 25 cm/10 inch frying pan with oil.

3 Over medium heat, heat both pans.

5 Using palette knife, work carefully round pancake to loosen it from pan.

6 Invert pancake into hot frying pan. Cook other side for about 30 seconds. While first pancake is cooking, start cooking another pancake in pancake pan.

7 Slide pancake on to non-stick baking parchment. Repeat until all batter is used, stacking pancakes, with non-stick baking parchment between them. Use immediately or wrap in foil and refrigerate or freeze.

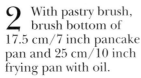

1 Put flour in bowl and make a well in centre. Add egg and gradually stir in half of the milk and water mixture. Using a whisk, blend in flour from sides of bowl. Beat well until mixture is smooth. Stir in remaining liquid and oil.

A handy measuring cup gives you an equal amount of batter every time

Tilt pan to coat bottom evenly

4 Pour 3-4 tablespoons batter into pancake pan; tilt pan to coat bottom evenly. Cook pancake for 2 minutes or until top is set and underside slightly browned.

CRÊPES SUZETTE

6 servings
Allow about 1 hour preparation and cooking time

---

12 pancakes (page 44)

---

1 large orange

---

60 g/2 oz butter

---

30 g/1 oz caster sugar

---

4 tablespoons orange liqueur

Orange slices and shredded orange zest to decorate

1 Prepare pancakes. (If using frozen pancakes, allow to stand, wrapped, at room temperature for about 2 hours until thawed.)

2 About 30 minutes before serving, grate ½ teaspoon zest from orange. Halve orange crossways; squeeze enough juice from orange halves to give 5 tablespoons.

3 Prepare sauce: in large frying pan or chafing dish, over low heat, place grated orange zest, juice, butter and sugar. Heat gently until butter melts.

4 Fold each pancake in half, then fold each one again into quarters.

5 Arrange pancakes in sauce in pan or chafing dish and heat through.

6 In very small saucepan over low heat, gently heat liqueur until warm; remove saucepan from heat. Ignite liqueur with match; pour flaming liqueur over pancakes.

FLAMBÉ

Flambé is the French word for flamed, and generally refers to foods that are bathed in flaming spirits, usually brandy, Cognac or high-proof liqueur. Flaming burns off some of the alcohol, and when the flames die down, the food, now deliciously flavoured, is ready to enjoy. Crêpes Suzette is one of the best-known desserts to use this classic French cooking technique, which is also used in Cherries Jubilee (see recipe below). Here are some tips for success.

• Use a frying pan or chafing dish, preferably a shallow one, to let more oxygen reach the flames and keep them alive longer so they burn off more alcohol.

• Serving dishes should be heatproof; do not use your fine crystal.

• Use wooden matches or long fireplace matches, not book matches, for igniting the spirit.

• Gently warm the spirit before igniting it. Heat it in a very small metal saucepan or ladle, over a low heat – such as a candle – until it is warm but not hot.

• Hold the lighted match over the spirit to ignite the vapours, then slowly pour the flaming spirit over the food. Or, if there isn't much liquid in the frying pan, pour the warm spirit into the pan (don't stir) and light it. Tilt the pan to keep the flames alive as long as possible.

• When the flames die, serve the food at once.

CHERRIES JUBILEE
Just before serving, scoop *vanilla ice cream* into 6 dessert bowls. In large frying pan or in chafing dish at the table, melt *300 g/ 10 oz redcurrant jelly;* stir until smooth. Add *one 425 g/ 15 oz can stoned black cherries, drained;* heat until simmering. Pour in *125 ml/4 fl oz brandy;* heat, without stirring, for 1 minute. Light brandy with match. Spoon flaming cherries over ice cream. Makes 6 servings.

> *TO SERVE*
> *When flames die down, place pancakes on warm dessert plates; decorate with orange slices and shredded orange zest.*

SWEET CHEESE BLINIS WITH CHERRY SAUCE

🍴 6 servings

⏰ Allow about 1 hour preparation and cooking time

12 pancakes (page 44)

350 g/12 oz curd cheese

175 g/6 oz full-fat soft cheese, softened

60 g/2 oz caster sugar

½ teaspoon vanilla essence

Cherry Sauce

1 x 425 g/15 oz can stoned black cherries in syrup

60 g/2 oz caster sugar

1 Prepare pancakes. (If using frozen pancakes, allow to stand, wrapped, at room temperature for about 2 hours until thawed.)

2 About 30 minutes before serving, in medium bowl, with electric mixer, beat curd cheese, full-fat soft cheese, sugar and vanilla essence until smooth.

3 Spread about 1 tablespoon of cheese mixture on each pancake.

4 Fold one side and then its opposite side slightly towards centre.

Blinis are rolled up Swiss roll fashion around a sweet cheese filling

5 Roll up pancake, Swiss roll fashion, starting from an unfolded side.

Here canned black cherries are used to make a simple sauce for pouring over blinis; fresh cherries can be used when they are in season

6 Prepare cherry sauce: put cherries and their syrup in a frying pan or skillet; add sugar and bring to the boil, stirring. Simmer for 5 minutes or until syrup has reduced slightly, stirring occasionally.

7 Add filled pancakes to cherry sauce in pan. Over low heat, simmer for 10 minutes to heat through.

TO SERVE
Place 2 pancakes on each plate and spoon over sauce.

PINEAPPLE PANCAKES

6 servings
Allow 1 ½ hours preparation and cooking time

12 pancakes (page 44)

Vanilla Custard Cream (see Box, right)

1 large pineapple

300 g/10 oz raspberries plus extra for decoration

6 tablespoons icing sugar

6 tablespoons brandy (optional)

1 Prepare pancakes. Prepare Vanilla Custard Cream and refrigerate.

2 About 45 minutes before serving, with sharp knife, cut crown and stalk ends from pineapple; cut off skin. Slice pineapple lengthways in half; remove core from each half. Cut pineapple halves crossways into slices about 5 mm/¼ inch thick; set aside.

3 Over bowl with, back of spoon, press and scrape 300 g/10 oz raspberries firmly against medium-mesh sieve to purée; discard pips left in sieve. Set purée aside.

4 Preheat grill to high. Place 3 pancakes on large baking sheet. On each pancake, spread about 2 tablespoons Vanilla Custard Cream; arrange several slices of pineapple on top of custard cream.

5 Spread about 2 more tablespoons custard cream over pineapple on each pancake; top with another pancake and slice of pineapple. Sift 1 tablespoon icing sugar over each filled pancake.

6 Place baking sheet under hot grill; grill filled pancakes for 6-8 minutes until sugar is caramelized. Remove baking sheet from grill; with fish slice, slide filled pancakes on to large dessert or dinner plates; keep warm. Repeat to make 3 more filled pancakes.

TO SERVE
Spoon raspberry purée round warm pancakes. Sprinkle each serving with about 1 tablespoon brandy and, if you like, sprinkle with more icing sugar. Decorate with fresh raspberries.

VANILLA CUSTARD CREAM
In medium saucepan over medium heat, bring *250 ml/8 fl oz milk* to the boil; remove from heat. In medium bowl, whisk *3 egg yolks*, *½ teaspoon vanilla essence* and *60 g/2 oz caster sugar* until mixture is thick and lemon-coloured; beat in *30 g/1oz plain flour*. Add half of the hot milk, whisking well; pour egg mixture back into remaining milk in pan, stirring constantly. Cook over medium-low heat, stirring, until mixture thickens and boils. Reduce heat to low; cook for 1 minute. Pour into small bowl. To keep skin from forming, press dampened greaseproof paper directly on to surface.

UPSIDE-DOWN APPLE PANCAKE

6 servings
Allow 40 minutes preparation and cooking time

3 large Golden Delicious apples

60 g/2 oz butter

1 teaspoon ground cinnamon

120 g/4 oz caster sugar

50 g/1 ⅔ oz plain flour

5 tablespoons milk

½ teaspoon baking powder

4 eggs, separated

1 Peel and core apples; cut each apple into slices about 3 mm/⅛ inch thick.

2 Place large frying pan with all-metal handle over medium-low heat (if handle is not all metal, cover it with heavy-duty foil).

3 Put butter in frying pan (do not use margarine because it separates from sugar during cooking). Melt butter, then stir in cinnamon and 60 g/2 oz sugar; remove pan from heat.

4 In butter mixture in pan, arrange apple slices, overlapping them slightly (see Box, below). Repeat with smaller circle of apple slices in centre.

5 Return pan to low heat; cook for 10 minutes or until apples are tender but still crisp (see Box, below).

6 Meanwhile, preheat oven to 200°C/ 400°F/gas 6. In medium bowl, with fork, beat flour, milk, baking powder and egg yolks until blended; set aside.

If apple slices are arranged carefully in pan before cooking, they will turn out beautifully

7 In large bowl, with electric mixer on full speed, beat egg whites and remaining sugar until soft peaks have formed. With rubber spatula, very gently fold egg whites into egg yolk mixture.

8 Cover apple slices in pan with egg mixture (see Box, below); with rubber spatula, spread mixture evenly.

9 Bake pancake in oven for 10 minutes or until golden brown. Remove pan from oven and carefully invert pancake on to warm platter.

PLACING APPLES AND PANCAKE MIXTURE IN PAN

Arranging apple slices: *round edge of pan, place apple slices in a circle. Do not crowd apple slices – overlap them slightly so they cook evenly.*

Spoon pancake mixture carefully over apple slices or slices will be dislodged and spoil the look of the finished dessert

Testing apple slices: *with prongs of fork, gently pierce apple slices. They are done when easy to pierce.*

Covering apple slices: *with large metal spoon, slowly pour egg mixture over apple slices, taking care not to shift them.*

Fruit Desserts

When eaten by itself at the peak of its freshness and flavour, fruit is truly a 'natural' dessert. But it can also be transformed into a myriad of different and delicious puddings, ranging from simple mixtures such as Gingered Fruit (below) and Festival Fruit Bowl (page 58), to more elaborate preparations like Grape Clusters in Shimmering Lemon Cheese (page 56), and Fresh Fruit Gâteau (page 60). Importing has extended the seasonal availability of many familiar fruits, and given us new and exotic kinds, to add flavour, colour and texture to desserts all year round.

GINGERED FRUIT

8 servings
Allow 1 ½ hours preparation and chilling time

2 x 425 g/15 oz cans apricot halves in syrup

1 x 475 g/17 oz can or jar figs in syrup

3 large Red Delicious apples

3 large pears

350 g/12 oz seedless red grapes

350 g/12 oz seedless green grapes

4 tablespoons chopped stem ginger in syrup

2 tablespoons lemon juice

1 Into large bowl, pour apricot halves with their syrup and figs with their syrup.

2 With sharp knife, cut unpeeled apples and pears into bite-sized chunks; discard cores.

3 Add apples and pears to fruit mixture in bowl with grapes, ginger and lemon juice; toss to mix well.

4 Cover and refrigerate for at least 1 hour to blend flavours.

This combination of fresh and canned fruits can be enjoyed all year round

CHERRIES EN GELÉE

4 servings
Can be made day before and kept in refrigerator

1 x 425 g/15 oz can stoned black cherries in syrup

1 x 142 g/4 ¾ oz packet cherry or blackcurrant jelly

4 tablespoons cream sherry

Snow-White Custard (see Box, right) or 300 ml/ ½ pint double or whipping cream

1 tablespoon bottled chocolate syrup or-sauce

Citrus Curls (page 62) to decorate (optional)

Wisps are made by drawing tip of knife or skewer through piped dots of chocolate syrup on custard or cream

1 Drain syrup from can of cherries into large measuring jug; set cherries aside.

2 Add enough *water* to cherry syrup to make 600 ml/1 pint liquid.

3 Heat liquid in large saucepan; add cubes of jelly and stir until dissolved. Remove pan from heat.

4 Stir cream sherry into dissolved jelly and syrup mixture.

For this presentation, each cherry jelly is given individual treatment by being set in a different shaped mould

5 Pour jelly mixture into large bowl; cover and refrigerate until jelly mixture mounds slightly when dropped from a spoon, about 1 hour, stirring occasionally.

6 When jelly mixture is ready, gently stir in cherries. Spoon mixture into 4 individual moulds. Cover and refrigerate until jelly is firm, about 3 hours or overnight.

7 Meanwhile, prepare Snow-White Custard, if using; refrigerate.

SNOW-WHITE CUSTARD

In medium non-stick saucepan, with wire whisk, beat *4 egg yolks* and *60 g/2 oz caster sugar* until evenly blended together. Stir in *450 ml/ ¾ pint single cream* and cook over medium-low heat, stirring constantly with wooden spoon, until mixture thickens and coats a spoon well, about 25 minutes (do not boil or mixture will curdle).

Remove saucepan from heat; stir in *½ teaspoon vanilla essence*. To keep skin from forming as custard cools, press dampened greaseproof paper directly on to surface of hot custard.

8 To serve, turn each jelly out into a large dessert glass or bowl. Spoon custard round jelly (if you are using cream, whip it lightly, then spoon round jelly).

9 With chocolate syrup or sauce in small piping bag with very small writing tube (or paper piping bag with tip cut to make 3 mm/⅛ inch hole), make wisps (see Cream Wisps, page 24). If you like, decorate each serving with a Citrus Curl.

Cherries and sherry account for the superb taste of this simple dessert

POACHED PEARS

🍴 12 servings
🕐 Allow 4 ½ hours preparation and chilling time

1 x 1 litre/1 ¾ pint carton cranberry juice drink or diluted blackcurrant cordial

100 g/3 ½ oz caster sugar

1 medium-sized lemon, cut in half

12 medium-sized firm pears

2 tablespoons redcurrant jelly

Mint to decorate

1 In large flameproof casserole, combine fruit juice or cordial, sugar, lemon halves and *450 ml/ ¾ pint water.*

2 Peel 6 pears, being careful to leave their stalks attached.

3 With sharp knife, cut peeled pears lengthways in half. With teaspoon, scoop out cores and stringy portions from pear halves.

4 As each pear half is peeled and cored, place it in fruit juice mixture, turning to coat completely to help prevent pears from discolouring.

5 Over high heat, bring pear mixture to the boil. Reduce heat to low; cover and simmer for 10-15 minutes until pears are tender. With slotted spoon, transfer pear halves to large bowl.

6 Repeat same procedure (steps 2 to 5) with remaining 6 pears.

7 After all pears are poached, over high heat, bring fruit juice mixture in casserole to the boil; cook, uncovered, for about 20 minutes or until liquid is reduced to about 350 ml/12 fl oz.

PEARS
William's and Cornice are the best varieties of pear for cooking.
If you have a melon bailer, you can use it to remove cores from pears easily and without waste, instead of a teaspoon. After scooping out core, run melon bailer from core to stalk and blossom end of pear to remove stringy portion.
To prevent peeled or chopped pears from browning if left to stand, sprinkle them with lemon juice.

8 Add redcurrant jelly to hot liquid; stir until dissolved. Pour hot syrup over pear halves in bowl; cool. Cover and refrigerate until pears are chilled, about 3 hours, turning them occasionally.

TO SERVE
Arrange pear halves in deep platter; pour syrup over pears. Decorate with mint leaves.

Stalks on some pear halves round edge of platter are left on to create interest

Pears have been poached in cranberry juice drink to colour them a delicate rosy pink

PEARS WITH ZABAGLIONE CREAM

🍴 4 servings

🕙 Begin about
10 minutes before
serving

2 large pears

125 ml/4 fl oz double or
whipping cream

1 tablespoon sweet Marsala

1 teaspoon icing sugar,
sifted

Mint to decorate

*Pears are sliced
lengthways, without
being cut at stalk end*

1 Cut each pear in half
lengthways; with
teaspoon or melon baller,
scoop out core, then run
spoon or melon baller
from core to stalk and
blossom ends of pears to
remove stringy portion.

2 With sharp knife, cut
each pear half length-
ways into thin slices,
almost but not all the way
through the stalk end.

3 Place each pear half,
cut side down, on
dessert plate; spread pear
slices open to form fans.

ZABAGLIONE

There are a number of
classic dessert recipes
using wine and eggs,
and Italian Zabaglione
is probably the most
well known. Its key
ingredient, Marsala, is a
fortified wine, which
means that it contains
both wine and brandy,
and has a dark, rich
flavour similar to sweet,
aged sherry.

Traditionally,
Zabaglione is made with
egg yolks, cooked in a
bowl over hot water
until thickened, but this
method of cooking eggs
is no longer recom-
mended. Using double
or whipping cream, as
in the recipe here, gives
a similar delicious taste.

4 In small bowl, whip
double or whipping
cream with Marsala and
sifted icing sugar until soft
peaks form.

5 Spoon some
zabaglione cream on
each plate with pear.
Decorate with
mint.

POACHED PEACHES IN ROSÉ WINE

6 servings
Can be made day
before and kept in
refrigerator

600 ml/1 pint rosé wine

*8 lemon balm, geranium or
bay leaves, plus extra for
decoration*

*About 75 g/2 ½ oz caster
sugar*

Grated zest of 1 lemon

6 large peaches

1 In flameproof
casserole into which
peaches will fit snugly, mix
wine, lemon balm, gera-
nium or bay leaves, sugar,
lemon zest and *450 ml/
¾ pint water.*

2 Peel peaches (see
Box, above right).
Add peaches to wine
mixture in casserole as
soon as they are
peeled to prevent
discolouring.

PEELING PEACHES

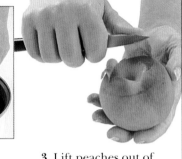

1 Into saucepan of
rapidly boiling water, with
slotted spoon, dip peaches
for about 15 seconds.

2 With slotted spoon,
immediately transfer
peaches to saucepan or
bowl of cold water.

3 Lift peaches out of
water; carefully peel off
skins with sharp knife.

3 Over high heat, bring
peaches and wine
mixture to the boil.
Reduce heat to low; cover
and simmer for 5-10
minutes, shaking pan
occasionally.

4 Spoon peaches and
wine mixture into
large bowl. Cover, then
refrigerate for at least
6 hours or overnight.
Discard leaves
before serving.

*Decorate peaches with
fresh leaves to echo
the flavour of
those used in
cooking*

FRUIT CONTAINERS

Many fruits come 'pre-packaged' in pretty casings which, once freed of their fillings, can be carved and cut for more spectacular servings.

The peel of melons and oranges can be given a scalloped edge, or formed into baskets, with or without a strip over the top for the handle; pineapples can be scooped out, part of their crowns intact, to make attractive 'fruit bowls', filled simply with their own chopped fruit to make easier eating.

Especially eye-catching effects are achieved by using contrasting fruits and shells: red fruits, such as watermelon and raspberries, stand out in green-fleshed melons, while rich green kiwi fruit contrasts well with the amber flesh of papaya in its shell; or for a more delicate effect, fill with mixed pastel-shaded balls of charentais, honeydew and watermelon.

Rock Melon Cup
Cut rock melon crossways in half. Hollow out halves, then fill with balls of charentais, honeydew or Gallia and watermelon. For added colour, sprinkle with a few blueberries, then decorate with a small sprig of mint.

Gallia Bowl
Cut slice off top of Gallia melon; scoop out seeds from centre. Heap centre with watermelon balls and raspberries, allowing them to spill out over top of melon flesh.

Watermelon Basket
Into small round watermelon, make horizontal cut from each end 5 cm/2 inches from top (do not cut through); leave 2.5 cm/1 inch strip in centre. Then make two vertical cuts from top of melon down to horizontal cuts, to create handle. Scoop out melon. If you like, cut scalloped edge round rim of basket. Fill with watermelon, charentais, honeydew or Gallia melon balls, and decorate with sprigs of mint.

Papaya Boat
Slice papaya (pawpaw) lengthways in half. Remove seeds; scoop out flesh and cut into bite-sized chunks. Fill papaya halves with chunks of papaya and honeydew melon. Top with kiwi fruit triangles and decorate with sprig of mint.

Grapefruit Half
Cut grapefruit crossways through centre in zig-zag pattern. Scoop out sections. Fill with clementines in liqueur and raspberries. Decorate with sprig of mint.

Pineapple Boat
Cut pineapple lengthways in half. Cut out core and chunks of flesh. Cut thin slice from underside. Fill shell with kiwi fruit and pineapple; crown with strawberry half.

Filled Fruits
Cut deep 'X' in top of figs, kiwi fruit and strawberries (peel kiwi fruit first). Gently spread fruit apart to make 'petals'; pipe whipped cream into centre of each fruit.

GRAPE CLUSTERS
IN SHIMMERING LEMON CHEESE

8 servings

Can be made day before and kept in refrigerator

Mint leaves

2 x 142 g/4 ¾ oz packets lemon jelly

450 g/1 lb full-fat soft cheese

300 ml/ ½ pint double cream

Grated zest and juice of 2 large lemons

120 g/4 oz seedless green grapes

350 g/12 oz seedless red grapes

1 Chop enough mint leaves to make 2 teaspoons; set aside.

2 Dissolve 1 packet lemon jelly in *150 ml/ ¼ pint boiling water*. In food processor or blender, work jelly liquid, cheese, cream, lemon zest and lemon juice and chopped mint until smooth. Pour mixture into 20 cm/8 inch springform cake tin; cover and chill until almost set, about 1 hour.

3 Meanwhile, in medium bowl, dissolve remaining packet lemon jelly in *600 ml/1 pint boiling water*. Chill until jelly is cool but not set, about 1 hour.

4 While cheese mixture and jelly are chilling, with sharp knife, carefully cut each green grape and 120 g/4 oz red grapes in half lengthways.

5 With kitchen scissors, cut remaining red grapes into small bunches for decoration; wrap and refrigerate.

6 Make grape clusters on cheese layer in springform tin (see Box, right). Carefully pour enough lemon jelly over grape design just to cover grapes but not so much that they will float.

7 Cover tin and chill in refrigerator until jelly is almost set, about 20 minutes. Leave remaining lemon jelly at room temperature so that it does not set.

8 Pour remaining lemon jelly over grapes (see Box, right). Cover and refrigerate until set, about 3 hours.

9 Turn dessert out of tin (see Box, right).

Layers of cheese and lemon jelly look beautiful topped with clusters of grapes

MOULDING DESSERT

Making grape clusters: *arrange green grape halves and red grape halves in 2 clusters on cheese layer in springform tin.*

Pouring lemon jelly over grapes: *carefully pour remaining lemon jelly over grape design; some grapes may not be submerged in jelly.*

Turning out dessert: *with palette knife dipped in hot water, gently loosen edge of dessert; remove side of tin.*

TO SERVE
Place dessert on serving
plate; decorate with
reserved grape bunches
and mint leaves.

FESTIVAL FRUIT BOWL

8 servings

Can be made day before and kept in refrigerator

300 g/10 oz caster sugar

3 tablespoons lemon juice

1 small pineapple

1 small honeydew melon

1 small charentais melon

2 oranges

2 large nectarines or 4 apricots

2 large red plums (optional)

225 g/8 oz seedless green grapes

2 kiwi fruit

1 In medium saucepan over medium heat, heat *450 ml/ ¾ pint water* with sugar and lemon juice to boiling point; cook for 15 minutes or until mixture becomes a light syrup. Pour into bowl; cool, then cover and refrigerate until well chilled.

2 Meanwhile, prepare pineapple (see Box, above right).

Festival Fruit Bowl is the perfect summer dessert – you can change the type of fruit according to whatever is freshest and best on the day

3 Cut honeydew and charentais melons into wedges; discard seeds. Cut rind from melon wedges, then cut flesh into bite-sized chunks.

4 With sharp knife, peel oranges, removing all white pith; cut along both sides of each dividing membrane and lift out orange segments from centre.

5 Cut nectarines or apricots and plums (if using) in half and remove stones; slice. Cut grapes in half.

6 In large serving bowl, combine prepared fruit. Pour chilled syrup through sieve over fruit. Cover and refrigerate until well chilled, stirring frequently.

Skin is left on nectarines and plums to provide colour contrast

PREPARING A PINEAPPLE

1 With sharp knife, cut crown and stalk ends from pineapple.

2 Stand pineapple on one cut end; cut off skin in large strips.

3 Cut pineapple from core in large strips; discard core.

4 Cut pineapple strips into bite-sized chunks.

TO SERVE
Peel and slice kiwi fruit. Gently stir kiwi fruit slices into fruit mixture.

SUMMER FRUIT
WITH ALMOND CHANTILLY YOGURT

8 servings

Allow about
30 minutes
preparation time

Almond Chantilly Yogurt
(see Box, right)

4 large kiwi fruit

4 medium-sized plums

2 large peaches

2 medium-sized bananas

1 small charentais melon

120 g/4 oz raspberries

120 g/4 oz blueberries

120 g/4 oz blackberries

Lemon leaves and flaked
almonds to decorate

1 Prepare Almond
Chantilly Yogurt;
spoon into small serving
bowl. Cover and chill in
refrigerator until ready
to serve.

2 About 20 minutes
before serving, with
sharp knife, peel kiwi fruit;
cut each one in half
lengthways.

3 Cut each plum and
peach in half; discard
stones. Peel bananas; cut
each in half crossways,
then cut each half lengthways into 2 pieces.

4 With sharp knife,
cut charentais melon
into thin wedges; remove
seeds and cut rind from
each wedge.

5 Arrange prepared
fruit decoratively on
large platter. Top with
raspberries, blueberries
and blackberries.

**ALMOND CHANTILLY
YOGURT**

Whip *300 ml/ ½ pint*
double or whipping cream
with *45 g/1 ½ oz icing*
sugar, sifted, and *1 tea-*
spoon almond essence
until stiff peaks form.
With rubber spatula or
wire whisk, fold in
300 ml/ ½ pint plain
yogurt until evenly
blended.

TO SERVE
Decorate dessert with
lemon leaves; decorate
Almond Chantilly Yogurt
with flaked almonds and
serve to spoon over fruit.

FRESH FRUIT GÂTEAU

This spectacular showpiece is an artfully arranged selection of juicy, ripe charentais and honeydew melons, red and blue berries, kiwi fruit and pineapple. It makes a wonderful centrepiece for a summer buffet table, and is ideal for barbecues and other informal events when guests can serve themselves. It can be prepared ahead of time too, as long as it is kept, well wrapped, in the refrigerator until you are ready to serve. The calorie-conscious will find the combination of fruit flavours absolutely delicious when eaten plain, but for those who don't mind throwing caution to the wind, a dollop of Crème Cointreau will make it sweeter.

 8-10 servings
Allow 3 hours preparation and chilling time

1 large charentais melon

1 medium-sized honeydew melon

1 large pineapple

2 large kiwi fruit

350 g/12 oz strawberries

225 g/8 oz blueberries

225 g/8 oz raspberries

Crème Cointreau (see Box, page 61)

Mint sprig to decorate

1 Cut each charentais and honeydew melon lengthways into 4 wedges. With spoon, scoop out seeds. Cut wedges crossways into 2.5 cm/1 inch thick slices; cut rind off each slice. Set aside.

2 Cut crown and skin off pineapple. Cut pineapple lengthways in half; cut crossways into 1 cm/ ½ inch thick slices. Cut out tough core of each slice. Cut about one-quarter of the pineapple slices into bite-sized pieces. Peel kiwi fruit; cut into wedges.

3 On large plate with rim (to catch any fruit juices), arrange half of the nice large honeydew slices round rim. Reserve small honeydew slices.

Arranging honeydew slices round edge of plate

ALTERNATIVE FRUIT ARRANGEMENT

Using only four different kinds of fresh fruit, you can create just as eye-catching an arrangement as in the main photograph on page 61. Neat wedges of charentais and honeydew melon can be combined with slices of fresh pineapple, with 'cherry blossoms' providing a pretty finishing touch.

Cherry Blossoms

Fresh mint leaf adds vibrant colour

Cherry is cut lengthways with stalk end left intact to form 'petals'

Four Fruit Gâteau

1 Cut *1 large charentais melon* lengthways into 3 wedges, and cut *1 medium-sized honeydew* lengthways into 4 wedges. With spoon, scoop out seeds. Cut wedges crossways into 2.5 cm/1 inch thick slices, then cut rind off each slice.

2 Cut crown and skin off *1 large pineapple*, reserve crown for decoration. Cut pineapple lengthways in half, then cut crossways into 2.5 cm/1 inch slices. Cut out tough core of each pineapple slice and discard.

3 On large round platter with rim (to catch any fruit juices), arrange large honeydew slices in a ring; fill centre of ring with end pieces; cut pieces to fit, if necessary. Repeat layering with charentais, pineapple and more honeydew slices, filling centre of ring with end fruit pieces as you assemble each layer.

4 Make Cherry Blossoms (page 62) from *450 g/1 lb fresh cherries*; arrange on top of gâteau. Cover tightly and refrigerate for at least 1 hour or until ready to serve.

4 Arrange layers of pineapple slices in centre of plate.

5 Arrange half of the large charentais slices over honeydew slices on rim of plate. Reserve small charentais slices.

6 Repeat with another layer of honeydew and charentais slices. With remaining pineapple and reserved small melon slices, fill in any gaps. Place kiwi fruit wedges on top.

7 Make neat piles of strawberries, blueberries, raspberries and bite-sized pieces of pineapple to cover rest of top of fruit gâteau.

8 Cover gâteau tightly; refrigerate for at least 1 hour or until ready to serve.

9 Meanwhile, prepare Crème Cointreau.

CRÈME COINTREAU
In medium bowl, whip *450 ml/ ¾ pint double or whipping cream* with *60 g/2 oz icing sugar, sifted*, just until soft peaks form. Gradually beat in *4 tablespoons orange liqueur.*

Spoon cream into bowl; cover and refrigerate until ready to serve.

Variegated mint is an unusual decoration for a dessert, but here it looks most effective perched on top of summer fruits

TO SERVE
Decorate centre of chilled fruit gâteau with mint sprig. Serve Crème Cointreau separately.

DECORATING WITH FRESH FRUIT

Fruit used for decoration adds little in the way of calories, but much in terms of colour, brightness and a fresh look to a wide range of desserts.

Like all carefully chosen decorations, fruit should be appropriate in size, shape, taste and colour to the food with which it is served.

Choose fruit that is as near perfect as possible, and leave it until the last moment to prepare, to prevent discoloration.

Small strawberries look very attractive left whole, with their stalks and hulls left on, as do cherries with their stalks left on. But cut into fans and blossoms or dipped into sugar, they take on a new dimension. The zest of citrus fruit such as lemons, limes and oranges is readily shaped into curls, julienne and twists, while slices, rounds and chunks of brightly coloured kiwi fruit, warmly shaded nectarine and coolly neutral pineapple can be used to good effect on contrasting bases or combined with berries.

Strawberry Fans
Starting just below hull, thinly slice strawberry lengthways several times, leaving strawberry connected at hull end. Press down gently to fan out slices slightly.

Citrus Curls
Using canelle knife, remove long thin strips of zest from citrus fruit. Coil zest round to create curls. Use curls individually or mix colours together.

Lemon Twists
With sharp knife, cut lemon crossways into thin slices. Cut from centre to edge of each slice; twist cut edges in opposite directions.

Lemon Cartwheels
With canelle knife, make vertical grooves at regular intervals in peel of whole lemon. With sharp knife, cut fruit crossways into thin slices.

Cherry Blossoms
Starting just below stalk end, make 8 cuts lengthways in cherry, leaving cherry connected at stalk end. Press down gently to fan out 'petals' slightly and expose stone. Place cherry on mint leaf.

Frosted Cherries
Wash cherries but do not remove stalks or stones. While still wet, dip bottoms in caster sugar until evenly coated; allow to dry before using.

Nectarine Slices
Cut nectarine (or peach) in half and twist apart; remove stone. Cut each half lengthways into thin slices; sprinkle with lemon juice if not using immediately. Arrange in fan shape; add mint sprig.

Strawberry Halves
Select firm berries with fresh green hulls and stalks. Cut strawberries lengthways through centres, being careful to leave some of the hull on each half. Arrange cut side up or cut side down, or alternate for a more striking effect.

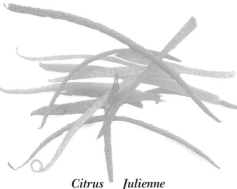

Citrus Julienne
With vegetable peeler, remove zest from citrus fruit in lengthways strips. Lay strips on top of each other; cut into julienne.

FRUIT COMBINATIONS

Eye-catching arrangements of fruit can be used to good effect as decorations on plates and platters when the dessert you are serving is simple. Experiment with different fruits, grouping them together to create dramatic designs and a variety of stunning shapes.

Pineapple and Raspberry Clusters
Cut crown and stalk ends from pineapple. Stand pineapple on one cut end; cut off skin in large strips. Cut pineapple crossways into thin slices and remove core. Cut slice into 4 wedges; arrange as slice. Fill centre with raspberries and mint sprig.

Honeydew Slices
Cut melon lengthways into wedges. Remove seeds and cut flesh from rind. Cut wedges into thin slices and arrange in fan shape, adding a few redcurrants for contrast.

Kiwi Fruit Slices
With sharp knife, remove fuzzy skin from kiwi fruit, then cut fruit crossways into thin slices. Combine with blueberries for extra effect.

SHORTCAKE WITH FRUIT AND CREAM

Whipped cream and strawberries are the usual filling and topping for a traditional American summer shortcake; this deluxe version goes one step further, combining a variety of different coloured fresh fruits with sweetened whipped cream for a more dramatic effect. Of course you don't have to use the fruits suggested here, as long as you are careful to choose ripe, juicy fruits in season and aim for a good contrast of bright colours and interesting shapes and flavours. This fresh, attractive dessert is perfect to serve at an informal gathering with friends, such as at a summer brunch party or al fresco lunch.

8 servings
Allow 1 hour preparation and cooking time

2 large nectarines

45 g/1 ½ oz caster sugar

30 g/1 oz light soft brown sugar

190 g/6 ½ oz self-raising flour

90 g/3 oz butter

1 teaspoon baking powder

½ beaten egg

85 ml/3 fl oz milk

120 g/4 oz cherries

1 small kiwi fruit

225 g/8 oz blackberries or blueberries

300 ml/ ½ pint double or whipping cream

1 Cut nectarines in half and remove stones; slice. In medium bowl, toss nectarines with 1 tablespoon caster sugar. Cover and refrigerate.

2 Preheat oven to 230°C/450°F/gas 8. Grease 20 cm/8 inch round cake tin.

3 Make crumble topping: in small bowl, with fork, mix brown sugar and 40 g/1 ¼ oz flour. With pastry blender or fingertips, cut or rub 30 g/1 oz butter into flour mixture until consistency of mixture resembles peas. Set aside.

MAKING SHORTCAKE

Spreading mixture: in greased cake tin, with rubber spatula, evenly spread shortcake mixture.

Sprinkling topping: over mixture in tin, evenly sprinkle crumble topping.

Sprinkle crumble topping evenly over shortbread so that it will brown nicely during baking

Testing if cooked: when shortcake is golden, insert cocktail stick in centre; it should come out clean.

Transferring to rack: after removing from cake tin, place shortcake, crumble side up, on wire rack to cool.

Handle shortcake gently so crumble topping is not dislodged

4 In large bowl, with fork, mix together baking powder, remaining flour and 1 tablespoon caster sugar.

5 With pastry blender or fingertips, cut or rub remaining butter into flour mixture until consistency of mixture resembles coarse crumbs.

6 In another small bowl, stir beaten egg into milk. Add egg and milk mixture all at once to flour mixture, then stir lightly together with fork until flour mixture is just moistened.

7 Spread shortcake mixture in tin and sprinkle with topping, then bake for 20 minutes or until golden (see Box, page 64). Cover with foil during last 5 minutes of baking if topping is browning too quickly.

8 Carefully remove shortcake from tin; transfer to wire rack (see Box, page 64); cool slightly, about 10 minutes. (Or cool completely to serve later.)

Luscious layers of fresh, juicy fruits, whipped cream and crumbly shortcake are topped with a trio of sweet red cherries

9 Reserve several cherries with stalks for decoration; remove stalks and stones from remaining cherries. Peel kiwi fruit; cut into bite-sized pieces. Gently stir stoned cherries, kiwi fruit and blackberries or blueberries into nectarine mixture.

10 In small bowl, whip double or whipping cream with remaining caster sugar until stiff peaks form.

11 With long serrated knife, carefully split shortcake in half horizontally.

12 Place bottom half of shortcake, cut side up, on dessert plate; top with all but about 60 g/2 oz fruit.

13 Spoon about two-thirds of whipped cream over top of fruit on shortcake.

Spooning whipped cream evenly over fruit so that it spills out over edge when shortcake is placed on top

14 Place top half of shortcake, crumble side up, on cream.

15 Pile reserved fruit in centre of shortcake. Top shortcake with remaining whipped cream and reserved cherries.

WINTER FRUIT COMPOTE

🍴 4 servings
⏱ Allow about 20 minutes preparation time

120 g/4 oz stoned prunes

120 g/4 oz dried apricot halves

125 ml/4 fl oz apple juice or orange juice

2 teaspoons light soft brown sugar

¼ teaspoon ground cinnamon

1 large banana

Whipped Topping (see Box, right)

Dried fruits retain their shape if they are poached gently and not overcooked

1 In medium saucepan over high heat, bring prunes, apricots, apple or orange juice, brown sugar and cinnamon to the boil.

2 Reduce heat to low; cover and simmer for 10 minutes, stirring fruit mixture occasionally.

3 Meanwhile, peel banana and cut into chunks 2.5 cm/1 inch thick. Prepare Whipped Topping.

4 Remove saucepan from heat. With rubber spatula, gently stir banana chunks into dried fruit mixture.

Stirring banana into dried fruit mixture

WHIPPED TOPPING

In small bowl, with electric mixer, beat *4 tablespoons well-chilled evaporated skimmed milk* with *1 tablespoon sifted icing sugar* until stiff peaks form.

Evaporated skimmed milk beats better if partially frozen.

TO SERVE
Spoon warm fruit and Whipped Topping on to 4 dessert plates.

SUMMER FRUIT MÉLANGE

6-8 servings
Allow about
30 minutes
preparation time

2 pink grapefruit

175 ml/6 fl oz apple juice

60 g/2 oz caster sugar

¼ teaspoon ground ginger

*About 1 kg/2 lb piece
watermelon*

*3-4 large nectarines or
peaches*

*About 450 g/1 lb medium-
sized plums*

350 g/12 oz strawberries

*Fresh mint leaves to
decorate*

1 Cut grapefruit
in half and
squeeze out juice.

2 Into large bowl, pour
grapefruit juice and
apple juice.

3 Add sugar and ginger
and stir well to mix.

4 Cut watermelon into
bite-sized pieces;
discard rind.

5 Cut nectarines or
peaches and plums
into wedges; discard stones
from fruit.

6 Hull strawberries; cut
each berry in half
lengthways if berries
are large.

7 Add fruit to juice
mixture in bowl. With
rubber spatula, gently toss
to mix well.

TO SERVE
*Transfer fruit mélange to
large serving bowl;
decorate with mint leaves.*

CHERRIES GLACÉS

 8 servings

Allow 35 minutes preparation, plus freezing time

900 g/2 lb cherries

350 g/12 oz plain chocolate, broken into pieces

300 ml/½ pint single cream

1 Wash cherries but do not remove stalks or stones; pat cherries dry with kitchen paper.

2 Place cherries in single layer on freezer tray; make sure they do not touch each other.

3 Place cherries in freezer until 15 minutes before serving.

4 Remove cherries from freezer; leave to stand at room temperature to soften slightly. Do not allow cherries to thaw completely.

5 Meanwhile, in heavy medium saucepan over low heat, heat chocolate pieces and single cream, stirring frequently, until chocolate is melted and smooth.

TO SERVE
Arrange cherries in large bowl. Pour chocolate sauce into small bowl. Let each person dip partially frozen cherries into chocolate sauce.

CREAM-FILLED STRAWBERRIES

6 servings
Allow about
30 minutes
preparation time

18 very large strawberries

*300 ml/ ½ pint double
cream*

*3 tablespoons lemon curd
(preferably home-made)
or lemon cheese*

1 Cut stalk ends off
strawberries so that
strawberries will stand
upright when filled. With
sharp knife, cut deep 'X'
in opposite (pointed) end
of each fruit.

2 With fingertips, gently
spread each straw-
berry apart to make
'petals'; set aside.

3 In small bowl, whip
double cream until
stiff peaks form.

4 Gently fold lemon
curd or lemon cheese
into whipped cream.

5 Spoon cream
mixture into piping
bag with large writing
tube.

6 Pipe cream mixture
into strawberries.

*Piping cream mixture
into strawberries*

7 Cover and refrigerate
strawberries if not
serving immediately.

ALTERNATIVE FRUIT

When figs are in season, you can fill them with
lemon-flavoured whipped cream, in the same way
as strawberries.

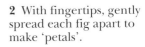
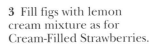

Cream-Filled Figs

1 With sharp knife, cut
stalk ends off *12 medium-
sized figs*, then cut deep
'X' in top of each fruit.

2 With fingertips, gently
spread each fig apart to
make 'petals'.

3 Fill figs with lemon
cream mixture as for
Cream-Filled Strawberries.

*Whipped cream is subtly
flavoured with lemon curd or
lemon cheese and softly piped
in swirls into strawberry
'flowers'*

*Here the flavours of
strawberry and
lemon are linked
together. For a
change, try filling
fresh apricots with
almond-flavoured
cream*

PUDDINGS

Of all the different kinds of desserts, puddings are the ones to call 'comfort food'. Look for variety in texture as well as flavour: smooth and custardy, like Hot Lemon Soufflé Puddings, substantial, like Cinnamon Rice Pudding, or sinfully rich, like Magic Chocolate Pudding.

ORANGE 'PUDDING' CUPS

8 servings
Allow 1 ½ hours preparation and chilling time

4 large oranges

300 ml/ ½ pint double cream

175 ml/ 6 fl oz canned custard

Orange zest to decorate

1 Prepare orange cups of your choice (see above right). With sharp knife, cut thin slice off base of each half so orange halves stand level. Carefully remove fruit from orange halves; cut fruit into small bite-sized pieces. Set fruit and orange cups aside.

2 In small bowl, whip cream until stiff peaks form. Reserve a few pieces of orange to decorate. With rubber spatula, fold remaining orange pieces and canned custard into cream.

Serve these eye-catching orange cups for a children's birthday party – children will love the patterns in the orange skins, especially if you make them different from each other as shown here

Zig-Zag Cups: *with sharp pointed knife, cut crossways through centre of each orange in sawtooth pattern, so that each orange half has zig-zag edge.*

Personalized Cups: *with canelle knife, carve initials of each guest in orange skin. Carve 2 sets of initials in each orange, then, with sharp knife, cut orange crossways in half.*

Striped Cups: *with canelle knife, cut thin strips from orange skin, working from top to bottom of orange. With sharp knife, cut orange crossways in half.*

3 Spoon mixture into orange cups; chill for about 1 hour. To serve, decorate with reserved fruit pieces and orange zest.

CINNAMON RICE PUDDING

6-8 servings

Allow 2 hours preparation and cooking time

1.2 litres/2 pints milk

---

120 g/4 oz short-grain or pudding rice

---

60 g/2 oz caster sugar

Ground cinnamon

Fresh or Maraschino cherries to decorate

1 In very large saucepan over medium heat, heat milk to simmering; stir in rice. Reduce heat to low; cover and simmer for 45-50 minutes until rice is very tender and mixture is thick, stirring occasionally.

2 Preheat oven to 180°C/350°F/gas 4. Grease large rectangular baking dish; set in large roasting tin.

3 Stir sugar gradually into hot rice mixture.

4 Place baking dish in tin on oven rack; carefully pour rice mixture into baking dish (mixture will almost fill dish). Fill roasting tin with boiling water to come halfway up sides of baking dish. Bake for 40-45 minutes until knife inserted in centre of pudding comes out clean.

5 Make Cinnamon Lattice on top of pudding (see Box, right).

Sweet fresh cherries nestle together in centre of rice pudding to give a touch of bright colour

> **TO SERVE**
> *Decorate pudding with cherries. Serve warm or cool and refrigerate to serve cold later.*

CINNAMON LATTICE

Hold ruler diagonally across 1 corner of dish, about 2.5 cm/1 inch in from edge of rice pudding. Holding cinnamon jar in other hand, evenly shake spice through sprinkler holes along ruler edge. Shake excess spice off ruler. Repeat at 2.5 cm/1 inch intervals.

Repeat in opposite direction to form lattice pattern.

Diamond lattice pattern of ground cinnamon both looks and tastes good

HOT LEMON SOUFFLÉ PUDDINGS

🥄 6 servings

🕐 Allow 1 ¾ hours preparation and chilling time

2 medium-sized lemons

2 eggs, separated

150 g/5 oz caster sugar

250 ml/8 fl oz milk

20 g/ ¾ oz plain flour

30 g/1 oz butter, melted

1 Preheat oven to 180°C/350°F/gas 4. Grease six 175 ml/6 fl oz mousse pots or ramekins.

2 Finely grate enough zest from lemons to give 1 tablespoon.

3 Squeeze juice from lemons to make 5 tablespoons; set aside.

4 In medium bowl, with electric mixer, beat egg whites on full speed until soft peaks form; gradually sprinkle in 100 g/3 ½ oz sugar, beating until sugar completely dissolves and whites stand in stiff peaks.

5 In large bowl, using electric mixer, beat egg yolks with remaining sugar until blended; add lemon zest and juice, milk, flour and butter, and beat until well mixed, occasionally scraping bowl with rubber spatula.

6 With wire whisk or with rubber spatula, gently fold beaten egg whites into egg yolk mixture just until mixed.

7 Into prepared mousse pots or ramekins, carefully pour mixture.

8 Set mousse pots in large roasting tin; place on oven rack. Fill tin with boiling water to come halfway up sides of mousse pots. Bake puddings for 40-45 minutes until tops are golden and firm. (Puddings separate into sponge layer on top, sauce layer underneath.)

9 Remove puddings from oven and cool in mousse pots on wire rack.

Individual puddings look really sweet in deep mousse pots, but if you do not have enough pots, make the pudding in 1 large baking dish and bake it for 55-65 minutes

MAGIC CHOCOLATE PUDDING

6 servings
Allow 1 ¼ hours
preparation and
cooking time

| 175 g/6 oz butter |
| 1 teaspoon vanilla essence |
| 400 g/14 oz caster sugar |
| 45 g/1 ½ oz cocoa powder |
| 25 g/ ¾ oz drinking chocolate powder |
| 300 g/10 oz plain flour |
| 5 teaspoons baking powder |
| 450 ml/ ¾ pint milk |
| Whipped cream (see Box, below right) or ice cream |

1 Preheat oven to
180°C/350°F/gas 4.
In large bowl, with electric
mixer, beat butter, vanilla
essence and 225 g/8 oz
sugar until soft. Sift in
cocoa powder, drinking
chocolate powder, flour,
baking powder and milk;
beat until smooth.

2 Pour mixture into
28 x 20 cm/
11 x 8 inch baking dish.

3 In small
bowl, mix
remaining
sugar and
cocoa;
sprinkle
over
mixture
in
baking
dish.

*Pouring mixture
into baking dish*

4 Over mixture
in baking dish,
carefully pour *450 ml/
¾ pint water*, do not stir.

TO SERVE
*Serve with whipped cream
or ice cream, whichever
you prefer.*

5 Bake for 45-55 min-
utes. (Mixture
separates into sponge
layer on top and sauce
layer underneath.)

6 Serve immediately or
sauce will become
absorbed by cake

WHIPPED CREAM

Indispensable as an ingredient in many dessert
dishes, whipped cream can be made from either of
two different creams of varying fat content. Double
cream contains about 48 per cent fat while whipping
cream is slightly lighter, at about 40 per cent fat.
When whipped, cream doubles in volume, and it
should stay whipped for a few hours before it begins
to 'weep'. The following should help ensure a
perfect outcome every time.

• Before starting to
whip, make sure that
cream, bowl and beaters
are well chilled.

• Start by whipping
slowly at first. This will
stabilize cream by
incorporating small air
bubbles into it.

• Finish whipping more
vigorously, until stiff
enough. Longer whip-
ping may break cream
down into butter and
whey.

• If not using whipped
cream immediately,
cover and refrigerate.

FRENCH BREAD PUDDING

🍴 6 servings

🕐 Allow 1 hour preparation and cooking time

1 x 60 cm/24 inch long loaf French or Italian bread (about 225 g/8 oz)

60-90 g/2-3 oz butter, softened

750 ml/1 ¼ pints single cream

75 g/2 ½ oz caster sugar

4 eggs

Grated zest of 1 lemon

Golden syrup for brushing

Double or whipping cream (optional)

Crusty French bread slices take on a glossy sheen when brushed with golden syrup just before serving

1 Preheat oven to 180°C/350°F/gas 4. Cut bread diagonally into 1 cm/½ inch thick slices, each slice about 12.5 cm/5 inches long. Spread one side of each slice with softened butter.

2 In 25 cm/10 inch round flan dish or baking dish at least 4 cm/1 ½ inches deep, arrange bread slices, buttered side up, to fill dish, overlapping slices if necessary.

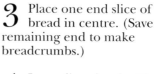

3 Place one end slice of bread in centre. (Save remaining end to make breadcrumbs.)

4 In medium bowl, with wire whisk or fork, beat single cream, sugar, eggs and lemon zest until well mixed.

5 Slowly pour egg mixture over bread slices in dish.

6 With fork, gently press bread slices into egg mixture.

7 Bake for 45-50 minutes until knife inserted in centre of pudding comes out clean. Remove pudding from oven and brush with golden syrup.

Concentric circles of overlapping bread slices accentuate the shape of this continental-style bread pudding

> **TO SERVE**
> *Serve pudding warm, or leave to cool and serve cold later. Serve with double or whipping cream, if you like.*

CAKES
75-130

CAKES

Here is a dazzling assortment of cakes for all occasions, from elegant dinner parties and special holidays to a cosy cup of tea with a friend – try indulgently rich Swiss Chocolate Cheesecake, or Calypso Fruit Cake, so colourful and tasty! Cappuccino Cake with its creamy coffee butter cream icing and Chocolate Buttermilk Gâteau – moist chocolate cake laced with orange liqueur – are as eye-catching as they are delicious. Recipes range from temptingly sumptuous Chocolate Truffle Cake to old-fashioned American Carrot Cake – there is even an ultra-light Angel Cake for the health-conscious dessert lover! In this chapter you will find every kind of cake and gâteau: easy but spectacular Celebration Buffet Cake, made from a packet of sponge cake mix, or the more fancifully decorated Fresh Strawberry Cream Cake, with helpful directions on piping whipped cream. And be sure to use the ideas for using chocolate and flower garnishes to make your luscious cakes even lovelier to look at!

CONTENTS

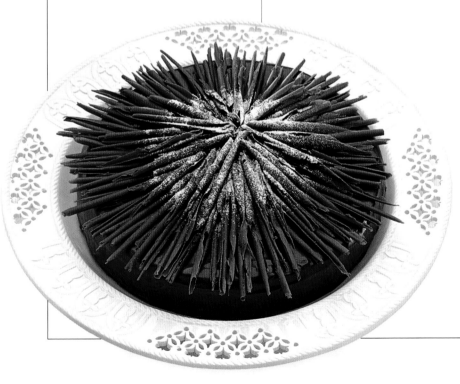

Cakes and Gâteaux

There's a cake or gâteau in this section for every occasion, every feast day, every season. There are lavish cakes to glorify grand celebrations such as weddings, and simple cakes to accompany a cup of morning coffee or afternoon tea, or bring a family meal to a happy ending. The gâteaux are richer and more elaborate, ideal for dinner parties and other such special occasions. Most of the recipes in this section start 'from scratch', but Celebration Buffet Cake cleverly turns a packet sponge mix into a spectacularly delicious (and deliciously spectacular) treat.

CINNAMON CREAM GÂTEAU

16 servings
Can be made up to 3 days ahead and kept in refrigerator

175 g/6 oz soft margarine
100 g/3 ½ oz caster sugar
1 tablespoon ground cinnamon
1 egg
215 g/7 ½ oz plain flour
450 ml/ ¾ pint double or whipping cream
Cocoa powder

1 Preheat oven to 190°C/375°F/gas 5. Tear 9 sheets of non-stick baking parchment, each about 21 cm/8 ½ inches long. On 1 sheet of baking parchment, trace circle, using base of 20 cm/8 inch round cake tin as a guide. Evenly stack all the baking parchment sheets with the marked sheet on top. With kitchen scissors, cut out rounds (see Box, above right).

2 In large bowl, combine margarine, sugar, cinnamon, egg and 150 g/5 oz flour. With electric mixer, beat ingredients until well mixed, constantly scraping bowl with rubber spatula. Continue beating until light and fluffy, about 3 minutes, occasionally scraping bowl. With spoon, stir in remaining flour to make a soft dough.

3 With wet cloth, dampen 1 large or 2 small baking sheets. Place 2 baking parchment rounds on large baking sheet, or 1 on each small baking sheet; with palette knife, spread 4 tablespoons dough in very thin layer on each round (see Box, right).

4 Bake for 6-8 minutes until lightly browned round the edges. Cool on baking sheet on wire rack for 5 minutes; with fish slice, carefully remove biscuit, still on paper, to wire rack to cool completely (see Box, right).

5 Let baking sheet cool before spreading parchment rounds with more dough. (The more baking sheets you have, the faster you can bake the biscuits.) Repeat until all dough is baked, to make 9 biscuits in all. If not assembling gâteau immediately, stack cooled biscuits carefully on flat plate; cover tightly and store in cool, dry place.

6 Early on day of serving, in medium bowl, whip cream until stiff peaks form.

7 Carefully peel parchment off 1 biscuit (see Box, page 78); place on cake plate. Spread with whipped cream. Repeat layering until all biscuits are used, ending with whipped cream.

8 Sift cocoa over whipped cream. If you like, with dull edge of knife, mark 16 wedges on top of gâteau. Refrigerate for at least 4 hours to let biscuits soften slightly for easier cutting.

GINGER CREAM GÂTEAU

If you like, you can change the flavour of this spectacular-looking gâteau from cinnamon to ginger.

Substitute *1 tablespoon ground ginger* for the ground cinnamon in the biscuit dough, then, for decoration, omit sprinkling whipped cream top with cocoa and instead make decorative pattern of finely chopped *crystallized ginger* on each marked wedge of gâteau.

Cocoa powder is sprinkled liberally over whipped cream on top of gâteau

After being sprinkled with cocoa, top of gâteau is marked into 16 wedges to make it easy to serve

Nine layers of crisp, cinnamon-flavoured 'biscuit' are sandwiched together with luscious whipped cream

DOUBLE CHOCOLATE MOUSSE CAKE

This luscious, rich mousse cake is the best chocolate dessert ever – dark, moist, very chocolatey, and soul satisfying! There is no flour in it; but the cake holds together beautifully when cut into slices for serving. Crystallized violets adorning the cream add an elegant finishing touch to the top of the cake.

8-10 servings

Can be made day before and kept in refrigerator

450 g/1 lb plain chocolate, broken into pieces

450 g/1 lb butter, cut into cubes

200 g/7 oz caster sugar

250 ml/8 fl oz single cream

8 eggs

Chocolate Glaze (see Box, page 81)

300 ml/ ½ pint double or whipping cream

Crystallized violets to decorate

1 Preheat oven to 180°C/350°F/gas 4. Grease 23 cm/9 inch springform cake tin.

2 In large heavy saucepan over low heat, heat chocolate, butter, sugar and single cream, stirring frequently, until chocolate melts and mixture is smooth.

3 In large bowl, with wire whisk or fork, beat eggs lightly; slowly beat warm chocolate mixture into eggs until well blended.

4 Pour mixture into springform tin so that it spreads evenly.

5 Bake for about 45 minutes or until skewer inserted in cake 5 cm/2 inches from edge comes out clean. Cool cake completely in tin on wire rack.

Pouring mixture into tin

> **TO SERVE**
> *Decorate piped cream round top edge of cake with crystallized violets.*

Ridged effect on chocolate glaze is made by swirling spatula over glaze while glaze is still warm

6 When cake is cool, carefully remove side of tin; wrap cake tightly, still on tin base, and refrigerate until it is well chilled, at least 6 hours.

7 Prepare Chocolate Glaze.

8 Line cake plate with strips of greaseproof paper. Unwrap cake; remove from tin base. Place cake on plate and spread with warm glaze (see Box, right). Discard greaseproof paper.

9 In small bowl, whip double or whipping cream until stiff peaks form. Spoon whipped cream into piping bag with medium star tube (see Box, right) and pipe cream round top edge of cake. Refrigerate cake if not serving immediately.

CHOCOLATE GLAZE

In heavy non-stick saucepan over very low heat, heat *175 g/6 oz plain chocolate chips* and *30 g/1 oz butter*, stirring frequently, until chocolate is melted and smooth. (If pan is too thin it will transfer heat too fast and burn chocolate.)

Remove pan from heat; beat in *3 tablespoons milk* and *2 tablespoons golden syrup.*

GLAZING AND DECORATING CAKE

Placing cake on plate: *on cake plate lined with strips of greaseproof paper (to catch glaze as it drips), carefully place well-chilled cake.*

Spreading glaze over cake: *with palette knife, evenly spread warm glaze over top and down side of cake.*

Don't worry if your cake sinks and looks unattractive at this stage; once glazed and decorated, it will look superb

Piping cream: *round top edge of cake, pipe scrolls of whipped cream to make continuous circle.*

Filling piping bag with cream: *into piping bag with medium star tube, spoon whipped cream. Twist end of bag to enclose cream.*

PILGRIM PUMPKIN TORTE

8 servings

Can be made day before and kept in refrigerator

Nutty Topping (see Box, right)

250 g/9 oz caster sugar
175 g/6 oz butter, softened
225 g/8 oz canned pumpkin or Mashed Cooked Pumpkin (see Box, page 83)
375 g/13 oz self-raising flour
125 ml/4 fl oz plain yogurt
1 tablespoon mixed spice
3 eggs
450 ml/ ¾ pint double or whipping cream
Rich tea biscuit crumbs to decorate

1 Prepare Nutty Topping; set aside in tins. Preheat oven to 180°C/350°F/gas 4.

2 In large bowl, with electric mixer, beat sugar and butter for 10 minutes or until light and fluffy, scraping bowl often with rubber spatula. Add pumpkin, flour, yogurt, mixed spice and eggs; beat until well mixed, constantly scraping bowl. Beat mixture for a further 2 minutes, occasionally scraping bowl (mixture will be thick).

*CAKE TINS
If you have only 2 cake tins, make 2 separate batches of both topping and cake mixture. Fill and bake 2 tins with 1 batch of each, cool in tins for 10 minutes, then turn out and bake remaining batch. Mixtures will not spoil when left to stand.

3 Spoon mixture over nutty topping in tins; spread evenly with rubber spatula.

4 Arrange 4 cake tins on 2 oven racks, so tins are not directly on top of one another. Bake for 20 minutes or until skewer inserted in centre of each cake comes out clean, swopping racks and, if necessary, position of tins after 10 minutes.

5 Cool cakes in tins on wire racks for 10 minutes. With palette knife, loosen each cake from edge of tin.

6 Turn cakes out on to wire racks; cool.

7 In medium bowl, whip double or whipping cream until stiff peaks form.

NUTTY TOPPING

175 g/6 oz walnut pieces, finely chopped
125 g/4 oz rich tea biscuits, finely crushed
350 g/12 oz light soft brown sugar
175 g/6 oz butter, melted

1 In large bowl, with spoon, mix walnuts, biscuit crumbs, light brown sugar and butter until well blended.

2 Into each of four 23 cm/9 inch round cake tins*, put one-quarter of topping.

3 With fingers, evenly pat topping to cover bottoms of tins.

8 On cake plate, place 1 cake, nutty topping side up; top with one-quarter of whipped cream and spread evenly.

9 Repeat layering, ending with a cake layer, topping side up. Spoon remaining cream round top edge of cake; sprinkle lightly with biscuit crumbs. Refrigerate if not serving immediately.

USING FRESH PUMPKIN

Fresh pumpkin is in season in October. Look for firm, bright pumpkins, free from blemishes. Store in a cool, dry place and cook within 1 month. Mashed cooked pumpkin can be frozen until you are ready to use it.

Mashed Cooked Pumpkin
With sharp knife, cut pumpkin in half; with spoon, scoop out seeds and fibres. Cut pumpkin into chunks. Place chunks in large saucepan in *2.5 cm/1 inch boiling water;* bring back to the boil. Reduce heat to low, cover and simmer for 25-30 minutes or until tender. Drain, cool slightly and remove peel. Return pumpkin to saucepan and mash with potato masher. Drain well.

The eight blobs of whipped cream around top edge of cake make it easy to cut cake into slices of equal size

Finely crushed rich tea biscuits are sprinkled over blobs of cream to add texture and flavour

Each of the four layers of cake has two layers of its own – a nutty, crunchy layer on top, and a spicy pumpkin sponge underneath

CHOCOLATE BUTTERMILK GÂTEAU

8-10 servings

Can be made day before and kept in refrigerator

300 g/10 oz caster sugar

150 g/5 oz butter, softened

250 g/9 oz self-raising flour

350 ml/12 fl oz buttermilk

60 g/2 oz cocoa powder

½ teaspoon coffee essence

2 eggs

120 g/4 oz plain chocolate flavour cake covering

Vanilla Butter Cream (see Box, above right)

3 tablespoons orange liqueur (optional)

Vanilla-flavoured butter cream is piped in large 'dollops' round edge of cake, in smaller 'dollops' in centre

1 Preheat oven to 180°C/350°F/gas 4. Grease 25 cm/10 inch springform cake tin; line bottom of tin with non-stick baking parchment.

2 In large bowl, with electric mixer, beat sugar and butter for 10 minutes or until light and fluffy, scraping bowl often with rubber spatula. Add flour, buttermilk, cocoa, coffee essence and eggs; beat until well mixed, constantly scraping bowl. Beat for a further 2 minutes, occasionally scraping bowl.

3 Spoon mixture into springform tin, spreading evenly.

4 Bake for 45 minutes or until skewer inserted in centre of cake comes out clean.

5 Cool cake in tin on wire rack for 10 minutes. With palette knife, loosen cake from edge of tin; turn out on to wire rack. Peel off paper. Cool completely.

6 Meanwhile, using plain chocolate flavour cake covering, make Dark Chocolate Curls (page 142).

7 Prepare Vanilla Butter Cream.

8 Place cake on large platter. If using liqueur, with skewer or fork, make holes all over top of cake. Sprinkle liqueur evenly over top of cake.

> **VANILLA BUTTER CREAM**
>
> In large bowl, with electric mixer, beat *450 g/1 lb icing sugar, sifted, 90 g/3 oz butter, softened, 3 tablespoons milk* and *1 ½ teaspoons vanilla essence* until smooth. Add more milk if necessary until butter cream is smooth, with an easy spreading consistency.

9 Spoon about one-third of butter cream into piping bag with large writing tube; set aside. Cover top and side of cake with remaining butter cream. With butter cream in piping bag, pipe circle of small 'dollops' round top edge of cake, then pipe another circle of smaller 'dollops' 7.5 cm/ 3 inches from edge of cake. Press some chocolate curls on to side of cake; sprinkle remaining chocolate curls in between 2 circles of dollops on top of cake. Refrigerate if not serving immediately.

AUSTRIAN CHOCOLATE CAKE

8 servings

Can be made day before and kept in a cool place

---

250 g/9 oz plain chocolate, broken into pieces

175 g/6 oz unsalted butter

6 eggs, separated

200 g/7 oz caster sugar

30 g/1 oz self-raising flour

60 g/2 oz plain chocolate flavour cake covering

1 tablespoon icing sugar

Whipped cream (see Box, page 73)

TO SERVE
Sift icing sugar over top of cake; decorate with chocolate curls. Serve with whipped cream.

---

1 Preheat oven to 170°C/325°F/gas 3. Grease and flour 23 cm/ 9 inch springform cake tin.

2 In heavy non-stick saucepan over low heat, heat plain chocolate and butter, stirring often, until melted and smooth. Remove pan from heat.

3 In large bowl, with electric mixer on full speed, beat egg whites until soft peaks form; gradually sprinkle in 60 g/2 oz caster sugar, beating until sugar completely dissolves and whites stand in stiff peaks.

4 In another large bowl, using electric mixer, beat egg yolks and remaining caster sugar until very thick and lemon-coloured, about 5 minutes. Add melted chocolate mixture, beating until well mixed.

5 Add flour to mixture; continue beating until blended, occasionally scraping bowl with rubber spatula.

6 With rubber spatula or wire whisk, gently fold beaten egg whites into chocolate mixture, one-third at a time.

7 Spoon mixture into tin, spreading evenly. Bake for 30-35 minutes (cake will rise and crack on top while baking).

8 Cake is done when mixture appears set and when skewer inserted in centre comes out moist (but centre should not be runny).

9 Cool cake completely in tin on wire rack (cake will fall and top will crack as it cools).

10 Meanwhile, using plain chocolate flavour cake covering, make Dark Chocolate Curls (page 142).

11 With palette knife, loosen cake from side of tin; remove tin side. Place cake on serving plate.

Icing sugar can be sifted over cake as liberally as you like

Cracks on top of cake are unavoidable, and quite acceptable with this type of very rich continental-style chocolate cake. No-one will notice once they have taken their first ecstatic bite

CAPPUCCINO CAKE

The layers of chocolate cake in this Italian-inspired gâteau are made without flour like a roulade. The cake will rise up in the oven then sink down after baking, giving a light, spongy texture – ideal for a layered cake with a rich filling.

 8 servings
Can be made day before and kept in refrigerator

5 eggs, separated

165 g/5 ½ oz icing sugar, sifted

45 g/ ¾ oz cocoa powder, sifted, plus extra for sprinkling

150 ml/ ¼ pint double or whipping cream

225 g/8 oz full-fat soft cheese, softened

30 g/1 oz plain chocolate, coarsely grated

Coffee Butter Cream (see Box, above right)

Chocolate 'coffee beans' to decorate

1 Preheat oven to 200°C/400°F/gas 6. Grease 33 x 23 cm/13 x 9 inch Swiss roll tin; line bottom with non-stick baking parchment.

2 In large bowl, with electric mixer on full speed, beat egg whites until soft peaks form.

3 Gradually sprinkle in 60 g/2 oz icing sugar, beating until sugar completely dissolves and whites stand in stiff peaks.

4 In another large bowl, using electric mixer, beat egg yolks until very thick and lemon-coloured. Beat in 60 g/2 oz icing sugar and cocoa.

COFFEE BUTTER CREAM

In cup, mix *2 tablespoons hot water* and *2 teaspoons instant coffee powder* until coffee dissolves. In large bowl, with electric mixer, beat *225 g/8 oz icing sugar, sifted*, and *225 g/8 oz butter, softened*, for 10 minutes or until fluffy, scraping bowl often. Gradually beat in coffee mixture until smooth, occasionally scraping bowl. If butter cream is made in advance, store until needed in tightly covered container to prevent crust forming on top.

5 With rubber spatula or wire whisk, gently fold beaten egg whites into egg yolk mixture, one-third at a time.

6 Spoon mixture into tin, spreading evenly. Bake for 15 minutes or until top of cake springs back when lightly touched with finger.

7 Sprinkle clean tea towel with cocoa. When cake is done, immediately turn cake out on to towel. Carefully peel baking parchment off cake. If you like, cut off crisp edges. Cool cake completely.

8 While cake is cooling, prepare soft cheese filling: in small bowl, whip double or whipping cream until stiff peaks form.

ASSEMBLING CAKE LAYERS

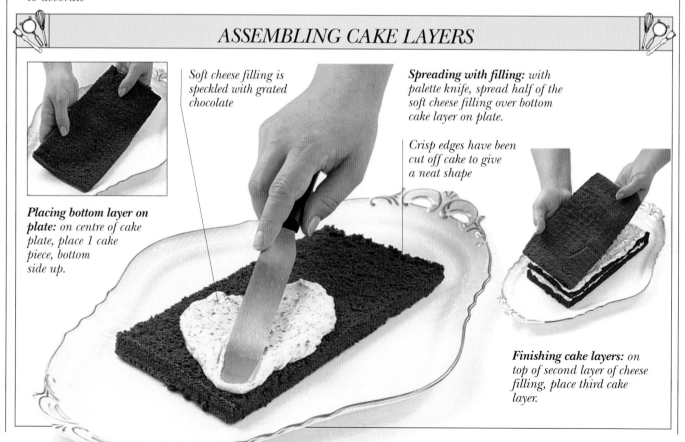

Placing bottom layer on plate: *on centre of cake plate, place 1 cake piece, bottom side up.*

Soft cheese filling is speckled with grated chocolate

Spreading with filling: *with palette knife, spread half of the soft cheese filling over bottom cake layer on plate.*

Crisp edges have been cut off cake to give a neat shape

Finishing cake layers: *on top of second layer of cheese filling, place third cake layer.*

9 In large bowl, with electric mixer, beat remaining icing sugar into full-fat soft cheese. Stir in grated chocolate. With rubber spatula, fold in whipped cream. Chill in refrigerator until ready to use.

10 Prepare Coffee Butter Cream. Spoon one-quarter of the butter cream into piping bag with small star tube.

11 With serrated knife, cut cake crossways into 3 equal pieces.

12 Place 1 cake piece on cake plate and spread with half of the soft cheese filling (see Box, page 86).

13 Repeat layering, finishing with cake layer (see Box, page 86).

14 Spread butter cream on sides and top of cake. Use butter cream in piping bag to pipe lattice top and border. Place a chocolate 'coffee bean' in each lattice diamond. Refrigerate cake if not serving immediately.

Piping butter cream with a small star tube gives lattice and border an attractive ridged effect

A chocolate 'coffee bean' in each 'window' of diamond lattice looks most effective

CHOCOLATE CARAQUE CAKE

The long, thin scrolls on this spectacular chocolate cake are called 'caraque' in French cooking. In this recipe they are made with chocolate cake covering, which is very easy to use.

 8 servings
Can be made day before and kept in a cool place

150 g/5 oz self-raising flour

150 g/5 oz caster sugar

175 ml/6 fl oz soured cream

120 g/4 oz butter, softened

30 g/1 oz cocoa powder

½ teaspoon baking powder

1 egg

175 g/6 oz plain chocolate flavour cake covering

Chocolate Glaze (see Box, above right)

Icing sugar for sifting

1 Grease 23 cm/9 inch round cake tin; line bottom of tin with non-stick baking parchment.

2 Preheat oven to 180°C/350°F/gas 4. In large bowl, with electric mixer, beat first 7 ingredients until blended, occasionally scraping bowl.

3 Spread mixture evenly in tin. Bake for about 30-35 minutes or until skewer inserted in centre comes out clean. Cool in tin on wire rack for 10 minutes. With palette knife, loosen cake from edge of tin; turn out on to wire rack; peel off parchment. Cool completely.

4 Meanwhile, in small bowl over pan of gently simmering water, heat chocolate, stirring often, until melted and smooth. Pour on to 2 large baking sheets, spread evenly and make Chocolate Scrolls (see Box, below).

CHOCOLATE GLAZE
In small heavy saucepan over very low heat, heat 90 g/3 oz plain chocolate, broken into pieces, 45 g/1 ½ oz butter and 2 teaspoons golden syrup, stirring frequently, until melted and smooth. Remove from heat; stir frequently until glaze cools and thickens slightly.

---

5 Make more Chocolate Scrolls with chocolate cake covering on second baking sheet. (Consistency of cake covering is very important. If it is too soft, it will not curl; if too hard, it will crumble. If too firm, leave it to stand at room temperature for a few minutes until soft enough to work with; if too soft, return to refrigerator.) Refrigerate scrolls until firm.

6 Make Chocolate Glaze.

7 Carefully brush away crumbs from cake. Place cake on wire rack over greaseproof paper.

8 Spoon Chocolate Glaze over top and side of cake (some glaze will drip on to greaseproof paper underneath).

9 Leave cake to stand at room temperature until glaze is firm, about 45 minutes.

10 Transfer cake to plate. Arrange Chocolate Scrolls on top and sift over icing sugar.

CHOCOLATE SCROLLS

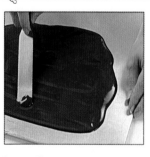

Spreading chocolate: with palette knife, spread melted chocolate flavour cake covering over baking sheets to cover evenly. Refrigerate until firm but not brittle, about 10 minutes.

Making scrolls: place 1 chocolate-covered baking sheet on damp cloth on work surface (damp cloth keeps baking sheet from moving while working). Using straight-edged knife or palette knife, push blade across chocolate to form long, thin scrolls.

Transferring scrolls: with cocktail stick, transfer scrolls to another baking sheet.

CHOCOLATE TRUFFLE CAKE

A gâteau for a special occasion, Chocolate Truffle Cake is a deep, three-layer cake filled and piped with a wickedly rich chocolate truffle mixture. The satiny smooth glaze, a luscious combination of cream and chocolate, gives the finished cake a professional look, yet it is remarkably simple to do.

10 servings
Can be made day before and kept in refrigerator

750 g/1 lb 10 oz plain chocolate, broken into pieces

325 g/11 oz butter, softened

3 eggs

400 g/14 oz self-raising flour

400 g/14 oz caster sugar

300 g/10 oz icing sugar, sifted

175 ml/6 fl oz double or whipping cream

Rose to decorate

1 Grease a deep 23 cm/9 inch round cake tin. Preheat oven to 170°C/325°F/gas 3.

2 In heavy non-stick saucepan over low heat, heat 350 g/12 oz chocolate, 225 g/8 oz butter and *600 ml/1 pint water*, stirring frequently, until melted and smooth. Remove from heat; cool slightly.

3 In large bowl, with wire whisk or fork, beat eggs. Gradually beat warm chocolate mixture into eggs.

4 To chocolate mixture, add flour and caster sugar; continue beating with wire whisk or fork until mixture is smooth and well blended.

5 Pour mixture into cake tin. Bake for 45 minutes or until skewer inserted in centre of cake comes out clean. Cool cake in tin on wire rack for 10 minutes. Remove from tin; cool cake completely on wire rack.

6 Meanwhile, prepare truffle mixture: in bowl over pan of gently simmering water, heat 120 g/4 oz chocolate, stirring frequently, until melted; cool slightly. With spoon, stir in icing sugar, remaining butter and 4 tablespoons double or whipping cream until mixture is smooth and well blended.

7 When cake is cool, slice horizontally into three layers.

8 Prepare glaze: in heavy medium saucepan over low heat, heat 225 g/8 oz chocolate and remaining double or whipping cream, stirring frequently, until melted, smooth and slightly thickened; keep warm.

9 Assemble and glaze cake (see Box, below). Refrigerate cake until glaze is set, about 30 minutes.

10 Remove cake to plate. Pipe border with remaining truffle mixture (see Box, below). Grate remaining chocolate; sprinkle round top edge of cake. Place rose in centre.

ASSEMBLING, GLAZING AND DECORATING CAKE

Glazing cake: over assembled cake, pour prepared glaze. With palette knife, spread glaze to cover top and side of cake completely.

Assembling cake: *with palette knife, spread 1 cake layer with about one-sixth of truffle mixture. Top with second cake layer, pressing down gently but firmly. Spread with another one-sixth of truffle mixture; top with third cake layer.*

Piping border: *with star tube, pipe border of remaining truffle mixture round bottom of cake.*

CHOCOLATE COCONUT CAKE

This four-layer treat boasts shreds of coconut in the cake mixture, chopped walnuts in the sweet filling, whipped cream to accent the chocolate flavour, and paper-thin, dainty 'ruffles' of slivered fresh coconut to crown the whole. If you cannot obtain buttermilk, use fresh milk soured with a few drops of lemon juice.

 8 servings
Can be made day before and kept in refrigerator

Cocoa powder

90 g/3 oz plain chocolate, broken into pieces

225 g/8 oz self-raising flour

300 g/10 oz caster sugar

300 ml/ ½ pint buttermilk

120 g/4 oz butter, softened

½ teaspoon baking powder

3 eggs

100 g/3 ½ oz shredded or desiccated coconut

Chocolate Walnut Filling (see Box, above right)

300 ml/ ½ pint double or whipping cream

Coconut Ruffles (see Box, page 93) to decorate

1 Preheat oven to 180°C/350°F/gas 4. Grease two 23 cm/9 inch round cake tins; dust bottoms and sides of tins with cocoa.

2 In small bowl over pan of gently simmering water, melt pieces of chocolate, stirring often, until smooth; remove bowl from pan.

3 In large bowl, combine next 6 ingredients; add melted chocolate. With electric mixer, beat until mixed, scraping bowl often with rubber spatula. Continue beating for 2 minutes, occasionally scraping bowl. Stir in coconut.

CHOCOLATE WALNUT FILLING
In large non-stick saucepan over medium heat, heat *250 ml/8 fl oz evaporated milk, 120 g/4 oz light soft brown sugar, 120 g/4 oz butter, 60 g/2 oz plain chocolate* and *3 egg yolks, lightly beaten,* until chocolate melts and mixture will coat a spoon well, about 10 minutes, stirring often (do not boil or mixture will curdle). Remove from heat and stir in *225 g/8 oz walnut pieces.* Cool slightly until thick enough to spread, stirring occasionally.

4 Spread mixture evenly in tins. Bake for 35 minutes or until skewer inserted in centres of cakes comes out clean.

5 Cool cakes in tins on wire racks for 10 minutes. With palette knife, loosen cakes from edges of tins; turn out on to wire racks to cool completely.

6 When cakes are cool, prepare Chocolate Walnut Filling. In small bowl, whip double or whipping cream until stiff peaks form.

7 Cut each cake horizontally into 2 layers; place 1 layer on cake plate and spread with half of the Chocolate Walnut Filling (see Box, page 93).

8 Top with a second cake layer; spread with half of the cream. Top with another cake layer; spread with remaining filling. Top with last cake layer; spread with remaining cream (see Box, page 93).

TO SERVE
Decorate top of cake with Coconut Ruffles. Sprinkle some cocoa through sieve over centre. Refrigerate if not serving immediately.

Four layers of Chocolate Coconut Cake are sandwiched together with alternate layers of Chocolate Walnut Filling and whipped cream

Inner skin is left on edges of coconut to give definition to coconut 'ruffles'

Top layer of whipped cream is spread just over edge of cake to give a gentle, curvy outline

ASSEMBLING CAKE LAYERS

Cutting cake into layers: *with serrated knife, cut each cake in half horizontally to make 4 thin layers in all.*

Starting to assemble cake: *on cake plate, place 1 cake layer, cut side up.*

Spreading with first layer of filling: *on first cake layer, with palette knife, evenly spread half of the Chocolate Walnut Filling.*

Topping with third cake layer: *over cream layer, place cake layer, cut side up.*

Spreading with cream: *on last cake layer, with palette knife, evenly spread remaining whipped cream.*

COCONUT RUFFLES

With skewer and hammer, puncture 'eyes' of fresh coconut. Drain off coconut milk (add to orange juice or other fruit drinks). Open shell by hitting very hard with hammer. Hit firmly all round middle.

With small sharp knife, prise out coconut meat piece by piece.

With vegetable peeler, draw blade along curved edge of coconut piece to make wafer-thin, wide ruffles with attractive edging.

Remaining coconut meat can be peeled and shredded or grated for later use; wrap tightly in foil or place in sealed container and keep in refrigerator; use within 1-2 days.

GRANNY'S CAKE

  8 servings
Can be made day
before

400 g/14 oz caster sugar

225 g/8 oz butter, softened

350 g/12 oz self-raising
 flour

250 ml/8 fl oz milk

½ teaspoon baking powder

4 eggs

Icing sugar for sprinkling

Cherries to decorate
 (optional)

1 Preheat oven to
180°C/350°F/gas 4.
Lightly grease and flour
23 cm/9 inch fluted
kugelhopf mould or
savarin mould.

2 In large bowl, with
electric mixer, beat
caster sugar and butter
for 10 minutes or until
light and fluffy, scraping
bowl frequently with
rubber spatula.

3 Add flour, milk,
baking powder and
eggs; beat ingredients until
well mixed, constantly
scraping bowl.

4 Beat mixture for a
further 2 minutes,
occasionally scraping bowl.

5 Spread mixture evenly
in mould.

6 Bake cake in oven for
50-55 minutes or until
skewer inserted in centre
comes out clean. Cool
cake in mould on wire
rack for 10 minutes, then
turn out on to wire rack to
cool completely.

7 Sift icing sugar
over cake.

*A pretty doiley sets off this cake
a treat, especially when the
colours tone so well with the
serving plate and cherry
decoration*

*A liberal
sprinkling of
icing sugar
adds an
attractive
decorative
touch to a
plain and
simple cake*

TO SERVE
*If you like, decorate side of
cake with cherries.*

ALMOND SCALLOP CAKES

Makes 8
Allow 2 hours preparation and cooking time

150 g/5 oz blanched almonds
215 g/7 ½ oz self-raising flour
200 g/7 oz caster sugar
2 eggs
150 ml/ ¼ pint milk
2 tablespoons vegetable oil
1 teaspoon almond essence
Strawberries to decorate

1 In small frying pan over medium heat, cook blanched almonds until golden, stirring often; cool. In food processor or blender, finely grind toasted almonds. (If using blender, grind nuts in 2 batches.)

2 Preheat oven to 180°C/350°F/gas 4. Generously grease eight 12.5 cm/5 inch or 125 ml/ 4 fl oz scallop shell-shaped moulds.

These pretty little teacakes are flecked with ground toasted almonds; if you prefer, you can use walnuts or pecans instead

3 In large bowl, mix ground almonds, flour and sugar.

4 In small bowl, beat eggs lightly; stir in next 3 ingredients.

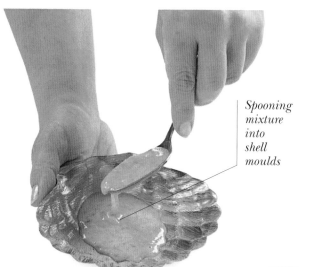

Spooning mixture into shell moulds

5 Stir liquid mixture into flour mixture just until flour is moistened. Spoon mixture evenly into moulds, leaving 1 cm/ ½ inch border all round moulds.

Golden-brown edges add to the visual appeal of the dainty scallop shapes

6 To keep moulds level while baking, arrange them on top of 2 large bun tins, or arrange them on crumpled pieces of foil in baking tray.

7 Bake cakes in oven for 20-25 minutes or until skewer inserted in centres comes out clean.

8 Cool cakes in moulds on wire racks for 5 minutes. Run tip of knife round edges of moulds to loosen cakes; turn cakes out on to wire racks to cool completely. Serve with strawberries.

MOCHA CREAM BUTTERFLY CAKE

16 servings
Can be made day
before and kept in
refrigerator

225 g/8 oz plain chocolate

8 eggs, separated

200 g/7 oz caster sugar

75 g/2 ½ oz plain flour

Chocolate Butterflies (see
  Box, right)

1 teaspoon white vegetable
  shortening

500 ml/16 fl oz double or
  whipping cream

45 g/1 ½ oz cocoa powder

2 teaspoons instant coffee
  granules or powder

1 Grate 175 g/6 oz
chocolate (or in food
processor with knife blade
attached, finely grind
chocolate). Set aside.

2 In large bowl, with
electric mixer on full
speed, beat egg whites
until stiff peaks form.

3 Preheat oven to
180°C/350°F/gas 4.
In another large bowl,
using electric mixer, beat
egg yolks and half of the
sugar until very thick and
lemon-coloured, about
5 minutes. Add flour; beat
until just mixed, occasionally scraping bowl with
rubber spatula. With
rubber spatula, stir in
grated chocolate. Gently
fold beaten egg whites into
egg yolk mixture, one-
third at a time.

4 Evenly spread mixture
in ungreased 25 cm/
10 inch springform cake
tin. Bake in the oven for
40-45 minutes or until top
of cake springs back when
touched with finger. Invert
cake in tin on to rack; cool
completely in tin.

CHOCOLATE BUTTERFLIES

Making rectangles: *cut
baking parchment into five
10 x 6 cm/4 x 2 ½ inch
rectangles. Fold each in half
crossways to form 5 x 6 cm/
2 x 2 ½ inch rectangle.*

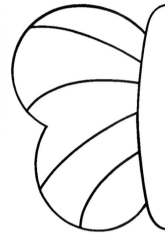

***Making tracing of
butterfly:*** *with pencil,
draw outline of half a
butterfly on each folded
rectangle using centre-fold
for butterfly body (pressure
of pencil point will mark
bottom half of paper as
well). Unfold rectangles and
place on clean flat surface,
tracing side down. Stick
rectangles to work surface
about 5 cm/2 inches apart
with small pieces of tape.*

***Piping chocolate
butterfly:*** *pipe some
chocolate mixture on to a
parchment rectangle in thin
continuous lines over
tracing and along centre-
fold to make a butterfly.
Repeat with remaining
chocolate to make several
butterflies. Remove and
discard tapes.*

Moulding butterflies:
*with fish slice, carefully lift
each piece of parchment and
place, chocolate side up, in
6 cm/2 ½ inch hole in deep
bun tin or in section of
empty egg carton so that
parchment is slightly bent
on centre-fold. Refrigerate
chocolate butterflies for at
least 1 hour or until
chocolate is set.*

Removing parchment:
*with cool hands, carefully
peel off parchment. Keep
butterflies refrigerated until
ready to use.*

5 Meanwhile, prepare Chocolate Butterflies: cut non-stick baking parchment into rectangles and use to make tracings of butterflies (see Box, page 96). In heavy non-stick saucepan over low heat, heat vegetable shortening and remaining chocolate, stirring frequently, until melted and smooth; cool for 10 minutes for easier piping. Spoon chocolate mixture into paper piping bag with tip cut to make 3 mm/⅛ inch hole (or use small piping bag with small writing tube). Pipe butterflies and leave to cool (see Box, page 96).

6 When cake is cooled, prepare mocha cream: in large bowl, whip double or whipping cream with cocoa, instant coffee and remaining sugar until stiff peaks form. Spoon one-quarter of the mocha cream into piping bag with medium star tube; set aside.

7 With palette knife, loosen cake from side of tin; remove tin side. Loosen cake from tin base; remove tin base. With serrated knife, cut cake horizontally into 3 layers.

8 Place bottom cake layer, cut side up, on cake plate; spread with about one-quarter of the mocha cream in bowl. Repeat layering, ending with third cake layer, cut side down.

9 Spread top of cake with thin layer of mocha cream; use remaining mocha cream to ice side of cake. Use mocha cream in piping bag to pipe pretty design on top of cake. Refrigerate cake if not serving immediately.

10 To serve, decorate cake with chocolate butterflies.

Chocolate 'butterflies' perched on cake are made by piping melted chocolate over tracings of butterflies on parchment paper

Mocha cream is piped with star tube to give this spiral effect on top of cake

DECORATING WITH CHOCOLATE

A chocolate butterfly perched on top of a simple dessert will delight the sophisticated dinner party guest as much as it will enchant children at a birthday party. Like the majority of chocolate decorations, butterflies require no special skill, but they do need time for the chocolate to harden. All chocolate decorations except curls can be made with real chocolate; for making curls, use plain chocolate flavour cake covering, which is more manageable.

To melt chocolate: break it into pieces and place in a small bowl over a pan of gently simmering water. Heat for about 5 minutes or until melted and smooth, stirring often with rubber spatula. If using for piping, leave to cool first.

NON-TOXIC LEAVES
These non-toxic leaves are safe for making chocolate leaves: gardenia, grape, lemon, magnolia, nasturtium, rose, violet.

Do not use the following leaves in contact with chocolate or other foods: amaryllis, azalea, caladium, daffodil, delphinium, dieffenbachia, English ivy, hydrangea, jonquil, larkspur, laurel, lily of the valley, mistletoe, narcissus, oleander, poinsettia, rhododendron.

Wash non-toxic leaves in warm, soapy water; rinse and dry well before use.

Chocolate Dipped Fruits
Small fruits like grapes, cherries and strawberries dipped in melted chocolate look very pretty arranged round edge of a cake or dessert, or grouped together in clusters in centre.

Chocolate Leaves
A variety of leaves is brushed with different kinds of melted chocolate to make interesting shapes and colours. Grouping chocolate leaves together in centre of dessert or cake to make a flower shape is especially effective.

Chocolate Cups
Miniature paper or foil cake cases are used as moulds for melted chocolate, then peeled off when chocolate is firm. Filled with piped whipped cream, icing or pieces of fruit, they look good on the edge of plates and platters.

Lacy Lattice
Melted chocolate piped free-hand in lattice design on non-stick baking parchment is refrigerated until firm, then carefully lifted off.

Chocolate Heart
Heart shape is cut out of melted and chilled plain chocolate with a biscuit cutter, then piped with melted white chocolate. Hole is punched with fine skewer for ribbon to be threaded through.

Chocolate Scrolls
Elegant curls are made by pushing knife or palette knife across surface of melted and cooled plain chocolate flavour cake covering.

Chocolate Ruffles
These are made like Chocolate Scrolls (left), but knife or palette knife is pushed only halfway across surface of melted and cooled plain chocolate flavour cake covering.

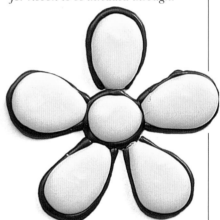

Dainty Daisy
Melted plain chocolate is piped over daisy design on non-stick baking parchment, then left to set before being flooded with melted white chocolate. Daisy is refrigerated until firm, then lifted off parchment.

Simple Curls
These can be made quickly by warming bar of milky white chocolate or plain chocolate flavour cake covering in your hands, then drawing a vegetable peeler along it to produce short, plump shapes.

Fleur-de-Lis
Shape of fleur-de-lis is drawn on non-stick baking parchment, then melted chocolate piped over. Decoration is refrigerated until firm before being carefully lifted off and placed on dessert.

Marbled Triangles
Melted plain and white chocolates are swirled together to make marbled design, then refrigerated until firm. Triangles are then stamped out with small cutter.

CHOCOLATE DIPPED FRUIT

Cherries dipped in melted plain and white chocolates

CHOCOLATE CURLS

Chocolate Scrolls (see Box, page 88), together with white Chocolate Curls

CHOCOLATE BUTTERFLIES

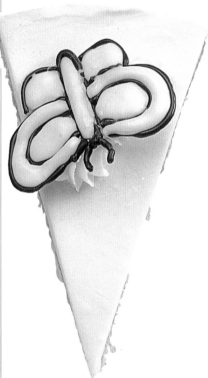

Two-Tone Butterfly made with piped melted plain and white chocolates

1 Rinse fruit under cold running water but do not remove stalks; pat completely dry with kitchen paper; set fruit aside. (For dipping, fruit should be at room temperature.)

2 Melt chocolate in small bowl over pan of gently simmering water (page 98); leave to cool slightly.

3 With fingers, hold stalk of 1 fruit at a time and dip it into chocolate, leaving part of fruit uncovered.

4 Shake off excess chocolate; place fruit on non-stick baking parchment. Leave to stand until chocolate is set, about 10 minutes; remove from parchment.

1 Hold bar or piece of milky white or Swiss white chocolate or plain chocolate flavour cake covering between palms of hands to soften chocolate slightly.

2 Slowly and firmly draw blade of vegetable peeler across wide side of chocolate for wide curls, thin side for thin curls.

3 Use cocktail stick to transfer curls, to avoid breaking them.

This technique is also shown, with dark chocolate, on page 142.

1 With pencil, draw butterflies on rectangles of baking parchment. Place rectangles on clean flat surface, pencil-side down; tape to work surface.

2 Spoon melted plain chocolate (page 98) into paper piping bag with tip cut to make 3 mm/ ⅛ inch hole (or small piping bag with small writing tube).

3 Pipe melted plain chocolate on to non-stick baking parchment rectangle in thin continuous lines over butterfly outline. Refrigerate until set.

4 Spoon melted white chocolate into clean paper piping bag; pipe inside outline. Refrigerate until firm, 1 hour.

CHOCOLATE TRIANGLES

Plain and white chocolate triangles

1 *Tape sheet of non-stick baking parchment to clean work surface.*

2 *With palette knife, spread melted chocolate (page 98) on sheet of non-stick baking parchment. Refrigerate until chocolate is set.*

3 *With small decorative cutter, cut out chocolate shapes. Refrigerate shapes until firm.*

CHOCOLATE SQUIGGLES

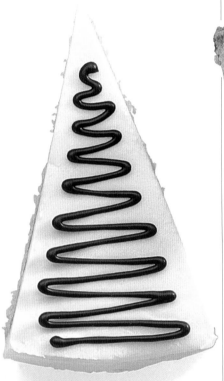

Plain chocolate squiggles

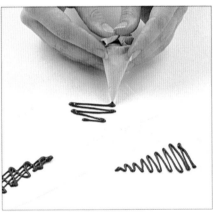

1 *Spoon melted chocolate (page 98) into paper piping bag with tip cut to 3 mm/ ⅛ inch hole.*

2 *On to non-stick baking parchment rectangles, pipe melted chocolate in free-hand squiggle designs.*

3 *Refrigerate chocolate squiggles until they are firm.*

4 *With palette knife, carefully lift chocolate squiggles off baking parchment.*

CHOCOLATE LEAVES

Chocolate leaves in different colours and shapes

1 *Rinse leaves of your choice (see Box, page 98); pat dry with kitchen paper.*

2 *With pastry brush, small painting brush or small palette knife, spread layer of melted chocolate (page 98) on underside of leaves (using underside will give a more distinctive leaf design).*

3 *Refrigerate chocolate-coated leaves until chocolate is firm, about 30 minutes.*

4 *With cool hands, carefully peel leaves away from chocolate.*

WALNUT CREAM GÂTEAU

10 servings
Can be made day before and kept in refrigerator

450 g/1 lb *walnut pieces*

50 g/1 ⅔ oz *self-raising flour*

½ teaspoon *baking powder*

5 eggs, *separated*

150 g/5 oz *caster sugar*

2 tablespoons *corn oil*

600 ml/1 pint *double or whipping cream*

30 g/1 oz *icing sugar, sifted*

1 In food processor or blender, finely grind three-quarters of walnuts with flour and baking powder. (If using blender, blend ingredients in batches.)

2 Preheat oven to 180°C/350°F/gas 4. Grease two 23 cm/9 inch round cake tins; line bottoms of tins with non-stick baking parchment.

3 In large bowl, with electric mixer on full speed, beat egg whites until soft peaks form; gradually sprinkle in one-third of caster sugar, beating until sugar completely dissolves and whites stand in stiff peaks.

4 In another large bowl, with electric mixer, beat egg yolks, corn oil and remaining caster sugar until very thick and lemon-coloured, about 5 minutes. With rubber spatula or wire whisk, gently fold nut mixture and beaten egg whites into egg yolk mixture just until blended.

5 Spoon mixture into tins, spreading evenly. Bake for 20-25 minutes or until tops of cakes spring back when lightly touched with finger. Immediately loosen edges of cakes from sides of tins; turn out cakes on to wire racks and peel off baking parchment. Cool completely.

6 In large bowl, whip double or whipping cream with icing sugar until stiff peaks form. Spoon about one-quarter of whipped cream into piping bag with large star tube; reserve for decoration. Chop remaining walnuts for decoration.

7 With serrated knife, cut each cake in half horizontally to make 4 thin layers in all.

8 Place 1 cake layer on cake plate; spread with one-quarter of whipped cream.

9 Repeat layering, ending with a cake layer. Spread remaining one-quarter of whipped cream on side of cake.

10 Reserve 30 g/1 oz chopped walnuts; press remaining chopped walnuts into cream on side of cake. Pipe whipped cream in piping bag on top of cake in parallel lines.

11 Sprinkle reserved chopped walnuts in between lines of cream on top of cake.

12 Refrigerate cake if not serving immediately.

Parallel lines of piped whipped cream are separated by chopped walnuts

CHOCOLATE MARSHMALLOW CAKE

8-10 servings
Can be made day before

350 g/12 oz *soft margarine*

90 g/3 oz *walnut pieces, finely chopped*

60 g/2 oz *rich tea biscuits, finely crushed*

165 g/5 ½ oz *light soft brown sugar*

215 g/7 ½ oz *self-raising flour*

200 g/7 oz *caster sugar*

30 g/1 oz *cocoa powder*

¼ teaspoon *baking powder*

4 *eggs*

100 g/3 ½ oz *shredded or desiccated coconut*

75 g/2 ½ oz *miniature marshmallows or ordinary marshmallows, halved*

Chocolate Glaze (see Box, below)

Chocolate Curls (see Box, page 104) to decorate

Squiggly chocolate curls are a simple way to dress up a plain glazed cake

CHOCOLATE GLAZE

In small bowl over saucepan of gently simmering water, heat 225 g/8 oz *plain chocolate, broken into pieces,* 45 g/1 ½ oz *butter* and 3 tablespoons *water,* stirring frequently, until melted and smooth. Remove bowl from pan of water. Let chocolate mixture cool to room temperature, then sift in 3 tablespoons *icing sugar,* beating with a spoon until glaze has a thick spreading consistency.

1 Preheat oven to 180°C/350°F/gas 4. Grease two 23 cm/9 inch round cake tins; line bottoms with non-stick baking parchment.

2 In medium saucepan over low heat, heat 120 g/4 oz margarine until melted. Remove from heat; stir in walnuts, biscuit crumbs and brown sugar. Divide mixture equally between cake tins and pat to cover bottoms of tins evenly.

3 In large bowl, with electric mixer, beat flour, caster sugar, cocoa, baking powder, eggs, coconut and remaining margarine until blended, constantly scraping bowl with rubber spatula. Continue to beat for 1 minute.

4 Spoon mixture into tins, spreading evenly. Bake for 30 minutes or until skewer inserted in centre comes out clean. Immediately, with palette knife, loosen cakes from edges of tins; turn out on to wire racks and carefully peel off parchment.

5 While still hot, carefully place 1 cake, crumb mixture side up, on cake plate; top with marshmallows.

6 Immediately place second cake, crumb mixture side up, on top of marshmallows so marshmallows will melt.

7 Insert long metal or wooden skewer in centre of cake to keep top layer from sliding off.

8 Cool cake, then refrigerate until completely cold and marshmallows are set.

9 When cake is completely cold, prepare Chocolate Glaze.

10 Remove skewer from cake. Spread glaze over top and side of cake. Decorate with chocolate curls. Allow glaze to set before serving.

SWISS CHOCOLATE TORTE

This prettily piped and decorated chocolate cake has soured cream in the cake batter, an ingredient that is often used in Swiss, German and Austrian cakes to add moistness. If you would like to intensify the orange flavour of the cake, substitute tiny pieces of candied orange for the crystallized violets in the decoration.

8-10 servings
Can be made day before and kept in refrigerator

120 g/4 oz plain chocolate, broken into pieces

2 eggs, separated

300 g/10 oz caster sugar

120 g/4 oz butter, softened

340 g/11 ½ oz self-raising flour

125 ml/4 fl oz soured cream

2 teaspoons orange-flower water for culinary use

175 g/6 oz plain chocolate flavour cake covering

Chocolate Cream (see Box, page 105)

300 ml/ ½ pint double or whipping cream

Crystallized violets to decorate

1 Grease and flour 25 cm/10 inch springform cake tin.

2 In small non-stick saucepan over very low heat, heat pieces of chocolate, stirring often, until melted and smooth. Remove saucepan from heat.

3 In medium bowl, with electric mixer on full speed, beat egg whites until stiff peaks form.

4 Preheat oven to 180°C/350°F/gas 4.

5 In large bowl, using electric mixer, beat egg yolks, 250 g/9 oz sugar and butter until light and fluffy, about 5 minutes, occasionally scraping bowl with rubber spatula.

6 Add melted chocolate, flour, soured cream, orange-flower water, and *250 ml/8 fl oz water*; beat until well mixed, constantly scraping bowl. Beat for a further 2 minutes, occasionally scraping bowl.

7 With rubber spatula or wire whisk, gently fold beaten egg whites into chocolate mixture.

8 Spoon mixture into tin, spreading evenly. Bake for 45 minutes or until cake springs back when lightly touched with finger. Cool cake in tin on wire rack for 10 minutes.

9 With palette knife, loosen cake from edge of tin; carefully remove side of tin, leaving cake on tin base. Cool completely on wire rack.

10 Meanwhile, break chocolate flavour cake covering into pieces; place in small bowl over saucepan of gently simmering water. Heat chocolate flavour cake covering gently, stirring frequently, until melted and smooth; use to make Chocolate Curls (see Box, below).

11 Prepare Chocolate Cream.

12 Remove cake from tin base. With serrated knife, cut cake horizontally into 2 layers. Place 1 cake layer on cake plate; spread with one-third of the chocolate cream. Top with second cake layer.

CHOCOLATE CURLS

Making chocolate block: *into foil-lined 15 x 8 cm/6 x 3 ¼ inch loaf tin, pour melted chocolate flavour cake covering. Cool, then refrigerate until set, about 2 hours.*

Unmoulding chocolate block: *remove chocolate block from tin; carefully peel off foil.*

Grating chocolate curls: *using coarse side of grater, grate along 1 long side of chocolate block to make long, thin curls (if chocolate appears too brittle to curl, leave to stand at room temperature for 30 minutes to soften slightly).*

13 Spread remaining chocolate cream over top and side of cake. Carefully press chocolate curls on to side of cake.

14 In small bowl, whip double or whipping cream with remaining sugar until stiff peaks form. Spoon whipped cream into piping bag with large star tube; use to pipe border and lattice design on top of cake. Decorate with crystallized violets.

CHOCOLATE CREAM

In non-stick saucepan over medium heat, bring *350 ml/ 12 fl oz double or whipping cream, 225 g/8 oz plain chocolate, broken into pieces*, and *60 g/2 oz butter* to the boil, stirring constantly until mixture is smooth. Pour mixture into large bowl; leave to cool completely at room temperature. With electric mixer, beat chocolate mixture until light and fluffy.

To achieve this looped scroll effect with piped whipped cream, double the scrolls back on themselves while piping

Crystallized violets are placed at the intersections of the whipped cream lattice

MANHATTAN ROULADE

10 servings
Can be made day
before and kept in
refrigerator

6 eggs, separated

215 g/7 ½ oz caster sugar

*120 g/4 oz self-raising
flour*

*45 g/1 ½ oz cocoa powder
plus extra for sifting*

*White Chocolate Butter
Cream (see Box, right)*

*White and dark Chocolate
Curls (pages 100
and 142) to decorate*

1 Grease two 33 x
23 cm/13 x 9 inch
Swiss roll tins; line tins
with non-stick baking
parchment.

2 In large bowl, with
electric mixer on full
speed, beat egg whites
until soft peaks form;
gradually sprinkle in
75 g/2 ½ oz sugar, beating
until sugar completely
dissolves and whites stand
in stiff peaks.

3 Preheat oven to
190°C/375°F/gas 5.
In another large bowl,
using electric mixer, beat
egg yolks and remaining
sugar until very thick and
lemon-coloured. Add flour
and 45 g/1 ½ oz cocoa;
beat until well mixed,
occasionally scraping bowl
with rubber spatula. With
rubber spatula or wire
whisk, gently fold beaten
egg whites into egg yolk
and sugar mixture, one-
third at a time.

WHITE CHOCOLATE BUTTER CREAM

In small heavy saucepan
over medium heat, heat
3 tablespoons milk until
tiny bubbles form round
edge of pan; remove
saucepan from heat.

With wire whisk, beat
in *60 g/2 oz white
chocolate, chopped*; mix
until chocolate melts.
Stir in *4 tablespoons coffee
liqueur*. Cool, then
refrigerate until cold,
about 30 minutes,
stirring occasionally.

In large bowl, place
*120 g/4 oz icing sugar,
sifted*, and *175 g/6 oz
butter, softened* (do not
use margarine; butter
cream will separate).

With electric mixer,
beat for 10 minutes or
until light and fluffy,
scraping bowl often with
rubber spatula.

Gradually beat white
chocolate mixture into
butter cream until
smooth, occasionally
scraping bowl with
spatula.

4 Spoon mixture into
tins, spreading evenly.
Bake for 8-10 minutes or
until tops of cakes spring
back when lightly touched
with finger.

5 Sift cocoa over
2 clean tea towels.
When cakes are done,
immediately turn cakes
out on to towels.

6 Carefully peel baking
parchment off cakes.
If you like, cut off crisp
edges. Starting at a narrow
end of each cake, roll
cakes with towels, Swiss roll
fashion. Place cake rolls,
seam-side down, on wire
racks; leave to cool
completely.

MAKING ROULADE

**Spreading first cake with
butter cream:** *with palette
knife, spread top of 1 cake
evenly with about one-
third of the butter
cream.*

Joining cakes: *along
narrow end of second cake,
place a narrow end of filled
cake roll.*

Rolling cakes together:
*roll second cake round first
cake roll.*

7 Meanwhile, prepare White Chocolate Butter Cream.

8 Unroll 1 cooled cake; spread with about one-third of the butter cream (see Box, page 106). Starting at same narrow end, roll cake without towel. Unroll second cake; spread with another third of the butter cream. Join cakes and roll together (see Box, page 106).

9 Place roulade on serving plate; spread remaining butter cream over roulade. Decorate with chocolate curls. Refrigerate cake if not serving immediately.

CUTTING ROULADE
It is important to slice roulade cleanly, so that filling is seen at its best. For perfect results, dip long serrated knife in hot water before slicing. Wipe blade with kitchen paper after cutting each slice and dip again in water.

Two contrasting colours of chocolate curls look striking when mixed together on top of roulade

Layers of roulade are extra thin and dainty because cake mixture is baked in two separate Swiss roll tins and cakes are joined together at the rolling stage

HAZELNUT AND CREAM SWISS ROLL

12 servings
Can be made day before and kept in refrigerator

4 eggs, separated

120 g/4 oz icing sugar plus extra for sprinkling

120 g/4 oz self-raising flour

300 ml/ ½ pint double cream

120 g/4 oz hazelnut kernels

1 tablespoon liquid honey

MAKING SWISS ROLL

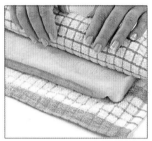

1 Sift icing sugar over clean tea towel. When cake is done, immediately turn out on to towel.

2 With fingers, carefully peel non-stick baking parchment off cake. If you like, cut off crisp edges.

3 Starting at a narrow end, roll cake with towel. Place roll, seam-side down, on wire rack; leave to cool completely.

1 Grease 33 x 23 cm/ 13 x 9 inch Swiss roll tin; line tin with non-stick baking parchment.

2 In large bowl, with electric mixer on full speed, beat egg whites until soft peaks form; gradually sift in 60 g/2 oz icing sugar, beating until sugar completely dissolves and whites stand in stiff peaks.

3 Preheat oven to 190°C/375°F/gas 5.

4 In another large bowl, using electric mixer, beat egg yolks and 60 g/ 2 oz sifted icing sugar until very thick and lemon-coloured. Add flour; beat until well mixed, constantly scraping bowl with rubber spatula.

5 With rubber spatula or wire whisk, gently fold beaten egg whites into egg yolk mixture, one-third at a time.

6 Spoon mixture into tin, spreading evenly. Bake for 12-15 minutes or until cake springs back when lightly touched with finger.

7 Make Swiss roll (see Box, above).

8 While Swiss roll is cooling, whip double cream until stiff peaks form.

9 In small frying pan over medium heat, cook hazelnuts until golden, stirring frequently; cool.

10 Coarsely chop 12 toasted hazelnuts and reserve for decoration; finely chop remaining toasted hazelnuts to use in filling.

11 Fold finely chopped hazelnuts and honey into half of the whipped double cream.

12 Unroll cooled Swiss roll; spread top of cake evenly with whipped cream, honey and hazelnut mixture.

13 Starting at same narrow end, roll cake without towel and then place on platter.

ALTERNATIVE FILLING

The whipped cream, hazelnut and honey filling in the main recipe on this page is very quick and easy to do. If you have more time and would like a richer flavour, try the following Maple Cream Filling.

Maple Cream Filling
In medium saucepan, place 2 tablespoons plain flour; with wire whisk or spoon, slowly stir in 150 ml/ ¼ pint milk and 5 tablespoons maple syrup until smooth.

Cook over medium heat, stirring constantly, until mixture boils; boil for 1 minute until thick. Remove saucepan from heat.

In cup, with fork, beat 2 egg yolks lightly; stir in small amount of hot maple mixture. Slowly pour egg mixture back into remaining maple mixture in pan, stirring rapidly with spoon to prevent lumping; cook over low heat, stirring constantly, until mixture thickens and coats back of spoon well, about 5 minutes (do not boil or mixture may curdle).

Remove saucepan from heat and pour filling into bowl. To keep skin from forming on top of filling as it cools, press a sheet of dampened greaseproof paper directly on to surface of hot filling.

14 Spoon remaining whipped cream into piping bag with large star tube; pipe whipped cream on Swiss roll to make attractive design. Refrigerate roll if not serving immediately.

TO SERVE
Just before serving, sprinkle reserved coarsely chopped hazelnuts over whipped cream on top of cake.

FRESH STRAWBERRY CREAM CAKE

 8-10 servings

Can be made day before and kept in refrigerator

175 g/6 oz soft margarine

175 g/6 oz caster sugar

3 eggs, beaten

175 g/6 oz self-raising flour

1 ½ teaspoons baking powder

700 g/1 ½ lb strawberries

750 ml/1 ¼ pints double or whipping cream

4 tablespoons strawberry jam

1 Grease two 18 cm/ 7 inch round cake tins and line with non-stick baking parchment.

2 Preheat oven to 180°C/350°F/gas 4.

3 In large bowl, place margarine, sugar, eggs, flour and baking powder. With electric mixer, beat well until all ingredients are thoroughly blended.

4 Spoon cake mixture into prepared cake tins, spreading evenly.

5 Bake for 25 minutes or until skewer inserted in centres of cakes comes out clean.

6 Cool cakes in tins on wire racks for 10 minutes.

7 With palette knife, loosen cakes from edges of tins; turn out on to wire racks to cool completely.

8 Hull half of the strawberries and cut each in half; set aside.

9 With serrated knife, cut each cake in half horizontally to make 4 thin layers in all.

10 In large bowl, whip double or whipping cream until stiff peaks have formed.

Strawberries are at their prettiest when hulls and stalks are left on for decoration

Gentle waves of whipped cream are piped with large star tube on top and side of cake

PIPING WHIPPED CREAM

Double or whipping cream can be whipped to double its volume and will stay stiff for several hours. For perfect results, chill bowl, beater and cream before beating. Whip until stiff peaks form, but be careful not to overwhip as this causes cream to become granular and it will then turn to butter. Refrigerate whipped cream if not using immediately. After piping design on to cake, refrigerate until ready to serve. Here we show you how, with piping bag and star tube, you can make a wide range of different shapes and designs.

Adaptor and tube

Piping bag fitted with adaptor and tube

11 Place 1 cake layer on plate; spread with whipped cream. Arrange half of the strawberry halves on top of cream.

12 Top strawberries with second cake layer, pressing down gently but firmly; spread strawberry jam over cake.

13 Top strawberry jam with third cake layer; repeat with whipped cream and strawberry halves. Top with remaining cake layer.

14 Cover top and side of cake with one-third of remaining whipped cream. Spoon rest of whipped cream into piping bag with large star tube; use to decorate top and side of cake.

15 Arrange 3 whole strawberries on top of cake. Cut remaining strawberries in half; use to decorate side of cake. Refrigerate cake if not serving immediately.

ALTERNATIVE FILLING

The simple Victoria sandwich cake on these two pages has a classic filling of jam and whipped cream. For a change, try the following filling.

Raspberry Custard Filling
Sprinkle *225 g/8 oz frozen raspberries* with *60 g/2 oz caster sugar*, thaw, then drain, reserving *125 ml/ 4 fl oz juice*. In saucepan, mix *1 tablespoon powdered gelatine, 4 teaspoons caster sugar* and *4 teaspoons plain flour*. Beat *2 egg yolks* with *250 ml/8 fl oz milk* and raspberry juice; stir into gelatine mixture. Set aside for 1 minute. Cook over low heat, stirring, until mixture thickens and coats a spoon well. Remove from heat; stir in raspberries. Cool, then cover and refrigerate until mixture mounds slightly, stirring occasionally. Whip *150 ml/ ¼ pint double or whipping cream*; fold into custard. Refrigerate until firm enough to spread, about 20 minutes.

CELEBRATION BUFFET CAKE

8-10 servings
Can be made day before and kept in refrigerator

450 g/1 lb plain chocolate, broken into pieces

350 ml/12 fl oz double or whipping cream

125 ml/4 fl oz cream liqueur

2 x 225 g/8 oz packets sponge cake mix

30 g/1 oz cocoa powder

Strawberries to decorate

1 Place chocolate in large bowl. In medium saucepan over medium heat, heat double or whipping cream and cream liqueur until tiny bubbles form round edge of pan; pour hot cream mixture into bowl with chocolate. With electric mixer, beat until chocolate melts and mixture is smooth. Cover and refrigerate chocolate ganache until thickened.

2 Preheat oven to 180°C/350°F/gas 4. Line two 33 x 23 cm/ 13 x 9 inch Swiss roll tins with non-stick baking parchment.

3 Prepare sponge mixture according to packet instructions. Spoon half of the mixture into 1 Swiss roll tin and spread evenly. Sift three-quarters of the cocoa into remaining mixture; stir well. Spread in second tin.

4 Bake cakes for 10 minutes or until skewer inserted in centre comes out clean. Cool in tins on wire racks for 10 minutes. With palette knife, loosen cakes; turn out on to wire racks, peel off parchment and cool.

5 With serrated knife, using cardboard strip as guide, cut each cake in half lengthways, to make 4 equal strips in all.

6 With electric mixer, beat chilled chocolate ganache until thick and with an easy spreading consistency.

7 Place 1 white cake strip on large baking sheet; spread with 5 tablespoons chocolate ganache. Top with 1 chocolate cake strip; spread with 5 tablespoons chocolate ganache.

8 Repeat layering, ending with chocolate cake strip. Set aside remaining ganache.

9 Cover cake and place in freezer until chocolate ganache filling is firm, about 1 hour.

10 Assemble and ice cake (see Box, right). Sift remaining cocoa powder over cake.

11 Transfer cake to serving plate; refrigerate if not serving immediately.

12 To serve, decorate cake with whole fresh strawberries.

ASSEMBLING CAKE

Cutting cake diagonally: *place frozen cake on work surface with long side parallel to edge. With long serrated knife, slice cake in half diagonally from upper rear corner to lower front corner, to make 2 long triangles. Place 1 cake half on foil-covered cardboard strip, cut side facing out.*

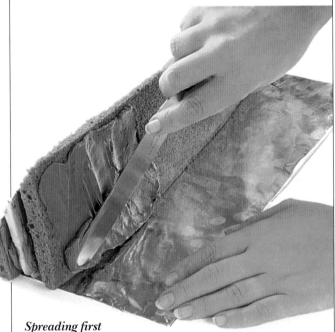

Spreading first cake half with chocolate ganache: *on uncut side of cake half on foil-covered cardboard strip, with palette knife, evenly spread 5 tablespoons chocolate ganache.*

Joining cake halves: *place second cake half, cut side facing outwards, alongside first cake half. Gently press 2 halves together to form 1 large triangle.*

Icing cake: *spread sloping sides of triangle cake with remaining chocolate ganache.*

No-one will believe that this dramatic-looking triangle cake is quick and easy to make – with a sponge mix from a packet!

CARROT CAKE

8-10 servings
Can be made up to
3 days before

450 g/1 lb self-raising flour

500 g/1 lb 2 oz caster
sugar

½ teaspoon baking powder

1 tablespoon ground
cinnamon

4 eggs

350 ml/12 fl oz vegetable
oil

3 medium-sized carrots,
peeled and grated

225 g/8 oz walnut pieces,
chopped

250 ml/8 fl oz apple sauce

150 g/5 oz icing sugar

1 Preheat oven to
170°C/325°F/gas 3.
Grease 25 cm/10 inch
bundt or kugelhopf
mould; dust lightly with
flour.

2 In large bowl, with
spoon, combine
flour, caster sugar,
baking powder and
ground cinnamon.

3 In medium bowl, with
fork, beat eggs lightly;
stir in oil. Stir egg mixture,
grated carrots, walnuts and
apple sauce into flour
mixture just until flour is
moistened.

4 Spoon mixture into
mould, spreading
evenly. Bake for 1 hour
20 minutes or until skewer
inserted in centre of cake
comes out clean.

5 Cool cake in mould
on wire rack for
10 minutes.

*Glacé icing should be just
runny enough to drizzle
down side of cake*

CREAMY CHEESE ICING
In large bowl, place
*350 g/12 oz full-fat soft
cheese, softened, 120 g/
4 oz butter, softened,* and
1 tablespoon lemon juice.
With electric mixer,
beat ingredients until
smooth. Gradually add
*625 g/1 lb 6 oz icing
sugar, sifted,* beating
constantly until
smooth; icing should
have an easy spreading
consistency.

6 With palette knife,
loosen cake from edge
of mould; turn out on to
wire rack and leave to cool.

7 Prepare icing: in small
bowl, with spoon, mix
sifted icing sugar with
5 teaspoons water until
smooth; icing should
have an easy spreading
consistency.

8 Place cake on plate.
With palette knife,
spread icing on cake.

ALTERNATIVE SHAPE

For a different look, you can bake two layers of
carrot cake mixture, then sandwich the layers
together with icing and spread icing over the
whole cake.

Carrot Sandwich Cake
In step 4, spoon mixture
into 2 greased and floured
23 cm/9 inch round cake
tins; bake for 40-45
minutes or until skewer
inserted in centres of
cakes comes out clean.
Cool cakes in tins on wire
racks for 10 minutes; turn
out on to wire racks to
cool completely. Make
Creamy Cheese Icing (see

Box, above left). Place
1 cake, rounded side
down, on serving plate.
With palette knife, spread
cake evenly with 250 ml/
8 fl oz icing. Place second
cake, rounded side up, on
top of first cake. With
palette knife, spread top
and side of cake with
remaining icing, swirling
to make attractive design.

CHOCOLATE CREAM CAKE

 16 servings
Can be made day before and kept in refrigerator

225 g/8 oz plain chocolate

6 eggs, separated

75 g/2 ½ oz caster sugar

50 g/1 ⅔ oz plain flour

120 g/4 oz flaked blanched almonds

Chocolate Cream Filling (see Box, right)

25 g/ ¾ oz cocoa powder

1 Preheat oven to 180°C/350°F/gas 4. Grease 25 cm/10 inch springform cake tin.

2 Grate half of the chocolate; set aside.

3 In large bowl, with electric mixer on full speed, beat egg whites until stiff peaks form.

4 In another large bowl, using electric mixer, beat egg yolks and sugar until very thick and lemon-coloured. Add flour; beat until well mixed, occasionally scraping bowl with rubber spatula. With spatula, stir in grated chocolate. With spatula or wire whisk, gently fold beaten egg whites into egg yolk mixture, one-third at a time.

5 Spoon mixture into tin, spreading evenly. Bake for 25 minutes or until skewer inserted in centre of cake comes out clean. Cool cake in tin on wire rack for 5 minutes. With palette knife, loosen cake from edge of tin; remove tin side. Loosen cake from tin base; slide on to wire rack to cool completely.

6 In frying pan over medium heat, cook almonds until golden, stirring frequently; cool.

7 Prepare Chocolate Cream Filling. Spoon a small quantity of filling into piping bag with small star tube; set aside for decoration. Spoon another small quantity of filling into small bowl; reserve to cover side of cake later.

8 Break remaining chocolate into pieces; place in bowl over saucepan of gently simmering water. Add *2 tablespoons water* to chocolate and heat, stirring frequently, until melted and smooth. Remove from heat.

9 With serrated knife, cut cake horizontally into 2 layers. Spread top cake layer with melted chocolate; leave to stand until chocolate sets slightly, about 10 minutes.

> ### CHOCOLATE CREAM FILLING
> In large bowl, with electric mixer, beat *750 ml/1 ¼ pints double cream, 60 g/2 oz cocoa powder, sifted*, and *150 g/5 oz caster sugar* until stiff peaks form.

10 Meanwhile, place bottom cake layer, cut-side up, on cake plate; spread with filling remaining in large bowl.

11 Cut top cake layer into 16 wedges. Place wedges on top of filling-covered cake layer. Use filling in small bowl to cover side of cake. Pat toasted almonds on to side of cake. Sift cocoa over top of cake. With knife, mark wedges to show servings. Use filling in piping bag to pipe rosette on top of each wedge. Refrigerate cake if not serving immediately.

Chocolate cream filling is piped in rosette shapes on each portion of cake

Cake is marked into serving portions after being sifted with cocoa powder

Toasted flaked almonds add crunch to this rich and creamy cake

CANNOLI CAKE

8-10 servings

Can be made day before and kept in refrigerator

6 eggs, separated

200 g/7 oz caster sugar

120 g/4 oz self-raising flour

2 large oranges

2 tablespoons orange liqueur (optional)

900 g/2 lb ricotta cheese

200 g/7 oz full-fat soft cheese, softened

120 g/4 oz icing sugar, sifted

100 g/3 ½ oz plain chocolate chips

Vanilla Cream Icing (see Box, page 117)

1 Preheat oven to 190°C/375°F/gas 5. Line base of 23 cm/9 inch springform cake tin with non-stick baking parchment.

2 In large bowl, with electric mixer on full speed, beat egg whites until soft peaks form; gradually sprinkle in half of the caster sugar, beating until sugar completely dissolves and whites stand in stiff peaks.

3 In another large bowl, using electric mixer, beat egg yolks, flour, remaining caster sugar and *2 tablespoons water* until blended. With rubber spatula, gently fold beaten egg whites into egg yolk mixture, one-third at a time.

4 Spoon mixture into cake tin. Bake for 30-35 minutes or until cake is golden and top springs back when lightly touched with finger.

MAKING FEATHER DESIGN

Piping circles on cake: *using greaseproof paper piping bag with tip cut to make 3 mm/ ⅛ inch hole, pipe melted chocolate on top of cake in concentric circles, starting in centre and moving to edge of cake.*

Drawing spokes towards centre: *before chocolate hardens, with tip of cocktail stick or small knife, quickly draw lines in spoke fashion, about 4 cm/1 ½ inches apart round edge of cake; alternate direction of each spoke, first from edge to centre of cake, then from centre to edge.*

Completing feather design: *continue round top of cake, alternating direction of each spoke to make attractive feather design.*

5 Invert cake in tin on to wire rack; cool completely in tin.

6 From oranges, grate 2 teaspoons zest and squeeze 5 tablespoons juice (if not using liqueur, increase orange juice to 8 tablespoons). Stir liqueur into juice; set aside.

7 In large bowl, with electric mixer, beat ricotta cheese, soft cheese, grated orange zest and icing sugar until smooth. Stir in 45 g/1 ½ oz chocolate chips.

PAPER PIPING BAG

Cut square of grease-proof paper; fold in half into triangle. Lay triangle on flat surface so wide side is at top. Fold left-hand corner down to centre point. Take right-hand corner; wrap it completely round folded left-hand corner, forming cone. Both corners meet at centre point of original triangle.

Fold in these ends twice to hold together.

Fill cone-shaped paper piping bag two-thirds full; fold top over.

8 With palette knife, loosen cake from edge of tin; remove tin side. Loosen cake from tin base; remove tin base. With serrated knife, cut cake horizontally into 2 layers. Brush orange juice mixture evenly over cut side of both layers.

9 Place bottom cake layer, cut side up, on cake plate. Spoon ricotta cheese filling on centre of cake layer. Spread some filling out to edge, leaving centre rounded to achieve a dome effect.

10 Cut a wedge out of remaining cake layer; place cake layer over the filling and replace wedge. (Cutting wedge will allow cake layer to bend, without cracking, to fit over dome shape.)

11 Prepare Vanilla Cream Icing; spread all over top and down side of cake.

12 In small bowl over pan of gently simmering water, heat remaining chocolate chips, stirring frequently, until melted and smooth.

13 Into paper piping bag (see Box, page 116), spoon melted chocolate. With melted chocolate, make feather design on top of cake (see Box, page 116).

14 Refrigerate cake until filling is firm so that cutting is easy, about 3 hours.

VANILLA CREAM ICING

In medium bowl, with electric mixer, beat *45 g/1 ½ oz butter, softened, 3 tablespoons milk, 200 g/7 oz icing sugar, sifted*, and *¾ teaspoon vanilla essence* until smooth; add more milk if necessary until mixture has an easy spreading consistency. Whip *450 ml/ ¾ pint double* or *whipping cream* until stiff peaks form; fold icing sugar mixture into whipped cream.

Melted chocolate is feathered to give a spider's web effect

Dome-shaped ricotta filling is flavoured with orange; chocolate chips are the surprise ingredient

EDIBLE FLOWERS FOR DECORATING

Many of the flowers that add colour and freshness to the table as the centrepiece can be used to decorate desserts.

When choosing flowers to use with or on foods, keep two important points in mind. First, be sure the ones you want to use are non-toxic. If in doubt, check with the Royal Horticultural Society, or a good reference book. All of the flowers shown in this picture are non-toxic and safe to use with foods.

Next, use flowers that have been grown without the help of pesticides and other chemical sprays. Flowers from the florist have usually been sprayed. Flowers from a home garden, grown without insecticides, are best.

Flowers from a garden should be picked early in the day. Rinse blossoms, leaves and stalks briefly in cool water and shake dry. Keep flowers in water in the refrigerator and use them as soon as you can, as they tend to wilt quickly.

Use flowers in many ways – as buds or open flower heads, with or without the stalk and/ or leaves; or pull off individual petals and sprinkle them over the dessert.

Carnation

Pansy

Viola

Borage

Chrysanthemum

Variegated Geranium

Cornflower

Pink
Geranium

Gypsophila

Lavender

Marigold

Nasturtium

Daylily
(Hemerocallis)

Honeysuckle

Gladiolus

Wild Rose

Freesia

Sweet Pea

Rose

AMERICAN ANGEL CAKE

 16 servings
Allow 3 hours preparation and cooking time

150 g/5 oz icing sugar, sifted

120 g/4 oz plain flour

385 ml/13 ½ fl oz egg whites (12-14 egg whites)

3 tablespoons instant coffee granules or powder

1 ½ teaspoons cream of tartar

250 g/9 oz caster sugar

Coffee Icing (see Box, above right)

75 g/2 ½ oz roasted or toasted almonds, coarsely chopped

1 Preheat oven to 190°C/375°F/gas 5. In small bowl, with fork, stir sifted icing sugar and flour; set aside.

2 In large bowl, with electric mixer on full speed, beat egg whites with instant coffee and cream of tartar until soft peaks form. Gradually sprinkle in caster sugar, 2 tablespoons at a time, beating until sugar completely dissolves and whites stand in stiff peaks. With rubber spatula or wire whisk, fold in flour mixture just until flour disappears.

3 Pour mixture into ungreased 25 cm/ 10 inch angel cake tin or 3.5 litre/6 pint ring mould. Bake cake for 35-40 minutes or until top springs back when lightly touched with finger. Invert cake in tin or mould on to funnel or bottle; cool completely in tin or mould.

4 With palette knife, carefully loosen cake from tin or mould, then place on cake plate.

5 Prepare Coffee Icing; spread icing on top of cake. Sprinkle chopped almonds on icing.

COFFEE ICING
In small bowl, stir *1 tablespoon instant coffee granules* or *powder* with *2 tablespoons very hot water* until coffee dissolves. Stir in *175 g/6 oz icing sugar, sifted*, until smooth.

Coarsely chopped toasted almonds and coffee icing add crunch and flavour to this light-as-air cake, but if you omit them the cake will be very low in calories

CHEESECAKES

Cheesecakes are the ideal party dessert! On the dessert table they catch the eye because they are handsome to look at and sizeable enough to please a large group. They are smooth and creamy in texture, deliciously rich and satisfying to eat; and the different flavours make it easy to fit cheesecake into menus for any occasion. All of these cheesecake recipes can be prepared in advance; they can also be made up to a month ahead and frozen. Make as directed and cool completely, then wrap closely in freezer foil and freeze. Thaw, wrapped, for several hours or overnight in the refrigerator, then add any fruit or decoration just before serving.

PECAN CHEESECAKE

12 servings
Can be made day before and kept in refrigerator

Pastry

150 g/5 oz plain flour

90 g/3 oz butter or block margarine, softened

45 g/1 ½ oz caster sugar

1 egg yolk

Filling

135 g/4 ½ oz pecan or walnut halves

3 ½ x 200 g/7 oz packages full-fat soft cheese, softened

100 g/3 ½ oz caster sugar

4 eggs

4 tablespoons golden syrup

15 g/ ½ oz plain flour

Extra pecans or walnuts to decorate (optional)

Pecan nuts make a pretty pattern round edge of cheesecake and plate

1 First prepare pastry dough: in small bowl, with electric mixer, beat flour, butter or margarine, sugar and egg yolk just until mixed. Shape dough into 2 balls; wrap and refrigerate for 1 hour.

2 Preheat oven to 200°C/400°F/gas 6. Press one ball of dough on to bottom of 25 cm/10 inch springform cake tin; keep remaining dough refrigerated.

3 Bake pastry base for 8 minutes or until golden; cool in tin on wire rack. Turn oven temperature down to 180°C/350°F/gas 4.

4 While pastry base is cooling, prepare filling: reserve 30 g/1 oz pecan or walnut halves for decoration; chop remaining nuts. In large bowl, with electric mixer, beat soft cheese just until smooth; slowly beat in sugar, scraping bowl often with rubber spatula. Add eggs, golden syrup and flour; beat for 2 minutes, occasionally scraping bowl. Stir in chopped nuts.

5 Press remaining dough round side of tin to within 1-2.5 cm/ ½-1 inch of top. Pour cheese mixture into tin.

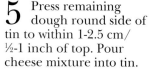

6 Bake cheesecake for 40-45 minutes; cover loosely with foil after 10 minutes, making sure it does not touch filling. Turn oven off; leave cheesecake in oven for 30 minutes. Remove cheesecake from oven; cool completely in tin on wire rack. Cover and refrigerate for at least 3 hours or until well chilled.

7 When cheesecake is firm, with palette knife, loosen tin side from cheesecake and remove; loosen cake from tin base; slide on to plate.

8 Just before serving, arrange reserved nuts on top of cheesecake, using a little extra golden syrup to help them stick. If you like, arrange extra nuts round edge of plate.

Stirring chopped pecans into cream cheese mixture

CHOCOLATE CHEESECAKE

10-12 servings
Can be made day before and kept in refrigerator

Pastry

300 g/10 oz plain flour
60 g/2 oz caster sugar
½ teaspoon baking powder
150 g/5 oz butter or block margarine
2 egg yolks
2 tablespoons milk

Filling

225 g/8 oz plain chocolate, broken into pieces
3 ½ x 200 g/7 oz packages full-fat soft cheese, softened
300 g/10 oz caster sugar
450 ml/ ¾ pint soured cream
3 eggs
Icing sugar for sprinkling

1 First prepare pastry dough: in medium bowl, with fork, stir flour, sugar and baking powder. With pastry blender or fingertips, cut or rub butter or margarine into flour mixture until mixture resembles coarse crumbs.

2 With fork, stir in egg yolks and milk. With hand, mix just until dough holds together. On lightly floured surface, knead dough until smooth, about 2 minutes. Shape dough into 2 balls; wrap and refrigerate for 1 hour.

3 Preheat oven to 190°C/375°F/gas 5. Lightly grease bottom of 23 cm/ 9 inch springform cake tin.

4 Press one ball of dough on to bottom of tin; keep remaining dough refrigerated. Bake pastry base 15-20 minutes until golden; cool in tin on wire rack. Turn oven temperature down to 170°C/325°F/gas 3.

5 While pastry base is cooling, prepare filling: place pieces of chocolate in bowl over saucepan of gently simmering water and heat, stirring frequently, until melted and smooth. Remove saucepan from heat; leave chocolate to cool to room temperature.

6 In large bowl, with electric mixer, beat soft cheese just until smooth; slowly beat in caster sugar, scraping bowl often with rubber spatula. Add soured cream and eggs; beat for 1 minute, occasionally scraping bowl. Stir melted chocolate into cheese mixture. Pour chocolate and cheese mixture into tin.

7 Divide remaining dough into 10 pieces. On lightly floured surface, with hand, roll each piece into 23 cm/9 inch log.

8 Place 5 pastry logs, 4 cm/1 ½ inches apart, across top of cheesecake filling.

TO SERVE
Sprinkle lattice with sifted icing sugar.

Pastry 'logs' arranged diagonally on top of cheesecake make an attractive diamond lattice

9 Lay remaining pastry logs diagonally across first pastry logs to form lattice top. Trim ends of logs even with side of tin.

10 Bake cheesecake for 50-60 minutes, covering tin loosely with foil after 45 minutes if pastry begins to brown too much. Turn oven off; leave cheesecake in oven for 50 minutes. Remove cheesecake from oven; cool completely in tin on wire rack. Cover and refrigerate for at least 4 hours or until well chilled.

11 When cheesecake is firm, with palette knife, loosen tin side from cheesecake and remove; loosen cake from tin base; slide on to plate.

GERMAN CHEESECAKE

12 servings
Can be made day before and kept in refrigerator

Pastry

185 g/6 ½ oz plain flour

120 g/4 oz butter or block margarine, softened

60 g/2 oz caster sugar

1 egg yolk

Grated zest of 1 large lemon

Filling

6 x 200 g/7 oz packages full-fat soft cheese, softened

350 g/12 oz caster sugar

5 eggs

4 tablespoons milk

25 g/ ¾ oz plain flour

2 egg yolks

Grated zest of 1 large lemon

Strawberries and kiwi fruit brushed with melted and sieved raspberry jam (optional)

1 First prepare pastry dough: in medium bowl, with electric mixer, beat flour, butter or margarine, sugar, egg yolk and grated lemon zest until well mixed. Shape dough into ball; wrap and refrigerate for 1 hour.

2 Preheat oven to 200°C/400°F/gas 6. Press one-third of pastry dough on to bottom of 25 cm/10 inch spring-form cake tin; keep remaining dough refrigerated.

3 Bake pastry base for 8 minutes or until golden; cool in tin on wire rack. Turn oven temperature up to 230°C/450°F/gas 8.

4 While pastry base is cooling, prepare filling: in large bowl, with electric mixer, beat soft cheese just until smooth; slowly beat in sugar, scraping bowl often with rubber spatula. Add eggs, milk, flour, egg yolks and lemon zest; beat for 5 minutes, occasionally scraping bowl.

5 Press remaining pastry dough round side of tin to within 1 cm/½ inch of top. Pour in cheese mixture.

Pouring cheese mixture into tin

6 Bake cheesecake for 12 minutes. Turn oven down to 150°C/300°F/gas 2; bake for a further 45 minutes. Turn oven off; leave cheesecake in oven for 30 minutes.

7 Remove cheesecake from oven; cool completely in tin on wire rack.

ALTERNATIVE TOPPING

Instead of the strawberry and kiwi fruit topping shown in the main picture below, you might like to try this delicious Black Cherry Topping.

Black Cherry Topping
Drain 150 ml/ ¼ pint juice from *1 x 425 g/15 oz can stoned black cherries* into small saucepan. Blend in *1 rounded teaspoon arrowroot.* Slowly bring to the boil, stirring until thickened. Add cherries and mix lightly; spoon over cheesecake and leave to cool completely. Chill before serving

8 Cover cheesecake and refrigerate for at least 4 hours or until well chilled.

9 When cheesecake is firm, with palette knife, loosen tin side from cheesecake and remove; loosen cake from tin base; slide on to serving plate.

10 If you like, arrange fruit on top of cheesecake and brush with melted and sieved jam.

LEMON CHEESECAKE

🍴 6-8 servings
🕐 Make day before
and keep in
refrigerator

---

175 g/6 oz digestive
biscuits

---

60 g/2 oz butter

---

25 g/1 oz demerara sugar

---

350 g/12 oz full-fat soft
cheese

Grated zest and juice of
3 large lemons

---

1 x 400 g/14 oz can
sweetened condensed milk

---

150 ml/¼ pint double
cream

---

150 ml/¼ pint soured
cream

Fresh seasonal fruit to
decorate

---

1 Place digestive biscuits in polythene bag; with rolling pin, roll biscuits until they are crushed to fine crumbs.

2 Melt butter in small saucepan, add sugar and biscuit crumbs and stir well to mix.

Garland of redcurrants, blueberries and strawberries looks very pretty on top of cheesecake

3 Turn biscuit mixture into 20 cm/8 inch springform cake tin and press firmly on to bottom with back of metal spoon.

4 In medium bowl, with electric mixer, beat soft cheese just until smooth; add lemon zest and juice and condensed milk and beat until well combined.

5 In another medium bowl, whip double cream until soft peaks form. Fold whipped cream into cheese mixture.

6 Slowly pour cheese mixture into spring-form cake tin so that it evenly covers biscuit crust in bottom of tin.

7 Smooth surface of cheese filling; cover and leave in refrigerator overnight, until well chilled and set.

8 Loosen tin side from cheesecake; remove. Loosen cheesecake from base; slide on to plate.

9 With palette knife, spread soured cream over top of cheesecake.

10 Decorate top of cheesecake with seasonal fresh fruit.

SWISS CHOCOLATE CHEESECAKE

12 servings
Can be made day before and kept in refrigerator

315 g/10 ½ oz crisp plain chocolate biscuits

200 g/7 oz butter, softened

450 g/1 lb Swiss white chocolate, broken into pieces

4 ½ x 200 g/7 oz packages full-fat soft cheese, softened

60 g/2 oz caster sugar

4 eggs

White Chocolate Curls (page 100) and cocoa powder to decorate

3 Preheat oven to 170°C/325°F/gas 3. Place pieces of chocolate in bowl over pan of gently simmering water and heat, stirring frequently, until melted and smooth. If necessary, with wire whisk, beat chocolate until smooth. Remove from heat; leave chocolate to cool to room temperature.

4 In large bowl, with electric mixer, beat soft cheese and remaining butter just until smooth; slowly beat in sugar, scraping bowl often with rubber spatula. Add melted white chocolate and eggs; beat just until smooth.

5 Pour cheese mixture into biscuit crust. Bake cheesecake for 1 hour; cool in tin on wire rack. Cover and refrigerate for at least 4 hours or until well chilled.

6 When cheesecake is firm, with palette knife, loosen tin side from cheesecake and remove. Loosen cake from tin base; slide on to plate.

7 Pile chocolate curls on top of cheese-cake; sift cocoa over chocolate curls.

White chocolate curls look fabulous on slices of white cheesecake, especially with dark cocoa powder dusted over them

1 Place chocolate biscuits, in batches, in polythene bag; with rolling pin, roll biscuits into fine crumbs. Or, in food processor or blender, blend biscuits, in batches if necessary, until fine crumbs form.

2 Lightly grease 25 cm/10 inch springform cake tin. Mix biscuit crumbs and 90 g/3 oz butter in tin; press mixture on to bottom and up side of cake tin to within 1 cm/½ inch of top of tin. Set aside.

Serve Swiss Chocolate Cheesecake on dark plates to create a dramatic colour contrast

COFFEE CHEESECAKE

 10-12 servings
Can be made day
before and kept in
refrigerator

315 g/10 ½ oz almond
macaroons

90 g/3 oz butter, softened

175 g/6 oz plain chocolate,
broken into pieces

4 ½ x 200 g/7 oz packages
full-fat soft cheese,
softened

135 g/4 ½ oz caster sugar

3 eggs

5 tablespoons milk

2 teaspoons instant coffee
powder

Icing sugar, Chocolate
Leaves (page 101) and
fresh raspberries to
decorate

TO SERVE
Sift icing sugar over top
of cheesecake, then
arrange chocolate leaves
and raspberries in centre.

1 Place almond maca-
roons, in batches, in
polythene bag and, with
rolling pin, roll macaroons
into fine crumbs. Or, in
food processor or blender,
blend almond macaroons,
in batches, until fine
crumbs form.

2 In 23 cm/9 inch
springform cake tin,
with hand, mix macaroon
crumbs and butter; press
mixture on to bottom and
up side of cake tin
to within 1 cm/
½ inch of top
of tin. Set aside.

3 Preheat oven to
170°C/325°F/
gas 3. Place pieces of
chocolate in bowl
over pan of gently
simmering water
and heat, stirring
frequently, until
melted and smooth.
Remove from heat.

4 In large bowl, with
electric mixer, beat
soft cheese just until
smooth; slowly beat in
sugar, scraping bowl often
with rubber spatula. Add
melted chocolate, eggs,
milk and instant coffee
powder; beat mixture for
3 minutes, occasionally
scraping bowl.

5 Pour chocolate and
cheese mixture into
biscuit crust.

6 Gently shake tin so
cheesecake mixture
levels out. Bake cheese-
cake for 1 hour. Cool in
tin on wire rack. Cover
and refrigerate for 4 hours
or until well chilled.

7 When cheesecake is
firm, with palette
knife, loosen tin side from
cheesecake and remove;
loosen cheesecake from
tin base; slide cheesecake
on to serving plate.

MELTING CHOCOLATE

Great care must be taken when melting chocolate to
prevent it from burning. Overheated chocolate
scorches easily and becomes bitter, so melt all forms
slowly, using gentle heat. You can use any of these ways.

• Break chocolate into
pieces; place in bowl and
set over saucepan of
gently simmering water.

• Or place in small non-
stick heavy saucepan;
melt over low heat – if
pan is too thin, it will
transfer heat too fast and
burn chocolate.

• Or, for small amounts,
leave chocolate in
original foil wrapper;
set in warm spot on
top of cooker.

• To speed melting, break
up chocolate into smaller
pieces; stir frequently.

• If melting chocolate in
double boiler or bowl over
pan of water, do not boil
water to speed melting.
Any moisture getting into
chocolate will thicken or
curdle chocolate.

• If chocolate thickens or
curdles, add white vege-
table fat (not butter or
margarine) a little at a
time and stir until of
desired consistency.

TORTA RICOTTA

 12 servings
Can be made day before and kept in refrigerator

Pastry

300 g/10 oz plain flour
175 g/6 oz butter or block margarine, softened
60 g/2 oz caster sugar
2 tablespoons dry Marsala wine
2 egg yolks

Filling

900 g/2 lb ricotta cheese
200 g/7 oz caster sugar
250 ml/8 fl oz double or whipping cream
50 g/1 ⅔ oz plain flour
6 eggs
Grated zest of 2 medium-sized oranges
Grated zest of 2 medium-sized lemons
Icing sugar for sprinkling
Orange twists to decorate

1 First prepare pastry dough: in large bowl, with electric mixer, beat flour, butter or margarine, sugar, Marsala and egg yolks just until mixed. Shape dough into a ball. Wrap tightly and refrigerate for 1 hour.

2 Preheat oven to 180°C/350°F/gas 4.

3 Into 25 cm/10 inch springform cake tin, press three-quarters of dough on to bottom and up side of tin to within 2 cm/ ¾ inch of top; keep remaining dough refrigerated.

4 Bake pastry case for 15 minutes or until golden; cool in tin on wire rack.

5 While pastry base is cooling, prepare filling: press ricotta through fine sieve into large bowl. With electric mixer, beat ricotta just until smooth; slowly beat in caster sugar, scraping bowl often with rubber spatula. Add double or whipping cream, flour, eggs and orange and lemon zest; beat until well blended, occasionally scraping bowl. Pour mixture into tin.

6 On lightly floured surface, with floured rolling pin, roll out remaining dough into 25 x 12.5 cm/10 x 5 inch rectangle. Cut dough lengthways into ten 1 cm/ ½ inch wide strips. Place 5 strips about 2.5 cm/ 1 inch apart across filling. Arrange remaining strips at right angles to make a lattice. Trim ends of strips even with pastry case.

7 Bake cheesecake for 1 ¼ hours. Turn oven off; leave cheesecake in oven for 1 hour. Remove cheesecake from oven; cool completely in tin on wire rack. Cover and refrigerate for at least 4 hours or until chilled.

8 When cheesecake is firm, with palette knife, loosen tin side from cheesecake and remove; loosen cake from tin base; slide on to plate.

9 Sprinkle cheesecake with sifted icing sugar. Arrange orange twists round cake.

RICOTTA CHEESE

Ricotta cheese is a pure white, creamy, satiny-smooth cheese with a fine, slightly moist texture and very bland, sweetish flavour. Its nearest 'relative' is curd cheese, but ricotta is creamier.

• Cheesecake made of ricotta – Torta Ricotta – is one of the great classic dishes of Italy. For another Italian-inspired dessert using ricotta, see Cannoli Cake (pages 116-117).

• Ricotta is made from the whey left from the making of other cheeses. It is uncured, and so should be used within a few days of purchase.

FRUIT CAKES

A beautifully decorated fruit cake makes a perfect centrepiece for any celebration, and a delicious dessert to crown a feast or to accompany mulled wine or cider, coffee or tea. Follow the storage tips below if you want to enjoy your fruit cake even after the celebrations are over.

AMERICAN FESTIVAL FRUIT CAKE

Makes one 25 cm/10 inch cake

Make day before or up to 1 month ahead

450 g/1 lb red glacé cherries

120 g/4 oz green glacé cherries

350 g/12 oz stoned prunes

300 g/10 oz stoned dates

120 ml/4 fl oz cream sherry

700 g/1 ½ lb mixed nuts

175 g/6 oz shelled pecans or walnut pieces

215 g/7 ½ oz self-raising flour

200 g/7 oz caster sugar

6 eggs, lightly beaten

1 In very large bowl mix first 5 ingredients; leave to stand for 15 minutes or until almost all liquid is absorbed, stirring often.

2 Meanwhile, brush 25 cm/10 inch angel cake tin or 3.5 litre/6 pint ring mould generously with oil and line with foil, smoothing it out as much as possible so cake does not have wrinkles on side and bottom; grease foil.

3 Preheat oven to 150°C/300°F/gas 2. Stir mixed nuts and pecans or walnuts into fruit mixture in bowl. Remove 225 g/8 oz fruit and nut mixture; set aside. Stir flour and sugar into remaining fruit and nut mixture in large bowl until well coated. Stir in eggs until well mixed.

4 Spoon mixture into tin or mould, spreading evenly. Sprinkle reserved fruit and nut mixture on top. Cover tin or mould loosely with foil. Bake for 2 hours.

5 Remove foil and bake for 30 minutes longer or until knife inserted in cake comes out clean.

6 Cool cake in tin or mould on wire rack for 30 minutes; remove from tin or mould and carefully peel off foil. Cool cake completely on rack.

7 Wrap fruit cake tightly; refrigerate overnight so cake will be firm and easy to slice.

TO STORE FRUIT CAKE

Keep cake, wrapped tightly, in airtight container in a cool place or refrigerator. If you like, sprinkle cake first with wine or brandy.

Alternatively, wrap cake with cloth soaked in brandy or wine, then overwrap with foil. Re-soak cloth weekly.

Top of cake is studded with an abundance of colourful fruit and nuts

CALYPSO FRUIT CAKE

🥄 Makes one 25 cm/
10 inch cake

⏱ Made day before
or up to 1 month
ahead

350 ml/12 fl oz dry
red wine

90 g/3 oz stoned prunes

120 g/4 oz raisins

100 g/3 ½ oz candied
citron, diced

300 g/10 oz caster sugar

225 g/8 oz butter or
margarine, softened

425 g/15 oz self-raising
flour

1 teaspoon ground
cinnamon

3 eggs

1 teaspoon grated lime zest

Lime Glaze (see Box, above
right)

100 g/3 ½ oz mixed glacé
fruit, chopped

1 tablespoon golden syrup

1 Bring first 4 ingredients to the boil in
medium saucepan
over high heat. Remove
saucepan from heat; leave
to soften for 30 minutes.

2 Process fruit mixture
in food processor or
blender, in 2 batches if
necessary, until smooth;
set aside.

3 Preheat oven to
170°C/325°F/gas 3.

4 Grease 25 cm/10 inch
kugelhopf mould or
savarin mould.

5 In large bowl, with
electric mixer, beat
sugar and butter or margarine for 10 minutes or
until light and fluffy
scraping bowl often with
rubber spatula.

6 To butter and sugar
mixture, add flour,
cinnamon, eggs and fruit
mixture; beat until well
mixed, constantly scraping
bowl. Continue beating for
1 minute, occasionally
scraping bowl. Stir in
grated lime zest.

LIME GLAZE

In medium bowl, with spoon, stir *175 g/6 oz icing
sugar, sifted, 4 teaspoons hot water, 2 teaspoons lime juice
and ½ teaspoon grated lime zest* until smooth.

7 Spoon mixture into
mould, spreading
evenly. Bake for 1 hour or
until skewer inserted in
centre of cake comes out
clean. Cool cake in mould
on wire rack for about
10 minutes; remove cake
from mould. Cool cake
completely on rack.

8 To serve, prepare
Lime Glaze. Spoon
glaze over cake.

9 In small bowl, stir
mixed glacé fruit with
golden syrup.

10 As quickly as
possible, before
glaze sets, arrange glacé
fruit in garland on top of
cake; leave to set before
serving.

*Calypso Fruit Cake is
drizzled with a lime
glaze and decorated
with glacé fruit*

SPICED MINCEMEAT CAKE

Makes one 25 cm/
10 inch cake

Make day before
or up to 1 month
ahead

---

300 g/10 oz stoned dates

225 g/8 oz dried figs, sliced

*175 g/6 oz pecan or
walnut halves*

*120 g/4 oz green glacé
cherries*

*120 g/4 oz red glacé
cherries*

*600 g/1 ¼ lb self-raising
flour*

*325 g/11 oz light soft
brown sugar*

200 g/7 oz caster sugar

225 g/8 oz soft margarine

6 eggs

*½ teaspoon ground
cinnamon*

½ teaspoon grated nutmeg

½ teaspoon ground allspice

*2 x 400 g/14 oz jars
mincemeat*

2 tablespoons golden syrup

*To give cake a party
look, tie a satin ribbon
round its waist*

1 Reserve 75 g/2 ½ oz
dates, 120 g/4 oz figs,
45 g/1 ½ oz pecans or
walnuts and 60 g/2 oz
each green and red glacé
cherries. Dice remaining
dates and cherries. In
bowl, combine diced dates
and cherries with remain-
ing figs and pecans or
walnuts; coat with
150 g/5 oz flour.

*Stirring flour into
fruit and nut
mixture*

2 Preheat oven to
150°C/300°F/gas 2.
Grease 25 cm/10 inch
loose-bottomed angel cake
tin or springform cake tin
with funnel base.

3 In large bowl, using
electric mixer, beat
brown sugar, caster sugar
and soft margarine for
10 minutes or until light
and fluffy, scraping bowl
often with rubber spatula.
Add eggs, cinnamon,
nutmeg and allspice;
beat until well mixed,
constantly scraping bowl.
With spoon, stir in mincemeat, fruit mixture and
remaining flour.

4 Spoon cake mixture
into cake tin, spread-
ing evenly with spoon so
mixture is level.

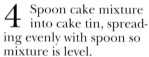

5 Bake for 2 hours or
until skewer inserted
in cake comes out clean
and cake pulls away slightly
from side of tin.

6 Cool cake in tin
on wire rack for
30 minutes; remove cake
from tin and cool com-
pletely on wire rack.

7 When cake is cool,
prepare topping: in
medium saucepan over
medium heat, heat
reserved fruit and nuts
with golden syrup for
5 minutes, stirring;
arrange on cake.

8 Let fruit and nut
topping cool and set.

9 Wrap fruit cake
tightly; refrigerate
overnight so cake will be
firm and easy to slice.

PIES, TARTS, PASTRIES AND HOT FRUIT PUDDINGS

131-198

PIES, TARTS, PASTRIES AND HOT FRUIT PUDDINGS

In this chapter, pastry – timeless and simple – can be used in so many different and exciting ways! Just start with the basic recipes and a variety of fillings, and you'll end up with time-honoured favourites like Apple Pie, Cherry Pie and Strawberry and Rhubarb Pie that your family will love. Make the most of summer and autumn harvests by trying Midsummer Fruit Pie, Ascot Fruit Tart and Individual Peach Cobblers – fruit desserts with a special touch. There are classic pastries from around the world like Baklava and Apple Strudel, comforting hot fruit puddings like Banana Brown Betty and Apple Cobbler that are so quick to make, and magnificent recipes like Swan Choux Puffs and Paris-Brest to add the crowning touch to an elegant meal.

CONTENTS

Sweet Pies

Sweet pies can be as simple and homely or as elaborate and elegant as you wish. Much of their success depends on the pastry, which should enhance, not compete with, the flavour of the filling and be crisp and tender, never soggy. For variety, try a plain top crust one time, a lattice top the next. For biscuit crust pies, try different fillings and toppings. Be creative!

SHORTCRUST PASTRY FOR DOUBLE CRUST PIE

300 g/10 oz plain flour

1 teaspoon salt (optional)

175 g/6 oz butter or block margarine

3-4 tablespoons cold water

1 Make dough as for Shortcrust Pastry for Pie Shell (see Box, right), steps 1 to 3.

2 Divide dough into 2 pieces, 1 slightly larger than the other.

3 On lightly floured surface, with floured rolling pin, roll out larger piece of dough into round about 3 mm/ ⅛ inch thick and 4 cm/1 ½ inches larger all round than upside-down shallow 20-23 cm/8-9 inch pie dish.

4 Roll dough round gently on to rolling pin; transfer to pie dish and unroll. Gently ease dough into bottom and up side of pie dish to line evenly; trim dough edge and fill according to individual recipe instructions.

5 For top crust, roll out smaller piece of dough as for bottom crust; with sharp knife, cut few slashes or design in centre of round; centre top crust over filling in bottom crust.

6 Make Decorative Pastry Edge (pages 136-137); bake pie according to recipe.

MAKING PASTRY IN FOOD PROCESSOR

To save time, pastry dough can be made in the food processor, with excellent results. This is especially helpful if you are catering for a crowd and have a large number of pies to make.

1 In food processor with knife blade attached, combine flour and butter or margarine. Process for 1-2 seconds until mixture forms fine crumbs.

2 Add cold water; process for 1-2 seconds until dough forms on blades.

3 Remove dough from bowl; with hands, shape dough into ball.

SHORTCRUST PASTRY FOR PIE SHELL

200 g/7 oz plain flour

1 teaspoon salt (optional)

120 g/4 oz butter or block margarine

2-3 tablespoons cold water

1 In medium bowl, stir flour and salt, if using.

2 With pastry blender or with fingertips, cut or rub butter or margarine into flour mixture until mixture resembles coarse crumbs.

3 Sprinkle cold water, a tablespoon at a time, into mixture. Mix lightly with fork after each addition, until dough is just moist enough to hold together.

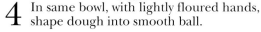

8 Roll dough round gently on to rolling pin; transfer to pie dish and unroll.

4 In same bowl, with lightly floured hands, shape dough into smooth ball.

5 On floured surface, with floured rolling pin, roll out dough into round about 3 mm/ ⅛ inch thick.

9 Gently ease dough into bottom and up side of pie dish to line evenly.

10 Make Decorative Pastry Edge (pages 136-137); fill and bake pie according to recipe.

6 Roll from centre to edge of dough to keep dough circular. Add more flour if dough begins to stick to work surface. Push sides in by hand if necessary and lift rolling pin slightly near edges to avoid making them too thin.

7 Cut dough round 4 cm/1 ½ inches larger all round than upside-down 20-23 cm/ 8-9 inch pie dish.

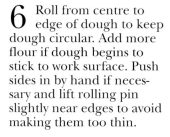

BAKING BLIND

Many pie shells are filled with an uncooked mixture, so you will need to bake the pie shell blind first. A crisp baked pastry shell that is to be filled with a chilled mixture should be thoroughly cooled before the filling is added.

1 Preheat oven to 220°C/425°F/gas 7. Line dish with dough.

2 With fork, prick dough liberally.

3 Line dough with foil and spread evenly with dried or baking beans.

4 Bake for 15 minutes or until golden.

5 Remove foil and beans, prick again and bake for a further 3-4 minutes.

6 Cool on wire rack.

DECORATIVE PASTRY EDGES

These eye-catching edges that finish off a pie so beautifully are not hard to make. Choose from Fluted, Sharp Fluted and Ruffled Edges for either pie shells or double crust pies; Leaf, Plaited and Heart Edges are suitable for pie shells only.

Pie Shells

1 Line pie dish with dough (page 135); trim dough edge with kitchen scissors, leaving about 2.5 cm/1 inch overhang all round rim of dish.

2 Fold overhang under, then bring up over rim of pie dish.

3 Make decorative edge of your choice, then bake pie as directed in recipe.

Double Crust Pies

1 Trim edge of top crust with kitchen scissors, leaving about 2.5 cm/1 inch overhang all round rim of pie dish. Fold overhang under, then bring up over rim of pie dish.

2 Make decorative edge of your choice, then bake pie as directed in recipe.

FLUTED EDGE

Canadian Peach Pie (page 158) with Fluted Edge

1 Pinch to form stand-up edge. Place index finger on inside edge of dough and, with index finger and thumb of other hand, pinch dough to make flute.

2 Repeat round edge of dough, leaving 5 mm/¼ inch space between each flute.

SHARP FLUTED EDGE

Old English Apple Pie (page 145) with Sharp Fluted Edge

1 Pinch to form stand-up edge. Place pointed edge of small star or diamond shaped biscuit cutter on inside edge of dough and, with index finger and thumb of other hand, pinch dough to make sharp flute.

2 Repeat round edge of dough, leaving 5 mm/¼ inch space between each flute.

LEAF OR HEART EDGE

*Pecan Pie (page 148)
with Leaf Edge*

1 Prepare Shortcrust Pastry for Double Crust Pie (page 134); use larger piece of dough to line pie dish.

2 Roll out remaining dough until it is 3 mm/ ⅛ inch thick. With sharp knife or small biscuit cutter, cut out shapes (leaves or hearts).

3 Press each shape on to lightly moistened pie shell edge, overlapping shapes slightly or varying angles.

RUFFLED EDGE

*Cherry Pie (page 156)
with Ruffled Edge*

1 Pinch to form stand-up edge. Place index finger under outside edge of dough and, with index finger and thumb of other hand, pinch dough to form ruffle.

2 Repeat round edge of dough, leaving 5 mm/ ¼ inch space between ruffles.

PLAITED EDGE

*Pumpkin Pie (page 149)
with Plaited Edge*

1 Prepare Shortcrust Pastry for Double Crust Pie (page 134); use larger piece of dough to line pie dish.

2 Roll out remaining dough until it is about 3 mm/ ⅛ inch thick; cut into strips that are 5 mm/ ¼ inch wide.

3 Gently plait strips together and press on to lightly moistened pie shell edge. Join ends of plait together to cover edge completely.

HARVEST PEAR AND PINEAPPLE PIE

10 servings
Allow 2 hours preparation and cooking time

Filling

| 2 x 820 g/29 oz cans pear halves |
| 2 x 400 g/14 oz cans pineapple pieces in juice |
| 1 rounded tablespoon cornflour |
| ½ teaspoon grated nutmeg |
| ½ teaspoon ground cinnamon |
| 45 g/1 ½ oz butter |

Pastry

| 225 g/8 oz plain flour |
| ½ teaspoon salt (optional) |
| 120 g/4 oz butter or block margarine |
| 1 egg yolk, lightly beaten |

Good for a crowd, this fruit pie is given a neat, professional finish with a Rope Edge

1 Drain pears, reserving 400 ml/14 fl oz juice; thinly slice pear halves. Drain pineapple.

2 In large saucepan, mix cornflour, nutmeg, cinnamon and reserved pear juice. Cook over medium heat, stirring constantly, until mixture thickens and boils. Remove saucepan from heat; stir in pear slices and pineapple pieces.

3 Into 23 cm/9 inch square baking dish, pour fruit mixture.

Pouring fruit mixture into baking dish

4 Cut butter into into small pieces; dot over fruit. Leave filling to cool to room temperature, about 30 minutes.

5 Meanwhile, prepare pastry dough: in bowl, mix flour with salt, if using. With pastry blender or with fingertips, cut or rub butter or margarine into flour until mixture resembles coarse crumbs. Sprinkle *3 tablespoons cold water*, a tablespoon at a time, into mixture, mixing lightly with fork after each addition until dough is moist enough to hold together. Shape dough into a ball.

6 Preheat oven to 220°C/425°F/gas 7. On floured surface, with floured rolling pin, roll out dough 3 mm/⅛ inch thick to fit dish, leaving 2.5 cm/1 inch overhang; place over filling.

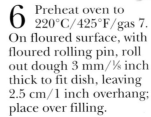

7 Turn overhang under to make stand-up edge. Make Rope Edge (see Box, right).

8 Cut a few slashes in crust to allow steam to escape during baking. Brush crust lightly with egg yolk.

9 Bake pie for 25-30 minutes until filling is bubbly and pastry is golden brown. Cool pie on wire rack for 15 minutes before serving, or cool completely to serve cold later.

ROPE EDGE

Press thumb into edge of crust at an angle, then pinch dough between thumb and knuckle of index finger. Place thumb in groove that has been left by index finger.

Repeat all round edge of crust to create twisted rope effect.

CHOCOLATE CHIFFON PIE

 8 servings
Make day before
and refrigerate

175 g/6 oz rich tea biscuits

120 g/4 oz butter, softened

60 g/2 oz plain chocolate,
broken into pieces

2 ½ x 200 g/7 oz packages
full-fat soft cheese,
softened

1 x 400 g/14 oz can
sweetened condensed milk

Candied Orange Zest (see
Box, right)

1 Preheat oven to
190°C/375°F/gas 5.
Place biscuits, in batches,
in polythene bag and with
rolling pin, roll biscuits
into fine crumbs. Or, in
food processor or blender,
blend biscuits, in batches,
until fine crumbs form.

2 In shallow 20-23 cm/
8-9 inch pie dish, mix
biscuit crumbs with butter;
press mixture on to
bottom and up side of
pie dish.

3 Bake crust for
8 minutes or until
golden; cool on wire rack.

4 Place pieces of chocolate in bowl over pan
of gently simmering water
and heat, stirring often,
until melted and smooth.

5 In large bowl, with
electric mixer, beat
soft cheese and condensed
milk until blended; beat in
melted chocolate until
smooth.

6 Pour chocolate
mixture into biscuit
crust. Cover and keep in
refrigerator overnight.

7 The next day,
prepare Candied
Orange Zest and arrange
on top of pie.

CANDIED ORANGE ZEST

With vegetable peeler,
thinly pare zest from
2 medium-sized oranges
in long pieces; cut zest
into 3 mm/⅛ inch-
wide matchstick strips.
In medium saucepan
over high heat, bring
orange zest, *125 ml/
4 fl oz water* and *60 g/
2 oz caster sugar* to the
boil. Reduce heat to
medium and cook for
10-15 minutes until
orange zest is limp and
translucent. Place *30 g/
1 oz caster sugar* in small
bowl. Drain orange zest;
place in bowl of sugar
and toss to coat.

Once orange zest is
evenly coated in sugar,
spread it out on a
baking sheet to dry.

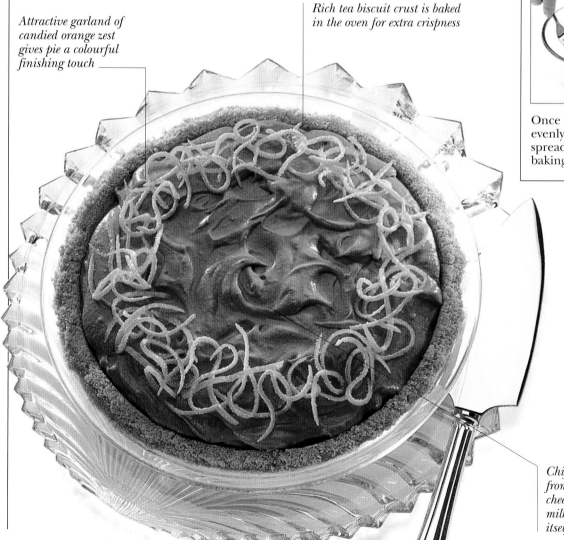

*Attractive garland of
candied orange zest
gives pie a colourful
finishing touch*

*Rich tea biscuit crust is baked
in the oven for extra crispness*

*Chiffon filling made
from chocolate, soft
cheese and condensed
milk is simplicity
itself to make*

STRAWBERRY AND RHUBARB PIE

Strawberries and rhubarb go together really well, both in terms of colour and flavour – and they're in season at the same time, making them the perfect combination for this luscious-tasting pie.

 8-10 servings
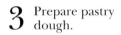 Allow 3 hours preparation and cooking time

Filling

450 g/1 lb strawberries

450 g/1 lb rhubarb (trimmed weight)

175 g/6 oz caster sugar

45 g/1 ½ oz plain flour

15 g/ ½ oz butter

Pastry

Shortcrust Pastry for Double Crust Pie (page 134)

1 tablespoon milk

1 Remove hulls from strawberries and cut each strawberry in half. Cut rhubarb stalks crossways into 1 cm/ ½ inch-thick pieces.

2 In large bowl, with rubber spatula, gently toss halved strawberries, rhubarb pieces, sugar and flour.

3 Prepare pastry dough.

4 On lightly floured surface, with floured rolling pin, roll out two-thirds of dough into 40 cm/16 inch round.

5 Gently ease dough into bottom and up side of 20-23 cm/8-9 inch pie dish that is at least 4 cm/1 ½ inches deep, to line evenly; trim dough edge, leaving 4 cm/ 1 ½ inch overhang.

6 Into pie shell, spoon strawberry and rhubarb mixture.

7 Cut butter into small pieces and dot evenly over strawberry and rhubarb mixture.

8 Preheat oven to 220°C/425°F/gas 7.

9 Roll out remaining dough into a 26.5 cm/ 10 ½ inch round. With fluted pastry wheel or knife, cut into ten 2 cm/ ¾ inch wide strips.

10 Place 5 strips over filling; do not seal ends.

11 With remaining 5 strips, make Diamond Lattice (see Box, page 141).

12 Trim ends of strips; moisten edge of pie shell with water; press ends of strips to pie shell to seal. Bring overhang up over strips; pinch edges to seal; make Ruffled or other Decorative Pastry Edge (pages 136-137). Brush lattice with milk.

13 Bake pie for 45-50 minutes or until fruit mixture bubbles and pastry is golden. After 30 minutes, cover pie loosely with foil if pastry is browning too quickly.

14 Leave pie to stand for 1 hour to allow juices to set slightly; serve warm or cold.

Tossing strawberry and rhubarb mixture

ALTERNATIVE TO LATTICE

A quick and easy alternative pastry topping to the Diamond Lattice in the main picture (page 141) is this Cartwheel, in which the pastry strips are placed over the filling like the spokes of a wheel.

Cartwheel

1 With fluted pastry wheel or knife, cut dough into twelve 1 cm/½ inch strips.

2 Arrange 6 strips over filling in 'V' shapes.

3 Use more strips to make smaller 'V' shapes inside larger ones.

4 If you like, cut out small shapes from dough trimmings and place in centre of pie.

DIAMOND LATTICE

Taking pastry strips back: fold back every other strip three-quarters of its length.

Placing central cross strip: arrange 1 strip diagonally across centre of filling to start forming diamond shape, then take folded part of strips over central strip.

Folding back alternate strips: fold back strips that were not folded back before.

Placing second cross strip: arrange another cross strip, parallel to central strip, 2.5 cm/1 inch away.

Replacing folded part of strips: take folded part of strips over second diagonal cross strip. Continue folding back alternate strips and placing cross strips diagonally across filling to weave diamond pattern.

Crinkled edges on pastry lattice are made by cutting out strips with a pastry wheel

Luscious filling of fresh strawberries and rhubarb can be seen through 'windows' of diamond lattice

BRANDY ALEXANDER PIE

8-10 servings
Can be made day
before and kept in
refrigerator

225 g/8 oz plain dark crisp
chocolate biscuits

175 g/6 oz butter, softened

225 g/8 oz icing sugar,
sifted

120 g/4 oz plain chocolate,
melted

3 tablespoons brandy

150 ml/ ¼ pint double or
whipping cream

Dark Chocolate Curls
(see Box, right)
to decorate

*This superbly
rich 'marquise'
filling is made from butter,
sugar, chocolate, whipped
cream - and brandy!*

1 Place chocolate
biscuits, in batches, in
polythene bag; with rolling
pin, roll biscuits into fine
crumbs. Or, in food
processor or blender,
blend biscuits, in batches
if necessary, until fine
crumbs form.

2 In bowl; mix together
biscuit crumbs and
60 g/2 oz butter. Press
biscuit crumb mixture on
to bottom and up side of
shallow 20-23 cm/8-9 inch
pie dish or ceramic
flan dish.

3 In food processor,
work icing sugar and
remaining butter until
creamy and smooth. Add
melted chocolate and
brandy to creamed sugar
and butter mixture and
work again in food processor until thick and smooth.

4 In small bowl, whip
double or whipping
cream until soft peaks
form. With wire whisk or
rubber spatula, gently fold
whipped cream into
chocolate mixture. Spoon
mixture into biscuit crust.

5 Decorate pie with
chocolate curls.
Refrigerate for at least
1 hour before
serving.

DARK CHOCOLATE CURLS

With heat of your hand,
slightly warm *60 g/2 oz
plain chocolate flavour
cake covering* to soften.

With vegetable peeler,
slowly and firmly draw
blade along smooth
surface of cake covering
to make curls.

Use wide side of cake
covering for wide curls,
thin side for thin curls.
Transfer curls with
cocktail stick.
   If you like, you can
use white chocolate
instead of plain choco-
late flavour cake
covering (see page 100).

TO SERVE
*Rich, dark and
chocolatey, Brandy
Alexander Pie should be
served chilled to be
enjoyed at its best.*

BLUEBERRY PIE

10 servings
Allow 3 hours
preparation and
cooking time

Pastry

300 g/10 oz plain flour
¾ teaspoon salt (optional)
175 g/6 oz butter or block margarine
1 egg
2 teaspoons caster sugar

Filling

700 g/1 ½ lb fresh or frozen (thawed) blueberries
100 g/3 ½ oz caster sugar
1 teaspoon grated lemon zest
15 g/ ½ oz butter

1 First prepare pastry dough: in large bowl, with fork, stir flour with salt, if using. With pastry blender or fingertips, cut or rub butter or margarine into flour mixture until mixture resembles coarse crumbs. In cup, beat egg lightly. Add egg to flour mixture, mixing lightly with fork until dough will hold together, adding a little *cold water* if necessary. With hands, shape dough into 2 balls, 1 slightly larger than the other.

2 On lightly floured surface, with floured rolling pin, roll out larger ball of dough into round about 4 cm/1 ½ inches larger all round than upside-down shallow 20-23 cm/8-9 inch pie dish. Ease dough into pie dish to line evenly.

3 If using frozen blueberries, they should be drained. In large bowl, with rubber spatula, gently toss blueberries with caster sugar and grated lemon zest.

4 Spoon blueberry mixture into pie shell. Cut butter into small pieces; dot on top of blueberry mixture.

5 Preheat oven to 220°C/425°F/gas 7. Roll out remaining dough as before. Moisten edge of pie shell with water; place top crust over filling.

6 Trim dough edge, leaving about 4 cm/1 ½ inch overhang. Fold overhang under; make Sharp Fluted or other Decorative Pastry Edge (pages 136-137).

7 With sharp knife, cut 10 cm/4 inch 'X' in centre of top crust.

8 Fold back points of 'X' to make square opening in centre of pie.

9 Sprinkle top of pie with 2 teaspoons caster sugar.

10 Bake pie for 40 minutes or until filling begins to bubble and pastry is golden. If pastry browns too quickly, cover edge loosely with foil. Cool pie on wire rack before serving. Serve warm or cold.

BANANA CREAM PIE

8 servings
Allow 4 hours preparation and cooking time

100 g/3 ½ oz shredded or desiccated coconut

60 g/2 oz quick-cooking porridge oats, uncooked

75 g/2 ½ oz butter, softened

750 ml/1 ¼ pints milk

45 g/1 ½ oz cornflour

100 g/3 ½ oz caster sugar

3 egg yolks

3 large bananas

150 ml/ ¼ pint double or whipping cream

Toasted flaked almonds to decorate

1 Preheat oven to 150°C/300°F/gas 2. In shallow 20-23 cm/ 8-9 inch pie dish, mix coconut, porridge oats and 45 g/1 ½ oz butter. Pat coconut mixture on to bottom and up side of pie dish to line evenly.

2 Bake pie shell for 15 minutes or until golden; cool on wire rack.

Coconut and porridge oat crust provides a crisp and crunchy contrast to soft and creamy banana filling

3 In medium saucepan, combine milk, cornflour, sugar and remaining butter. Cook over medium-low heat, stirring constantly, until mixture boils and thickens; boil for 1 minute longer.

4 Remove saucepan from heat; stir in egg yolks.

5 Peel 2 bananas and cut into slices 5 mm/ ¼ inch thick. Line cooled pie shell with sliced bananas; pour custard filling over bananas.

6 Cover custard filling tightly; refrigerate until cold.

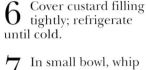

7 In small bowl, whip double or whipping cream until stiff peaks form.

8 With palette knife, evenly spread whipped cream over custard filling.

9 Cover and refrigerate pie until ready to serve.

> *TO SERVE*
> *Slice remaining banana. Decorate pie with banana slices and toasted almonds.*

OLD ENGLISH APPLE PIE

8 servings
Allow 2 hours preparation and cooking time

Filling

8 medium-sized Bramley apples

2 teaspoons lemon juice

1 tablespoon cornflour

100 g/3 ½ oz caster sugar

15 g/ ½ oz butter

Pastry

Shortcrust Pastry for Double Crust Pie (page 134)

Milk for glazing

1 tablespoon caster sugar

7 slices processed cheese (optional)

1 Peel and core apples; cut into thin slices. In large bowl, with rubber spatula, lightly toss apple slices, lemon juice, cornflour and sugar; set aside.

2 Prepare pastry dough. Divide into 2 pieces, 1 slightly larger. On lightly floured surface, with floured rolling pin, roll out larger piece of dough into round about 4 cm/ 1 ½ inches larger all round than upside-down shallow 20-23 cm/8-9 inch pie dish. Ease dough into pie dish to line evenly; trim dough edge, leaving 2.5 cm/1 inch overhang. Reserve dough trimmings.

Pastry crust is sprinkled with sugar before baking to give finished pie a frosted top

3 Spoon apple mixture into pie shell. Cut butter into small pieces; dot over apple filling.

4 Preheat oven to 220°C/425°F/gas 7. Roll out remaining dough as before; place over filling. Trim dough edge, leaving 2.5 cm/1 inch overhang. Fold overhang under; make Sharp Fluted or other Decorative Pastry Edge (pages 136-137).

Cheese and apples make good partners; here cheese leaves are placed under pastry leaves to look – and taste – good

5 Reroll dough trimmings. With floured leaf-shaped biscuit cutter or knife, cut 7 leaves, rerolling dough if necessary. Arrange leaves on top of pie. Lightly brush top of pie with milk.

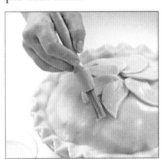

6 With tip of knife, cut hole in top crust to allow steam to escape during baking.

7 Evenly sprinkle caster sugar over pie. Set pie dish on baking sheet and bake for 45 minutes or until pastry is golden and apples are tender.

8 Transfer pie to wire rack; cool slightly. If using cheese slices, cut each slice into leaf shape using biscuit cutter or knife. Gently tuck cheese leaves under pastry leaves, taking care not to break pastry.

CUSTARD PEACH PIE

8 servings
Allow 3 hours preparation and cooking time

Pastry

Shortcrust Pastry for Pie Shell (see Box, page 134)

Filling

5 medium-sized peaches (about 700 g/1 ½ lb)

150 ml/ ¼ pint soured cream

3 egg yolks

200 g/7 oz caster sugar

30 g/1 oz plain flour

Streusel Topping

60 g/2 oz butter

75 g/2 ½ oz plain flour

60 g/2 oz caster sugar

½ teaspoon ground cinnamon

1 Prepare pastry dough.

2 Preheat oven to 220°C/425°F/gas 7. On lightly floured surface, with floured rolling pin, roll out dough into round about 4 cm/1 ½ inches larger all round than upside-down shallow 20-23 cm/8-9 inch pie dish; ease dough into pie dish to line evenly.

3 Trim dough edge, leaving 2.5 cm/1 inch overhang. Fold overhang under; make Fluted or other Decorative Pastry Edge (pages 136-137).

4 Peel 4 peaches (see Box, page 53); cut peaches into 5 mm/ ¼ inch-thick slices with sharp knife.

5 In pie shell, arrange peach slices in concentric circles, overlapping them slightly.

6 In medium bowl, beat soured cream, egg yolks, sugar and flour just until blended; pour slowly over peaches in pie dish, taking care not to dislodge them.

7 Bake pie for 30 minutes, or just until custard mixture is beginning to set.

8 Meanwhile, prepare streusel topping: in small bowl, rub together butter, flour and sugar until mixture resembles coarse crumbs. Stir in ground cinnamon.

STREUSEL TOPPING
Streusel is a crisp topping of flour, butter and sugar, often mixed with spices such as cinnamon, nutmeg and cloves, which is sprinkled on breads, cakes and puddings before baking. The topping is of German origin, and is very similar to crumble toppings for fruit.

9 After pie has baked for 30 minutes, evenly sprinkle streusel topping over peaches and custard.

Sprinkling streusel topping over peaches and custard

10 Bake for 15 minutes longer or until streusel is golden and knife inserted in centre of pie comes out clean.

11 If pastry browns too quickly, cover edge loosely with foil.

12 Cool pie on wire rack for 1 hour; serve warm, or cool completely to serve cold later.

At end of baking time, insert tip of knife into centre of pie; if custard is set, tip of knife will come out clean

TO SERVE
*Cut remaining peach
into 5 mm/ ¼ inch thick
slices; use to decorate
centre of pie.*

PECAN PIE

8 servings
Allow 4 hours
preparation and
cooking time

Pastry

Shortcrust Pastry for
Double Crust
Pie (page 134)

Filling

4 eggs

250 ml/8 fl oz golden syrup

60 g/2 oz light soft brown
sugar

60 g/2 oz caster sugar

30 g/1 oz butter, melted

90 g/3 oz shelled pecans or
walnuts, chopped

Honey Pecan Topping (see
Box, above right)

1 Prepare pastry dough.
Divide dough into
2 pieces, 1 slightly larger.

2 Preheat oven to
180°C/350°F/gas 4.
On lightly floured surface,
with floured rolling pin,
roll out larger piece of
dough into round about
4 cm/1 ½ inches larger all
round than upside-down
shallow 20-23 cm/8-9 inch
pie dish.

3 Ease dough into pie
dish to line evenly;
trim dough edge,
leaving 1 cm/ ½ inch
overhang. Fold over-
hang under. Make Leaf or
other Decorative
Pastry Edge (pages
136-137) with
remaining
dough.

Spreading Honey
Pecan Topping over
pie filling

4 In medium bowl, beat
eggs lightly; stir in
golden syrup, brown sugar,
caster sugar and butter;
stir in chopped pecans or
walnuts. Spoon into pie
shell; bake pie for
40 minutes.

5 Meanwhile, prepare
Honey Pecan
Topping.

6 When pie has baked
for 40 minutes,
remove from oven; spread
topping over filling.

HONEY PECAN TOPPING

In medium saucepan
over medium heat,
combine 75 g/2 ½ oz
light soft brown sugar,
3 tablespoons honey and
45 g/1 ½ oz butter;
cook for 2-3 minutes,
stirring constantly,
until sugar dissolves. Stir
in 150 g/5 oz shelled
pecan or walnut halves.
Remove saucepan
from heat.

7 Return pie to oven
and bake for
10-15 minutes longer until
topping is bubbly and
golden brown. Cover edge
of pastry with foil, if
necessary, to prevent
overbrowning.

8 Cool pie on wire rack
before serving.

Golden-brown leaf edge
accents the autumnal look of
this popular American pie

Pecan Pie, perfect for a
winter party

PUMPKIN PIE

8 servings
Allow 3 hours preparation and cooking time

Pastry

Shortcrust Pastry for Double Crust Pie (page 134)

Filling

450 g/1 lb canned pumpkin or Mashed Cooked Pumpkin (page 83)

1 x 400 g/14 oz can evaporated milk

2 eggs

165 g/5 ½ oz light soft brown sugar

1 ½ teaspoons ground cinnamon

½ teaspoon ground ginger

½ teaspoon grated nutmeg

Walnut Crunch Topping (see Box, below)

150 ml/ ¼ pint double or whipping cream to decorate

Chopped walnuts, brown sugar and butter make up this topping, a deliciously crunchy contrast to the soft texture of the pumpkin filling underneath

1 Prepare pastry dough. Divide dough into 2 pieces, 1 slightly larger than the other.

2 Preheat oven to 200°C/400°F/gas 6. On lightly floured surface, with floured rolling pin, roll out larger piece of dough to round about 4 cm/1 ½ inches larger all round than upside-down shallow 20-23 cm/8-9 inch pie dish.

3 Line pie dish with dough; trim edge, leaving 1 cm/ ½ inch overhang. Fold overhang under. With remaining dough, make Plaited or other Decorative Pastry Edge (pages 136-137).

4 In large bowl, with electric mixer, beat pumpkin and next 6 ingredients.

5 Place pie dish on oven rack; pour filling into pie shell. Bake pie for 40 minutes or until knife inserted 2.5 cm/1 inch from edge comes out clean.

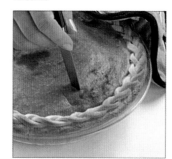

6 Cool pie on wire rack for about 1 ½ hours.

7 When pie is cool, preheat grill to high. Prepare Walnut Crunch Topping; spoon evenly over pie. Place pie about 15 cm/6 inches below source of heat and grill for 3 minutes or until topping is golden and sugar dissolves. Cool pie again on wire rack.

8 In small bowl, whip double or whipping cream until stiff peaks form. Decorate pie with cream.

Piped swirls of cream complement the plaited edge of this traditional American Thanksgiving pie

WALNUT CRUNCH TOPPING

In small saucepan over low heat, melt *60 g/2 oz butter.* Stir in *120 g/4 oz walnut pieces, chopped,* and *165 g/5 ½ oz light soft brown sugar* until well mixed; cook for a few minutes until butter is absorbed.

LEMON MERINGUE PIE

6-8 servings
Allow 50 minutes preparation and cooking time

Crumb Crust

175 g/6 oz digestive biscuits	
75 g/2 ½ oz butter	
45 g/1 ½ oz demerara sugar	

Lemon Filling

Grated zest and juice of 2 large lemons	
45 g/1 ½ oz cornflour	
2 egg yolks	
75 g/2 ½ oz caster sugar	

Topping

3 egg whites	
120 g/4 oz caster sugar	

Meringue topping is swirled over lemon filling, but it can be piped for a more formal effect

1 Make crumb crust: place digestive biscuits in polythene bag; with rolling pin, roll biscuits into fine crumbs.

2 Melt butter in small saucepan over gentle heat, add sugar and biscuit crumbs and mix well.

3 Turn biscuit mixture into deepish 23 cm/ 9 inch flan dish; with back of metal spoon, press mixture on to bottom and up side of dish.

4 Make lemon filling: put lemon zest and juice in bowl with cornflour; blend to a smooth paste.

5 In medium saucepan, bring 300 ml/ ½ pint water to the boil; pour on to cornflour mixture. Return cornflour mixture to pan, bring to the boil and simmer for 3 minutes until thick, stirring.

Pressing crushed biscuit mixture on to bottom and up side of flan dish

6 Remove saucepan from heat; add egg yolks and caster sugar. Return to heat; cook for 1 minute, to thicken sauce. Cool slightly, then spoon into biscuit crust.

7 Preheat oven to 170°C/325°F/ gas 3.

8 Make topping: in large bowl, with electric mixer on full speed, beat egg whites until soft peaks form. Add caster sugar, 1 table-spoon at a time, beating well after each addition until sugar dissolves completely and egg whites stand in stiff, glossy peaks.

9 Spoon topping over lemon filling, taking care to spread it right to edge of crust, leaving no spaces.

10 Bake pie for about 30 minutes or until meringue is golden brown. Serve warm or cold.

WALNUT FUDGE PIE

8-10 servings
Allow 4 hours preparation and cooking time

225 g/8 oz walnut pieces

Shortcrust Pastry for Double Crust Pie (page 134)

60 g/2 oz butter

60 g/2 oz plain chocolate, broken into pieces

200 g/7 oz caster sugar

5 tablespoons milk

4 tablespoons bottled chocolate syrup

4 eggs

Vanilla ice cream (optional)

TO SERVE
If you like, top each serving of pie with a scoop of vanilla ice cream.

---

1 Preheat oven to 180°C/350°F/gas 4. Place walnuts in baking tray; toast in oven for about 10 minutes or until golden brown, shaking tray occasionally. Set aside to cool. Do not turn oven off.

2 Meanwhile, prepare pastry dough. Divide into 2 pieces, 1 slightly larger than the other.

3 On lightly floured surface, with floured rolling pin, roll out larger piece of dough into round about 4 cm/1 ½ inches larger all round than upside-down shallow 20-23 cm/8-9 inch pie dish.

4 Ease dough into pie dish to line evenly; trim dough edge, leaving 1 cm/½ inch overhang. Fold overhang under.

5 In medium saucepan over low heat, heat butter and chocolate, stirring often, until melted and smooth. Remove saucepan from heat. With wire whisk, beat in sugar, milk, chocolate syrup and 3 eggs until blended. Stir in toasted walnuts. Pour walnut mixture into pie shell.

6 Roll out remaining dough 3 mm/⅛ inch thick. With different sized heart-shaped pastry cutters, cut out hearts for decorating edge of pie shell and top of pie.

7 Place hearts on edge of pie and on filling to make pretty design.

Placing heart shapes over filling

8 In cup, with fork, lightly beat remaining egg. Brush egg lightly over edge of pie shell.

9 Brush hearts in centre and on edge with beaten egg.

10 Bake pie for 1 hour or until knife inserted in centre of pie comes out clean. Cool pie on wire rack. Serve warm or cold.

MIDSUMMER FRUIT PIE

8-10 servings
Allow 4 hours
preparation and
cooking time

Almond Pastry

225 g/8 oz plain flour
1 tablespoon caster sugar
½ teaspoon salt (optional)
120 g/4 oz butter
2 tablespoons finely chopped blanched almonds

Fruit Filling

300 g/10 oz fresh or frozen (thawed) blueberries or blackcurrants
30 g/1 oz caster sugar
1 tablespoon cornflour
1 tablespoon lemon juice
1 tablespoon grated lemon zest
30 g/1 oz butter

White Chocolate Filling

215 g/7 ½ oz white chocolate, broken into pieces
15 g/ ½ oz butter
30 g/1 oz blanched almonds, toasted and coarsely chopped
150 ml/ ¼ pint double or whipping cream

Cream Layer

300 ml/ ½ pint double or whipping cream
30 g/1 oz icing sugar

1 Prepare pastry dough: in large bowl, with fork, stir flour, sugar and salt, if using. With pastry blender or fingertips, cut or rub butter into flour mixture until mixture resembles coarse crumbs. Stir in almonds. Sprinkle *3 tablespoons cold water*, a tablespoon at a time, into mixture, mixing lightly with fork after each addition until dough is just moist enough to hold together. With hands, shape dough into ball.

2 Preheat oven to 220°C/425°F/gas 7.

3 On lightly floured surface, with floured rolling pin, roll out dough into round about 4 cm/ 1 ½ inches larger all round than upside-down shallow 20-23 cm/8-9 inch pie dish.

4 Ease dough into pie dish to line evenly. Trim dough edge, leaving 1 cm/ ½ inch overhang; reserve dough trimmings. Fold overhang under.

5 At regular intervals round edge of dough, cut out narrow sections, about 1 cm/½ inch long.

Cutting out sections from edge of dough

6 Place 1 thumb on inside edge of each section of dough, and, with index finger and thumb of other hand, pinch dough and press upwards to make rounded 'petal' shape.

7 Prick bottom and side of pie shell liberally with fork to prevent puffing and shrinkage during baking.

8 Line pastry with foil; spread evenly with dried or baking beans.

9 Bake blind for 15 minutes or until pastry is golden; remove foil and beans, prick bottom again and bake for further 3-4 minutes. Cool on wire rack.

10 Roll out dough trimmings. With small biscuit cutters or knife, cut out a few flowers and leaves for decoration. Bake pastry shapes on ungreased baking sheet for about 10 minutes or until golden; cool.

11 Prepare fruit filling; if using frozen fruit, it should be drained. In medium saucepan, mix sugar, cornflour, lemon juice and lemon zest; add half of the fruit. Cook over low heat, mashing fruit with spoon and stirring, until mixture boils and thickens. Remove pan from heat; stir in butter and remaining fruit, reserving a few blueberries for decoration. Cool.

12 For white chocolate filling: place pieces of chocolate, butter and *2 tablespoons water* in bowl over saucepan of gently simmering water and heat, stirring often, until melted and smooth. Remove saucepan from heat; cool completely. Stir in chopped toasted almonds. In small bowl, whip double or whipping cream until stiff peaks form. Stir a few spoonfuls of whipped cream into chocolate mixture to lighten, then with wire whisk or rubber spatula, gently fold in remaining cream.

13 For cream layer: in same bowl, whip double or whipping cream with sifted icing sugar until stiff peaks form.

14 In cooled pie shell, with spoon, evenly spread fruit filling.

15 Top fruit filling with white chocolate filling. Spread with whipped cream mixture, reserving 1 tablespoon for decoration.

16 Decorate pie with pastry flowers, reserved whipped cream and blueberries, and pastry leaves.

Arranging blueberries and pastry flowers and leaves on whipped cream topping

BLUEBERRIES

Big, sweet, succulent blueberries are purplish-blue in colour with a powdery bloom – the 'aristocrats' of soft fruit. They come in many varieties, cultivated and wild, and can be found at most good supermarkets and greengrocers.

• Blueberries are traditionally a summer fruit, at their best from June to September.

• Just before using blueberries, remove any stalks and discard any bruised, soft or damaged berries; rinse blueberries gently in cold water, drain well and dry on kitchen paper.

• To freeze blueberries, overwrap berries in containers as bought; freeze. Or place them in à single layer in a baking tray, freeze until firm, then transfer to freezer container; use within 12 months.

• When using frozen blueberries, thaw only if recipe tells you to do so.

Here's a pie with a hidden secret – the whipped cream topping hides a white chocolate filling and a luscious layer of sweet summer berries

PARISIENNE APPLE PIES

6 servings
Allow 2 hours preparation and cooking time

Pastry

375 g/13 oz plain flour

225 g/8 oz unsalted butter, softened

75 g/2 ½ oz caster sugar

2 egg yolks, lightly beaten

1 tablespoon milk

Filling

8 large Golden Delicious apples

100 g/3 ½ oz caster sugar plus extra for sprinkling

60 g/2 oz unsalted butter

1 Prepare pastry dough: in large bowl, with fingertips, quickly mix flour, butter and sugar until mixture resembles coarse crumbs. Add egg yolks and milk; mix until dough will hold together.

2 Shape two-thirds of dough into ball; wrap and set aside. On non-stick baking parchment, with rolling pin, roll out remaining one-third of dough 3 mm/⅛ inch thick. With 6 x 4 cm/ 2 ½ x 1 ½ inch leaf-shaped biscuit cutter, cut out 36 leaves. With cocktail stick, press 'vein' into each leaf; place on baking sheet and refrigerate.

3 Divide larger ball of dough into 6 equal pieces. Press one piece of dough on to bottom and up side of each of six 10-11 cm/4-4 ½ inch loose-bottomed tartlet tins; refrigerate.

4 Prepare filling: peel and core apples; cut into 5 mm/¼ inch thick slices. In large frying pan over medium-high heat, heat sugar and butter until butter melts, stirring occasionally (do not use margarine because it separates from sugar during cooking). Sugar will not be completely dissolved.

5 Arrange apple slices on top of sugar mixture; heat to boiling (do not stir). Cook for about 20 minutes, depending on juiciness of apples, until sugar mixture is caramel-coloured; stir to mix apples with caramelized sugar. (Apples should still be slightly crunchy.) Remove pan from heat.

6 Preheat oven to 200°C/400°F/gas 6. Spoon apple mixture into tartlet shells. Arrange 6 dough leaves on top of each pie, leaving some of filling uncovered. Arrange apple pies in baking tray for easier handling. Bake pies for 25-30 minutes until pastry is golden (cover leaves with foil after 15 minutes, if necessary, to prevent overbrowning).

7 Cool pies on wire rack for 10 minutes; lightly sprinkle with caster sugar. Serve warm, or cool completely to serve cold later. Remove sides and bases of tins before serving.

Parisienne Apple Pies are lightly dusted with caster sugar just before serving, to give pastry leaves a frosted look

Pies are baked in fluted, loose-bottomed tartlet tins so they can be removed from tins before serving; this way they look their best for serving

KEY LIME PIE

6-8 servings
Can be made day before and kept in refrigerator

135 g/4 ½ oz digestive biscuits, finely crushed

60 g/2 oz caster sugar

75 g/2 ½ oz butter, softened

1 x 400 g/14 oz can sweetened condensed milk

125 ml/4 fl oz freshly squeezed lime juice (3-4 limes)

2 teaspoons grated lime zest

2 eggs, separated

Green food colouring (optional)

300 ml/ ½ pint double or whipping cream

Lime decoration of your choice (see Box, above right)

1 Preheat oven to 170°C/325°F/gas 3. In shallow 20-23 cm/ 8-9 inch pie dish, mix biscuit crumbs, sugar and butter; press mixture on to bottom and up side of pie dish, making small rim.

2 In medium bowl, with wire whisk or fork, stir sweetened condensed milk with lime juice, grated lime zest and egg yolks until mixture thickens. If liked, add sufficient green food colouring to tint mixture pale green.

3 In small bowl, with electric mixer on full speed, beat egg whites until stiff peaks form. With rubber spatula or wire whisk, gently fold egg whites into lime mixture.

4 Into biscuit crust, pour lime filling; smooth top. Bake pie for 15-20 minutes until lime filling is just firm.

5 Cool pie in pie dish on wire rack, then refrigerate until well chilled, about 3 hours.

6 In small bowl, whip double or whipping cream until stiff peaks form. Pipe border of whipped cream round edge of filling, or spread cream completely over top of pie and swirl to make attractive design.

TO SERVE
Top cream with Lime Kites or other lime decoration of your choice.

LIME DECORATIONS

The contrasting greens of lime peel and flesh make this a good choice for decorating desserts, and a welcome change from the more usual orange and lemon decorations.

Lime Cones
With sharp knife, cut lime crossways into thin slices. Make 1 cut from centre to edge of each slice, then curl slice round from centre to form cone shape.

Lime Kites and Bow-Ties
With sharp knife, cut lime crossways into thin slices, then cut each slice into quarters. Use singly, or place 2 kites together as shown above to make bow-tie shape.

CHERRY PIE

8 servings
Allow 4 hours
preparation and
cooking time

Filling

2 x 425 g/15 oz cans
   stoned cherries in juice

75 g/2 ½ oz light soft
   brown sugar

60 g/2 oz caster sugar

30 g/1 oz cornflour

15 g/ ½ oz butter

1 teaspoon almond essence

Pastry

Shortcrust Pastry for
   Double Crust Pie
   (page 134)

Milk for glazing

2 teaspoons caster sugar

1 Drain juice from
canned cherries;
reserve 250 ml/8 fl oz
juice.

2 In medium saucepan,
combine brown sugar,
caster sugar, cornflour and
reserved cherry juice.
Cook over low heat,
stirring constantly, until
mixture boils and thick-
ens; boil for 1 minute
longer. Remove pan from
heat; stir in butter and
almond essence. Fold
in cherries.

3 Prepare pastry dough.
Divide dough into
2 pieces, 1 slightly larger
than the other.

4 Preheat oven to
220°C/425°F/gas 7.
On lightly floured surface,
with floured rolling pin,
roll out larger piece of
dough into round about
4 cm/1 ½ inches larger all
round than upside-down
shallow 20-23 cm/8-9 inch
pie dish; ease dough into
pie dish to line evenly.
Trim dough edge even
with rim of pie dish;
reserve dough trimmings.

5 Spoon filling into
pie shell. Roll out
remaining dough as
before. With leaf-shaped
biscuit cutter, cut out
leaves in top crust; reserve
cut out shapes. Place top
crust over filling. Trim
edge of top crust, leaving
1 cm/½ inch overhang;
reserve dough trimmings.
Fold overhang under;
make Ruffled or other
Decorative Pastry Edge
(pages 136-137).

6 With reserved dough
trimmings, make
'berries' (see Box, right).
Score veins on reserved cut
out leaves and arrange
with berries on top crust.
Brush top crust with milk
and sprinkle with sugar.
Bake pie for 15 minutes.
Turn oven to 180°C/
350°F/gas 4; bake for
25 minutes longer or until
pastry is golden brown.

7 Cool pie in pie dish
on wire rack before
serving.

PASTRY LEAVES AND BERRIES

Pastry 'leaves' can be
made by cutting out
shapes from top crust
of pie with biscuit cutter
as in the recipe here
for Cherry Pie, or by
rolling out pastry dough
trimmings, then cutting
pastry dough into leaf
shapes with sharp knife
or biscuit cutter. After
making leaf shapes,
score 'veins' on surface
of leaf shapes with tip of
sharp knife.

Between fingertips of
both hands, roll dough
trimmings into 'berry'
shapes. Arrange leaves
and berries together,
twisting leaves at base to
give a more realistic
look.

To decorate a large pie
for a special occasion,
group lots of berries
together to make a
cluster of grapes; for a
Christmas pie, create a
seasonal look by deco-
rating top or edge of pie
with pastry holly leaves
and berries.

CHOCOLATE CREAM PIE

8 servings
Can be made day
before and kept in
refrigerator

120 g/4 oz rich tea biscuits
120 g/4 oz butter, softened
50 g/1 ⅔ oz cornflour
100 g/3 ½ oz plus
1 teaspoon caster sugar
450 ml/ ¾ pint milk
90 g/3 oz plain chocolate,
broken into pieces
2 egg yolks
½ teaspoon vanilla essence
30 g/1 oz walnut pieces
150 ml/ ¼ pint double or
whipping cream

1 Preheat oven to 190°C/375°F/gas 5. Place biscuits, in batches, in polythene bag and with rolling pin, roll biscuits into fine crumbs. Or in food processor or blender, blend biscuits, in batches if necessary, until fine crumbs form.

2 In shallow 20-23 cm/ 8-9 inch pie dish, mix biscuit crumbs and 90 g/3 oz softened butter; press mixture on to bottom and up side of pie dish, making small rim.

3 Bake biscuit crust for 8 minutes; cool on wire rack.

4 While crust is cooling, prepare filling: in large non-stick saucepan, mix cornflour and 100 g/3 ½ oz sugar. Stir in milk and chocolate. Cook over medium heat, stirring constantly, until chocolate melts and mixture thickens and boils; boil for 1 minute longer. Immediately remove saucepan from heat.

5 In cup, with fork, beat egg yolks; stir in small amount of hot chocolate mixture. Slowly pour egg mixture back into remaining chocolate mixture in pan, stirring rapidly to prevent lumping. Cook, stirring constantly, until mixture thickens and coats a spoon well (do not boil or mixture will curdle). Stir in vanilla essence and remaining butter until blended.

6 Into biscuit crust, pour chocolate filling; smooth top with rubber spatula.

Pouring chocolate filling into baked biscuit crust

7 To keep skin from forming as filling cools, press dampened greaseproof paper directly on to surface of hot filling. Refrigerate pie for at least 3 hours or until well chilled.

8 Meanwhile, in small saucepan over medium heat, cook walnuts until toasted, stirring frequently; cool. Chop walnuts.

9 In small bowl, whip double or whipping cream with remaining 1 teaspoon sugar until soft peaks form.

10 Discard grease-proof paper from filling. Spoon or pipe whipped cream on to filling and swirl to make attractive design.

TO SERVE
Sprinkle top of pie with
toasted chopped walnuts.

CANADIAN PEACH PIE

 8 servings
Allow 3 hours preparation and cooking time

Filling

14 large peaches

30 g/1 oz cornflour

2 tablespoons lemon juice

1 teaspoon ground cinnamon

200 g/7 oz caster sugar

15 g/ ½ oz butter

Pastry

175 g/6 oz plain flour

½ teaspoon salt (optional)

1 teaspoon caster sugar

90 g/3 oz butter

1 egg yolk, beaten

1 Prepare filling: peel peaches (see Box, page 53). With sharp knife, cut peeled peaches into thick slices.

2 In bowl, gently toss peaches, cornflour, lemon juice, cinnamon and sugar. Set aside.

3 Prepare pastry dough: in medium bowl, with fork, stir flour, salt (if using) and sugar. With pastry blender or finger-tips, cut or rub butter into flour mixture until mixture resembles coarse crumbs. Sprinkle *2-3 table-spoons cold water*, a table-spoon at a time, into mixture, mixing lightly with fork after each addition until dough is just moist enough to hold together. With hands, shape dough into ball.

4 Spoon peach mixture into deep 20-23 cm/8-9 inch pie dish. Cut butter into small pieces; dot on top of peach mixture.

5 Preheat oven to 220°C/425°F/gas 7. Roll out dough into 28-32 cm/11-12 ½ inch round. Cut a few small slashes in centre of round to allow steam to escape during baking.

6 Place dough round over peach filling; trim dough edge, leaving 2.5 cm/1 inch overhang. Fold overhang under; make Fluted or other Decorative Pastry Edge (pages 136-137).

7 Reroll dough trimmings; cut out a few leaves. Arrange leaves on top of pie. Brush all over with beaten egg yolk.

8 Because peaches vary in juiciness, place sheet of foil underneath pie dish; crimp edges to form rim to catch any drips during baking. Bake pie for 50 minutes or until pastry is golden and peaches are tender. If pastry begins to brown too much, cover loosely with foil.

9 Slightly cool pie on wire rack; serve warm. Or cool pie completely to serve cold later.

Slashes are made in top crust before baking. This lets steam from fruit escape and helps keep pastry dry and crisp

Deep-dish pies with juicy fruit fillings need only a top crust as here; pastry on bottom of dish would be soggy from the juice of the fruits

TARTS AND FLANS

Tarts and flans – crisp, rich and sweet pastry filled with creamy custards, juicy fresh fruits, fine chocolate and crunchy nuts – make the most delectable of desserts. In this collection of recipes you will find old favourites as well as new and exciting ideas, each one of them as good to look at as it is to eat, and you don't have to be a pastry chef to make them!

TART OR FLAN SHELL

| 175 g/6 oz plain flour |
| 1 tablespoon caster sugar |
| ¼ teaspoon salt (optional) |
| 120 g/4 oz cold butter |
| 2-3 tablespoons cold water |

1 In medium bowl, with fork, stir flour with sugar and salt, if using. With pastry blender or with fingertips, cut or rub butter into flour mixture until mixture resembles coarse crumbs.

2 Sprinkle cold water, a tablespoon at a time, into mixture, mixing lightly with fork after each addition, until dough just holds together. With hands, shape dough into ball. Wrap and refrigerate for 1 hour.

3 Preheat oven to 220°C/425°F/gas 7. On lightly floured surface, with floured rolling pin, roll out dough into round about 2.5 cm/1 inch larger all round than 23-25 cm/ 9-10 inch loose-bottomed tart or flan tin.

4 Ease dough into tin to line evenly; press dough on to bottom and up side of tin.

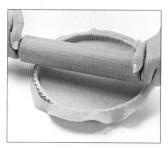

5 Roll rolling pin across top of tin to trim off excess dough; reserve trimmings for decoration.

6 With fork, prick dough liberally to prevent puffing and shrinkage during baking.

7 Line shell with foil; fill with dried or baking beans. Bake shell for 10 minutes. Remove foil and beans; again prick dough. Bake shell for 10-15 minutes longer until golden brown.

8 If pastry puffs up, gently press it to tin with spoon.

9 Cool tart or flan shell in tin on wire rack.

TARTLET SHELLS

1 In bowl, with fork, stir 75 g/2 ½ oz plain flour, 1 teaspoon caster sugar and ¼ teaspoon salt (optional). With pastry blender or fingertips, cut or rub 60 g/2 oz cold butter into flour mixture until mixture resembles coarse crumbs. Sprinkle 4-5 teaspoons cold water, a teaspoon at a time, into mixture, mixing lightly with fork after each addition until dough is just moist enough to hold together. With hands, shape dough into ball. Wrap and refrigerate for 1 hour.

2 Preheat oven to 190°C/375°F/gas 5. On lightly floured surface, with floured rolling pin, roll out half of the dough 3 mm/ ⅛ inch thick. With floured 7.5 cm/3 inch round pastry cutter, cut out as many rounds as possible. Repeat with remaining dough and trimmings to make 18 rounds.

3 Press each round of dough on to bottom and up side of eighteen 6 cm/2 ½ inch round tartlet tins (2 cm/ ¾ inch deep).

4 With fork, prick tartlet shells in many places to prevent puffing and shrinkage during baking. Place tartlet tins in baking tray for easy handling. Bake for 12-15 minutes until lightly browned.

5 Cool tartlet shells in tins on wire racks for 10 minutes. With knife, gently loosen tartlet shells from sides of tins; remove from tins and cool completely on wire racks.

6 If not using tartlet shells immediately, store them in airtight container.

WICKED TRUFFLE TARTS

Makes 18
Can be made day
before and kept in
refrigerator

350 g/12 oz plain
  chocolate, broken
  into pieces

300 ml/ ½ pint double
  cream

90 g/3 oz butter

2 tablespoons orange
  liqueur or brandy

18 Tartlet Shells
  (see Box, page 159)

Shredded orange zest
  to decorate

*These dainty little tartlet shells
are home-made, but if you are
short of time, you can buy
ready-made tartlet shells*

1 In non-stick
saucepan over low
heat, heat pieces of chocolate, double cream and
butter, stirring frequently,
until melted and smooth.
Remove saucepan from
heat; stir in liqueur or
brandy.

2 Refrigerate chocolate
mixture for about
2 ½ hours or until very
thick and an easy piping
consistency, stirring
occasionally.

3 Meanwhile, prepare
and bake Tartlet
Shells as directed; cool on
wire rack.

ALTERNATIVE FILLING

For a change, use white rather than plain
chocolate to make the truffle filling for these elegant
tartlets.

White Truffle Tartlets
In step 1, substitute
*350 g/12 oz white
chocolate* for the plain
chocolate, and
2 teaspoons vanilla essence
for the orange liqueur

or brandy. For decora-
tion, use chocolate
'coffee beans', grated
chocolate, Chocolate
Curls (page 100), or a
cluster of raspberries.

4 Spoon chocolate
mixture into large
piping bag fitted with large
star tube; pipe into shells.

5 Serve tartlets while
truffle mixture is
velvety soft, or refrigerate
filled tartlets for several
hours so truffle mixture
has firmer consistency.
Decorate with orange zest
before serving.

PLUM AND ALMOND FLAN

8 servings
Allow 3 hours
preparation and
cooking time

Cinnamon Shortbread

175 g/6 oz plain flour
120 g/4 oz butter, softened
60 g/2 oz caster sugar
½ teaspoon ground cinnamon

Filling

700 g/1 ½ lb Victoria plums
100 g/3 ½ oz caster sugar
1 tablespoon cornflour
½ teaspoon ground cinnamon
¼ teaspoon almond essence
30 g/1 oz slivered blanched almonds
Whipped cream for serving (optional)

Flan case is rich and buttery, more like shortbread than pastry

1 Prepare cinnamon shortbread dough: in medium bowl, combine flour, butter, sugar and cinnamon. With fingertips, mix until dough just holds together.

2 Press shortbread on to bottom and up side of 20 cm/8 inch loose-bottomed tart or flan tin.

3 Preheat oven to 190°C/375°F/gas 5. Prepare filling: cut each plum in half and remove stone; slice plums.

4 In large bowl, toss plums, sugar, corn-flour, cinnamon and almond essence.

5 Arrange plum slices, closely overlapping, to form concentric circles in shortbread shell.

PLUMS

These plump, fragrant fruits are in season from the beginning of May until the end of October, but are at their plentiful best in August.

- Plums come in a wide range of sizes, shapes and colours, with skin ranging from bright yellow-green to reddish-purple to purplish-black, depending on variety.

- It doesn't matter which variety of plum you choose for cooking – all types of plum can be used interchangeably in recipes, including dam-sons and greengages.

- A perfect plum is richly coloured and firm, with a slight softening at stalk end.

- Five or six plums weigh 450 g/1 lb.

- Store ripe plums in refrigerator, for 3-5 days.

- Plums can be frozen – halve and remove stones, then freeze plums in small quantities in freezer bags.

Sprinkling almonds over plums

6 Evenly sprinkle slivered almonds over plum slices.

7 Bake in the oven for 45 minutes or until pastry is golden and plums are tender. Cool flan in tin on wire rack.

8 Carefully remove side of tin. Transfer flan to serving plate.

9 Serve Plum and Almond Flan cut into wedges, with whipped cream if you like.

ASCOT FRUIT TART

8 servings
Allow 3 ½ hours preparation and cooking time

Coconut Pastry

150 g/5 oz plain flour
75 g/2 ½ oz shredded or desiccated coconut
90 g/3 oz butter
30 g/1 oz caster sugar
1 egg yolk

Lemon Custard Filling

1 large lemon
90 g/3 oz butter
60 g/2 oz caster sugar
1 tablespoon cornflour
4 egg yolks
300 ml/ ½ pint double or whipping cream

Fruit Topping

350 g/12 oz raspberries
225 g/8 oz blueberries

1 Prepare coconut pastry dough: in medium bowl, combine flour, coconut, butter, sugar and egg yolk. With fingertips, mix together just until blended.

2 Press dough on to bottom and up side of 25 cm/10 inch loose-bottomed tart or flan tin. With fork, prick pastry shell in many places to prevent puffing and shrinkage during baking.

3 Preheat oven to 180°C/350°F/gas 4. Line pastry shell with foil and spread evenly with dried or baking beans; bake for 10 minutes. Remove beans and foil; again prick dough. Bake for 10-15 minutes longer until golden (if pastry puffs up, press it to tin with spoon). Cool pastry shell in tin on wire rack.

4 While pastry shell is baking, prepare lemon custard filling: from lemon, grate 1 teaspoon zest and squeeze 2 tablespoons juice; set aside. In heavy medium saucepan over medium-low heat, heat butter, sugar and cornflour, stirring constantly, until mixture thickens and boils; boil for 1 minute longer.

5 In small bowl, with fork, beat egg yolks; stir in small amount of hot sugar mixture.

6 Slowly pour egg yolk mixture back into sugar mixture in pan, stirring rapidly with wooden spoon to prevent lumping.

7 Cook, stirring constantly, until mixture thickens and coats spoon well, about 1 minute. Remove saucepan from heat.

8 Stir lemon zest and lemon juice into custard; cool, then cover and refrigerate until very cold, about 1 hour.

9 In small bowl, whip double or whipping cream until stiff peaks form. With rubber spatula or wire whisk, fold whipped cream into chilled lemon custard.

RASPBERRIES

These small, juicy, thimble-shaped berries come in red, black, purple and yellow varieties, and are best during June to July and September to October.

• Choose plump, fresh-looking berries.

• Do not buy berries that are crushed or bruised, or that have leaked moisture through container.

• Keep refrigerated and use within 1-2 days.

• Eat raspberries plain or use in fruit salads, pies, flans, crumbles, jams, jellies and sweet sauces.

10 Evenly spoon lemon custard filling into cooled pastry shell.

Spooning lemon custard filling into pastry shell

Whipped cream is folded into egg custard to make this rich filling

11 Arrange raspberries in circular pattern round edge of tart.

12 Fill in centre with blueberries and raspberries; refrigerate for 1 hour until custard is set.

With different fruits to match the seasons, this can be a year-round treat. Use bananas and oranges in winter; pineapple and papaya in spring; apricots and cherries in summer; grapes and pears in autumn. Slice or dice fruit as necessary, to make it look as pretty as possible, and for easy serving

ROYAL RASPBERRY TART

8-10 servings

Allow 3 ½ hours preparation and cooking time

1 x 25 cm/10 inch Tart or Flan Shell (see Box, page 159)

60 g/2 oz caster sugar

20 g/ ⅔ oz cornflour

1 tablespoon powdered gelatine

2 eggs plus 1 egg yolk

350 ml/12 fl oz milk

150 ml/ ¼ pint double or whipping cream

450 g/1 lb raspberries

1 Prepare and bake Tart or Flan Shell according to recipe instructions; cool on wire rack.

2 In medium saucepan, combine sugar, cornflour and gelatine. In medium bowl, with wire whisk or fork, beat eggs and egg yolk with milk until well mixed; stir into gelatine mixture. Leave to stand for 5 minutes to soften gelatine slightly.

3 Cook over low heat, stirring constantly, until mixture thickens and coats spoon well, about 20 minutes. Remove saucepan from heat.

4 Pour custard into large bowl; cool, then cover and refrigerate until mixture mounds slightly when dropped from spoon, about 1 hour, stirring occasionally.

5 In small bowl, whip double or whipping cream until stiff peaks form. With rubber spatula or wire whisk, fold whipped cream into custard.

ALTERNATIVE RASPBERRY TOPPINGS

In the main picture below, raspberries are piled high on top of custard. For a more formal effect, raspberries can be arranged in a pattern, as here.

Windmill
Arrange raspberries in 4 triangular shapes, working from centre of filling towards outside.

In the Round
Arrange raspberries in concentric circles, working from outside edge of filling to centre.

6 Carefully remove pastry shell from tin; place on serving plate. Spoon custard into pastry shell; top with raspberries.

7 Refrigerate tart for 1 hour or until custard is completely set.

Fresh summer raspberries are piled high in centre of tart; if you like, sprinkle them with caster sugar just before serving

NUTCRACKER TART

8 servings
Allow 3 hours
preparation and
cooking time

Ginger Pastry

175 g/6 oz plain flour

2 tablespoons caster sugar

1 teaspoon ground ginger

120 g/4 oz butter

1 egg

Filling

60 g/2 oz butter

60 g/2 oz black treacle

175 g/6 oz golden syrup

60 g/2 oz caster sugar

3 eggs

120 g/4 oz shelled pecans
or walnut halves

100 g/3 ½ oz shelled
unsalted macadamia
nuts or hazelnuts

Whipped cream and non-
toxic flowers (pages 118-
119) to decorate

1 Prepare ginger pastry dough: in medium bowl, with fork, stir flour, sugar and ginger. With pastry blender or with fingertips, cut or rub butter into flour mixture until mixture resembles coarse crumbs. Add egg; mix lightly with fork until dough just holds together.

Rich-tasting macadamia nuts look good arranged with pecans because of their perfect round shape, but for a less expensive alternative you could equally well use a combination of hazelnuts and walnuts

2 With hand, pat dough on to bottom and up side of 25 cm/10 inch loose-bottomed tart or flan tin. Set aside.

3 Preheat oven to 180°C/350°F/gas 4.

4 Prepare filling: in medium saucepan over low heat, melt butter; remove from heat.

5 Into melted butter, with wire whisk, beat treacle, syrup, sugar and eggs just until blended.

6 Arrange pecans or walnuts and macadamia nuts or hazelnuts on bottom of pastry shell in concentric circles.

7 Slowly pour treacle mixture over nuts in pastry shell, taking care not to disturb pattern.

8 Bake tart for 35 minutes or until knife inserted in filling 2.5 cm/1 inch from edge comes out clean. Cool tart in tin on wire rack.

9 To serve, remove side of tin; decorate centre of tart with whipped cream and flower.

Tiger lily gives an exotic touch to the centre of this tart, but you can use any flower you like, as long as it is non-toxic

FRENCH APPLE PUFFS

8 servings
Allow 1 ½ hours preparation and cooking time

450 g/1 lb frozen puff pastry

4 medium-sized dessert apples

3 digestive biscuits, finely crushed

45 g/1 ½ oz butter, melted

About 3 tablespoons orange marmalade

Icing sugar for sprinkling

Whipped cream for serving (optional)

1 Thaw puff pastry according to packet instructions.

2 Preheat oven to 220°C/425°F/gas 7. On floured surface, with floured rolling pin, roll half of the pastry out to 36 cm/14 ½ inch square.

3 Using 17.5 cm/7 inch round plate as a guide, cut out 4 rounds from pastry square.

Finely crushed digestive biscuits add crunch to apple filling, and help prevent apple juices seeping into pastry and making it soggy

4 Cut 2 apples in half lengthways; remove cores and peel. Cut apple halves lengthways into paper-thin slices.

5 Place pastry rounds on large baking sheet Top each pastry round with 1 tablespoon biscuit crumbs, then with one-quarter of the apple slices.

6 Brush apple slices with some melted butter.

7 Bake apple puffs for 15 minutes or until pastry is lightly browned and crisp and apple slices are tender. With fish slice, transfer apple puffs to wire racks.

8 In small saucepan over low heat, heat orange marmalade until melted. Brush over apple slices while they are still hot.

9 Repeat with remaining ingredients to make 4 more apple puffs.

> **TO SERVE**
> *Sift icing sugar over apple slices. Serve puffs warm, with whipped cream.*

Icing sugar melts and caramelizes on hot marmalade glaze

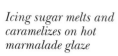

PEACH GALETTE

 8 servings
Allow 3 hours preparation and cooking time

Pastry

175 g/6 oz plain flour	
30 g/1 oz caster sugar	
120 g/4 oz butter	
1 egg	

Filling

2 x 825 g/1 lb 13 oz cans peach halves	
1 teaspoon lemon juice	
¼ teaspoon ground ginger	
3 heaped tablespoons peach or apricot jam	

Pastry 'scallops' follow shape of peaches

1 Prepare pastry dough: in medium bowl, with fork, stir flour and sugar. With pastry blender or with fingertips, cut or rub butter into flour mixture until mixture resembles coarse crumbs. Add egg; mix lightly with fork until dough just holds together. (Or, in food processor with knife blade attached, blend flour, sugar and butter, cut into 8 pieces, for about 10 seconds. Add egg through feed tube; blend for 15 seconds longer or until dough holds together.) Shape dough into ball. Wrap and refrigerate for 1 hour.

2 Meanwhile, prepare filling: drain peaches; set aside 8 peach halves. Slice remaining peaches.

3 Put sliced peaches in saucepan; add lemon juice, ground ginger and 1 tablespoon jam. Bring to the boil, then cook over medium heat for 5-10 minutes or until mixture is reduced to 300 ml/ ½ pint, mashing frequently with potato masher. Leave to cool.

4 Preheat oven to 180°C/350°F/gas 4. On lightly floured surface, with floured rolling pin, roll pastry dough out to 35 cm/14 inch round; transfer to large baking sheet.

5 With fingertips, roll edge towards centre until round measures 25 cm/10 inches and edge is 2 cm/¾ inch high; push edge in towards centre to make 7 large, evenly spaced scallops.

6 Bake for 25 minutes or until pastry is golden. Cool on baking sheet on wire rack.

7 Melt remaining peach or apricot jam in small saucepan over medium heat, then press through sieve into small jug. Spoon cooled peach mixture over pastry.

8 Cut reserved peach halves into slices, taking care to maintain peach shape. Slip flat side of broad-bladed knife under each peach half and arrange on filling.

9 Fan peach slices slightly; brush with peach or apricot jam glaze. Transfer galette to serving plate.

Pushing pastry edge in to make 'scallop' shapes

UPSIDE-DOWN APPLE TART

8-10 servings
Allow 1 ½ hours preparation and cooking time

300 g/10 oz frozen puff pastry

10 large Golden Delicious apples

200 g/7 oz caster sugar

120 g/4 oz butter

¼ teaspoon almond essence

Chilled pouring cream for serving (optional)

1 Thaw puff pastry according to packet instructions.

2 Meanwhile, peel and core apples (Golden Delicious apples with very green skin retain their shape best; do not use other apples). Cut each apple in half lengthways.

3 In 25 cm/ 10 inch heavy frying pan with metal handle (or with handle covered with heavy-duty foil) over medium heat, heat sugar, butter and almond essence until butter melts, stirring occasionally (do not use margarine because it will separate from sugar during cooking). Sugar will not be completely dissolved. Remove pan from heat.

4 Arrange apple halves on their sides round side and in centre of pan, fitting apples very tightly together.

5 Return frying pan to medium heat and bring to the boil; boil for 20-40 minutes, depending on juiciness of apples, until butter and sugar mixture becomes caramel-coloured. Remove from heat.

6 Preheat oven to 230°C/450°F/gas 8.

7 On lightly floured surface, with floured rolling pin, roll pastry out to 30 cm/12 inch round.

8 Carefully place pastry round over apple halves in frying pan.

9 With prongs of fork, press pastry to edge of frying pan.

10 Cut slits in pastry. Bake in the oven for 20-25 minutes until pastry is golden. Remove pan from oven; allow to cool on wire rack for 10 minutes.

11 Place dessert platter upside-down over frying pan; holding them firmly together, carefully invert tart on to dessert platter (do this over sink since tart may be extremely juicy).

TO SERVE
Serve Upside-Down Apple Tart warm or cold, with chilled cream if you like.

When tart is turned out upside-down for serving, apples are caramelized yet still retain their shape

MINCEMEAT AND PEAR FLAN

8-10 servings
Allow 2 hours preparation and cooking time

Pastry

175 g/6 oz plain flour	
30 g/1 oz caster sugar	
120 g/4 oz butter	
1 egg	

Streusel Topping

30 g/1 oz plain flour	
20 g / ⅔ oz light soft brown sugar	
30 g/1 oz butter	

Filling

450 g/1 lb mincemeat	
1 x 400 g/14 oz can pear halves	

Sweet and buttery streusel topping adds crunch and texture to soft mincemeat and pears

1 Prepare pastry dough: in medium bowl, with fork, stir flour and sugar. With pastry blender or with fingertips, cut or rub butter into flour mixture until mixture resembles coarse crumbs. Add egg; mix lightly with fork until dough just holds together. (Or, in food processor with knife blade attached, blend flour, sugar and butter, cut into 8 pieces, until mixture resembles coarse crumbs, about 10 seconds. Add egg through feed tube; blend for 15 seconds longer or until dough holds together and leaves side of bowl.) With hands, shape dough into ball. Wrap and refrigerate for 1 hour.

2 Prepare streusel topping: in small bowl, combine flour and brown sugar. With pastry blender or with fingertips, cut or rub butter into flour mixture until mixture resembles coarse crumbs. Refrigerate.

3 Preheat oven to 180°C/350°F/gas 4.

4 On lightly floured surface, with floured rolling pin, roll pastry dough out to round 2.5 cm/1 inch larger all round than 23 cm/9 inch loose-bottomed tart or flan tin.

5 Ease dough into tin to line evenly; trim edge. With fork, prick pastry shell liberally to prevent puffing and shrinkage during baking.

6 Line pastry shell with foil and spread evenly with dried or baking beans; bake for 10 minutes.

7 Remove foil and beans; prick dough again. Bake for a further 10 minutes. Remove pastry shell from oven; turn oven up to 220°C/425°F/gas 7.

8 Spoon mincemeat into pastry shell and spread evenly.

9 Drain pears; pat dry with kitchen paper. Cut each pear half lengthways into 5 mm/¼ inch thick slices, taking care to keep slices from each half together. Arrange pears on mincemeat, fanning slices slightly.

10 With spoon, evenly sprinkle streusel topping over sliced pears in pastry shell.

11 Bake flan for 15-20 minutes until filling is heated through and pastry and topping are lightly browned. Cool flan slightly in tin on wire rack.

12 Remove side of tin. Serve flan warm or cool completely to serve cold later.

Fanning pear halves in circle on top of mincemeat filling

FRUIT TARTLETS

Petite and prettily shaped, tartlets filled with a variety of colourful fruits and topped with a sparkling glaze make an irresistible display on the table. Here are a few ideas for presentation, to inspire you to create your own filling and topping combinations. Use tartlet tins of as many different shapes as you can, and choose small whole fruits that lend themselves to the shape of the shells, or cut up larger fruits to fit. Make the pastry shells from the recipe for Tartlet Shells (see Box, page 159), leave them to cool, then fill them with Lemon Custard Filling (page 162) or sweetened whipped cream. Once fruits have been arranged on top, brush them with a little melted jelly – use redcurrant jelly for dark fruits, or sieved apricot jam for light-coloured fruits. The thin glaze will provide an instant gloss and keep fruit looking its best for a few hours if necessary.

Raspberry and blackberry

Blueberry

Strawberry

Orange and grapefruit

Red and green seedless grapes

FRUIT TOPPINGS

Choose fruits that suit the size and shape of the tartlet shell. Dainty small whole fruits such as berries and grapes can be used singly, or heaped or clustered on filling. Dice larger fruits, or cut them into slices for dramatic effect.

Grapes can be left whole or sliced, according to their size

Star fruit slices have a beautiful shape

Passion fruit pulp can be sprinkled over other fruits as a decoration

PEAR CRUMBLE TART

  8-10 servings
Allow 3 hours
preparation and
cooking time

Filling

30 g/1 oz caster sugar	
1 teaspoon ground cinnamon	
300 ml/ ½ pint double or whipping cream	
2 egg yolks	
2 x 400 g/14 oz cans pear halves	

Crumble Crust

215 g/7 ½ oz plain flour	
¼ teaspoon salt (optional)	
45 g/1 ½ oz caster sugar	
90 g/3 oz butter	

Crumble base is rich, sweet and buttery, with a short texture

Pear slices are set in a creamy egg custard, subtly flavoured with cinnamon

1 Prepare filling: in small bowl, with fork, mix sugar and cinnamon; set aside.

2 In another small bowl, with wire whisk or fork, beat double or whipping cream with egg yolks until blended; cover and refrigerate.

3 Preheat oven to 200°C/400°F/gas 6. Prepare crumble crust: in medium bowl, with fork, stir flour, salt, if using, and sugar. With pastry blender or with fingertips, cut or rub butter into flour mixture until mixture resembles coarse crumbs. (Mixture will be dry and crumbly.)

4 With hand, firmly press crumble mixture on to bottom and up side of shallow 25 cm/10 inch pie dish.

5 Drain pears; pat dry with kitchen paper. Slice pears, then arrange in pie dish, fanning slices slightly.

6 Over pear slices in bottom of crumble crust, with spoon, evenly sprinkle sugar and cinnamon mixture.

7 Bake tart for about 5 minutes or until sugar and cinnamon mixture is melted.

8 With pie dish still on oven rack, carefully pour cream mixture over pears.

9 Bake tart for 20-30 minutes until top is browned and knife inserted in centre of filling comes out clean.

10 Cool tart in dish on wire rack. Serve warm, or cover and refrigerate to serve cold later.

APRICOT LINZER TORTE

8 servings
Allow 3 hours preparation and cooking time

Filling

350 g/12 oz dried apricot halves

250 ml/8 fl oz orange juice

100 g/3 ½ oz caster sugar

Almond Pastry

120 g/4 oz blanched almonds, ground

265 g/9 ½ oz plain flour

200 g/7 oz caster sugar

175 g/6 oz butter, softened

30 g/1 oz cocoa powder

1 teaspoon ground cinnamon

1 teaspoon grated lemon zest

1 egg

Icing sugar for sprinkling

1 Prepare filling: in large saucepan bring apricots, orange juice, sugar and *250 ml/8 fl oz water* to the boil. Cook, uncovered, over medium heat for 30 minutes or until apricots are very tender and liquid is absorbed, stirring frequently.

2 Press apricot mixture through food mill or coarse sieve into bowl; cover and refrigerate.

3 Generously grease 28 cm/11 inch loose-bottomed tart or flan tin.

4 Prepare almond pastry dough: in large bowl, with electric mixer, beat almonds, flour, caster sugar, butter, cocoa, cinnamon, lemon zest and egg until well mixed, occasionally scraping bowl.

5 Divide dough in half; press half of the dough on to bottom and up side of tin. Spoon apricot mixture into pastry shell.

6 Preheat oven to 200°C/400°F/gas 6. On lightly floured surface, with floured rolling pin, roll out remaining dough into 25 cm/10 inch round. With knife, cut dough round into 1 cm/½ inch wide strips.

7 Carefully place half of the dough strips, about 1 cm/½ inch apart, over apricot filling.

8 Place remaining strips diagonally across first row of strips about 1 cm/½ inch apart.

9 Press down with finger on either side of each crossing to create rippled lattice effect.

10 Press ends of strips to inside edge of pastry shell.

11 Bake torte in the oven for 10 minutes. Turn oven down to 180°C/350°F/gas 4; bake for 20 minutes longer. Cool torte in tin on wire rack.

12 To serve, remove side of tin; place torte on serving platter. Sift icing sugar over lattice, covering top strips only.

If you use a small sieve and are very careful when sifting icing sugar over lattice, sugar will settle on top row of lattice strips only, and look most effective

FRESH CHERRY FLAN

8 servings
Allow 2 hours
preparation and
cooking time

*1 x 25 cm/10 inch Tart or
Flan Shell (see Box,
page 159)*

450 g/1 lb cherries

3 eggs

*300 ml/ ½ pint double or
whipping cream*

60 g/2 oz caster sugar

*2 tablespoons almond
liqueur or 1 teaspoon
almond essence*

*For the best creamy texture,
egg custard should be firm
and set at edge when removed
from oven, but still slightly
soft in centre; it will set
throughout if left to stand
for 10-15 minutes*

1 Prepare and bake Tart
or Flan Shell accord-
ing to recipe instructions;
cool. Turn oven down to
180°C/350°F/gas 4.

2 Meanwhile, with
cherry stoner, remove
stones from cherries.

3 In large bowl, with
electric mixer, beat
eggs with double or
whipping cream, sugar and
almond liqueur or almond
essence until blended.

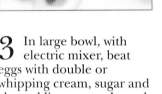

CUSTARDS AND CUSTARD TARTS

Because custards are so delicate in texture, and can
easily be overcooked, they should be removed from
the oven when they are set at the sides – and still
slightly soft in the centre.

Testing Custards
When custard looks
firm and set, double-
check by inserting
knife 2.5 cm/1 inch
from edge – custard is
ready if knife comes
out clean. Custard will
continue cooking after
it has been removed from
the oven, so that after
10-15 minutes it will be
set throughout.

4 Place cher-
ries in pastry
shell, arran-
ging them
in concentric
circles.

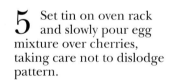

5 Set tin on oven rack
and slowly pour egg
mixture over cherries,
taking care not to dislodge
pattern.

6 Bake flan in the oven
for 30 minutes or
until knife inserted in
filling 2.5 cm/ 1 inch from
edge comes out clean.

7 Cool flan slightly in
tin on wire rack.

8 Remove side of tin.
Serve flan warm, or
cover and leave to cool to
serve cold later.

*Sweet juicy cherries are stoned and set in an
almond-flavoured creamy egg custard*

CLAFOUTIS FLAN

- 8-10 servings
- Allow 4 hours preparation and cooking time

Pastry

215 g/7 ½ oz plain flour
¾ teaspoon salt (optional)
1 teaspoon caster sugar
120 g/4 oz butter, softened
1 egg

Filling

6 eggs
200 g/7 oz caster sugar
450 ml/ ¾ pint milk
150 ml/ ¼ pint soured cream
1 teaspoon vanilla essence
175 g/6 oz blueberries or stoned cherries

1 Prepare pastry dough: in medium bowl, with fork, stir flour, salt, if using, and sugar. With pastry blender or with fingertips, cut or rub butter into flour mixture until mixture resembles coarse crumbs. In cup, with fork, beat egg; add to flour mixture and mix lightly with fork until dough just holds together, adding a little water if necessary. With hands, shape dough into ball. Wrap and refrigerate for 1 hour.

Here, fresh blueberries are used for this French 'clafoutis', but you can use stoned cherries if they are more easy to obtain

2 On lightly floured surface, with floured rolling pin, roll out dough into round 2.5 cm/1 inch larger all round than 30 cm/12 inch flan dish. Ease dough into dish to line evenly; trim edge. With fork, prick pastry shell in many places to prevent puffing during baking. To prevent pastry from shrinking during baking, place shell in freezer for 15 minutes.

3 Preheat oven to 220°C/425°F/gas 7. Line pastry shell with foil and evenly spread dried or baking beans over bottom.

4 Bake pastry shell for 20 minutes. Remove beans and foil and again prick pastry shell. Bake for a further 3-4 minutes until pastry is lightly browned and no longer soft and raw (if pastry puffs up, gently press it to dish with spoon).

5 Prepare filling: in large bowl, with electric mixer, beat eggs and caster sugar until very thick and lemon-coloured, about 3 minutes. Gradually add milk, soured cream and vanilla essence; beat until well blended.

6 Place blueberries or cherries in warm pastry shell. Slowly pour over egg mixture.

Pouring egg mixture over blueberries

7 Bake in the oven for 30-35 minutes until filling is set and pastry is golden brown; cover with foil after 20 minutes to prevent overbrowning.

8 Cool flan in dish on wire rack.

Flan is served topped with extra blueberries and sifted with icing sugar

ORANGE AND ALMOND FLAN

 10 servings
Allow 2 ¼ hours preparation and cooking time

Ginger Pastry

150 g/5 oz plain flour

¼ teaspoon salt

¼ teaspoon ground ginger

1 tablespoon caster sugar

60 g/2 oz butter

Filling

2 eggs

225 g/8 oz almond paste

125 ml/4 fl oz double or whipping cream

2 medium-sized oranges

2 tablespoons golden syrup

60 g/2 oz caster sugar

1 First prepare pastry dough: in medium bowl, with fork, stir flour, salt, ginger and sugar. With pastry blender or with fingertips, cut or rub butter into flour mixture until it resembles coarse crumbs.

2 Sprinkle *2-3 tablespoons cold water*, a tablespoon at a time, into mixture, mixing lightly with fork after each addition until dough is just moist enough to hold together. Shape dough into ball. Wrap and chill in refrigerator for 1 hour.

3 Preheat oven to 190°C/375°F/gas 5. On lightly floured surface, with floured rolling pin, roll out dough into round about 2.5 cm/1 inch larger all round than 24 cm/9 ½ inch loose-bottomed tart or flan tin. Ease dough into tin; trim edge.

4 Prepare filling: in large bowl, with electric mixer, beat eggs, almond paste and double or whipping cream until mixture is smooth, occasionally scraping bowl with rubber spatula.

5 Pour almond mixture into pastry shell. Bake for 35 minutes or until filling and pastry are golden brown. Cool flan in tin on wire rack.

6 While flan is cooling, prepare candied orange zest: with vegetable peeler, thinly pare zest from oranges in long strips. Cut orange zest into matchstick-thin strips.

7 With knife, cut white pith from oranges; cut along both sides of each dividing membrane and lift out segments from centre. Place orange segments on kitchen paper to absorb excess juice.

8 In medium saucepan over medium heat, bring orange zest, golden syrup, sugar and *5 tablespoons water* to the boil, stirring frequently. Reduce heat to medium-low; cook for 15 minutes or until zest is tender.

9 With fork, remove orange zest and place in single layer on wire rack to drain.

10 Brush flan with sugar syrup remaining in saucepan.

11 Carefully remove side of tin; slide flan on to serving plate.

> *TO SERVE*
> *Arrange candied orange zest round edge of flan; arrange orange segments in centre.*

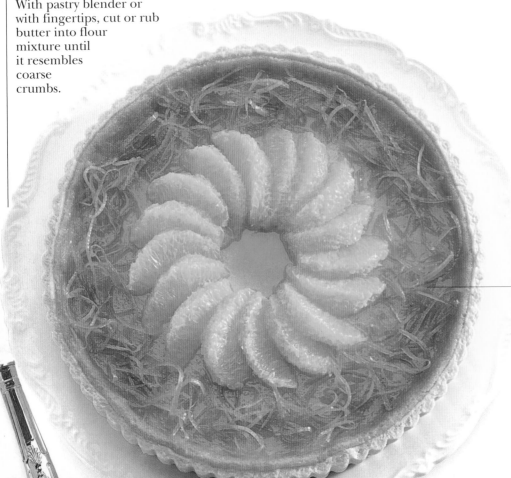

Matchstick-thin strips of candied orange zest are arranged round circle of orange segments to make the pretty topping for this superb-tasting flan

ITALIAN WALNUT TART

8 servings
Allow 3 hours preparation and cooking time

Sweet Cornmeal Pastry

215 g/7 ½ oz plain flour	
40 g/1 ⅓ oz cornmeal	
60 g/2 oz caster sugar	
175 g/6 oz butter	
1 egg	
1 tablespoon milk	

Filling

150 g/5 oz caster sugar	
250 ml/8 fl oz double cream	
90 g/3 oz liquid honey	
450 g/1 lb walnut pieces, coarsely chopped	

1 Prepare sweet cornmeal pastry dough: in large bowl, with fork, stir flour, cornmeal and sugar. With pastry blender or with fingertips, cut or rub butter into flour and cornmeal mixture until mixture resembles coarse crumbs.

2 Add egg to flour and cornmeal mixture; mix lightly with fork until dough just holds together.

3 With your hands, press two-thirds of dough on to bottom and 3 cm/1 ¼ inches up side of 25 cm/10 inch springform cake tin.

4 Place pastry shell and remaining pastry dough in refrigerator to chill while preparing filling.

5 Prepare filling: in large frying pan over medium heat, heat sugar, without stirring, just until it begins to melt. Cook, stirring constantly, for 6-8 minutes until golden brown. Remove pan from heat; slowly and carefully stir in double cream (mixture will spatter). Return pan to medium heat; cook for 5 minutes or until mixture is smooth, stirring frequently.

Stirring walnuts into filling

6 Remove frying pan from heat; stir in honey until well blended. Stir in chopped walnuts until evenly mixed.

7 Leave walnut filling in frying pan to cool slightly.

8 Preheat oven to 180°C/350°F/gas 4. Evenly spread walnut filling in pastry shell. On lightly floured surface, with floured rolling pin, roll out remaining dough into 25 x 12.5 cm/ 10 x 5 inch rectangle; cut lengthways into ten 1 cm/½ inch wide strips.

Sweet cornmeal pastry gives this lattice-topped tart a golden colour and accentuates the nutty flavour of the filling

9 Twist strips; arrange in lattice design on top of filling.

10 Brush strips lightly with milk. Bake tart for 45 minutes or until golden brown. Cool tart in tin on wire rack.

11 To serve, carefully remove side from springform tin. Serve warm, or leave to cool, cover and refrigerate to serve cold later.

DELUXE APPLE FLAN

This beautiful apple flan is a classic piece of French pâtisserie, yet it is easy to make at home. Take care to cut the apple slices really thinly, and take time to arrange them in overlapping circles; your efforts will be rewarded.

 8-10 servings
Allow 4 hours preparation and cooking time

Pastry

150 g/5 oz plain flour

75 g/2 ½ oz butter, softened

30 g/1 oz caster sugar

⅛ teaspoon salt (optional)

Filling

6 large dessert apples

120 g/4 oz apricot jam

1 teaspoon lemon juice

1 Prepare pastry dough: in medium bowl, combine flour, butter, sugar, salt, if using, and *2 tablespoons cold water*. With fingertips, mix together just until blended, adding more water, 1 teaspoon at a time, if needed.

2 Press dough on to bottom and up side of 23 cm/9 inch loose-bottomed tart or flan tin; refrigerate.

3 Prepare filling: peel and core 3 apples; cut into chunks. In saucepan, cook apple chunks with half of the apricot jam and *4 tablespoons water* until apples are tender.

4 In food processor or blender, blend apple mixture until smooth. Pour apple purée into medium non-stick saucepan; cook, uncovered, until very thick, stirring frequently to prevent purée catching on bottom of pan.

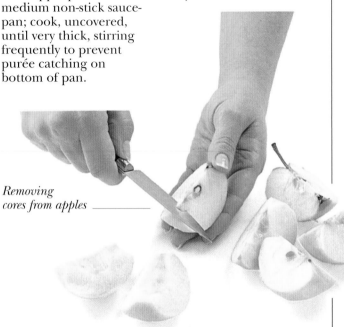

Removing cores from apples

5 Peel remaining 3 apples. Cut each apple into quarters lengthways; remove cores.

FILLING AND GLAZING FLAN

Spreading apple purée in pastry shell: *spoon apple purée into pastry shell, then spread evenly with back of spoon.*

Arranging apples in centre of flan: *place apple slices, closely overlapping, in small circle in centre of apple purée filling.*

Arranging remaining apple slices: *place remaining apple slices, closely overlapping, in large circle round first small circle, to cover apple purée completely and fill pastry shell.*

Glazing apples: *with pastry brush, gently spread hot apricot glaze over apple slices until evenly coated.*

6 Cut each quarter lengthways into 3 mm/⅛ inch thick slices.

7 In large bowl, gently toss apple slices with lemon juice.

8 Preheat oven to 200°C/400°F/gas 6.

9 Fill pastry shell with apple purée and cover with apple slices (see Box, page 178).

10 Bake flan in the oven for 45 minutes or until apple slices are tender and browned. Transfer tin to wire rack.

11 In small saucepan, melt remaining apricot jam; with spoon, press through sieve if liked.

12 Brush jam glaze evenly over apple slices (see Box, page 178). Cool flan in tin on wire rack.

13 To serve, carefully remove side of tin.

VIENNESE CARAMEL NUT TART

 8 servings
Allow 3 hours preparation and cooking time

Filling

225 g/8 oz shelled pecans or walnut halves	
135 g/4 ½ oz caster sugar	
300 ml/ ½ pint double or whipping cream	
15 g/ ½ oz butter	

Pastry

300 g/10 oz plain flour
30 g/1 oz caster sugar
½ teaspoon salt (optional)
175 g/6 oz butter

Chocolate Coating

175 g/6 oz plain chocolate, broken into pieces
60 g/2 oz butter

Tart is turned upside-down after baking; pastry on top is then glazed and piped

1 Prepare filling: reserve 10 pecan or walnut halves for decoration; finely chop remaining nuts. Set aside.

2 In medium saucepan over high heat, bring sugar and *4 tablespoons water* to the boil, stirring frequently until sugar completely dissolves. Reduce heat to medium; cook sugar syrup for 10 minutes, without stirring, until syrup turns medium amber in colour. Remove saucepan from heat; slowly and carefully pour in double or whipping cream (mixture will spatter). Return saucepan to heat; cook until caramel dissolves, stirring occasionally. Increase heat to high; cook, stirring frequently, until mixture boils and thickens slightly.

3 Remove saucepan from heat; stir in chopped nuts and butter. Set aside to cool.

4 Prepare pastry dough: in medium bowl, with fork, stir flour, sugar and salt, if using. With pastry blender or with fingertips, cut or rub butter into flour mixture until mixture resembles coarse crumbs. Sprinkle *4-6 tablespoons cold water*, a tablespoon at a time, into mixture, mixing lightly with fork after each addition until dough holds together. With hands, shape dough into ball.

5 Preheat oven to 200°C/400°F/ gas 6. On lightly floured surface, with floured rolling pin, roll out two-thirds of pastry dough into round about 5 cm/ 2 inches larger all round than 20 cm/ 8 inch loose-bottomed tart or flan tin. Ease dough into tin to line evenly (you will have a 2.5 cm/1 inch overhang).

6 Spoon nut mixture into pastry shell. Roll out remaining dough into 19 cm/7 ½ inch round; place on top of nut filling. Fold overhang over round; press gently to seal.

7 Bake tart in the oven for 40 minutes or until lightly browned. Cool tart in tin on wire rack.

8 When tart is cool, prepare chocolate coating: in bowl over saucepan of gently simmering water, heat pieces of chocolate and butter, stirring frequently, until melted and smooth. Remove bowl from pan; cool chocolate mixture slightly.

9 Carefully turn tart out upside-down on to cake plate; remove tin. Spoon 4 tablespoons chocolate mixture into piping bag fitted with small writing tube; spread remaining chocolate mixture over top and sides of tart. Arrange reserved pecan or walnut halves on top. Drizzle chocolate mixture in piping bag over top of tart to make pretty design. Leave for 15 minutes until chocolate sets before serving.

LEMON CUSTARD TART

 8 servings
Make day before and keep in refrigerator

Pastry

90 g/3 oz butter, softened

45 g/1 ½ oz caster sugar

½ teaspoon grated lemon zest

1 egg yolk

120 g/4 oz plain flour

Filling

4 eggs

4 egg yolks

175 ml/6 fl oz lemon juice

190 g/6 ½ oz caster sugar

60 g/2 oz butter

2 tablespoons apricot jam

Lemon slices to decorate

1 Prepare pastry dough: in medium bowl, with electric mixer, beat butter, sugar and lemon zest until well blended; beat in egg yolk. Stir in flour until just blended. Shape pastry dough into ball; wrap and refrigerate for 1 hour.

2 Preheat oven to 220°C/425°F/gas 7. On lightly floured surface, with floured rolling pin, roll out dough into round 2.5 cm/1 inch larger all round than 23 cm/9 inch loose-bottomed tart or flan tin. Ease dough into tin to line evenly; trim edge even with rim. With fork, prick pastry shell in many places to prevent puffing and shrinkage during baking. Line pastry shell with foil and spread evenly with dried or baking beans.

3 Bake pastry shell for 10 minutes; remove beans and foil and again prick shell. Bake for a further 5 minutes or until pastry is golden (if pastry puffs up, gently press it to tin with spoon). Cool pastry shell in tin on wire rack.

4 Prepare filling: in non-stick saucepan, with wire whisk or fork, beat eggs and egg yolks until blended; stir in lemon juice and 150 g/5 oz sugar. Cook over medium-low heat, stirring constantly, until mixture thickens and coats a spoon well, about 15 minutes (do not boil or mixture will curdle). Stir in butter until melted.

5 Into baked pastry shell, pour lemon custard filling.

6 Refrigerate tart overnight so that filling is well chilled and firm.

Here lemon slices are 'vandyked' with canelle knife to make cartwheel shapes – see page 62 for instructions

7 About 1-2 hours before serving, preheat grill to high. Cover edge of pastry shell with foil to prevent overbrowning. Evenly sprinkle remaining caster sugar over chilled lemon custard filling.

8 Place tart under grill for 6-8 minutes until sugar melts and begins to brown, making a shiny crust. (Take care not to let filling scorch.) Cool, then refrigerate.

9 Carefully remove side of tin; slide tart on to cake plate. Melt apricot jam, then work through sieve. Brush top of tart with jam glaze and decorate with lemon slices.

GRAPE AND KIWI FRUIT FLAN

8 servings
Allow 3 ½ hours
preparation and
cooking time

1 x 25 cm/10 inch Tart or
Flan Shell (see Box,
page 159)

60 g/2 oz caster sugar

25 g/ ¾ oz plain flour

1 tablespoon powdered
gelatine

2 eggs plus 1 egg yolk

450 ml/ ¾ pint milk

2 tablespoons almond
liqueur or ½ teaspoon
almond essence

About 225 g/8 oz seedless
green or red grapes

3 medium-sized kiwi fruit

150 ml/ ¼ pint double or
whipping cream

2 tablespoons redcurrant
jelly

1 Prepare and bake Tart or Flan Shell according to recipe instructions; cool on wire rack.

2 While pastry shell is baking, prepare filling: in heavy medium saucepan, combine sugar, flour and gelatine. In small bowl, with wire whisk or fork, beat eggs and egg yolk with milk until well mixed; stir into gelatine mixture. Leave to stand for 5 minutes to soften gelatine slightly.

3 Cook over low heat, stirring constantly, until mixture thickens and coats a spoon well, about 15 minutes (do not boil or mixture will curdle).

The contrasting shades of two green fruits look stunning in Grape and Kiwi Fruit Flan

4 Remove saucepan from heat; stir in almond liqueur or almond essence. Cool, then cover and refrigerate until mixture mounds slightly when dropped from a spoon, about 1 hour, stirring occasionally.

5 Meanwhile, cut each grape in half lengthways. Peel and thinly slice kiwi fruit. Set grapes and kiwi fruit aside.

6 In small bowl, whip double or whipping cream until stiff peaks form. With rubber spatula or wire whisk, fold whipped cream into almond custard.

Melted redcurrant jelly gives these artfully arranged fruits a glossy finish

7 Carefully remove side of flan tin; slide pastry shell on to serving plate. Evenly spoon custard into cooled pastry shell. Arrange grapes, cut side down, and kiwi fruit slices on custard to make attractive design.

8 In small saucepan over medium heat, melt redcurrant jelly, stirring occasionally. With pastry brush, carefully brush fruit with melted jelly. Refrigerate flan until filling is completely set, about 1 hour.

PASTRIES

All pastries are made with some kind of dough; and the different doughs, coupled with the wide variety of fillings that can be used, add up to an almost limitless choice of eye-catching, taste-tempting desserts. Melt-in-the-mouth shortcrust can be used for fruit-filled rolls and dumplings.

Flaky puff pastry makes handsome pies, tarts and turnovers. Light and airy shells made from choux pastry take to luscious fillings from whipped cream to ice cream; and delicious desserts made with paper-thin phyllo range from classic Strudel to the incomparable Baklava.

PEARS EN CROÛTE À LA CRÈME

Makes 6
Allow 1 ½ hours preparation and cooking time

Filling

15 g/ ½ oz caster sugar	
¼ teaspoon ground cinnamon	
3 medium-sized William's pears	
6 whole cloves	

Pastry

215 g/7 ½ oz plain flour
120 g/4 oz butter, softened
1 x 85 g/3 oz package full-fat soft cheese, softened
1 egg white

Custard

1 egg yolk
450 ml/ ¾ pint single or half cream
4 teaspoons cornflour
45 g/1 ½ oz caster sugar
¼ teaspoon almond essence

1 Prepare filling: in cup, with fork, stir sugar with cinnamon; set aside. Peel pears. Cut each pear in half lengthways; remove cores.

2 Prepare pastry dough: in medium bowl, combine flour, butter and soft cheese; with fingertips, mix together just until blended.

3 On lightly floured surface, with floured rolling pin, roll out half of the dough 3 mm/⅛ inch thick. Using 18 cm/7 inch round plate as a guide, cut 3 rounds from dough; reserve trimmings.

4 Sprinkle rounds of dough with half of the sugar and cinnamon mixture; place a pear half, cut side up, on each round. Carefully fold round of dough over each pear half. Pinch dough edges to seal.

5 Place wrapped pears, seam side down, on ungreased large baking sheet. Repeat with remaining pears and dough to make 6 altogether.

Pastry made with soft cheese is rich and melt-in-the mouth, an ideal casing for a sweet William's pear

6 Preheat oven to 190°C/375°F/gas 5. Reroll dough trimmings; cut to make leaves. Brush dough with egg white; decorate with dough leaves and brush them with egg white.

7 Bake pears for 35 minutes or until pastry is golden. Transfer to wire rack; cool slightly.

8 Meanwhile, make custard: in medium saucepan, combine egg yolk, single or half cream, cornflour and sugar.

9 Cook over medium-low heat, stirring constantly, until mixture thickens and coats a spoon well, about 15 minutes. Remove saucepan from heat; stir in almond essence. Cool custard slightly.

> **TO SERVE**
> On to each of 6 dessert plates, spoon some custard. Place pear in centre of custard; insert whole clove in tip of each to resemble stalk. Or refrigerate pears and custard separately to serve chilled later.

PEAR JALOUSIE

🍴 8 servings
🕐 Allow 1 ½ hours preparation and cooking time

Pastry

2 x 225 g/8 oz packets frozen puff pastry

1 egg

Caster sugar for sprinkling

Filling

6 medium-sized pears

45 g/1 ½ oz currants

100 g/3 ½ oz caster sugar

To Serve

Spiced Cream (see Box, below)

1 Thaw puff pastry according to packet instructions.

2 Meanwhile, prepare pear filling: core and thinly slice pears (do not peel them). In large bowl, toss pear slices with currants and caster sugar.

3 Preheat oven to 220°C/425°F/gas 7. On lightly floured surface, with floured rolling pin, roll 1 packet of pastry out into 33 x 25 cm/ 13 x 10 inch rectangle; place on ungreased large baking sheet.

SPICED CREAM

In large saucepan over high heat, bring 350 ml/ 12 fl oz double cream, 2 tablespoons caster sugar and 1 teaspoon ground cinnamon to the boil, stirring occasionally. Boil until cream is reduced to about 300 ml/½ pint. Strain cream into serving bowl. Leave cream to cool slightly to serve warm, or refrigerate to serve cold later.

Thinly sliced pears and currants peep through slats in pastry jalousie (jalousie means 'Venetian blind' in French)

Jalousie is best served sliced on individual plates, as it is difficult to find a serving plate that is the right shape and size for the whole dessert

4 On lightly floured surface, with floured rolling pin, roll out remaining packet of pastry into 35 x 28 cm/ 14 x 11 inch rectangle; sprinkle lightly with flour. Fold pastry in half lengthways.

5 Cut pastry crossways through folded edge to within 2.5 cm/1 inch of unfolded edge at 1 cm/ ½ inch intervals.

6 In cup, with fork, beat egg and 1 teaspoon water. Spoon pear filling on to pastry rectangle on baking sheet to about 2.5 cm/1 inch from edges. Brush edges of pastry with some egg mixture.

7 Place folded piece of pastry over filling with fold at centre; unfold pastry. Press edges of pastry together to seal.

8 Brush pastry all over with remaining egg mixture; sprinkle lightly with caster sugar. Bake in the oven for 30 minutes or until pastry is golden and puffed.

9 While jalousie is baking, prepare Spiced Cream.

10 Cut jalousie into slices; serve warm, or cool on wire rack to serve cold later. Serve Spiced Cream separately.

CONTINENTAL FRUIT SLICE

8 servings
Allow 4 hours preparation and cooking time

Filling

225 g/8 oz dried figs, coarsely chopped

150 g/5 oz stoned dates, coarsely chopped

120 g/4 oz dried apricots, coarsely chopped

30 g/1 oz sultanas

2 tablespoons lemon juice

1 teaspoon ground cinnamon

100 g/3 ½ oz caster sugar

120 g/4 oz walnut pieces, chopped

Pastry

300 g/10 oz plain flour

1 teaspoon salt (optional)

30 g/1 oz caster sugar

175 g/6 oz butter

1 egg

1 tablespoon milk

1 Make filling: in large saucepan over high heat, bring figs, dates, apricots, sultanas, lemon juice, cinnamon, sugar and *600 ml/1 pint water* to the boil. Reduce heat to low; simmer, uncovered, stirring occasionally, for 30 minutes or until mixture is thick. Remove saucepan from heat; stir in chopped walnuts. Leave to cool for at least 1 hour.

2 Meanwhile, prepare pastry dough: in medium bowl, with fork, stir flour, salt, if using, and sugar. With pastry blender or with fingertips, cut or rub butter into flour mixture until mixture resembles coarse crumbs. Sprinkle *5-6 tablespoons cold water*, a tablespoon at a time, into flour mixture, mixing lightly with fork after each addition until dough just holds together. With hands, shape dough into ball. Wrap and refrigerate until dried fruit filling is cool.

3 Preheat oven to 220°C/425°F/gas 7. Reserve a little dough for making leaves and berries. On lightly floured surface, with floured rolling pin, roll out remaining dough into 40 x 30 cm/ 16 x 12 inch rectangle.

4 Transfer dough rectangle to ungreased large baking sheet. Spoon dried fruit filling lengthways in 10 cm/4 inch wide strip over centre of rectangle to about 6 cm/ 2 ½ inches from each end. Fold one long side of dough rectangle over filling, then roll over to enclose filling, seam side down. Fold dough under on each end of roll.

5 In cup, with fork, beat egg and milk. Brush roll with some egg mixture. With tip of knife, cut few shallow lines in top of roll. On floured surface, with floured rolling pin, roll out reserved dough. With knife, cut out small leaves and roll small pieces of dough into berries. Arrange leaves and berries on top of roll; brush with some egg mixture.

6 Bake roll for 25-30 minutes until pastry is golden. With fish slices, transfer pastry roll to wire rack to cool completely. Serve at room temperature.

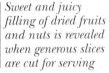
Sweet and juicy filling of dried fruits and nuts is revealed when generous slices are cut for serving

APPLE TURNOVERS

Makes 8
Allow 5 hours preparation and cooking time

Flaky Pastry

| 300 g/10 oz plain flour |
| 1 teaspoon salt (optional) |
| 225 g/8 oz butter |
| 1 egg |

Filling

| 2 large cooking apples |
| 100 g/3 ½ oz caster sugar |
| 1 tablespoon cornflour |
| 1 teaspoon lemon juice |
| ¼ teaspoon ground cinnamon |

Topping

Glacé Icing (see Box, below)

Triangles of flaky pastry encase apples flavoured with cinnamon and lemon; glacé icing is drizzled over before serving

1 Prepare pastry dough: in medium bowl, with fork, stir flour and salt. With pastry blender or with fingertips, cut or rub half of the butter into flour mixture until mixture resembles coarse crumbs. Sprinkle *125 ml/4 fl oz cold water*, a tablespoon at a time, into mixture, mixing lightly with fork after each addition until dough just holds together. With hands, shape dough into ball.

2 On lightly floured surface, with floured rolling pin, roll out pastry dough into 45 x 20 cm/ 18 x 8 inch rectangle. Cut 60 g/2 oz butter into thin slices.

3 Starting at one of the 20 cm/8 inch sides, place butter slices over two-thirds of rectangle to within about 1 cm/ ½ inch of edge of dough.

4 Fold unbuttered third of dough over middle third.

5 Fold opposite end of dough over to make 20 x 15 cm/8 x 6 inch rectangle.

6 Roll out dough again into 45 x 20 cm/ 18 x 8 inch rectangle. Slice remaining butter; place slices on dough and fold as before. Wrap dough and refrigerate for 15 minutes.

7 Roll out folded dough into 45 x 20 cm/ 18 x 8 inch rectangle. Fold rectangle lengthways and then crossways; wrap and refrigerate for 1 hour.

8 Meanwhile, prepare filling: peel, core and slice apples. In small saucepan over low heat, cook apples with sugar, cornflour, lemon juice and cinnamon, stirring frequently, until apples are tender. Set aside until filling is cool.

9 Preheat oven to 230°C/450°F/gas 8. Cut dough in half cross-ways. On lightly floured surface, with floured rolling pin, roll out half into 30 cm/12 inch square (keep remaining dough refrigerated); cut into four 15 cm/6 inch squares. In cup, with fork, beat egg and *1 tablespoon water*; brush some egg mixture over dough squares.

10 Spoon one-eighth of apple mixture in centre of each square; fold diagonally in half and press edges to seal. Place on ungreased baking sheet; refrigerate. Repeat with remaining dough and apple mixture.

11 Brush turnovers with egg mixture. Bake for 20 minutes or until pastry is golden. Cool on wire rack.

12 Prepare Glacé Icing; with spoon, drizzle over turnovers; leave to set before serving.

GLACÉ ICING
In small bowl, mix together *60 g/2 oz icing sugar, sifted,* and *about 1 tablespoon water.*

RASPBERRY CREAM SLICES

 Makes 6
Allow 2 hours
preparation and
cooking time

1 x 225 g/8 oz packet
frozen puff pastry

325 g/11 oz caster sugar

150 ml/ ¼ pint single
cream

300 ml/ ½ pint double or
whipping cream

300 g/10 oz raspberries

1 Thaw pastry according to packet instructions.

2 Preheat oven to 220°C/425°F/gas 7. On lightly floured surface, with floured rolling pin, roll out pastry to 24 x 20 cm/9 ½ x 8 inch rectangle. With sharp knife, cut thin strip of pastry, about 5 mm/ ¼ inch wide, from each side of pastry (freshly cut edges give maximum puffing). Cut pastry into 6 rectangles in all.

3 Place pastry rectangles on ungreased large baking sheet. Bake for 15 minutes or until pastry is puffed and golden. Cool on wire rack.

4 About 30 minutes before serving, prepare caramel sauce: in large saucepan over medium heat, bring 300 g/ 10 oz sugar and 5 table-spoons water to the boil, stirring frequently. Cook, without stirring, until mixture becomes caramel-coloured. Remove sauce-pan from heat; gradually stir in single cream (sugar mixture will harden). Cook over medium heat, stirring constantly, until caramel sauce is smooth; keep sauce warm.

5 In small bowl, with mixer on medium speed, whip double or whipping cream with remaining caster sugar until soft peaks form.

6 With serrated knife and using a sawing action, carefully split each puff pastry rectangle in half horizontally.

Use rectangles of puff pastry or, alternatively, use circles

7 Spoon whipped cream on to bottom half of each puff pastry rectangle, spreading it out evenly.

8 With fingers, carefully place raspberries on top of whipped cream, spacing them evenly.

9 Gently replace pastry tops over whipped cream and raspberries.

TO SERVE
Pour warm caramel sauce on to 6 dessert plates. Arrange pastries on plates; decorate with remaining raspberries.

FRESH FRUIT PUFF PASTRY TARTS

The melt-in-the-mouth layers of puff pastry in these glorious French tarts are filled with cream and juicy, colourful fruits. Here there's a mixture of fresh and canned fruits – fresh strawberries, apples, grapes and kiwi fruit with canned mandarin oranges and peaches, but you can ring the changes according to the season.

 Makes 16
Pastry can be made up to 1 week ahead; allow about 3 hours to make tarts

Rough Puff Pastry

550 g/1 lb 3 oz plain flour
1 teaspoon salt (optional)
450 g/1 lb cold butter
1 egg, beaten

Filling

300 ml/ ½ pint double or whipping cream
30 g/1 oz caster sugar
¼ teaspoon almond essence
Fresh or canned fruits
Mint leaves to decorate

1 First make pastry dough: in medium bowl, with fork, stir flour and salt, if using. With pastry blender or with fingertips, cut or rub 120 g/4 oz butter into flour until mixture resembles coarse crumbs. Add *250 ml/8 fl oz cold water*, a few tablespoons at a time, mixing lightly with fork after each addition until soft dough is formed (add more water if needed, a tablespoon at a time).

2 With hands, shape dough into ball. Wrap and refrigerate for 30 minutes.

3 Meanwhile, between 2 sheets of grease-proof paper, roll remaining butter into 15 cm/ 6 inch square; wrap and refrigerate.

MAKING PASTRY TARTS

1 Fold 1 square of dough in half diagonally to form triangle.

2 Starting at folded side, cut 1 cm/½ inch border strip on both sides of triangle, leaving 1 cm/ ½ inch uncut dough at triangle point so strips remain attached.

3 Unfold triangle. Lift up both loose border strips and slip one under the other, gently pulling to matching corners on base. Attach points of dough with drop of water.

4 On lightly floured surface, with floured rolling pin, roll out dough into 30 cm/12 inch square.

5 Place square of butter diagonally in centre of dough; fold corners of dough over butter so that they meet edges in centre, overlapping slightly.

Square of butter is placed diagonally in centre of dough, then corners of dough are folded over butter to meet in the centre

6 Press dough with rolling pin to seal seams.

7 Roll into 45 x 30 cm/ 18 x 12 inch rectangle. Fold one-third over centre, then fold opposite third over first to form 30 x 15 cm/ 12 x 6 inch rectangle of three layers.

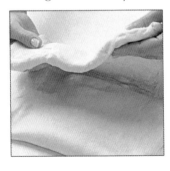

8 Press rectangle of dough with rolling pin to seal seam. Give dough quarter turn. Roll out dough into 37.5 x 20 cm/ 15 x 8 inch rectangle; fold into thirds to form 20 x 12.5 cm/8 x 5 inch rectangle. Wrap and refrigerate, at least 1-hour.

9 Repeat, rolling out dough into 37.5 x 20 cm/15 × 8 inch rectangle and folding into thirds, twice. Wrap and refrigerate for 2 hours.

10 Repeat rolling, folding and refrige-rating twice more, or 6 times in all. After sixth time, wrap well and refrigerate for at least 4 hours (or up to 1 week) before using.

11 Cut dough cross-ways in half. On floured surface, with floured rolling pin, roll out half of the dough into rectangle of 51 x 26 cm/ 20 ½ x 10 ½ inches, gently lifting dough occasionally.

12 With sharp knife or pastry wheel, trim edges to make 50 x 25 cm/20 x 10 inch rectangle.

13 Cut rectangle into eight 12.5 cm/ 5 inch squares; place on large baking sheet. Refrigerate for 30 minutes.

14 Repeat with remaining dough. (Or wrap and freeze remaining dough for up to 6 months; thaw dough in refrigerator overnight before using.)

15 Make pastry tarts (see Box, page 188). Refrigerate for 30 minutes.

16 Preheat oven to 200°C/400°F/gas 6. Bake tarts for 20 minutes. Turn oven down to 190°C/ 375°F/gas 5; brush top of borders with beaten egg. Bake for 20 minutes longer or until centres of tarts are lightly browned. Cool tarts on wire rack.

17 In small bowl, whip double or whipping cream with sugar and almond essence until soft peaks form. Fill tarts with whipped cream; top with fruit and decorate with mint leaves.

Sliced fresh strawberries, canned mandarin orange segments and fresh mint leaves make a colourful combination

Apple, kiwi, peach slices and grapes fit neatly into puff pastry tarts

BAKLAVA

Makes 24
Allow 3 ½ hours preparation and cooking time

450 g/1 lb walnut pieces, finely chopped

100 g/3 ½ oz caster sugar

1 teaspoon ground cinnamon

450 g/1 lb fresh or frozen (thawed) phyllo pastry

225 g/8 oz butter, melted

350 g/12 oz liquid honey

In Baklava, layer upon layer of phyllo pastry and chopped walnuts are made sweet and sticky with melted butter and honey

1 In large bowl, with fork, mix finely chopped walnuts, sugar and cinnamon; set aside.

2 Cut sheets of phyllo into 33 x 23 cm/ 13 x 9 inch rectangles. In greased 33 x 23 cm/ 13 x 9 inch baking dish, place 1 phyllo sheet; brush with some melted butter. Repeat with more phyllo and butter until there are 6 rectangular sheets of phyllo in dish.

3 Over phyllo pastry in baking dish, sprinkle one-quarter of chopped walnut mixture.

4 Repeat steps 2 and 3 to make 3 more layers (4 layers in total). Place remaining phyllo on top of last amount of walnuts; brush with butter.

5 Preheat oven to 150°C/300°F/gas 2. With sharp knife, cut just halfway through layers in triangle pattern to make 24 servings (cut lengthways into 3 strips; cut each strip crossways into 4 rectangles; then cut each rectangle diagonally into 2 triangles).

6 Bake for 1 hour and 25 minutes or until top is golden brown.

7 In small saucepan over medium-low heat, heat honey until hot but not boiling. Evenly spoon hot honey over hot Baklava.

ALTERNATIVE SHAPES

For a change from triangles, you can cut Baklava into diamond shapes, which are more traditional.

Diamond Baklava
In step 5, with sharp knife, cut just halfway through layers in diamond pattern (cut lengthways into 4 strips, then cut diagonally across strips in parallel lines); finish cutting through layers in step 9.

Spooning honey over Baklava

8 Cool Baklava in dish on wire rack for at least 1 hour; cover with foil and leave at room temperature until serving.

9 To serve, with sharp knife, finish cutting through layers to make 24 Baklava triangles.

APPLE STRUDEL

10 servings
Allow 2 hours
preparation and
cooking time

3 large cooking apples

100 g/3 ½ oz caster sugar

*75 g/2 ½ oz seedless
raisins*

*60 g/2 oz walnut pieces,
chopped*

*½ teaspoon ground
cinnamon*

¼ teaspoon grated nutmeg

*About 75 g/2 ½ oz white
breadcrumbs*

*225 g/8 oz fresh or frozen
(thawed) phyllo pastry*

120 g/4 oz butter, melted

Icing sugar for sprinkling

*Icing sugar is sifted
over top of strudel to
help hide cracks in
phyllo pastry*

1 Grease large baking
sheet. Peel, core and
thinly slice apples. In bowl,
toss apples with caster
sugar, raisins, walnuts,
cinnamon, nutmeg and
25 g/ ¾ oz breadcrumbs.

2 Cut two 60 cm/24 inch
lengths of greaseproof
paper. Place 2 long sides
together, overlapping them
by about 5 cm/2 inches;
join with adhesive tape.

3 On sheet of grease-
proof paper, arrange
1 sheet of phyllo. (It
should be a 43 x 30 cm/
17 x 10 inch rectangle; if
necessary, trim or overlap
small pieces of phyllo to
make it this size.) Brush
with some melted butter.

4 Sprinkle phyllo with
scant tablespoon
breadcrumbs. Continue
layering phyllo, brushing
each sheet with melted
butter and sprinkling every
other sheet with crumbs.

*Spooning apple
mixture on to
phyllo*

5 Preheat oven to
190°C/375°F/gas 5.
Spoon apple mixture
along 1 long side of phyllo
rectangle to within 1 cm/
½ inch of edges to cover
about half of rectangle.

6 From apple mixture
side, roll phyllo, Swiss
roll fashion, using greaseproof to help lift roll.

7 Place roll on
baking sheet,
seam side down.
Brush with remaining
melted butter. Bake for
40 minutes or until
golden. Cool on baking
sheet for 30 minutes.

SWAN CHOUX PUFFS

Makes 8
Allow 3 hours preparation and cooking time

Choux Pastry Dough (see Box, below right)

300 ml/ ½ pint double cream

150 ml/ ¼ pint canned Devon custard

Pretty as a picture, Swan Choux Puffs are filled with the most luscious cream and custard mixture

1 Preheat oven to 190°C/375°F/gas 5. Prepare Choux Pastry Dough. Spoon some dough into piping bag fitted with large writing tube (tip about 1 cm/ ½ inch in diameter). On to greased large baking sheet, pipe eight 7.5 cm/ 3 inch long 'question marks' for swans' necks, making small dollop at beginning of each for head.

Piping 'question mark' shapes for swans' necks

2 Drop remaining dough by large spoonfuls, pushing off with rubber spatula, into 8 large mounds on baking sheet, about 7.5 cm/ 3 inches apart.

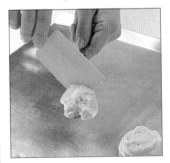

3 With moistened finger, gently smooth dough to round slightly.

4 Bake swans' necks and choux puffs in the oven for 20 minutes or until necks are golden. Transfer necks to wire rack to cool.

5 Continue baking choux puffs for 45-50 minutes until golden; transfer to racks and leave to cool.

6 When choux puffs are cool, prepare filling: in small bowl, whip double cream until stiff peaks form. With rubber spatula or wire whisk, gently fold into custard.

7 Cut off top third from each choux puff; set aside.

CHOUX PASTRY DOUGH

In medium saucepan over medium heat, heat 120 g/4 oz butter and 250 ml/8 fl oz water until butter melts and mixture boils. Remove saucepan from heat. Add 150 g/5 oz plain flour all at once; with wooden spoon, vigorously stir until mixture leaves side of pan and forms a ball. Add 4 eggs, 1 egg at a time, beating well with wooden spoon after each addition until choux pastry dough is smooth and satiny.

8 Spoon some filling into each of the choux puff bottoms (swans' bodies). Cut each reserved top piece in half; set into filling for wings. Place swans' necks into filling. Refrigerate if not serving immediately.

PARIS-BREST

10 servings
Allow 3 hours
preparation and
cooking time

*Choux Pastry Dough (see
Box, page 192)*

*450 ml/ ¾ pint double
cream*

2 tablespoons brandy

*Chocolate Glaze (see Box,
above right)*

1 Preheat oven to
200°C/400°F/gas 6.
Grease and flour large
baking sheet.

2 Prepare Choux Pastry
Dough according to
recipe instructions. Using
17.5 cm/7 inch plate as
guide, trace circle in flour
on baking sheet. Drop
dough by heaping table-
spoons, pushing off with
rubber spatula, into
10 mounds, inside circle,
to form ring.

3 Bake ring for
40 minutes or until
golden. Turn oven off;
leave ring in oven for
15 minutes. Cool ring on
wire rack.

4 With long serrated
knife, slice ring
horizontally in half.

CHOCOLATE GLAZE
In heavy non-stick
saucepan, gently heat
*90 g/ 3 oz plain choco-
late, broken into pieces,
15 g/ ½ oz butter,
1 ½ teaspoons golden
syrup* and *1 ½ teaspoons
milk,* stirring often, until
melted and smooth.

5 In small bowl, whip
double cream until
stiff peaks form; fold in
brandy. Spoon on to
bottom of pastry ring.

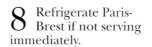

6 Replace top
of pastry ring.

7 Prepare Chocolate
Glaze; with spoon,
carefully drizzle glaze
over top of choux
pastry ring to give
it a smooth,
glossy coating.

8 Refrigerate Paris-
Brest if not serving
immediately.

*Paris-Brest, a ring of choux
pastry filled with brandy-
flavoured whipped cream and
coated with a rich chocolate
glaze, was created by a
Parisian baker in 1891. The
wheel-shaped cake was
designed in honour of the
annual bike race between the
cities of Paris and Brest.*

APPLE DUMPLINGS WITH CHEDDAR PASTRY

 Makes 6
Allow 2 hours
preparation and
cooking time

Pastry

365 g/12 ½ oz plain flour
1 teaspoon salt (optional)
175 g/6 oz butter
120 g/4 oz mature Cheddar cheese, grated
1 egg
6 whole cloves

Filling

75 g/2 ½ oz light soft brown sugar
30 g/1 oz seedless raisins
30 g/1 oz walnut pieces
60 g/2 oz butter, softened
1 teaspoon ground cinnamon
6 small Golden Delicious apples

Sauce

300 ml/ ½ pint apple juice
125 ml/4 fl oz maple syrup

1 Prepare pastry dough: in large bowl, with fork, stir flour and salt, if using. With pastry blender or with fingertips, cut or rub butter into flour mixture until mixture resembles coarse crumbs; stir in cheese. Sprinkle *8-9 tablespoons cold water*, a tablespoon at a time, into mixture, mixing lightly with fork after each addition until dough just holds together. With hands, shape dough into ball.

2 In small bowl, with fork, mix brown sugar, raisins, walnuts, butter and cinnamon.

TO SERVE
Serve apple dumplings hot on individual plates, with hot sauce spooned round.

3 Peel apples; remove cores but do not cut all the way through apples.

4 Preheat oven to 200°C/400°F/gas 6. Reserve 45 g/1 ½ oz pastry dough. On well-floured surface, with floured rolling pin, roll out remaining dough into 52.5 x 35 cm/21 x 14 inch rectangle. Cut dough into six 17.5 cm/7 inch squares.

5 In cup, with fork, beat egg and *1 teaspoon water*. Centre an apple on square of dough.

6 Spoon one-sixth of sugar mixture into cavity in apple. Brush edges of dough square with some egg mixture.

7 Bring points of dough square up over apple, pinching edges together to seal well.

8 Repeat with remaining dough squares, apples and sugar mixture. With fish slice, place dumplings in greased 33 x 23 cm/13 x 9 inch baking dish.

9 On floured surface, with floured rolling pin, roll out reserved dough 5 mm/¼ inch thick. Cut 12 leaves from dough; score with tip of knife to make 'veins'. Brush dumplings with some egg mixture; press 2 leaves on top of each dumpling and brush them with egg mixture. Press cloves, rounded side down, into dumplings to look like stalks. Bake dumplings for 35 minutes.

10 In bowl, with spoon, stir apple juice and maple syrup; pour mixture over dumplings. Bake dumplings for 15 minutes longer (cover with foil after 5 minutes if dumplings are browning too much), basting occasionally with sauce in baking dish, until pastry is golden brown and apples are tender when pierced with skewer.

PROFITEROLES GLACÉES

  Makes 18
Can be made up to
1 month ahead and
kept in freezer

Sauce

225 g/8 oz frozen
  raspberries

60 g/2 oz caster sugar

1 scoop vanilla ice cream

Choux Pastry

60 g/2 oz butter

75 g/2 ½ oz plain flour

2 eggs

Filling and Topping

60 g/2 oz plain chocolate,
  broken into pieces

2 tablespoons milk

15 g/ ½ oz butter

600 ml/1 pint vanilla
  ice cream

30 g/1 oz shelled pistachio
  nuts, chopped

1 Sprinkle raspberries
with sugar; set aside
to thaw. Preheat oven to
200°C/400°F/gas 6.
Grease and flour large
baking sheet.

2 Prepare choux pastry
dough: in medium
saucepan over medium
heat, heat butter and
125 ml/4 fl oz water until
butter melts and mixture
boils. Remove from heat.
Add flour all at once; with
wooden spoon, vigorously
stir until mixture leaves
side of pan and forms a
ball. Add eggs, 1 at a time,
beating well after each
addition until dough is
smooth and satiny.

TO SERVE
*Spoon raspberry sauce on
to 6 dessert plates;
arrange 3 profiteroles on
each plate.*

3 Drop 18 teaspoonfuls
of dough on baking
sheet, 5 cm/2 inches
apart.

4 Bake for 30 minutes
or until golden. Turn
oven off; leave puffs in oven
for 10 minutes. Cool on
wire rack.

5 While puffs are
cooling, make sauce:
over large bowl, with back
of spoon, press and scrape
thawed raspberries with
their juice firmly against
medium-mesh sieve to
purée; discard pips left in
sieve. Add ice cream to
raspberry purée; stir to
mix. Cover sauce and
refrigerate.

ALTERNATIVE SERVING IDEA

As an alternative to raspberry sauce, you can serve
Profiteroles Glacées with other fruit sauces such as
strawberry, apricot or mango. This peach sauce goes
especially well, both in colour and flavour.

Peach Sauce
In blender at low speed,
blend *450 g/1 lb ripe
peaches, peeled and stoned,
¼ teaspoon almond
essence* and *⅛ teaspoon
grated nutmeg* until all
ingredients are smooth.

6 When puffs are cool,
make topping: in non-
stick saucepan over low
heat, heat pieces of
chocolate, milk and butter,
stirring frequently, until
melted and smooth.

7 Cut each puff in half
horizontally; fill
bottom halves with ice
cream; replace tops.
Drizzle profiteroles with
chocolate mixture and
sprinkle with nuts. Freeze.

*Profiteroles nestled together
on a pool of raspberry sauce
are drizzled with chocolate
sauce and sprinkled with nuts*

HOT FRUIT PUDDINGS

Here you'll find homely and satisfying puddings: sweet fruit blanketed with a crunchy topping in a crumble, or covered with a tender scone crust in a cobbler, or layered with buttered breadcrumbs, sugar and spices in a 'brown Betty'. Reheating at the same temperature at which they were baked will give puddings made ahead, or leftovers, a freshly baked goodness.

BANANA BROWN BETTY

4 servings
Allow 40 minutes preparation and cooking time

2 large oranges

6 medium-sized bananas

45 g/1 ½ oz caster sugar

90 g/3 oz butter

25 g/ ¾ oz fresh breadcrumbs

20 g/ ⅔ oz rolled oats

45 g/1 ½ oz soft brown sugar

½ teaspoon ground cinnamon

Whipped cream (optional)

1 From oranges, grate 1 teaspoon zest and squeeze 175 ml/6 fl oz juice. Cut bananas into chunks.

2 In large frying pan over medium-high heat, cook caster sugar, 3 tablespoons orange juice and 30 g/1 oz butter, stirring frequently, until light caramel colour, about 3-4 minutes. To orange juice mixture, add banana chunks; toss until banana is evenly coated.

3 Remove frying pan from heat; set aside. Preheat oven to 200°C/400°F/gas 6.

4 Divide half of the caramelized banana mixture equally among four 250 ml/8 fl oz ramekins or baking dishes.

5 Sprinkle each with 1 tablespoon breadcrumbs. Top with remaining banana mixture. Spoon 2 tablespoons orange juice over banana mixture in each ramekin.

Chunks of juicy, caramelized bananas peep through crunchy topping

6 Into remaining breadcrumbs, with fingertips, mix oats, brown sugar, cinnamon, orange zest and remaining butter until mixture resembles coarse crumbs; sprinkle over bananas.

Spooning cinnamon-flavoured oat and breadcrumb topping over bananas

7 Place ramekins in baking tray for easier handling. Bake for 15 minutes or until topping is crisp and golden. Serve warm, with whipped cream if you like.

APPLE COBBLER

RHUBARB CRUMBLE

🍴 6 servings
⏱ Allow 50 minutes preparation and cooking time

700 g/1 ½ lb rhubarb
1 teaspoon lemon juice
100 g/3 ½ oz caster sugar
Custard or pouring cream for serving
Crumble Topping
185 g/6 ½ oz plain flour
45 g/1 ½ oz caster sugar
120 g/4 oz butter

1 Wash rhubarb; trim and discard leaves and discoloured ends. Cut rhubarb into 2.5 cm/1 inch pieces. In saucepan over medium heat, bring rhubarb, lemon juice, sugar and *4 tablespoons water* to the boil. Reduce heat to low; cover and simmer for about 10 minutes or until rhubarb is tender.

2 Preheat oven to 220°C/425°F/gas 7. While rhubarb is cooking, make crumble mixture: in medium bowl, with fork, stir flour and sugar. With pastry blender or with fingertips, cut or rub butter into flour mixture until mixture resembles coarse crumbs.

3 Pour rhubarb mixture into 20 cm/8 inch square baking dish. Sprinkle crumble mixture over rhubarb.

4 Bake for 25 minutes or until crumble topping is golden.

> *TO SERVE*
> *Serve Rhubarb Crumble hot with custard or pouring cream.*

🍴 6 servings
⏱ Allow 1 hour preparation and cooking time

225 g/8 oz light soft brown sugar
45 g/1 ½ oz plain flour
30 g/1 oz butter
1 teaspoon lemon juice
¼ teaspoon ground cinnamon
Pinch of grated nutmeg
5 large cooking apples
Pouring cream or vanilla ice cream (optional)
Dough
150 g/5 oz plain flour
2 teaspoons baking powder
45 g/1 ½ oz butter
175 ml/6 fl oz milk

1 In small saucepan, mix brown sugar and flour; stir in *250 ml/8 fl oz water*. Bring to the boil over medium heat, stirring constantly; cook until thick.

2 Remove pan from heat. Stir butter, lemon juice, cinnamon and nutmeg into sauce.

3 Peel, core and thinly slice apples. Arrange in 30 x 20 cm/12 x 8 inch baking dish; pour sauce mixture over apples.

4 Preheat oven to 190°C/375°F/gas 5. Make dough: in medium bowl, combine flour and baking powder. With pastry blender or with fingertips, cut or rub butter into flour mixture until size of peas. Add milk; stir until moistened but still lumpy.

5 Evenly drop large spoonfuls of cobbler dough on top of apples, not covering completely. Bake for 40 minutes or until topping is golden.

> *TO SERVE*
> *Serve Apple Cobbler warm, with cream or ice cream, if you like.*

INDIVIDUAL PEACH COBBLERS

 Makes 4
Allow 1 hour preparation and cooking time

4 large peaches
25 g/ ¾ oz plain flour
60 g/2 oz caster sugar
Scone Dough
120 g/4 oz plain flour
1 teaspoon baking powder
2 teaspoons caster sugar
45 g/1 ½ oz butter
5-6 tablespoons whipping cream plus extra for glazing

1 Peel peaches (see Box, page 53); slice thinly. In large bowl, toss peaches, flour and sugar. Spoon into four 250 ml/8 fl oz ramekins. Set aside.

2 Prepare scone dough: in large bowl, with fork, mix flour, baking powder and sugar. With pastry blender or with fingertips, cut or rub in butter until mixture resembles coarse crumbs. Stir in 5-6 tablespoons whipping cream; quickly mix just until a stiff dough is formed that leaves side of bowl.

3 Preheat oven to 200°C/400°F/gas 6. Turn dough on to lightly floured surface. With floured rolling pin, roll out dough to about 2 cm/⅜ inch thickness.

4 Using floured pastry cutter with diameter about 5 mm/¼ inch smaller than diameter of top of ramekin, cut out 4 rounds.

Cutting out rounds of scone dough for cobbler topping

5 Place dough rounds over peaches; brush dough rounds lightly with whipping cream.

6 If you like, press trimmings together; roll and cut into desired shapes to decorate top of cobblers.

7 Place cobblers in baking tray for easier handling. Bake for 15-20 minutes until peach mixture begins to bubble and scone topping is golden.

Tiny aspic cutters are used to cut dough trimmings into pretty shapes to top cobbler dough

BISCUITS AND COOKIES
199-216

Biscuits and Cookies

Biscuits and cookies – perfect for after school, as a snack, with dessert, for anytime! Around the holidays, festive Gingerbread Christmas Biscuits and Sweet and Spicy Peppernuts are crowd-pleasers for children and adults alike. Elegant Chocolate and Nut Shortbread and Almond Butter Shortbread are ideal to accompany afternoon tea or after-dinner coffee, and delicate Brandy Snaps and dainty Waffle Hearts taste as good as they look – why not make a second batch to wrap as take-home gifts for guests? For all-round favourites, nothing can beat Apricot Croissants and Nutty Oat Crunchies – home-baked goodness your family and friends will love.

CONTENTS

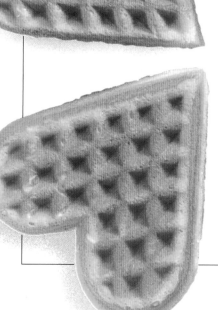

BISCUITS AND COOKIES

In this biscuit collection, you'll find dainty, elegant morsels for the tea table, sturdy favourites for the school lunchbox, and jolly sugary snowmen to delight the children at Christmas. There are different shapes, sizes and decorations to catch the eye and match any occasion. Every palate is sure to be pleased with the choice of buttery, nutty, chocolatey or sugar-and-spicy flavours and the variety of textures, from tender and chewy to crisp and crunchy.

BRANDY SNAPS

Makes about 36
Allow 2 hours preparation and cooking time

120 g/4 oz butter

3 tablespoons golden syrup

75 g/2 ½ oz plain flour

100 g/3 ½ oz caster sugar

1 teaspoon ground ginger

2 tablespoons brandy

Lacy-textured Brandy Snaps are good served with after-dinner coffee and liqueurs

1 Preheat oven to 180°C/350°F/gas 4. Line large baking sheet with non-stick baking parchment. In small saucepan over medium heat, heat butter and golden syrup, stirring occasionally, until butter melts. Remove saucepan from heat; with spoon, stir in flour, sugar, ginger and brandy until smooth. Return saucepan to very low heat to keep mixture warm.

2 Drop 1 teaspoon mixture on to baking sheet; spread in circular motion to make 10 cm/ 4 inch round (mixture spreads during baking to fill in any thin areas). Repeat to make 3 more rounds, about 5 cm/2 inches apart.

3 Bake biscuits for about 5 minutes or until golden brown. Remove baking sheet from oven; allow biscuits to cool briefly, only until edges set. With fish slice, flip biscuits over quickly so lacy texture will be on outside after rolling.

4 Working as quickly as possible, roll each biscuit into cylinder around handle of wooden spoon (1 cm/ ½ inch in diameter). If biscuits become too hard to roll, return to oven briefly to soften. As each biscuit is shaped, remove from spoon handle; cool on wire racks.

5 Repeat until all mixture is used.

TWO-TONE HEARTS

 Makes 30
Allow 4 hours preparation and cooking time

60 g/2 oz plain chocolate, broken into pieces

325 g/11 oz plain flour

175 g/6 oz butter, softened

1 tablespoon milk

1 ½ teaspoons baking powder

1 egg

150 g/5 oz caster sugar plus extra for sprinkling

1 Place pieces of chocolate in bowl over pan of gently simmering water and heat, stirring frequently, until melted and smooth. Remove bowl from pan.

2 In large bowl, combine flour, butter, milk, baking powder, egg and 150 g/5 oz sugar. With electric mixer, beat ingredients until well blended, occasionally scraping bowl with rubber spatula. With hands, shape half of the dough into ball; wrap and refrigerate for 2 hours or until dough is firm enough to handle. (Or place dough in freezer for 40 minutes.)

Eye-catching Two-Tone Hearts are rich and buttery, the perfect present for your sweetheart on Valentine's Day

3 With electric mixer, beat melted chocolate into dough remaining in bowl until blended. With hands, shape chocolate dough into ball; wrap and refrigerate for 2 hours.

4 Grease and flour 2 large baking sheets. On lightly floured surface, with floured rolling pin, roll out half of the plain dough 3 mm/ ⅛ inch thick; keep remaining dough refrigerated. With floured 8 cm/3 ¼ inch heart-shaped cutter, cut dough into hearts. Place hearts, about 5 mm/ ¼ inch apart, on 1 baking sheet. Repeat with remaining plain dough and trimmings. Repeat with chocolate dough, placing hearts on second baking sheet. Refrigerate until hearts are firm, about 20 minutes.

5 Preheat oven to 180°C/350°F/gas 4. With 2.5 cm/1 inch heart-shaped pastry cutter, cut small heart in centre of each plain and chocolate heart biscuit; set small hearts aside. With 5 cm/ 2 inch heart-shaped pastry cutter, cut another heart in centre of each biscuit. Remove medium-sized heart from each plain biscuit and replace it with one from chocolate biscuit. Fit 2.5 cm/1 inch plain hearts into centres of medium-sized chocolate hearts; repeat with 2.5 cm/ 1 inch chocolate hearts and medium-sized plain hearts.

6 Sprinkle biscuits lightly with sugar. Bake biscuits for 10 minutes or until golden. With fish slice, transfer biscuits to wire racks to cool. Store in airtight container.

CHRISTMAS SUGAR COOKIES

Makes about 48

Can be made several days before and kept in airtight container

525 g/1 lb 2 ½ oz plain flour

225 g/8 oz butter, softened

150 g/5 oz caster sugar

125 ml/4 fl oz golden syrup

1 tablespoon lemon juice

2 eggs

Ornamental Icing (see Box, right)

1 In large bowl, combine flour, butter, sugar, golden syrup, lemon juice and eggs. With electric mixer, beat ingredients until well blended, occasionally scraping bowl with rubber spatula. Wrap dough; refrigerate for 2 hours or until dough is firm enough to handle. (Or place dough in freezer for 40 minutes.)

2 Preheat oven to 180°C/350°F/gas 4. On well floured surface, with floured rolling pin, roll out one-quarter of dough 3 mm/⅛ inch thick, keeping remaining dough refrigerated. With floured pastry cutters, cut dough into different shapes (or use 7.5 cm/ 3 inch round cutter). With fish slice, place cookies, about 1 cm/½ inch apart, on ungreased baking sheet.

3 Bake cookies for 5-7 minutes until golden. With fish slice, transfer cookies to wire racks to cool. Repeat with remaining dough and trimmings.

ORNAMENTAL ICING

In large bowl, with electric mixer, beat 450 g/1 lb icing sugar, sifted, 5 tablespoons warm water and 3 tablespoons albumen powder. Beat until mixture is so stiff that when knife is drawn through mixture it will leave a clean path.

Divide icing among small bowls; tint each bowl of icing with *food colouring* as liked. Keep all bowls covered with damp tea towels or cling film, to prevent icing drying out during standing.

4 Prepare Ornamental Icing.

5 Place cookies on baking sheets lined with non-stick baking parchment. With small palette knife or small and medium artist's paint brushes and piping bags fitted with writing tubes, decorate cookies with Ornamental Icing as desired. (If icing is too stiff for brushing on cookies, dilute it with a little water.) Set cookies aside to allow icing to dry completely, about 2 hours. Store cookies in airtight container.

Jingle Bells
With skewer, make small hole in dough at top of each bell before baking. After cookies have cooled, coat with yellow icing; leave to dry. With piping bag and small writing tube, pipe decorative designs in different colours on top of yellow; leave to dry. Thread string or ribbon through holes.

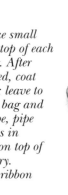

Holly Wreaths
Coat each wreath shape with green icing; leave to dry. With piping bag and small writing tube, pipe white icing in zig-zag design over green. Pipe red dots in between white icing to resemble holly berries.

Christmas Presents
With piping bag and small writing tube, pipe decorative designs in different coloured icings on plain rectangular-shaped cookies. If you like, tie presents with ribbon.

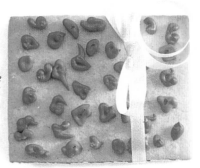

Jolly Snowmen
Coat each cookie with white icing; leave to dry. With piping bag and small writing tube and different coloured icings, pipe hats, faces, scarves, buttons and other trimmings on snowmen.

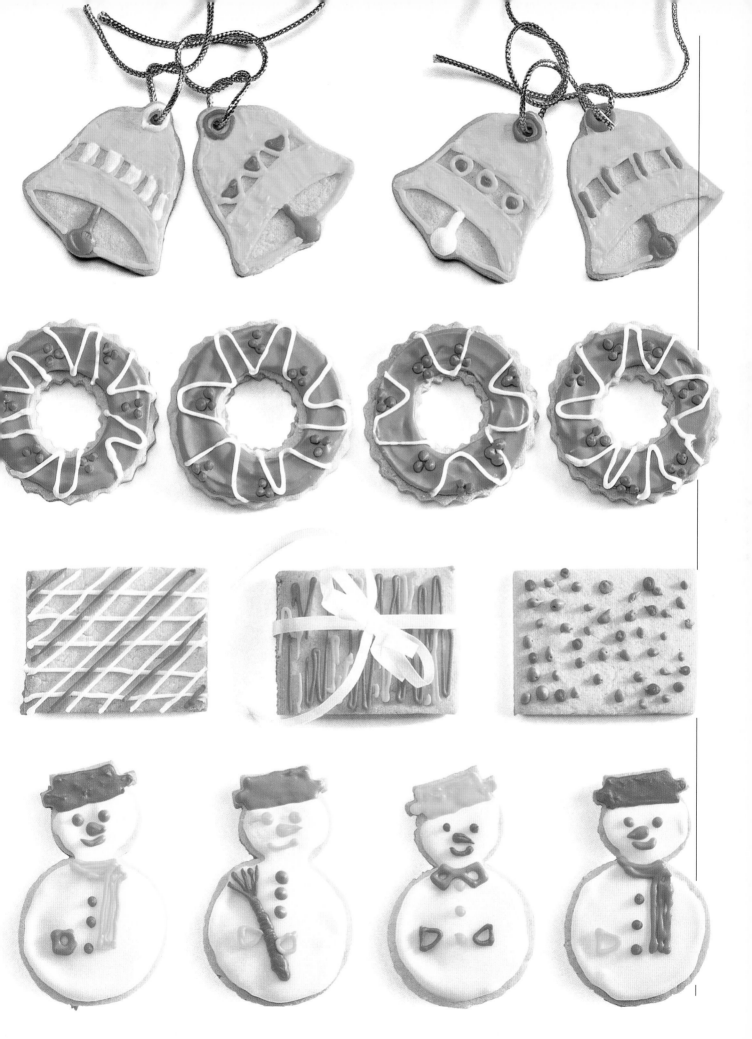

CHOCOLATE AMARETTI

Makes about 30
Allow 1 ½ hours
preparation and
cooking time

140 g/4 ½ oz blanched
    whole almonds

100 g/3 ½ oz caster sugar

2 egg whites

⅛ teaspoon cream of tartar

½ teaspoon vanilla essence

½ teaspoon almond essence

15 g/ ½ oz cocoa powder

30 g/1 oz icing sugar plus
    extra for sifting

1 In large frying pan over medium heat, cook almonds until lightly browned, shaking pan frequently. Remove from heat; cool almonds.

2 In food processor, blend almonds with half of the caster sugar, pulsing on and off, until almonds are finely ground.

3 Preheat oven to 170°C/325°F/gas 3. Line large baking sheet with non-stick baking parchment or foil.

4 In small bowl, with electric mixer on full speed, beat egg whites with cream of tartar until soft peaks form; gradually sprinkle in remaining caster sugar, beating until sugar completely dissolves and whites stand in stiff, glossy peaks. Beat in both vanilla and almond essences. With rubber spatula or wire whisk, gently fold in ground almond mixture, cocoa powder and 30 g/1 oz sifted icing sugar.

5 Spoon almond mixture into piping bag fitted with medium writing tube (tip about 1 cm/ ½ inch in diameter). On to baking sheet, pipe mixture in 4 cm/1 ½ inch mounds, about 2.5 cm/ 1 inch apart.

6 Bake for 15 minutes or until amaretti are crisp. Cool for 10 minutes on baking sheet on wire rack; with fish slice, transfer amaretti to wire rack to cool completely. Sift icing sugar over amaretti until coated. Store in airtight container.

CAPPUCCINO SQUARES

Makes 24
Allow 2 hours
preparation and
cooking time

225 g/8 oz butter

225 g/8 oz plain chocolate,
    broken into pieces

700 g/1 ½ lb caster sugar

6 eggs

225 g/8 oz walnut pieces

250 g/9 oz plain flour

30 g/1 oz instant coffee
    powder

½ teaspoon ground
    cinnamon

Icing sugar to decorate

1 Preheat oven to 180°C/350°F/gas 4. Grease and flour 33 x 23 cm/13 x 9 inch baking tin.

2 In heavy non-stick saucepan over low heat, heat butter and chocolate, stirring often, until melted and smooth; remove saucepan from heat. With wire whisk or spoon, beat in caster sugar and eggs until well blended. Stir in walnuts, flour, coffee powder and cinnamon.

3 Evenly spread mixture in baking tin. Bake for 45-50 minutes until skewer inserted in centre comes out clean. Cool completely in tin on wire rack.

4 When cold, cut crossways into 6 strips, then cut each strip into 4 pieces. With fish slice, remove squares from tin; carefully sift icing sugar over half of each square. Store in single layer in airtight container.

APRICOT CROISSANTS

Makes 36
Allow 2 ½ hours preparation and cooking time

300 g/10 oz plain flour

275 g/9 oz butter

175 ml/6 fl oz soured cream

120 g/4 oz apricot jam

60 g/2 oz plain chocolate chips or polka dots

30 g/1 oz flaked almonds

30 g/1 oz caster sugar

1 Into large bowl, sift flour. With pastry blender or with fingertips, cut or rub 225 g/8 oz butter into flour until mixture resembles fine breadcrumbs. Add soured cream and mix lightly with fork until dough just holds together. Divide dough into 3 pieces. Wrap and refrigerate for 1 hour or until firm enough to handle.

2 On lightly floured surface, with floured rolling pin, roll out 1 piece of dough into 27.5 cm/ 11 inch round, keeping remaining pieces of dough refrigerated.

3 Spread dough round with one-third of apricot jam; sprinkle with one-third of chocolate chips. Cut dough round into 12 equal wedges; starting at curved edge, roll up each wedge croissant fashion. Place croissants, point side up, about 4 cm/1 ½ inches apart, on large ungreased baking sheet. Repeat with remaining dough, jam and chocolate chips.

4 Preheat oven to 190°C/375°F/gas 5. In small saucepan over low heat, melt remaining butter; remove saucepan from heat. In small bowl, mix almonds and sugar.

5 Brush croissants with melted butter, then sprinkle with almond mixture. Bake croissants for 25 minutes or until golden brown. With fish slice, immediately transfer croissants to wire racks to cool.

These miniature 'croissants' are perfectly divine – melt-in-the-mouth buttery pastry around a gooey chocolate and apricot filling; they are best served warm

CHOCOLATE AND NUT SHORTBREAD

Makes about 18
Allow 2 hours preparation and cooking time

180 g/6 ¼ oz plain flour

90 g/3 oz icing sugar, sifted

30 g/1 oz cornflour

45 g/1 ½ oz shelled pecans or walnut pieces, finely chopped

175 g/6 oz butter

175 g/6 oz plain chocolate, broken into pieces

1 Preheat oven to 170°C/325°F/gas 3. In large bowl, with fork, stir flour, icing sugar, cornflour and chopped nuts. With knife, cut butter into small pieces; add to flour mixture. With hand, rub in ingredients until well blended, then knead together.

2 Pat dough evenly into 28 x 18 cm/ 11 x 7 inch Swiss roll tin. Bake shortbread for 35-40 minutes or until golden. With sharp knife, immediately cut short-bread lengthways into 3 strips, then cut each strip crossways into 12 pieces. Cool shortbread in dish on wire rack. When cold, with fish slice, remove short-bread from baking dish.

3 Place pieces of choco-late in bowl over pan of gently simmering water and heat, stirring often, until melted and smooth; remove bowl from pan. Dip 1 corner of each piece of shortbread diagonally into chocolate until half is coated with chocolate. Place shortbread on baking sheet lined with greaseproof paper or foil. Refrigerate until chocolate is set, about 15 minutes.

FUNNEL CAKES

Makes 7
Allow 30 minutes preparation and cooking time

Oil for deep frying

165 g/5 ½ oz plain flour

175 ml/6 fl oz milk

1 teaspoon baking powder

1 teaspoon almond essence

1 egg

Icing sugar for sifting

1 In deep-fat fryer or deep frying pan over medium heat, heat oil to 170°C/325°F on a deep-frying thermometer.

2 Meanwhile, in bowl, with wire whisk or fork, mix flour, milk, baking powder, almond essence and egg until well blended.

Funnel Cakes are a speciality from Pennsylvania Dutch country in the USA

3 Holding funnel with 1 cm/½ inch narrow spout, close spout with finger; pour about 4 tablespoons batter into funnel. Over hot oil, remove finger to let batter run out in a stream, to make a spiral about 15 cm/ 6 inches in diameter.

4 Fry for 3-5 minutes until golden brown, turning once with tongs. Drain well on kitchen paper; keep warm. Repeat with remaining batter, stirring well each time before pouring.

5 Sift icing sugar lightly over Funnel Cakes. Serve warm.

Crisp and dainty, these deep-fried bow ties are sprinkled with icing sugar for extra sweetness

FRIED BOW TIES

Makes about 40
Allow 4 hours preparation and cooking time

2 size-6 eggs

2 tablespoons caster sugar

2 tablespoons milk

185 g/6 ½ oz plain flour

Oil for deep frying

Icing sugar for sifting (optional)

1 In medium bowl, combine eggs, caster sugar, milk and 135 g/ 4 ½ oz flour. With wooden spoon, stir until ingredients are well blended; stir in enough of remaining flour until mixture holds together. With hands, shape dough into ball; wrap dough and refrigerate for 2 hours or until easy to handle. (Or place dough in freezer for 40 minutes.)

2 On floured surface, with floured rolling pin, roll out half of the dough until paper thin, keeping remaining dough refrigerated. Cut dough into 10 x 4 cm/ 4 x 1½ inch rectangles. Twist each strip to form bow tie shape, pinching centre firmly to flatten and seal. Repeat with remaining dough.

3 In deep-fat fryer or deep frying pan over medium heat, heat oil to 180°C/350°F on a deep-frying thermometer.

4 Gently place several bow ties in hot oil; fry for about 1½ minutes or until golden. Drain bow ties on kitchen paper; cool. Fry remaining bow ties in batches; drain and cool. Store in airtight container.

5 If you like, sift icing sugar over bow ties just before serving.

CRISPY SNOWFLAKES

Makes 32
Allow 4 hours preparation and cooking time

3 eggs

400 g/14 oz plain flour

50 g/1 ⅔ oz caster sugar

4 tablespoons milk

Oil for deep frying

Icing sugar for sifting (optional)

1 In medium bowl, combine eggs, flour, caster sugar and milk. With wooden spoon, stir ingredients until well blended and mixture holds together. With hands, shape dough into ball; wrap and refrigerate for 2 hours or until dough is easy to handle. (Or place dough in freezer for 40 minutes.)

2 Divide dough into 32 pieces. On lightly floured surface, with floured rolling pin, roll out 16 dough pieces into 13.5 cm/5 ½ inch rounds; cover and refrigerate remaining dough pieces. Allow dough rounds to stand, uncovered, until tops are fairly dry.

3 Fold each dough round in half, folding dry top side together; fold again into quarters, then into eighths. With sharp knife, scissors or petit four cutter, cut designs along edges of dough. Unfold snowflakes and set aside at room temperature. Meanwhile, repeat with remaining dough.

4 In deep-fat fryer or deep frying pan over medium heat, heat oil to 180°C/350°F on deep-frying thermometer.

5 Gently place 2 or 3 snowflakes in hot oil; fry for about 1 ½ minutes or until golden. Drain snowflakes on kitchen paper; cool. Fry remaining snowflakes in batches; drain and cool. Store in airtight container.

6 If you like, sift icing sugar over snowflakes just before serving.

Snowflake shapes are made by folding dough and cutting out design exactly as you would when making paper snowflakes. One helpful tip: it is essential to let the dough get really dry before folding and cutting or you will not get good shapes

WAFFLE HEARTS

Makes about
48 heart- or wedge-
shaped waffles
Allow 2 hours
preparation and
cooking time

| 250 g/8 ½ oz plain flour |
| 150 g/5 oz caster sugar |
| 120 g/4 oz butter, melted |
| 2 teaspoons baking powder |
| 3 eggs |

WAFFLE IRON
Waffle irons are avail-
able in electric and non-
electric models in
various shapes and sizes.
Be sure to follow
manufacturer's instruc-
tions for exact amount
of batter to use, and
cooking times.

1 Preheat 17.5 cm/
7 inch waffle iron
according to manufac-
turer's instructions (see
Box, above right).

2 In large bowl,
mix all ingredients.
With electric mixer, beat
ingredients until blended,
occasionally scraping bowl
with rubber spatula.

3 Pour about 2 table-
spoons batter at a
time on to waffle iron.
Cover; cook according to
manufacturer's instruc-
tions (do not lift cover
during cooking).

4 When done, lift cover
and loosen waffle with
fork; transfer to wire rack
to cool.

5 When waffles are
cold, break each into
4 pieces to serve. (The
17.5 cm/7 inch iron makes
round waffles, each with
4 heart- or wedge-shaped
sections.)

*These waffles are made in
a heart-shaped waffle
iron; if you do not
have a waffle iron,
use a frying pan,
and turn the waffles
halfway through
cooking*

NUTTY OAT CRUNCHIES

Makes about 30
Allow 2 hours
preparation and
cooking time

| 175 g/6 oz butter, softened |
| 165 g/5 ½ oz light soft brown sugar |
| 1 tablespoon grated lemon zest |
| 1 teaspoon baking powder |
| 1 egg |
| 260 g/9 oz quick-cooking porridge oats |
| 45 g/1 ½ oz ground almonds |
| 2 egg yolks, lightly beaten, or a little milk |

1 In bowl, combine
first 5 ingredients.
With electric mixer, beat
ingredients for 10 minutes
or until light and fluffy,
occasionally scraping bowl
with rubber spatula. Add
oats and almonds; with
hand, knead until well
blended and mixture
holds together.

2 Preheat oven to
180°C/350°F/gas 4.
Grease well 2 large baking
sheets. Between 2 sheets of
non-stick baking parch-
ment, roll out half of the
dough until 5 mm/¼ inch
thick. With 6 cm/2 ½ inch
round cutter, cut dough
into as many rounds as
possible; place rounds,
2.5 cm/1 inch apart, on
baking sheets. Brush tops
with egg yolk or milk.

3 Bake for 12 minutes
or until golden.
Quickly, with fish slice,
transfer oat crunchies to
wire racks to cool. Repeat
with remaining dough and
trimmings. Store in
airtight container.

ALMOND BUTTER SHORTBREAD

Makes 30
Allow 1 ½ hours preparation and cooking time

300 g/10 oz plain flour

300 g/10 oz butter, softened

150 g/5 oz cornflour

150 g/5 oz caster sugar

½ teaspoon almond essence

60 g/2 oz flaked almonds

Icing sugar or caster sugar

1 Preheat oven to 170°C/325°F/gas 3. In food processor, combine flour, butter, cornflour, sugar and almond essence until mixture is well blended and will hold together.

2 Form dough roughly into a ball. Place in ungreased 33 x 23 cm/ 13 x 9 inch Swiss roll tin. With fingers, pat and press dough into tin (if dough is sticky, cover with cling film and press through it). Prick dough all over with fork; sprinkle with almonds and sifted icing sugar or caster sugar.

3 Bake shortbread for 40-45 minutes or until very pale golden. Leave in tin until lukewarm, then cut into 30 pieces. Leave in tin until almost cold, then lift out and place on wire rack; leave to cool completely. Store in airtight container.

Shortbread must be made with butter to taste really good; it keeps extremely well, so it is worth baking a big batch

Toasted sesame seeds give these crunchy cookies a distinctive 'oriental' flavour

TOASTED SESAME COOKIES

Makes about 36 small cookies
Allow 2 hours preparation and cooking time

130 g/4 ¼ oz sesame seeds

300 g/10 oz plain flour

150 g/5 oz caster sugar

120 g/4 oz butter, softened

1 teaspoon baking powder

½ teaspoon vanilla essence

1 egg

1 In large frying pan over medium heat, cook sesame seeds until golden, shaking pan and stirring often. Remove pan from heat; set aside.

2 In large bowl, combine flour, sugar, butter, baking powder, vanilla essence, egg and *2 tablespoons water*. With electric mixer, beat ingredients until well blended, occasionally scraping bowl with rubber spatula. With wooden spoon, stir in half of the toasted sesame seeds.

3 Preheat oven to 180°C/350°F/gas 4. Shape 2 teaspoons dough at a time into 5 cm/2 inch long oval; roll ovals in remaining sesame seeds. Place ovals, about 2.5 cm/ 1 inch apart, on ungreased baking sheets.

4 Bake cookies for 20 minutes or until lightly browned. With fish slice, transfer cookies to wire rack to cool. Store in airtight container.

SWEET AND SPICY PEPPERNUTS

Makes about
8 large cupfuls
Allow 2 ½ hours
preparation and
cooking time

250 g/8 ½ oz plain flour

200 g/7 oz light soft brown
sugar

60 g/2 oz butter, softened

¼ teaspoon bicarbonate of
soda

¼ teaspoon ground
cinnamon

¼ teaspoon ground cloves

¼ teaspoon ground ginger

Good pinch of white pepper

1 egg, beaten

1 Preheat oven to 190°C/375°F/gas 5. In large bowl, combine all ingredients. With electric mixer, beat ingredients until well blended, occasionally scraping bowl with rubber spatula. (Mixture may be crumbly; if necessary, add a little more egg and, with hand, knead lightly until mixture holds together.) Shape dough into ball.

2 For each peppernut, pinch off walnut-sized pieces of dough; with hands, shape into ball. Place dough balls, about 1 cm/½ inch apart, on baking sheets lined with non-stick baking parchment.

3 Bake peppernuts for about 7 minutes or until lightly browned. Leave to cool on baking sheets. Store in airtight container.

These German sweetmeats are perfect as petits fours with after-dinner coffee and liqueurs

These Canadian biscuits are richly flavoured with maple syrup; serve them with morning coffee

MAPLE LEAVES

Makes about 24
Allow 3 ½ hours
preparation and
cooking time

300 g/10 oz plain flour

120 g/4 oz butter, softened

75 g/2 ½ oz light soft
brown sugar

4 tablespoons maple syrup

1 teaspoon cream of tartar

½ teaspoon bicarbonate of
soda

1 egg

1 In large bowl, mix all ingredients. With electric mixer, beat ingredients until blended, occasionally scraping bowl with rubber spatula.

2 With hands, shape dough into ball; wrap and refrigerate for 1 hour or until dough is easy to handle. (Or place dough in freezer for 30 minutes.)

3 Preheat oven to 180°C/350°F/gas 4. Grease large baking sheet. On lightly floured surface, with floured rolling pin, roll out half of the dough 3 mm/⅛ inch thick; keep remaining dough in refrigerator. With floured 8 cm/3½ inch leaf-shaped pastry cutter, cut dough into leaves; score leaf 'veins' in dough with tip of knife. Place leaf shapes, 2.5 cm/1 inch apart, on baking sheet.

4 Bake leaf shapes for 10 minutes or until golden. With fish slice, transfer to wire racks; cool. Repeat with remaining dough and trimmings. Store in airtight container.

POPPY SEED CATHERINE WHEELS

Makes about 30
Allow about 4 hours preparation and cooking time

50 g/1 ⅔ oz caster sugar

90 g/3 oz butter, softened

135 g/4 ½ oz plain flour

½ beaten egg

¼ teaspoon vanilla essence

30 g/1 oz walnut pieces

40 g/1 ¼ oz poppy seeds

45 g/1 ½ oz honey

½ teaspoon grated orange zest

Pinch of ground cinnamon

1 In large bowl, with electric mixer, beat sugar and 60 g/2 oz butter for 10 minutes or until light and fluffy, scraping bowl often with rubber spatula. Add flour, egg and vanilla essence; beat just until blended, occasionally scraping bowl. With hands, shape dough into ball; wrap and refrigerate for 1 hour or until dough is firm enough to handle. (Or place dough in freezer for 30 minutes.)

2 Meanwhile, in food processor, finely grind walnuts. In small bowl, stir walnuts, poppy seeds, honey, orange zest, cinnamon and remaining butter until mixed; set aside.

3 On sheet of non-stick baking parchment, with floured rolling pin, roll out dough into a 25 x 20 cm/10 x 8 inch rectangle; spread rectangle with poppy seed mixture. Starting at a 20 cm/8 inch side, roll dough Swiss roll fashion. Wrap roll and refrigerate for 1 hour or until dough is firm enough to slice. (Or place roll in freezer for 30 minutes.)

4 Preheat oven to 190°C/375°F/gas 5. With sharp knife, slice roll crossways into slices about 5 mm/¼ inch thick. Place slices, about 1 cm/½ inch apart, on ungreased baking sheets.

5 Bake for 10-12 minutes until lightly browned. With fish slice, transfer to wire racks to cool. Store in airtight container.

Poppy seeds spiral their way through these crisp, nutty cookies

WINDMILLS

Makes about 36
Allow 3 ½ hours preparation and cooking time

300 g/10 oz plain flour

225 g/8 oz light soft brown sugar

120 g/4 oz butter, softened

½ teaspoon bicarbonate of soda

1 egg

45 g/1 ½ oz walnut pieces, chopped

1 In large bowl, mix all ingredients except nuts. With electric mixer, beat ingredients until well blended, occasionally scraping bowl with rubber spatula.

2 With hands, shape dough into ball; wrap and refrigerate for 1 hour or until dough is easy to handle. (Or place dough in freezer for 30 minutes.)

3 Preheat oven to 180°C/350°F/gas 4. Grease large baking sheet. On lightly floured surface, with floured rolling pin, roll out one-third of dough 3 mm/⅛ inch thick; keep remaining dough in refrigerator. With floured 8 cm/3 ½ inch round pastry cutter, cut dough into rounds. Place rounds, 2.5 cm/1 inch apart, on baking sheet. With knife, cut 4 lines from edge of each round almost to centre, forming quarters; fold left corner of each quarter to centre; press to form windmill. Sprinkle with nuts.

4 Bake windmills for 10-12 minutes until golden. Transfer windmills to wire racks to cool. Repeat with remaining dough and nuts. Store in airtight container.

GINGERBREAD CHRISTMAS BISCUITS

Makes about 24
Can be made up to 1 week before and kept in airtight container

75 ml/2 ½ fl oz black treacle

60 g/2 oz dark soft brown sugar

60 g/2 oz butter, softened

¾ teaspoon bicarbonate of soda

¼ teaspoon ground allspice

¼ teaspoon ground cinnamon

¼ teaspoon ground cloves

¼ teaspoon ground ginger

1 egg

About 325 g/11 oz plain flour

Ornamental Icing (see Box, above right)

ORNAMENTAL ICING
In large bowl, with electric mixer, beat *450 g/1 lb icing sugar, sifted, 5 tablespoons warm water* and *3 tablespoons albumen powder.* Beat until mixture is so stiff that when knife is drawn through mixture it will leave a clean path.
If not using icing immediately, keep bowl covered with damp tea towel or cling film.

1 In large bowl, combine black treacle, brown sugar, butter, bicarbonate of soda, allspice, cinnamon, cloves, ginger, egg and 100 g/ 3 ½ oz flour. With electric mixer, beat ingredients for 2 minutes, frequently scraping bowl with rubber spatula. With wooden spoon, stir in enough of remaining flour to make stiff dough. Shape dough into ball; wrap. Use dough immediately or refrigerate to use within 2 days.

2 Preheat oven to 180°C/350°F/gas 4. On lightly floured surface, with floured rolling pin, roll out half of the dough 3 mm/⅛ inch thick.

3 With desired shape pastry cutter (about 8.5 cm/3½ inches), cut out as many biscuits as possible. With fish slice, place biscuits, about 1 cm/½ inch apart, on ungreased large baking sheet.

4 Bake biscuits for 12 minutes or until edges are firm. With fish slice, immediately loosen biscuits from baking sheet and transfer to wire racks to cool. Repeat with remaining dough and trimmings.

5 If not decorating biscuits immediately, wrap in freezer paper or foil, seal, label and freeze. Before decorating, unwrap frozen biscuits and thaw for 1 hour.

6 Prepare Ornamental Icing. Spoon icing into piping bag with small writing tube, or use paper piping bag with tip cut to make 3 mm/⅛ inch hole; pipe decorative outlines and designs on each biscuit. Set biscuits aside to allow icing to dry completely, about 1 hour.

Christmas Tree

Twinkling Star

Rocking Horse

Father Christmas

Reindeer

PINOLIS

 Makes 16
Allow 2 ½ hours preparation and cooking time

120 g/4 oz plain flour
75 g/2 ½ oz butter, softened
50 g/1 ⅔ oz caster sugar
4 tablespoons golden syrup
1 egg
90 g/3 oz pine kernels

1 Preheat oven to 180°C/350°F/gas 4. In medium bowl, combine flour, 60 g/2 oz butter and 40 g/1 ⅓ oz sugar. With hand, knead ingredients until well blended and mixture holds together.

2 Divide dough into 16 pieces. Press dough pieces on to bottom and up sides of each of sixteen 4.5 cm/1¾ inch holes in deep bun tin.

3 In small saucepan over low heat, heat remaining butter until just melted. Remove saucepan from heat; into melted butter, stir golden syrup, egg and remaining caster sugar.

4 Into dough cups in deep bun tin, sprinkle pine kernels.

5 Spoon syrup mixture over pine kernels. Bake pinolis for about 25 minutes or until edges are browned and skewer inserted in centre of filling comes out clean.

6 Cool pinolis in tin on wire rack for about 5 minutes or until firm. With tip of knife or small palette knife, loosen pinolis from bun tin holes; place on wire racks to cool completely.

HAZELNUT CRESCENTS

 Makes about 18
Allow about 2 hours preparation and cooking time

15 g/ ½ oz shelled hazelnuts
90 g/3 oz plain flour
60 g/2 oz butter, softened
30 g/1 oz icing sugar, sifted

1 Preheat oven to 200°C/400°F/gas 6. Place hazelnuts in small baking tray. Bake for 8-10 minutes until lightly toasted. Remove nuts from oven; turn oven down to 180°C/350°F/gas 4. Cool nuts; chop finely.

2 In large bowl, combine flour, butter and icing sugar; add hazelnuts. With hand, knead ingredients until well blended and mixture holds together. (Mixture may be crumbly; if necessary, add 1 tablespoon water while kneading ingredients together.)

3 Shape dough into 4.5 x 1 cm/1 ¾ x ½ inch crescents (about 2 level teaspoons each). Place crescents, about 2.5 cm/1 inch apart, on ungreased baking sheets.

4 Bake crescents for 10 minutes or until lightly browned. With fish slice, transfer crescents to wire racks to cool. Store in airtight container.

FROZEN DESSERTS
217-240

Frozen Desserts

Summertime or winter, cool and creamy frozen desserts will delight everyone. Many of the fabulous frozen cakes and bombes are made with bought ice cream, making them much easier than they look, while pretty decorations, such as mint leaves, fruit slices, and chocolate 'coffee beans' give even the simplest of iced drinks a sophisticated look. Florida Fruit Cups and Lemon Ice in Lemon Cups are ideal for casual entertaining and everyday eating. On the lighter side, Raspberry Sorbet and Two-Tone Granitas – elegant layers of icy coffee and citrus sorbet – are so refreshing in hot weather or to balance out a lavishly rich meal. When you're feeling especially creative, try Hazelnut Icebox Cake, smooth, frozen coffee and chocolate custards with a hazelnut crunch topping. Or, for a special treat, Fudge Sundae Pie, a deluxe concoction of vanilla and chocolate ice creams with a rich and chewy fudge centre, all in a walnut crust. Scrumptious!

CONTENTS

Frozen Desserts

Nothing beats ice cream, frozen yogurt or sorbet for an 'instant' dessert: just dish it up, serve and enjoy. You'll find all your favourite flavours in this chapter, plus recipes to turn them (or their bought counterparts) into chilly treats that money can't buy, such as dacquoises, frozen tortes and more. For freezer storage, wrap them well to prevent freezer burn, and keep them on hand to serve with easy elegance at very short notice, or to end a feast superbly.

CHESTNUT GLACÉ

Makes 6
Allow 15 minutes preparation, plus freezing time

300 ml/ ½ pint double or whipping cream

1 x 439 g/15 ½ oz can unsweetened chestnut purée

120 g/4 oz caster sugar

2 tablespoons brandy

Dark Chocolate Curls (page 142) and lemon leaves (optional) to decorate

1 In small bowl, whip double or whipping cream until stiff peaks form. In large bowl, with fork, mash chestnut purée; stir in sugar and brandy until smooth.

Gold foil tartlet tins give these quick-and-easy frozen desserts a ritzy look

2 With rubber spatula or wire whisk, fold whipped cream into chestnut mixture.

3 Spoon chestnut and cream mixture into foil tartlet tins or small freezerproof ramekins. Cover; freeze until firm, at least 3 hours.

4 Leave to stand at room temperature for about 10 minutes to soften slightly for easier eating.

> **TO SERVE**
> *Decorate with chocolate curls and lemon leaves, if you like.*

RAINBOW ICE CREAM TORTE

16 servings
Allow about 2 hours preparation, plus final freezing time

600 ml/1 pint chocolate ice cream

600 ml/1 pint mint chocolate chip ice cream

600 ml/1 pint strawberry ice cream

600 ml/1 pint vanilla ice cream

15 gingernut biscuits

60 g/2 oz butter, softened

1 x 425 g/15 oz can stoned black cherries, drained

60 g/2 oz walnut pieces, chopped

1 Place ice creams in refrigerator to soften slightly.

2 Meanwhile, place biscuits in polythene bag; with rolling pin, roll biscuits into fine crumbs.

3 Or in food processor or blender, blend gingernut biscuits until fine crumbs form.

4 In 23 cm/9 inch springform cake tin, with hand, mix biscuit crumbs with butter; press mixture firmly on to bottom of tin. Freeze until firm, about 10 minutes.

5 Evenly spread chocolate ice cream on top of crumb mixture. Place tin in freezer to harden ice cream slightly, about 15 minutes.

6 Spread mint chocolate chip ice cream on chocolate ice cream layer; top with cherries.

7 Return springform tin to freezer to harden ice creams and cherries slightly.

This party cake is a bit of a cheat in that it is made from bought ice cream, but it looks so spectacular that your guests are bound to be impressed!

8 With palette knife, evenly spread strawberry ice cream over layer of cherries.

Spreading strawberry ice cream over cherries

9 Place tin in freezer to harden ice cream slightly, about 15 minutes. Evenly spread vanilla ice cream on strawberry ice cream layer. Sprinkle top with walnuts. Cover and freeze until firm.

10 To serve, run knife or palette knife, dipped in hot water, round edge of tin to loosen ice cream cake; remove side of tin. Leave cake to stand at room temperature for about 10 minutes for easier slicing.

VANILLA ICE CREAM

 8-10 servings

Allow 30 minutes preparation, plus freezing time

4 eggs, separated

120 g/4 oz vanilla sugar, or caster sugar and 1 teaspoon vanilla essence

300 ml/ ½ pint double cream

1 In small bowl, with wire whisk, beat egg yolks until well blended.

2 In large bowl, with electric mixer on full speed, beat egg whites until soft peaks form.

3 Into beaten egg whites, gradually sprinkle vanilla sugar, 1 tablespoon at a time, beating well after each addition. (This will take about 10 minutes.)

4 In another large bowl, whip cream until soft peaks form. (If using vanilla essence, add to cream before whipping.)

5 With rubber spatula or wire whisk, fold beaten egg whites and egg yolks into whipped cream.

6 If you are making one of the variations (see right and Box, right), add the extra ingredients.

7 Turn mixture into 1.5 litre/2 ½ pint plastic container; cover and freeze overnight.

8 To serve, scoop ice cream into individual dessert bowls or dishes; serve immediately.

SIMPLE VARIATIONS

If you are making one of the following variations on basic vanilla ice cream, use caster sugar instead of vanilla sugar (or omit vanilla essence). Add extra ingredients after folding beaten egg whites and egg yolks into whipped cream.

Ginger Ice Cream
Add *1 teaspoon ground ginger* and *120 g/4 oz stem ginger in syrup, drained and chopped*, to basic ice cream.

Mocha Ice Cream
Add *2 tablespoons coffee essence* and *2 tablespoons coffee liqueur* to basic ice cream.

Fresh Lemon Ice Cream
Add *grated zest* and *juice of 2 lemons* to basic ice cream.

Mango Ice Cream
Peel and stone *1 ripe mango*; lightly mash flesh and add to basic ice cream.

Passion Fruit Ice Cream
Halve *3 passion fruit*; with small spoon, scoop out flesh and add to basic ice cream.

Tutti Frutti Ice Cream
Chop *120 g/4 oz mixed glacé pineapple, raisins, dried apricots, glacé cherries* and *angelica*; in small bowl, soak overnight in *4 tablespoons brandy* to plump them. Add to basic ice cream.

Blackcurrant Ice Cream
Add *3 tablespoons blackcurrant cordial* and *3 tablespoons crème de cassis* to basic ice cream.

SPECIAL VARIATIONS

Once you've mastered the art of ice cream making, you can ring the changes by adding different fresh fruits, chocolate, nuts or fudge to vanilla ice cream. Here are 3 special varieties for you to try.

Chocolate Ice Cream
Make basic vanilla ice cream using caster sugar instead of vanilla sugar (or omit vanilla essence). In small bowl, with spoon, stir *15 g/ ½ oz cocoa powder, 30 g/1 oz caster sugar* and about *3 tablespoons boiling water* to a smooth paste; cool. Stir sweetened cocoa paste mixture into ice cream until evenly blended.
Makes 8-10 servings

Fudge-Swirl Ice Cream
Make basic vanilla ice cream using caster sugar instead of vanilla sugar (or omit vanilla essence); freeze until softly set.
Meanwhile, prepare fudge sauce: in heavy saucepan over medium-high heat, bring *200 g/7 oz caster sugar, 300 ml/ ½ pint double or whipping cream, 30 g/1 oz butter, 1 tablespoon golden syrup* and *120 g/4 oz plain chocolate, chopped*, to the boil, stirring constantly. Reduce heat to medium; cook for 5 minutes, stirring occasionally. Remove saucepan from heat; stir in *1 teaspoon vanilla essence*.
Leave sauce to cool, stirring occasionally, then with spoon or knife, quickly swirl fudge sauce into ice cream to create marbled design. Cover container of ice cream again, return to freezer and freeze overnight.
Makes 8-10 servings

Strawberry Ice Cream
Make basic vanilla ice cream using caster sugar instead of vanilla sugar (or omit vanilla essence). Add *150 ml/ ¼ pint strawberry purée*, beating well to mix.
For Raspberry Ice Cream, substitute *raspberry purée* for strawberry. For Gooseberry, Plum or Rhubarb Ice Cream, add *150 ml/ ¼ pint sweetened cooked gooseberry, plum or rhubarb purée*.
Makes 8-10 servings

FROZEN DESSERTS · 223

Chocolate Ice Cream

A piped chocolate design only hints at the rich taste of *Chocolate Ice Cream.* Make the designs as shown, using directions for Chocolate Squiggles (page 101); chill and place on servings at the last minute.

Vanilla Ice Cream

Home-made Vanilla Ice Cream is everybody's favourite, so delicious that it can be served absolutely plain. Yet it's equally good topped with sweet sauces, fruit, nuts, honey, liqueur or even crumbled biscuits.

Strawberry Ice Cream

For incomparable flavour, use the reddest, ripest (but not over-ripe), juiciest berries you can find for Strawberry Ice Cream. Here, scoops of varied sizes make a pretty plateful.

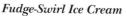

Fudge-Swirl Ice Cream

The decoration is built right into Fudge-Swirl Ice Cream, with thick, fudgy sauce rippled through the frozen mixture. Elegant rolled biscuits make a perfect partner.

HAZELNUT ICEBOX CAKE

10 servings
Allow about 2 ½ hours preparation, plus final freezing time

Hazelnut Praline (see Box, below right)

12 egg yolks

175 ml/6 fl oz golden syrup

2 tablespoons coffee liqueur

2 teaspoons instant coffee powder

175 g/6 oz plain chocolate, broken into pieces

750 ml/1 ¼ pints double or whipping cream

Toasted hazelnuts for decoration

1 Prepare Hazelnut Praline.

2 In large bowl, with electric mixer, beat egg yolks and golden syrup until slightly thickened and light-coloured, about 4 minutes.

3 Pour egg yolk mixture into large non-stick saucepan. Cook over low heat, stirring constantly, until mixture thickens and coats a spoon well, about 30 minutes. Remove saucepan from heat.

4 Pour two-thirds of egg yolk mixture into large bowl.

5 In cup, stir coffee liqueur and coffee powder; stir into egg yolk mixture in large bowl.

6 In bowl over pan of gently simmering water, heat half of the chocolate, stirring frequently, until melted and smooth.

7 Stir melted chocolate into remaining egg yolk mixture in saucepan until blended.

8 In another large bowl, whip 600 ml/1 pint double or whipping cream until stiff peaks form.

9 With rubber spatula or wire whisk, fold two-thirds of whipped cream into coffee mixture until blended. Fold remaining whipped cream into chocolate mixture.

10 Spoon half of the coffee mixture into 23 cm/9 inch springform cake tin, spreading evenly; freeze until set, about 15 minutes.

11 Evenly spread chocolate mixture over coffee layer in springform tin; freeze until set, about 15 minutes.

12 Sprinkle chocolate layer with hazelnut praline; evenly spread with remaining coffee mixture. Cover and freeze until firm, at least 4 hours.

13 In bowl over pan of gently simmering water, heat remaining chocolate, stirring often, until melted and smooth; remove saucepan from heat. Cut non-stick baking parchment into two 10 cm/4 inch squares. Moisten large baking sheet with water; place parchment squares on baking sheet (water will prevent paper from slipping). Use melted chocolate and parchment squares to make Chocolate Triangles (see Box, page 225); refrigerate.

14 In small bowl, whip remaining double or whipping cream until stiff peaks form. Spoon whipped cream into piping bag fitted with star tube.

HAZELNUT PRALINE
Coarsely chop 135 g/ 4 ½ oz shelled hazelnuts.

In large frying pan over medium heat, heat 60 g/2 oz caster sugar until sugar melts and turns golden brown. Stir in chopped hazelnuts; toss to coat well.

Pour into baking tin; leave to cool. Break into small pieces.

15 Run knife or palette knife, dipped in hot water, round edge of springform tin to loosen cake; remove side of tin.

16 Pipe whipped cream into 8 'flowers' round edge on top of cake; place chocolate triangles between whipped cream flowers. Decorate with toasted hazelnuts.

17 Leave cake to stand at room temperature for about 10 minutes for easier slicing.

CHOCOLATE TRIANGLES

Removing baking parchment: *carefully peel parchment from chocolate squares.*

Spreading melted chocolate: *with small palette knife, evenly spread chocolate to cover baking parchment squares. Refrigerate until chocolate is firm but not brittle, about 10 minutes. Remove chocolate from refrigerator; leave to stand for about 5 minutes to soften slightly.*

Cutting triangles: *with sharp knife, quickly but gently cut each chocolate square into 8 triangles.*

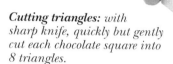

Cutting chocolate into triangle shapes

Top of cake is beautifully decorated with whipped cream 'flowers', toasted hazelnuts and chocolate triangles

DACQUOISE GLACÉE

10 servings

Allow about 4 hours preparation, plus freezing time

5 egg whites

300 g/10 oz caster sugar

25 g/ ¾ oz cocoa powder, sifted

60 g/2 oz flaked almonds

1 litre/2 pints coffee ice cream

450 ml/ ¾ pint double or whipping cream

30 g/1 oz icing sugar, sifted

2 tablespoons coffee liqueur

1 Line 1 large and 1 small baking sheet with non-stick baking parchment or foil.

2 Using 20 cm/8 inch round plate as guide, outline 2 circles on parchment or foil on large baking sheet and 1 circle on small baking sheet.

3 In large bowl, with electric mixer on full speed, beat egg whites until soft peaks form.

4 Into beaten egg whites, gradually sprinkle caster sugar, 1 tablespoon at a time, beating well after each addition until sugar completely dissolves and whites stand in stiff, glossy peaks.

5 With rubber spatula or wire whisk, gently fold sifted cocoa into meringue until blended.

6 Preheat oven to 140°C/275°F/gas 1. Spoon one-third of meringue inside each circle on baking sheets; spread to fill circle.

7 Bake layers for 1 ¼ hours or until meringue is crisp.

8 Cool meringue layers on baking sheets on wire racks for 10 minutes; carefully loosen and lift meringue layers from parchment or foil.

9 Place meringue layers on wire racks; leave to cool completely.

ASSEMBLING DACQUOISE GLACÉE

Spreading meringue with ice cream: with palette knife, quickly and evenly spread first meringue layer with softened ice cream.

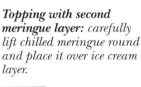

Topping with second meringue layer: carefully lift chilled meringue round and place it over ice cream layer.

Icing frozen dessert: evenly swirl whipped cream all over side and top of frozen dessert.

10 While meringue is cooling, turn oven up to 180°C/350°F/gas 4. Spread almonds in baking tray. Bake almonds for 10-15 minutes until browned, stirring occasionally. Cool; set aside.

11 Chill meringue layers in freezer for about 30 minutes for easier handling. Place half of the coffee ice cream in refrigerator to soften slightly, about 30 minutes.

12 On freezerproof cake plate, place 1 meringue layer; spread with softened ice cream (see Box, page 226).

13 Place meringue with ice cream in freezer until firm, about 30 minutes. Meanwhile, place remaining coffee ice cream in refrigerator to soften.

14 Remove meringue with ice cream from freezer. Top with second meringue layer (see Box, page 226).

15 Quickly and evenly spread with remaining ice cream; place remaining meringue layer on top. Return to freezer until completely frozen, at least 4 hours.

16 In bowl, whip double or whipping cream with icing sugar and coffee liqueur until stiff peaks form.

17 Ice frozen dessert with whipped cream (see Box, page 226). Evenly sprinkle toasted almonds on top of whipped cream.

Sprinkling toasted almonds on top of frozen dessert

18 Return dessert to freezer; when whipped cream has hardened, cover. Keep in freezer until ready to serve.

Ridged effect on whipped cream is made by drawing a serrated icing spreader round side of cake

TO SERVE
Leave cake to stand at room temperature for about 10 minutes for easier slicing.

AMERICAN ICED DRINKS

VELVET HAMMER

 4 servings
Make just before serving

600 ml/1 pint vanilla ice cream, slightly softened

2 tablespoons orange liqueur

2 tablespoons brandy

Orange wedges and curls (see Citrus Curls, page 62) to decorate

1 In food processor or blender on medium speed, blend all ingredients just until smooth. Do not overblend; mixture should be thick.

2 Pour immediately into chilled wine glasses for sipping; decorate each serving with orange wedge and curls.

STRAWBERRY SODA

 6-8 servings
Make just before serving

300 ml/ ½ pint milk

300 g/10 oz frozen sliced strawberries, partially thawed

600 ml/1 pint strawberry ice cream

450 ml/ ¾ pint soda water or fizzy strawberry drink, chilled

Velvet Hammer looks coolly elegant with orange wedge and curl on rim of glass

1 In food processor or blender on high speed, blend milk and strawberries for 15 seconds until smooth. Pour into 5 tall glasses.

2 Add scoop of strawberry ice cream to each; slowly add soda or fizzy drink to fill almost to top. Serve immediately.

Strawberry Soda is topped with scoop of strawberry ice cream

Milk and strawberries are blended to a very smooth consistency

DECORATIONS FOR ICED DRINKS

A pretty decoration on top of an iced drink, or arranged on the rim of the glass, adds greatly to its appeal. Sprigs of fresh herbs and fruit slices go well with fruity drinks, while chocolate 'coffee beans' taste good with chocolate- and coffee-flavoured drinks.

Mint sprig

Star fruit slice

Chocolate 'coffee beans'

BLACK COW

1 serving

Make just before serving

150 ml/ ¼ pint root beer or cola, chilled

Scoop of vanilla ice cream

1 Into chilled tall glass, pour chilled root beer or cola.

2 Top with generous scoop of slightly softened vanilla ice cream. Serve immediately with straw and long-handled spoon.

Black Cow, a very popular soft drink in America, is a dark soda, root beer or chocolate drink with white ice cream floating on top

Scoop of slightly softened ice cream makes a delicious froth on the top of root beer or cola

MOCHA FLOAT

1 serving

Make just before serving

1 teaspoon drinking chocolate powder

¾ teaspoon instant coffee powder

½ teaspoon caster sugar

Soda water, chilled

2 small scoops of chocolate ice cream

1 In 300 ml/ ½ pint glass, combine first 3 ingredients. Gradually add enough soda to fill glass three-quarters full; stir vigorously until sugar is dissolved.

2 Add chocolate ice cream; stir. Serve with spoon and straw.

Chocolate ice cream tops this coffee- and chocolate-flavoured drink

FLORIDA FRUIT CUPS

12 servings
Allow 20 minutes preparation, plus freezing time

600 ml/1 pint plain yogurt

3 tablespoons liquid honey

Grated zest of 1 small lemon

300 g/10 oz assorted fresh fruit (halved strawberries, chopped peaches, chopped nectarines, blueberries or raspberries)

Decoration: lemon leaves, halved strawberries, blueberries, raspberries and nectarine wedges

1 Place fluted paper cake cases in each of 12 holes in deep bun tin.

2 Into large bowl, pour yogurt; add honey and grated lemon zest (honey prevents yogurt from crystallizing in freezer). With wire whisk, mix until blended. Gently stir in 175 g/6 oz fruit.

3 Spoon fruit and yogurt mixture into paper cake cases; top with remaining fruit (some fruit will stay above mixture for pretty colour).

4 Cover bun tin; freeze until firm, about 3 hours.

5 With your fingers, carefully peel off paper cake cases from dessert.

Ridges from paper cases look attractive

6 Leave fruit cups to stand at room temperature for 10-15 minutes to soften slightly for easier eating.

TO SERVE
Decorate each serving with lemon leaves, strawberry halves, blueberries, raspberries and nectarine wedges.

RASPBERRY ARCTIC ROLL

8 servings
Allow 2 ½ hours preparation, plus freezing time

100 g/3 ½ oz self-raising flour

120 g/4 oz caster sugar

15 g/ ½ oz cocoa powder plus extra for sprinkling

4 eggs

300 ml/ ½ pint Cornish dairy ice cream

300 ml/ ½ pint raspberry or strawberry ice cream

1 Preheat oven to 220°C/425°F/gas 7. Line 33 x 23 cm/ 13 x 9 inch Swiss roll tin with non-stick baking parchment.

2 In small bowl, stir flour, 60 g/2 oz sugar and 15 g/ ½ oz cocoa powder until evenly blended; set aside.

3 In large bowl, with electric mixer, beat eggs with remaining sugar until thick and lemon-coloured, occasionally scraping bowl with rubber spatula.

4 With wire whisk or rubber spatula, gently fold flour mixture into egg mixture.

5 Spoon mixture into tin, spreading evenly. Bake for about 12 minutes until top of cake springs back when lightly touched with finger.

6 Sprinkle clean tea towel with cocoa. When cake is done, immediately turn out on to towel. Carefully peel baking parchment from cake. If you like, cut off crisp edges. Starting at 1 narrow end, roll cake with towel, Swiss roll fashion. Place cake roll, seam side down, on wire rack; cool completely.

7 Place ice creams in refrigerator to soften slightly, about 30 minutes. Carefully unroll cooled cake; with palette knife, spread half of the cake crossways with one flavour ice cream; evenly spread other half of the cake with remaining flavour ice cream.

8 Starting at same narrow end, roll cake without towel.

9 Place rolled cake, seam side down, on long freezerproof platter. Cover and freeze cake until firm, at least 4 hours.

TO SERVE
Leave arctic roll to stand at room temperature for 15 minutes for easier slicing.

LEMON ICE IN LEMON CUPS

6 servings
Allow 45 minutes preparation, plus freezing time

6 large lemons

1 tablespoon powdered gelatine

200 g/7 oz caster sugar

Lemons are cut lengthways to make deep cup shapes

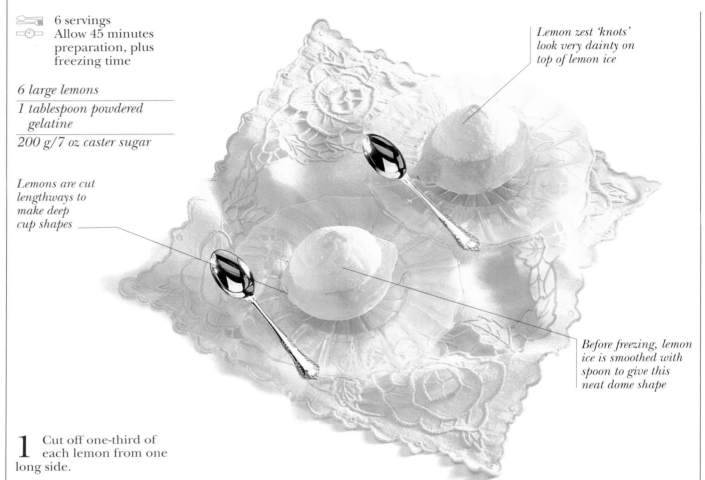

Lemon zest 'knots' look very dainty on top of lemon ice

Before freezing, lemon ice is smoothed with spoon to give this neat dome shape

1 Cut off one-third of each lemon from one long side.

2 With canelle knife, remove 6 strips of zest from cut off pieces of lemons. Wrap; refrigerate for decoration. Grate remaining zest from cut off pieces of lemons; set aside.

3 Squeeze 175 ml/ 6 fl oz juice from bottom pieces of lemons. Remove all crushed pulp and membrane.

4 Cut thin slice off base of each lemon cup so it can stand level. Place lemon cups in polythene bag; refrigerate until ready to fill.

5 In medium saucepan, with wire whisk, mix gelatine and sugar; stir in *550 ml/18 fl oz water*. Leave to stand for 1 minute to soften gelatine slightly. Cook over medium heat, stirring constantly, until gelatine completely dissolves. Remove saucepan from heat; stir in grated lemon zest and juice.

6 Pour lemon mixture into 23 cm/9 inch baking tin; cover with foil or cling film. Freeze until partially frozen, about 2 hours, stirring occasionally.

7 Spoon lemon mixture into chilled large bowl; with electric mixer, beat mixture until smooth but still frozen.

8 Return mixture to baking tin; cover and freeze until partially frozen, about 2 hours. Spoon mixture into chilled large bowl; beat again as before. Cover and freeze until firm.

9 With spoon, fill lemon cups with lemon ice.

10 Tie each strip of reserved lemon zest into loose knot; use to decorate top of each lemon ice. Serve immediately or freeze to serve later. If not serving on same day, when filled cups have hardened, wrap and return to freezer.

ITALIAN TARTUFO

6 servings
Allow 2 ¾ hours preparation, plus final freezing time

900 ml/1 ½ pints vanilla ice cream

6 amaretti biscuits

2 tablespoons almond liqueur or orange juice

175 g/6 oz plain chocolate, broken into pieces

45 g/1 ½ oz butter

1 tablespoon golden syrup

90 g/3 oz walnut pieces, toasted

1 Place ice cream in refrigerator to soften slightly. Chill small baking sheet in freezer.

2 Meanwhile, place amaretti biscuits on plate; pour over almond liqueur or orange juice. Leave to stand until liqueur is absorbed, turning biscuits occasionally.

3 Line chilled baking sheet with non-stick baking parchment. Working quickly, with large ice cream scoop, scoop a ball of ice cream. Gently press an amaretti into centre.

4 Reshape ice cream into ball around amaretti; place on lined baking sheet. Repeat with remaining ice cream and amaretti to make 6 ice cream balls. Freeze until firm, about 1 ½ hours.

5 In bowl over pan of gently simmering water, heat chocolate pieces, butter and golden syrup, stirring frequently, until melted and smooth. Remove bowl from pan.

6 Remove baking sheet with ice cream balls from freezer.

7 Place 1 ice cream ball on metal spatula over bowl of melted chocolate. With large metal spoon, quickly scoop up melted chocolate and pour over ice cream ball to coat completely.

8 Place chocolate-coated ice cream ball on same baking sheet. Firmly pat some walnuts on to chocolate coating.

9 Repeat with remaining ice cream balls, chocolate mixture and nuts. Freeze until ice cream balls are firm, about 1 hour.

10 If not serving on same day, wrap ice cream balls with foil; return to freezer to use within 1 week.

TO SERVE
Leave ice cream balls to stand at room temperature for about 10 minutes to soften slightly for easier eating.

Toasted walnuts are pressed on to chocolate coating before ice cream ball is frozen, so they will be secure for serving

ICE CREAM BOMBE

8-10 servings
Allow 3 hours preparation, plus final freezing time

3 eggs

90 g/3 oz caster sugar, warmed

75 g/2 ½ oz self-raising flour

15 g/ ½ oz cocoa powder

300 ml/ ½ pint strawberry ice cream

600 ml/1 pint vanilla ice cream

3 tablespoons coffee liqueur (optional)

1 x 425 g/15 oz can stoned black cherries, drained

300 ml/ ½ pint chocolate ice cream

Chocolate Bow and Ribbon Streamers (see Box, right)

60 g/2 oz desiccated coconut

120 g/4 oz icing sugar, sifted

120 g/4 oz butter, softened

¼ teaspoon vanilla essence

1 Preheat oven to 220°C/425°F/gas 7. Lightly grease 33 x 23 cm/ 13 x 9 inch Swiss roll tin and line with non-stick baking parchment.

2 In large bowl, with electric mixer, beat eggs and caster sugar until very thick and lemon-coloured. Sift over flour and cocoa powder; with large metal spoon, fold into egg mixture. Spoon mixture into tin, spreading evenly. Bake for 10 minutes or until top of cake springs back when lightly touched with finger. Immediately turn cake out on to wire rack; peel off baking parchment and leave cake to cool.

3 Place both strawberry and vanilla ice creams in refrigerator to soften slightly.

4 Line medium bowl with cling film. Cut chocolate cake into pieces to line bowl, keeping large piece aside for top; trim pieces of cake to fit, if necessary and press trimmings into gaps. Brush cake with coffee liqueur.

5 Spoon half of the strawberry ice cream into cake-lined bowl. Spoon one-quarter of vanilla ice cream in dollops on to strawberry ice cream. Scatter one-quarter of cherries between vanilla ice cream dollops.

6 Repeat with remaining strawberry ice cream, one-quarter of vanilla ice cream and one-quarter of cherries; press down mixture to eliminate air pockets. Place bowl in freezer to harden ice cream slightly, about 20 minutes.

DECORATION FOR ICE CREAM BOMBE

The bow and ribbon streamers on the Ice Cream Bombe (page 235) add a professional touch to the finished dessert, yet they are simple to make. If you use white marzipan or almond paste rather than yellow, you will get a better 'chocolate' colour.

Chocolate Bow and Ribbon Streamers

Knead *2 teaspoons sifted cocoa powder* into *120 g/ 4 oz marzipan* or *almond paste* until evenly blended. If mixture seems very dry, lightly dampen hands, but do not use too much water or paste will be too sticky to roll.

Sift *a very little extra cocoa powder* on to work surface; with rolling pin, roll out paste to 20 x 11 cm/ 8 x 4 ½ inch rectangle.

Trim edges; cut paste into 8 long strips of equal width. Use 5 strips for ribbon streamers; cut ends on the diagonal. Arrange on bombe, some full length and some shorter. Make loops with remaining strips; place on top of bombe to resemble bow.

7 Meanwhile, place chocolate ice cream in refrigerator to soften slightly, and return remaining vanilla ice cream to freezer.

8 Remove bowl from freezer. Repeat layering as for strawberry ice cream, but use chocolate ice cream with remaining vanilla ice cream and cherries.

9 Place reserved chocolate cake on top of chocolate ice cream, pressing cake down firmly against ice cream. Cover bowl with freezer film; place bowl in freezer until ice cream is firm, at least 4 hours.

10 Prepare Chocolate Bow and Ribbon Streamers.

Spooning vanilla ice cream over chocolate ice cream in bowl

11 Heat grill. Evenly sprinkle coconut in baking tray; grill for 3 minutes or until lightly toasted, stirring frequently. Set aside.

12 Prepare butter cream: in medium bowl, with electric mixer, beat icing sugar, butter and *2 teaspoons hot water* until light and fluffy, scraping bowl often with rubber spatula. Beat in vanilla essence until smooth.

13 Remove ice cream cake from freezer. Turn cake out on to chilled freezerproof cake stand or platter; remove cling film. With palette knife, thinly spread butter cream over cake, covering a small area at a time and immediately pressing toasted coconut on to butter cream.

14 Continue until cake is completely covered with butter cream and toasted coconut. Decorate cake with chocolate bow and ribbon streamers. Keep cake in freezer until ready to serve

---

TO SERVE
Leave cake to stand at room temperature for 20 minutes for easier slicing.

When Ice Cream Bombe is cut, it reveals its pretty coloured layers of cake, ice cream and cherries

MELON SORBET

🍴 6 -8 servings
⏲ Allow 15 minutes preparation, plus freezing time

1 ripe gallia, charentais or cantaloupe melon (800 g/1 ¾ lb)

Juice of ½ lemon

4 egg whites

100 g/3 ½ oz caster sugar

1 Remove and discard rind and seeds from melon; cut melon into chunks. In food processor, blend melon chunks and lemon juice until smooth.

2 Turn blended melon and lemon mixture into 1.7 litre/3 pint rigid freezer container and level surface; place in freezer until mixture is just beginning to set round edges.

3 In large bowl, with electric mixer on full speed, beat egg whites until soft peaks form.

4 Into beaten egg whites, gradually sprinkle caster sugar, 1 tablespoon at a time, beating well after each addition until sugar completely dissolves and whites stand in stiff, glossy peaks.

5 Return partially frozen melon mixture to food processor; blend until mixture is broken down. Fold in beaten egg whites until evenly blended. Return melon mixture to rigid container; cover and freeze until firm, about 3 hours.

6 Leave sorbet to stand at room temperature for 10 minutes for easier scooping.

For this attractive presentation, different-sized scoops of sorbet were placed on chilled baking sheet lined with non-stick baking parchment and put in freezer to harden; they were then lifted off and piled on top of each other

Colourful wedges of melon are arranged like spokes of a wheel round edge of serving bowl

TWO MELON GRANITA

WATERMELON ICE

🍴 8 servings
⏱ Allow 20 minutes preparation, plus final freezing time

1 x 900 g/2 lb piece watermelon

15 g/ ½ oz icing sugar, sifted

1 ½ teaspoons lemon juice

1 Remove and discard rind and seeds from watermelon; cut watermelon flesh into bite-sized chunks. In food processor, blend half of the watermelon chunks with icing sugar and lemon juice until smooth.

2 Pour watermelon mixture into rigid freezer container. Blend remaining watermelon chunks until smooth. Stir into mixture in container. Cover with lid; freeze until partially frozen, about 2 hours, stirring occasionally.

3 Return partially frozen watermelon mixture to food processor; blend until mixture is broken down. Return mixture to rigid container; cover and freeze until firm, about 3 hours.

4 Leave ice to stand at room temperature for about 10 minutes to soften slightly. Then, with spoon, scrape across surface of ice to create fine 'snow-like' texture; spoon into dessert dishes.

'Snow-like' texture is made by scraping spoon across surface of water ice when removing it from container for serving

🍴 8 servings
⏱ Allow 30 minutes preparation, plus freezing time

200 g/7 oz caster sugar

4 tablespoons lemon juice

1 ripe charentais or gallia melon (about 900 g/2 lb)

1 ripe honeydew melon (about 900 g/2 lb)

1 In small saucepan over high heat, bring sugar and *500 ml/16 fl oz water* to the boil. Reduce heat to medium; cook for 5 minutes. Remove saucepan from heat; stir in lemon juice.

2 Remove and discard rind and seeds from charentais or gallia melon; cut flesh into chunks. In food processor or blender, blend melon flesh until smooth; pour into rigid freezer container.

3 Repeat with honeydew melon; pour into another rigid freezer container.

4 Pour half of the sugar mixture into each rigid container; stir until well mixed. Cover with lids; freeze melon mixtures until firm, about 5 hours, stirring occasionally so mixtures freeze evenly.

5 Leave granitas to stand at room temperature for about 10 minutes to soften slightly.

6 With spoon, scrape across surface of granitas to create pebbly texture.

7 Spoon some charentais granita and some honeydew granita into each of 8 chilled dessert bowls.

RASPBERRY SORBET

8 servings
Allow 20 minutes preparation, plus freezing time

2 x 250 g/8.8 oz packets frozen raspberries

120 g/4 oz caster sugar

1 tablespoon powdered gelatine

4 tablespoons golden syrup, dissolved in 4 tablespoons hot water

5 tablespoons raspberry liqueur

3 tablespoons lemon juice

Kiwi fruit, papaya and fresh raspberries

1 Sprinkle raspberries with sugar; set aside to thaw.

2 In small saucepan, evenly sprinkle gelatine over 250 ml/ 8 fl oz water, allow to stand for 1 minute to soften. Cook over medium heat until gelatine completely dissolves, stirring often. Remove saucepan from heat.

3 Over large bowl, with back of spoon, press and scrape raspberries with their syrup firmly against medium-mesh sieve to purée; discard pips left in sieve.

4 Stir golden syrup, liqueur and lemon juice into raspberry purée, then stir in dissolved gelatine, a little at a time, until well mixed.

Adding dissolved gelatine to raspberry mixture

5 Pour raspberry mixture into rigid freezer container. Freeze until partially frozen, about 2 hours, stirring occasionally.

6 Transfer partially frozen raspberry mixture to food processor; blend until mixture is broken down. Return mixture to rigid container; cover and freeze until firm, about 3 hours.

7 Arrange some kiwi fruit, papaya and fresh raspberries on individual plates. Place small scoops of sorbet next to fruit.

Slices of peeled papaya and kiwi fruit add extra colour to individual servings of sorbet

SERVING SORBET AND ICE CREAM

For an attractive presentation, sorbet and ice cream look best served in scoops. For easy serving, with ice cream scoop, take balls of sorbet or ice cream from container and place on chilled baking sheet lined with non-stick baking parchment.

Immediately place baking sheet in freezer; leave until sorbet or ice cream hardens. To serve, lift scoops off parchment and place on dessert plates or in dishes at last minute.

FUDGE SUNDAE PIE

 8-10 servings

Allow about 3 hours preparation, plus freezing time

120 g/4 oz digestive biscuits, finely crushed

60 g/2 oz walnut pieces, finely chopped

60 g/ 2 oz soft brown sugar

90 g/3 oz butter, softened

600 ml/1 pint vanilla ice cream

175 g/6 oz caster sugar

45 g/1 ½ oz cocoa powder

450 ml/ ¾ pint double or whipping cream

600 ml/1 pint chocolate or coffee ice cream

Chocolate Curls (page 104) to decorate

1 Preheat oven to 200°C/400°F/gas 6. In shallow 23 cm/9 inch pie dish, with hand, mix biscuits, walnuts, brown sugar and 75 g/2 ½ oz butter. Press mixture on to bottom and up side of pie dish. Bake for 8 minutes. Cool crust on wire rack.

2 Meanwhile, place vanilla ice cream in refrigerator to soften slightly.

3 With rubber spatula or palette knife, evenly spread softened vanilla ice cream in crust; freeze until firm, about 1 ½ hours.

4 In non-stick saucepan over medium heat, place 150 g/5 oz caster sugar, cocoa powder, 125 ml/4 fl oz double or whipping cream and remaining butter. Bring to the boil, stirring constantly until smooth. Remove saucepan from heat. Cool fudge sauce to room temperature.

5 Over vanilla ice cream layer in biscuit crust, pour fudge sauce.

6 Return pie to freezer; freeze until fudge sauce hardens, about 30 minutes.

7 Remove chocolate or coffee ice cream from container to medium bowl; leave to stand at room temperature, stirring occasionally, until a smooth spreading consistency (but not melted). Spread chocolate or coffee ice cream over fudge layer; return pie to freezer.

8 In small bowl, whip remaining double or whipping cream with remaining caster sugar until stiff peaks form.

9 With palette knife, spread whipped cream smoothly and evenly over pie.

10 Decorate pie with chocolate curls.

11 Return pie to freezer, uncovered; freeze until firm, about 3 hours. If not serving pie same day, wrap frozen pie with foil and freeze until ready to serve.

TO SERVE
Let pie stand at room temperature 15 minutes for easier slicing.

Spreading whipped cream over pie

TWO-TONE GRANITAS

COFFEE

 6 servings
Allow 10 minutes preparation, plus freezing time

60 g/2 oz caster sugar

4 tablespoons instant coffee powder

1 In medium saucepan over high heat, bring sugar, coffee powder and *750 ml/1 ¼ pints water* to the boil, stirring occasionally. Reduce heat to medium; cook for 5 minutes.

2 Pour mixture into rigid freezer container.

3 Cool mixture. Cover with container lid; freeze until firm, about 5 hours, stirring occasionally.

TO SERVE
Leave granitas to stand at room temperature for 10 minutes to soften slightly. Then, with spoon, scrape across surface of granitas to create pebbly texture; spoon into tall glasses, alternating layers.

LEMON

 6 servings
Allow 15 minutes preparation, plus freezing time

200 g/7 oz caster sugar

4 large lemons

1 In medium saucepan over high heat, bring sugar and *500 ml/16 fl oz water* to the boil, stirring occasionally. Reduce heat to medium; cook for 5 minutes. Cool.

2 From lemons, grate 2 teaspoons zest and squeeze 175 ml/6 fl oz juice. Stir lemon zest and juice into cooled sugar syrup.

3 Pour mixture into freezer container.

4 Cover and freeze until firm, about 5 hours, stirring occasionally.

USEFUL INFORMATION AND BASIC RECIPES

241-259

DESSERTS

The recipes in this book fall into the following categories: mousses and soufflés, custards and creams, meringues, pancakes and crêpes, fruit desserts, puddings, cakes and gâteaux, cheese-cakes, fruit cakes, sweet pies, tarts and flans, pastries, hot fruit puddings, biscuits and cookies, and frozen desserts. Within each category the recipes range from simple everyday desserts to classic dishes, and popular recipes calling for slightly more advanced techniques. On these two pages, you will find useful information on general dessert-making techniques.

USING GELATINE

Many desserts, such as mousses and cold soufflés, depend on gelatine to make them set. Gelatine is available as powder or leaf, and the two can be used interchangeably. To substitute leaf gelatine for powder, use 2 leaves for each 7 g/ ¼ oz powdered gelatine (1 tablespoon).

DISSOLVING GELATINE

For properly set, jellied mixtures, gelatine must be dissolved completely in hot liquid such as water, milk or fruit juice in a bowl or saucepan; no visible bits of gelatine should remain in the mixture or they will spoil its clarity and/or smoothness.

Constant stirring is essential to make sure gelatine is completely dissolved.

Gelatine granules that splash up the side of bowl or saucepan are difficult to dissolve, so always stir mixture steadily but not too vigorously.

For best results, powdered gelatine should not be added directly to hot liquid. The granules could lump together and not dissolve completely, and could then spoil the dessert.

Leaf gelatine should always be soaked in water to soften it, then squeezed out before being added to hot liquid.

To check powdered gelatine has dissolved completely: *run rubber spatula through mixture, next to side of pan or bowl, to see if granules are all dissolved*

TURNING OUT GELATINE DESSERTS

Individual desserts set with gelatine can be turned out right on to dessert plates for serving. Turn out large desserts on to serving platter (moisten platter first so that if dessert comes out off-centre on platter, it can be moved easily to centre).

- Fill sink or large basin with warm, not hot, water.

- Carefully loosen edges of dessert from mould with palette knife.

- Dip mould into warm water just to rim for about 10 seconds. Be careful not to melt dessert.

- Lift mould out of water and shake it gently to loosen dessert.

- Invert serving platter on top of mould.

- Quickly invert mould and platter together; gently lift off mould.

ADDING INGREDIENTS TO GELATINE

In most recipes, a gelatine mixture should be partially set before other ingredients are added, or solid ingredients such as sliced fruit might sink to the bottom, and whipped cream could lose its volume by the time it is thoroughly blended in. When solids are to be added, gelatine mixture should have thickened to consistency of unbeaten egg white. This partially thickened stage allows for even distribution of solids. When adding whipped cream, chill mixture slightly longer, until it mounds when dropped from spoon.

If gelatine mixture thickens too much before other ingredients are folded in or it is turned into a mould, place bowl of mixture in hot water and stir occasionally for 1 minute or less to melt gelatine. Then chill mixture again, stirring occasionally.

CHILLING GELATINE DESSERTS

In order to set, a gelatine mixture must be chilled. Stir mixture occasionally while it chills, so that it cools and thickens evenly. For faster thickening, place saucepan or bowl containing mixture in larger bowl of iced water. Stir mixture often until it reaches desired consistency. Or place saucepan or bowl in freezer and stir often until mixture is of desired consistency. Do not leave mixture in freezer until it sets; ice crystals will form and make mixture watery, spoiling the dessert.

To test consistency of gelatine mixture: *take up spoonful of mixture and drop it on top. It should 'mound', not disappear*

EGGS: HANDLE WITH CARE

Raw or undercooked eggs may pose a risk of salmonellosis, food poisoning caused by salmonella bacteria found in some eggs. While this risk is extremely small, it does exist, so it is a good idea to follow some simple rules. When making a custard, be sure that the eggs are cooked and the custard thickened properly, but do not allow the custard to boil or it will curdle. Proper storage and cooking of eggs and handling of egg-rich foods is necessary to prevent growth of potentially harmful bacteria. For safety first, take these precautions.

• Buy only clean, uncracked eggs from a reputable source.

• Don't buy too many eggs at a time; buy only as many as you need.

• When you bring eggs home, put them a cool place or in the refrigerator as soon as possible.

• Keep eggs in their box, pointed ends downwards.

• Use eggs within 1 week of purchase.

• To test an egg for freshness: place in a bowl of cold water; if it begins to float, it is not fresh.

• If an egg is fresh, its white will not be runny.

• If a speck of yolk gets into egg whites while separating eggs, use a spoon, not the egg shell, to remove it. The egg shell might not be clean.

• Serve eggs and egg-rich foods as soon as they are cooked; or, if you've made them ahead, refrigerate them at once and use within 3 days.

• The following, in particular, are advised not to eat raw or undercooked eggs:
  a) elderly whose immune systems are weakened with age
  b) infants whose immune systems are not yet fully developed
  c) pregnant women
  d) anyone with an immune system weakened by disease or anticancer treatments.

THICKENING WITH EGGS

Many different desserts use eggs as a thickening agent in the form of a custard. The key to successful custards is careful control of heat; too high a heat causes eggs to curdle, resulting in a lumpy, thin mixture. However, it is also important that the heat is high enough (see Eggs: Handle with Care, left).

For successful custards, always use a heavy, non-stick saucepan, or double boiler, and stir mixture constantly with a whisk until it thickens and coats a metal spoon well. Take care not to let mixture boil or it will curdle. Check thickness by lifting spoon from custard and holding it up for 15-20 seconds; if back of spoon does not show through it, custard has thickened to right consistency.

To test consistency of custard: *lift spoon from pan and hold it up for 15-20 seconds; back of spoon should not show through mixture*

HOT SOUFFLÉS

Raised high with beaten egg whites, light, fluffy, hot dessert soufflés need to be carefully timed since they should be served as soon as they are taken from the oven: they tend to collapse if left to stand for more than a few minutes. Both the basic sauce and the soufflé dish itself can be prepared well in advance. Don't open oven door before end of specified baking time; a rush of cold air into the oven could cause soufflé to collapse.

With wire whisk, gradually folding soufflé mixture into egg whites

With back of spoon, making 2.5 cm/1 inch indentation round top of soufflé for 'top hat' effect

MOUSSES

The light, creamy texture of a mousse comes from eggs, custard or whipped cream, or a combination of these, blended into melted chocolate, fruit purée or nuts.

To achieve a smooth, creamy texture, it is essential to fold and blend ingredients in as evenly as possible; for best results, use a wire whisk or rubber spatula when folding in or blending, and a 'figure of eight' action.

SAUCES

A repertoire of sweet sauces enables the cook to put a special finishing touch to a wide variety of desserts. On these pages you will find sauces to enhance the flavour and appeal of fresh, canned and frozen fruits; home-made or bought pastries, flans and cakes; frozen desserts; and bread and rice puddings.

Today's sauces aren't just poured over foods. They can be puddled on the plate or spooned round food to frame it like in a picture. More, sauces themselves can be decorated, with designs piped or stirred in; see Decorating with Sauces (pages 24-25) for ideas to copy or to spark your own imagination.

CHOCOLATE SAUCES

CHOCOLATE CREAM SAUCE

175 g/6 oz plain chocolate, broken into pieces

125 ml/4 fl oz golden syrup

4 tablespoons single cream

15 g/ ½ oz butter

1 In bowl over saucepan of gently simmering water, melt pieces of chocolate with golden syrup, stirring. Remove bowl from pan; stir in remaining ingredients.

2 Serve warm over profiteroles or ice cream.

CHOCOLATE RUM SAUCE

120 g/4 oz plain chocolate, broken into pieces

3 tablespoons caster sugar

30 g/1 oz butter

1 tablespoon rum

1 In non-stick saucepan over medium heat, bring *5 tablespoons water* to the boil with all the other ingredients, stirring. Reduce heat to medium-low; simmer, stirring, until mixture thickens and is smooth, about 3 minutes. Remove from heat; stir in rum.

2 Serve warm over bananas, ice cream or poached pears.

CHOCOLATE MARSHMALLOW SAUCE

60 g/2 oz plain chocolate, broken into pieces

100 g/3 ½ oz marshmallows, cut into small pieces

5 tablespoons double or whipping cream

5 tablespoons honey

1 In non-stick saucepan over low heat, cook chocolate, marshmallows, cream and honey, stirring, until both chocolate and marshmallows have melted.

2 Serve hot over bananas or ice cream.

CREAM AND CUSTARD SAUCES

CHANTILLY CREAM

300 ml/ ½ pint double or whipping cream

1-2 tablespoons caster sugar

½ teaspoon vanilla essence

1 In bowl, with whisk, rotary beater or electric mixer, whip cream with sugar and vanilla essence until soft peaks form. (Over-whipping causes cream to curdle and turn to butter.)

2 On hot days, chill bowl and beaters. Serve cream on fruit or nut pies or ice cream sundaes.

Brandy Chantilly Cream
Whip cream with sugar as above until soft peaks form; fold in *2 tablespoons brandy*.

Chocolate Chantilly Cream
Place *2 tablespoons drinking chocolate powder* (or 2 tablespoons caster sugar and 2 tablespoons cocoa powder) in bowl; add 300 ml/ ½ pint double or whipping cream. Whip as above.

Coffee Chantilly Cream
Place *2 teaspoons instant coffee powder* and 2 tablespoons caster sugar in bowl; add 300 ml/ ½ pint double or whipping cream. Whip as above.

CUSTARD SAUCE

3 tablespoons caster sugar

450 ml/ ¾ pint milk

1 egg yolk

1 tablespoon cornflour

½ teaspoon vanilla essence

1 In heavy non-stick saucepan, combine all ingredients except vanilla essence. Cook over medium heat, stirring, until mixture coats back of spoon well, about 15 minutes (do not boil or custard will curdle).

2 Remove from heat; stir in vanilla essence. Chill. Serve with fruit pies and crumbles, fruit tarts and flans and poached or stewed fruit.

EGG CUSTARD SAUCE

4 egg yolks

5 tablespoons caster sugar

450 ml/ ¾ pint milk

1 teaspoon vanilla essence

1 In heavy non-stick saucepan over low heat, or in double boiler over hot, not boiling, water, with wire whisk, stir egg yolks and sugar.

2 Gradually add milk and cook, stirring, until mixture thickens and coats back of spoon well, about 25 minutes (do not boil or custard will curdle). Stir in vanilla essence. Serve warm or cold with apple or other fruit pies, or with poached or stewed fruit.

SUGAR SAUCES

BUTTERSCOTCH SAUCE

225 g/8 oz light soft brown sugar

125 ml/4 fl oz single cream

30 g/1 oz butter

2 tablespoons golden syrup

1 In non-stick saucepan over medium heat, heat brown sugar, single cream, butter and golden syrup just to boiling point, stirring occasionally.

2 Serve warm over vanilla or rum and raisin ice cream, or with baked custard.

HOT FUDGE SAUCE

300 g/10 oz caster sugar

125 ml/4 fl oz milk

5 tablespoons golden syrup

60 g/2 oz plain chocolate, broken into pieces

15 g/ ½ oz butter

1 teaspoon vanilla essence

1 In non-stick saucepan over medium heat, bring first 4 ingredients to the boil, stirring constantly. Set sugar thermometer in place and continue boiling, stirring occasionally, until temperature reaches 109°C/ 228°F or until small amount of mixture dropped from tip of spoon back into mixture spins 5 mm/¼ inch thread.

2 Remove from heat; stir in butter and vanilla essence. Serve hot over vanilla ice cream or poached pears.

CARAMEL SAUCE

30 g/1 oz butter

2 tablespoons plain flour

450 ml/ ¾ pint single cream

165 g/5 ½ oz light soft brown sugar

150 g/5 oz caster sugar

1 In medium saucepan over medium heat, melt butter; stir in flour.

2 Gradually stir in cream; cook, stirring constantly, until mixture thickens.

3 Stir in brown and caster sugars. Serve warm or cover and refrigerate to serve cold; serve over baked bananas or apples, or vanilla or chocolate ice cream.

PRALINE SAUCE

225 g/8 oz light soft brown sugar

125 ml/4 fl oz golden syrup

15 g/ ½ oz butter

60 g/2 oz shelled pecan or walnut pieces, finely chopped

1 In small saucepan over medium heat, stir all ingredients, except nuts, with *2 tablespoons water* until sugar dissolves. Stir in nuts.

2 Serve hot over rice pudding, ice cream or waffles.

BRANDY BUTTER

120 g/4 oz icing sugar, sifted

90 g/3 oz butter, softened

2 tablespoons brandy

1 In medium bowl, with electric mixer, beat icing sugar with butter until creamy; beat in brandy.

2 Spoon into small bowl and refrigerate if not serving immediately. Serve with hot mince pies or Christmas pudding.

Deluxe Brandy Butter
Prepare as above; fold in *4 tablespoons double or whipping cream, whipped,* after brandy.

Rum Butter
Prepare as for Brandy Butter, but using *rum* instead of brandy.

FRUIT SAUCES

BLACKBERRY SAUCE

600 g/1 ¼ lb fresh or frozen blackberries

120 g/4 oz caster sugar

2 tablespoons lemon juice

1 In medium saucepan over medium heat, heat berries, sugar and lemon juice, stirring occasionally, until hot and bubbly. Work through sieve. Cover; chill.

2 Serve over ice cream and other fruits.

CHERRY SAUCE

450 g/1 lb cherries, stoned

4 tablespoons caster sugar

1 In medium saucepan over medium heat, in *150 ml/ ¼ pint water*, bring cherries to the boil.

2 Reduce heat to low; cover pan and simmer cherries for about 5 minutes or until tender.

3 During last minute of cooking, add sugar. Serve hot, poured over pancakes; or serve cold over ice cream or creamy puddings.

PEACH SAUCE

1 x 400 g/14 oz can peaches in natural juice

¼ teaspoon almond essence

1 In food processor or blender, blend ingredients together until smooth.

2 Serve over ice cream.

RASPBERRY SAUCE

300 g/10 oz raspberries

1 tablespoon caster sugar

1 In food processor or blender, blend raspberries and sugar until smooth, adding *a little water* if needed to thin sauce.

2 Press sauce through fine sieve with wooden spoon to remove pips. Serve with peaches or strawberries, or over ice cream.

COMPOTE SAUCE

3 large nectarines

3 large plums

125 ml/4 fl oz orange juice

100 g/3 ½ oz caster sugar

2 tablespoons brandy

1 Cut fruit into wedges, discarding stones.

2 In medium saucepan over low heat, cook fruit and juice for 10 minutes or until tender, stirring occasionally. Remove from heat.

3 Add sugar and brandy; stir until sugar is dissolved. Serve over vanilla ice cream.

MAPLE AND ORANGE SAUCE

1 x 325 g/11 oz can mandarin orange segments, drained and chopped

175 ml/6 fl oz maple syrup

30 g/1 oz butter

1 In medium saucepan over low heat, heat all ingredients until hot and butter melts.

2 Serve warm over pancakes, French toast or ice cream sundaes.

MELBA SAUCE

75 g/2 ½ oz redcurrant jelly

300 g/10 oz raspberries

30 g/1 oz icing sugar, sifted

Juice of 1 lemon

1 In small saucepan over low heat, heat redcurrant jelly until melted.

2 In food processor, blend raspberries, melted redcurrant jelly, icing sugar and lemon juice until smooth. Press through sieve.

3 Serve over ice cream or poached peaches or pears.

ORANGE SAUCE

60 g/2 oz butter

175 g/6 oz icing sugar, sifted

5 tablespoons orange juice

2 tablespoons grated orange zest

1 In small saucepan over low heat, melt butter. Stir in icing sugar, orange juice and orange zest.

2 Cook over low heat, stirring frequently, until heated through. Serve over pancakes.

CAKES

The cake recipes in this book generally follow one of two basic methods. Most contain butter or soft margarine and are mixed and beaten in one bowl. Others, such as sponges, roulades and angel cakes, have beaten egg whites folded in at the end to give them a light and fluffy texture. Whichever type you bake, if you follow the directions given here you can be assured of success every time.

Before you start, read the recipe carefully and assemble all ingredients and equipment. Prepare tins, put oven racks in correct position, and preheat oven if necessary.

BEFORE YOU START

INGREDIENTS
In the recipes in this book size 3 eggs are used. Don't be tempted to substitute different ingredients for the ones given in the recipe; they will give different results.

MEASURING
Weigh and measure dry and liquid ingredients carefully. Spoon measures used in the recipes are metric spoons (1 tablespoon = 15 ml and 1 teaspoon = 5 ml). All spoon measures of dry ingredients are level.

TINS
Use shiny metal tins or tins with non-stick finish. Avoid old-fashioned tins with insulated bases. If using glass or porcelain-coated aluminium tins with a non-stick finish, reduce oven temperature by 10°C/25°F. Cake tins are available in round, square or rectangular shapes. Be sure your tins are the size and shape called for in the recipe. Measure the top inside of a tin for length, width or diameter; measure perpendicular inside for depth. Prepare tins according to recipe instructions (see How to Grease and Line Tins, page 248).

Springform tin: *has side section which can be removed without disturbing contents*

Angel cake or tube tin: *has centre tube; may or may not have removable bottom*

Swiss roll tin: *shallow rectangular tin, usually 2.5 cm/1 inch deep*

German Bundt or kugelhopf mould: *fluted, with centre tube; for elegant cakes and desserts*

STORING AND FREEZING CAKES

Storing
Sandwich cakes and ring cakes filled and/or iced with butter cream or glacé icing should be kept under an inverted bowl or tin to protect icing; store cakes filled and/or iced with butter cream in a cool place or the refrigerator, to prevent butter from becoming rancid.

Cakes covered with whipped cream or soft cheese icing, or those that have any sort of cream filling, should be kept refrigerated and are best eaten within 1-2 days.

Wrap rich fruit cakes closely and store in airtight containers in cool place; they will improve with storage. For very rich cakes, before storing, sprinkle cake with wine or brandy, or wrap in wine- or brandy-dampened cloth, then overwrap and store in airtight container for up to 2 months. Re-dampen cloth weekly with more wine or brandy, if you like. Ice or decorate cake just before serving.

Freezing
Cakes in the freezer make wonderful standby desserts. For freezer storage, all cakes must be wrapped or packaged in materials specifically designed for freezer use. Wrapping materials for foods must be moisture-proof: use heavy-duty freezer foil, freezer paper or freezer wrap. Secure packages with freezer or masking tape. Use waterproof felt-tip pens or markers for writing on labels, freezer tape or freezer paper.

Un-iced cakes should be closely wrapped in freezer paper, freezer wrap or foil, and securely sealed with tape.

Most cakes will keep in the freezer for 4-6 months, fruit cakes for up to 12 months.

Open freeze cakes iced and/or piped with butter cream or whipped cream on tray or sheet of card covered with foil until icing hardens, then place frozen cake in rigid container, seal and return to freezer. Iced cakes can be stored in the freezer for 2-3 months.

Do not freeze cakes which have either jam or fruit fillings; they can become soggy when thawed.

Never freeze uncooked cake mixture or cakes with fillings made with cornflour or flour.

Thaw un-iced cakes and fruit cakes in their freezer wrappings at room temperature. Un-iced cakes take about 1 hour to thaw, fruit cakes, 2-3 hours.

Cakes with butter cream and whipped cream icings should be carefully unpacked before they are thawed and placed on their serving plate so that their decoration will not be spoiled. Thaw in refrigerator for 3-4 hours and keep refrigerated until serving time. Be sure to cover and refrigerate leftovers.

MEASURING TINS

Be sure your tins are the kind and size specified in recipe. Measure top inside for length, width or diameter; measure perpendicular inside for depth.

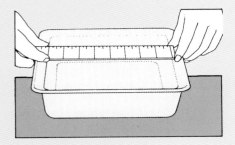

HOW TO GREASE AND LINE TINS

Make sure tins are size called for in recipe, and prepare them before you start mixing cake ingredients. Prepare tins according to instructions in individual recipes.

If tins are to be greased and floured, grease both bottom and sides with softened butter or margarine, using brush, crumpled greaseproof paper or kitchen paper. You can also grease tins with melted butter or margarine using pastry brush to grease evenly. Sprinkle tin with a little flour or, for dark-coloured cakes, with sifted cocoa powder so cake does not have white coating. Shake tin until coated, then invert it and tap to remove excess flour or cocoa. For fruit cakes, grease tins well, line with foil, then grease foil. Some recipes call for bottoms of tins to be lined with baking parchment; grease tin first, then parchment will stick to bottom.

Greasing tin: using brush, crumpled greaseproof paper or kitchen paper, spread tins evenly with melted butter or margarine

Lining tin: where specified, line bottom of greased tin with non-stick baking parchment

Flouring tin: in some recipes, tins are floured after greasing. Sprinkle with flour and shake and turn tin until evenly coated; knock out surplus

HOW TO BEAT MIXTURE

When preparing cake mixture, beat it with electric mixer for length of time specified in recipe. During beating, scrape bowl frequently with rubber spatula so that all cake ingredients are well mixed together. If you use a wooden spoon instead of mixer, you will need to give ingredients a very good beating until mixture is smooth and ingredients are blended thoroughly. Before adding large fruits and nuts to mixture, toss them in about 1 tablespoon of the measured flour, so that they do not sink in mixture.

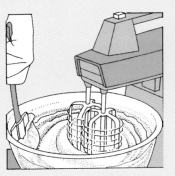

To beat mixture: beat with electric mixer for specified time, constantly scraping sides of bowl with rubber spatula to make sure ingredients are well mixed in

HOW TO FOLD IN

For cakes made with egg whites, beat egg whites into stiff peaks in bowl. In separate bowl, beat remaining ingredients according to recipe instructions. Using rubber spatula, gently fold egg whites into beaten mixture, cutting down through centre, across bottom and up side of bowl. Give bowl a quarter turn and repeat until mixture is uniformly blended, but do not overfold or egg whites will break down.

To fold mixture: use rubber spatula to fold egg whites into beaten ingredients

FILLING TINS

Pour mixture into prepared tin and tap tin sharply on work surface or cut through it several times with rubber spatula or knife to break any large air bubbles. Spread evenly with spatula.

For mixtures containing beaten egg white, push mixture into tin with rubber spatula. Smooth and level it very lightly, then cut through it with rubber spatula to break any large air bubbles.

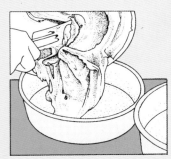

To fill tin: with rubber spatula, push mixture into tin, then smooth and level it very lightly

BASIC SANDWICH CAKE RECIPES

The cake recipes on this page provide a good basis for making a variety of different desserts at short notice. Sandwiched together with jam, lemon curd or fresh fruit and whipped cream – nothing could be more simple. The ingredients are carefully balanced, so follow instructions exactly for successful results every time.

VICTORIA SANDWICH

Made by the all-in-one method, this cake is a great stand-by for quick-and-easy desserts and party cakes.

175 g/6 oz soft margarine

175 g/ 6 oz caster sugar

3 eggs, beaten

175 g/ 6 oz self-raising flour

1 rounded teaspoon baking powder

1 Preheat oven to 180°C/350°F/gas 4.

2 Grease bottoms of two 18 cm/7 inch straight-sided sandwich tins; line with non-stick baking parchment.

3 In large bowl, beat margarine, sugar, eggs, flour and baking powder for about 2 minutes or until mixture is smooth and all ingredients are thoroughly blended.

4 Divide mixture evenly between prepared tins and smooth tops. Bake for 25-30 minutes or until cake is pale golden and centre springs back when lightly pressed with finger.

5 Turn cakes out on to wire rack. Carefully peel off baking parchment; leave cakes to cool.

Orange or Lemon Sandwich
To creamed mixture, add *finely grated zest of 1 orange or lemon.*

Chocolate Sandwich
In large bowl, blend *1 rounded tablespoon cocoa powder* with *2 tablespoons hot water.* Cool; add remaining cake ingredients and proceed as above.

Coffee Sandwich
Dissolve *1 heaped teaspoon instant coffee powder* in beaten eggs before adding to mixture.

WHISKED SPONGE

4 eggs

120 g/4 oz caster sugar

120 g/4 oz self-raising flour

1 Preheat oven to 190°C/375°F/gas 5. Grease bottoms of two 20 cm/8 inch straight-sided sandwich tins; line with non-stick baking parchment.

2 Put eggs and sugar in large bowl; beat with electric mixer until mixture is thick, white and creamy and leaves a thick ribbon trail. Sift in flour; carefully fold in with large metal spoon.

3 Divide mixture between tins. Bake for 20 minutes or until centres spring back when lightly pressed. Turn cakes out on to wire rack. Peel off parchment; leave cakes to cool.

CHOCOLATE CAKE

2 eggs

150 ml/ ¼ pint sunflower oil

150 ml/ ¼ pint milk

2 tablespoons golden syrup

150 g/5 oz caster sugar

190 g/6 ½ oz self-raising flour

30 g/1 oz cocoa powder, sifted

1 teaspoon baking powder

1 teaspoon bicarbonate of soda

1 Preheat oven to 170°C/325°F/gas 3. Grease bottoms of two 20 cm/8 inch straight-sided sandwich tins; line with non-stick baking parchment.

2 Break eggs into large bowl; add all other ingredients. Beat well for about 2 minutes or until mixture is smooth and all ingredients are thoroughly blended.

3 Divide mixture between tins. Bake for 30-35 minutes or until cakes shrink away slightly from sides of tins and wooden cocktail stick inserted in centres comes out clean.

4 Turn cakes out on to wire rack; cool, then peel off parchment.

When using electric mixer, occasionally scrape side of bowl with rubber spatula

To test if cake is done, insert wooden cocktail stick in centre – it should come out clean

ICINGS AND FROSTINGS

Most uncooked icings such as butter cream can be made in advance and stored until needed in a tightly covered container to prevent a crust forming on top. If they are refrigerated and become too firm to spread easily, leave them to stand at room temperature, or stir well to soften to spreading consistency.

Allow your cake to cool completely before icing or filling. Trim off any crisp edges with knife or kitchen scissors and brush away all loose crumbs. Keep cake plate clean by covering edges with strips of greaseproof paper. Lay cake on paper strips, placing it in centre of plate. After icing cake, carefully slide out paper strips. Cakes iced with soft cheese, soured cream or whipped cream icings should be refrigerated until served.

Recipes on this and the following page make enough to ice a 33 x 23 cm/13 x 9 inch cake or fill and ice a 20-23 cm/8-9 inch sandwich cake.

To ice cake: cover plate edges with strips of greaseproof paper; lay cake on strips

After icing, carefully slide out strips; if necessary, touch up base with icing

WHIPPED CREAM 'ICING'

450 ml/ ¾ pint double or whipping cream	In small bowl, with whisk or electric mixer, whip double or whipping cream with sugar until stiff peaks form; fold in vanilla essence, if you like. Keep iced cake refrigerated until ready to serve.
30 g/1 oz icing sugar, sifted	
1 teaspoon vanilla essence (optional)	

TECHNIQUES

Sandwich cake
Place one layer of cake, top side down, on serving plate. Cover this layer with either filling or icing, spreading it almost to edge. If filling is soft, spread it only to within 2.5 cm/1 inch of edge. Place second cake layer, top side up, on filling, so that flat bases of two layers face each other, keeping top layer from cracking or sliding off. Ice sides of cake thinly to set any loose crumbs, then apply second, more generous layer of icing, swirling it up to make 1 cm/½ inch ridge above rim of cake. Finally, ice top of cake, swirling icing or leaving it smooth, as you like. Decorate iced cake if desired.

Oblong cake
Ice top and sides of cake as for sandwich cake, or leave cake in tin and just ice top.

Tube or ring cake
Ice sides, then top and inside centre of cake as for sandwich cake.

Cup cakes
Dip top of each cake in icing, turning it slightly to coat evenly.

Glazing
Brush crumbs from top of cake. Spoon or pour glaze on to top of cake, letting it drip down sides. Spread thicker glazes over top and sides of cake with palette knife.

Drizzling
To make decorative pattern, pour thin icing or glaze from spoon, quickly waving spoon back and forth over cake.

Chocolate Whipped Cream 'Icing'
Prepare as left; fold in *2 tablespoons drinking chocolate powder*, instead of vanilla essence.

Coffee Whipped Cream 'Icing'
Prepare as left; add *1 teaspoon instant coffee powder* with sugar and omit vanilla essence.

Orange Whipped Cream 'Icing'
Prepare as left; add *1 teaspoon grated orange zest* and *½ teaspoon orange flower water* instead of vanilla essence.

Peppermint Whipped Cream 'Icing'
Whip cream as left; fold in *4 tablespoons crushed peppermints* or *seaside rock* and omit vanilla essence.

BUTTER CREAM

450 g/1 lb icing sugar, sifted	In large bowl, with electric mixer (or spoon), beat icing sugar and butter until smooth, adding a little milk if necessary until butter cream is smooth with an easy spreading consistency.
300 g/10 oz butter, softened	
A little milk	

Lemon Butter Cream
Prepare as for Butter Cream, but substitute *lemon juice* for milk.

Mocha Butter Cream
Prepare as for Butter Cream, but add *45 g/1 ½ oz cocoa powder*, substitute *cold black coffee* for milk.

CHOCOLATE SOURED CREAM ICING

175 g/6 oz plain chocolate, broken into pieces	**1** In bowl over saucepan of gently simmering water, heat chocolate and butter until melted and smooth, stirring occasionally. Remove bowl from pan.
15 g/ ½ oz butter	
150 ml/ ¼ pint soured cream	**2** In medium bowl, with electric mixer, beat melted chocolate mixture, soured cream and icing sugar until smooth.
30 g/1 oz icing sugar, sifted	

SOFT CHEESE ICING

175 g/6 oz full-fat soft cheese, softened	**1** In small bowl, with electric mixer, beat soft cheese and milk just until smooth.
2 tablespoons milk	
225 g/8 oz icing sugar, sifted	**2** Beat in icing sugar and vanilla essence until blended.
1 ½ teaspoons vanilla essence	

Coffee Soft Cheese Icing
Prepare as for Soft Cheese Icing, but add *4 teaspoons instant coffee powder* with icing sugar; omit vanilla essence.

COFFEE FUDGE ICING

90 g/3 oz butter	**1** In medium bowl, put butter, sifted icing sugar, milk and coffee essence.
225 g/8 oz icing sugar, sifted	
1 tablespoon milk	**2** With electric mixer or spoon, beat ingredients until smooth and with an easy spreading consistency.
1 tablespoon coffee essence	
60 g/2 oz walnut pieces, pecans or hazelnuts, finely chopped	**3** To icing, add finely chopped walnuts, pecans or hazelnuts; fold in until evenly distributed.
Walnut or pecan halves, or shelled whole hazelnuts for decoration	**4** After spreading icing on cake, immediately press walnut or pecan halves or shelled whole hazelnuts into icing, around edge of cake or in attractive design over top. Leave to set before serving cake.

DARK CHOCOLATE ICING

175 g/6 oz plain chocolate, broken into pieces	**1** In heavy non-stick saucepan over low heat, or in double boiler over hot, not boiling, water, heat chocolate and butter until melted and completely smooth, stirring occasionally. Remove from heat.
30 g/1 oz butter	
2 tablespoons golden syrup	**2** With wire whisk or fork, beat in golden syrup and milk until mixture is smooth. Spread while icing is still warm.
3 tablespoons milk	

MOCHA ICING

350 g/12 oz icing sugar	**1** Into large bowl, sift icing sugar, cocoa and coffee powders; stir well to mix.
4 tablespoons cocoa powder	
1 teaspoon instant coffee powder	**2** Gradually add *about 3 tablespoons warm water*, mixing until icing has a coating consistency; stir in vanilla essence.
1 ½ teaspoons vanilla essence	

CHOCOLATE ICING

350 g/12 oz icing sugar	**1** Into large bowl, sift icing sugar and cocoa powder.
2 tablespoons cocoa powder	**2** Gradually add *about 3 tablespoons warm water*, mixing until icing has a coating consistency.

GLAZES

These recipes make enough for a 33 x 23 cm/
13 x 9 inch or a 20-23 cm/8-9 inch round cake.

LEMON GLAZE

175 g/ 6 oz caster
sugar

Juice of 1½ lemons

1 In bowl, mix sugar and lemon juice until sugar dissolves.

2 With back of spoon, spread glaze over warm plain cake. Heat of cake causes lemon juice to run, giving cake a lovely lemon flavour and making it moist; sugar remains on top as a shiny crust.

RICH CHOCOLATE GLAZE

275 g/9 oz plain
chocolate, broken
into pieces

2 tablespoons icing
sugar, sifted

3 tablespoons orange
liquer

3 tablespoons milk

1 teaspoon instant
coffee powder

1 In bowl over saucepan of gently simmering water, heat all ingredients until chocolate melts and mixture is smooth, stirring constantly.

2 Remove bowl from pan. Leave glaze to stand at room temperature to cool slightly until of spreading consistency, then spread while still warm.

Spreading chocolate glaze over cake: *stand cake on wire rack over sheet of greaseproof paper; spread glaze over top and sides with palette knife, letting excess glaze drip on to paper*

DECORATIVE TOUCHES

It is easy to add decorative touches to cakes that are covered in icing. To make spiral patterns below left, place cake on a turntable if you have one.

Press tip of palette knife into centre – turn cake, slowly moving knife outwards

Draw prongs of fork across icing in parallel rows; repeat rows at right angles

GLACÉ ICINGS

You only need a very small amount of glacé icing to make a plain cake look special.

GLACÉ ICING

60 g/2 oz icing
sugar

Food colouring
(optional)

1 Into bowl, sift icing sugar.

2 Gradually add about *1½ teaspoons warm water,* beating vigorously until icing reaches a coating consistency. Beat in a few drops of food colouring, if you like.

Coffee Glacé Icing
Prepare as for Glacé Icing, but substitute *1 teaspoon coffee essence* for the same amount of water.

Lemon Glacé Icing
Prepare as for Glacé Icing, but substitute *lemon juice* for water; use *yellow food colouring,* if you like.

Liqueur Glacé Icing
Prepare as for Glacé Icing, but use *liqueur of your choice* instead of water.

Orange Glacé Icing
Prepare as for Glacé Icing, but substitute *orange juice* for water; use *orange food colouring,* if you like.

TOPPINGS

Each of the following recipes makes enough to spread on top of a 33 x 23 cm/13 x 9 inch cake.

NUTTY FUDGE TOPPING

250 ml/8 fl oz double or whipping cream

100 g/3 ½ oz caster sugar

30 g/1 oz butter

1 tablespoon golden syrup

120 g/4 oz plain chocolate, broken into pieces

200 g/7 oz shelled nuts, finely chopped

1 In non-stick saucepan over medium-high heat, bring first 5 ingredients to the boil, stirring constantly.

2 Reduce heat to medium and cook for 5 minutes, stirring constantly. Remove pan from heat. Cool slightly, about 10 minutes, then stir in nuts.

3 Quickly pour topping evenly over cake, allowing some to run down sides. Refrigerate until topping is firm, about 1 hour.

PRALINE AND COCONUT TOPPING

120 g/4 oz butter

100 g/3 ½ oz desiccated coconut

90 g/3 oz shelled nuts, finely chopped

165 g/5 ½ oz soft brown sugar

1 Start to prepare topping about 10 minutes before end of cake's baking time. In medium saucepan over low heat, melt butter.

2 Stir in coconut, chopped nuts and sugar. Remove saucepan from heat.

3 When cake is done, spread coconut mixture over hot cake. Grill cake for 2 minutes or until golden.

CRACKED CARAMEL

60 g/2 oz sugar

1 In small heavy saucepan over medium heat, heat sugar until melted and a light brown colour (about 6 minutes), stirring constantly.

2 Immediately pour caramel on to greased baking sheet; cool.

3 With rolling pin, crack caramel. If not using immediately, store in tightly covered container.

FILLINGS

Each of the following recipes makes enough filling for a 20-23 cm/8-9 inch sandwich cake.

ALMOND FILLING

120 g/4 oz blanched almonds, toasted

120 g/4 oz icing sugar, sifted

60 g/2 oz butter, softened

About 2 tablespoons orange juice or orange liqueur

1 In food processor, finely grind toasted almonds.

2 In bowl, mix ground almonds with remaining ingredients until evenly blended, adding enough orange juice or liqueur to reach an easy spreading consistency.

VANILLA CUSTARD FILLING

450 ml/ ¾ pint milk

50 g/1 ⅔ oz caster sugar

25 g/ ¾ oz cornflour

2 egg yolks

1 teaspoon vanilla essence

1 In non-stick saucepan, stir together all ingredients except vanilla essence.

2 Over medium-low heat, cook until mixture thickens and coats back of spoon well, about 20 minutes (do not boil or mixture will curdle). Stir in vanilla essence. Cool, then chill for 30 minutes.

FRESH LEMON FILLING

1 tablespoon grated lemon zest

4 tablespoons lemon juice

50 g/1 ⅔ oz caster sugar

4 teaspoons cornflour

15 g/ ½ oz butter

1 In small saucepan over medium heat, stir all ingredients except butter with *125 ml/4 fl oz water* until well blended. Cook until mixture thickens and boils, stirring.

2 Reduce heat; simmer for 1 minute, stirring occasionally. Remove from heat; stir in butter. Allow mixture to cool at room temperature.

Fresh Orange Filling
Prepare as for Fresh Lemon Filling, but substitute *orange zest and juice* for lemon zest and juice.

PASTRY-MAKING

You can make your own 'designer' pies, tarts and flans with the recipes and ideas on these pages. Pick a pastry to make the crust for any type of pie, whether served hot or cold; or choose a crumb crust to hold chilled fillings prepared separately. (An unbaked crumb crust, incidentally, is the quickest pie shell you can make.) The basic pastries for sweet pies are on pages 134-135; for tarts, flans and tartlets on page 159. These can be filled with fruit, custard, ice cream or mousse and then given the decorative touches – edges, tops, decorations, arrangements – that make a pie, tart or flan your very own creation. If you take a short cut and use bought frozen pastry, follow the same techniques for rolling and using the dough in double or single crust pies and tarts and flans.

EQUIPMENT

Using the right utensils can help make pastry-making easy and quick. Here are some of the most useful items. The pastry blender is a very clever invention, available at most good kitchenware shops; it is an excellent tool for cutting fat into flour.

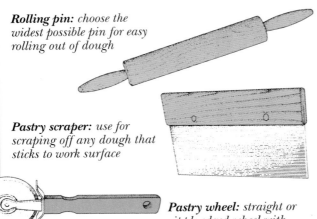

Rolling pin: choose the widest possible pin for easy rolling out of dough

Pastry scraper: use for scraping off any dough that sticks to work surface

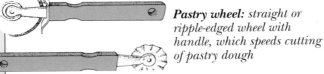

Pastry wheel: straight or ripple-edged wheel with handle, which speeds cutting of pastry dough

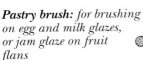

Pastry blender: for cutting fats evenly into dry ingredients

Pastry brush: for brushing on egg and milk glazes, or jam glaze on fruit flans

PASTRY-MAKING TECHNIQUES

ROLLING OUT DOUGH

Dough should be rolled with floured rolling pin on lightly floured surface. Slightly flatten ball of dough and roll it out, moving from centre to edge, keeping it circular. Push sides in occasionally by hand, if necessary, and lift rolling pin slightly as you near edge to avoid making dough too thin. Lift dough occasionally to ensure that it is not sticking. If it does stick, loosen it with pastry scraper and sprinkle more flour on surface underneath. Mend any cracks in dough as they appear, patching with dough cut from edge. Moisten torn edges, lay patch over tear and press it into position.

Rolling out dough: roll dough from centre to edge, keeping it circular. Push sides in occasionally by hand, if necessary, and lift rolling pin slightly as you near edge to avoid making dough too thin

LINING PIE DISHES AND TINS

If you are making a double crust pie, divide dough into 2 pieces, 1 slightly larger than the other. Use larger piece for lining pie dish or tin.

Roll out dough into round about 3 mm/⅛ inch thick and 4 cm/1 ½ inches larger all round than upside-down pie dish or tin. Roll dough loosely round rolling pin and lift on to dish. Unroll and ease into dish, pressing on to bottom and up side with fingertips. Do not stretch dough; it will shrink back while baking. Make Decorative Pastry Edge (pages 136-137) and fill pie, or make top crust if it is a double crust pie.

PIE DISHES

Be sure your pie dish or tin is size specified in recipe. To check size, if it has not been marked on pie dish or tin by manufacturer, use a ruler to measure dish or tin from inside edge to inside edge.

Pie dishes of the same diameter may differ in capacity; the recipes in this book are for shallow pie dishes.

For nicely browned pastry top and bottom, use metal such as anodized aluminium, tin or enamel pie dishes and tins.

Don't grease pie dishes or tins unless recipe says to do so. Most pastry contains enough fat to keep it from sticking to pie dish or tin.

BAKING BLIND

A pie, tart or flan shell may be baked blind, that is, baked first without a filling. If it is to be filled with a very juicy filling, it should not be pricked with a fork before baking. Instead, after lining the pie dish or tin with dough and making a decorative edge, cut a sheet of foil and place it in the pie shell, pressing it gently on to the bottom and side. Then, according to recipe instructions, half fill the foil-lined shell with dried or baking beans or uncooked rice. Bake in preheated 220°C/425°F/gas 7 oven for 10 minutes; carefully remove foil, with beans or rice if used, and continue baking pie shell until golden. Cool pie shell completely before filling. Dried and baking beans and rice can be stored, after cooling, in covered container and used time and again for baking blind; do not use in cooking.

Half filling foil liner with dried beans for baking blind

A BAKING PRECAUTION

Sometimes, despite the cook's best efforts, juices from very ripe fruit will bubble over the rim of the pie dish on to the oven floor. If you are using very juicy fruit and suspect that this might happen, tear off a 30 cm/12 inch square of foil and turn the edges up 1 cm/½ inch on all sides; place on another oven rack directly below the pie to catch any dripping juices, and bake the pie as directed. Even if the pie does bubble over, the foil should catch all the drips and save on oven cleaning.

GLAZING AND BAKING

For a golden glaze, brush top crust (not edge) with milk, undiluted evaporated milk, or lightly beaten egg white; sprinkle crust with sugar, if you like. If pie crust edges begin to brown too much during baking, cover them with strips of foil to prevent burning. If top crust seems to be browning too much, cover pie loosely with foil for the last 15 minutes of baking time.

Covering pie crust edges with strips of foil to prevent burning

FREEZING PASTRY

Uncooked Pastry Dough

Roll out pastry dough into rounds 4 cm/1 ½ inches larger all round than upside-down pie dishes or tins, stack with 2 sheets of greaseproof paper between each, wrap and freeze. Use within 2-3 months.

To use, place round of dough on pie dish or tin; thaw for 10-15 minutes before shaping.

Pie Crusts

Freeze baked or unbaked shells in their dishes or tins, or in reusable foil pie tins. Store baked shells for 4-6 months; thaw, unwrapped, at room temperature for 15 minutes. Store unbaked shells for 2-3 months.

To use, prick unfilled shells well with fork and bake, without thawing, for about 20 minutes in preheated 220°C/425°F/gas 7 oven; or fill and bake as instructed in individual recipes.

Fruit Pies and Tarts

Freeze baked or unbaked fruit pies for 2-3 months. To freeze unbaked fruit pies, if fruit is very juicy, add 1-2 tablespoons extra flour or cornflour to filling. Do not cut slits in top crust. Wrap and freeze. Or, if pie is fragile, first open freeze until firm, then cover top with paper plate for protection, wrap and return to freezer.

To cook unbaked fruit pie, unwrap, cut slits in top crust and bake in preheated oven from frozen, allowing 15-20 minutes additional baking time or until fruit is hot and bubbling.

Thaw baked pies, unwrapped, at room temperature for about 30 minutes, then bake in preheated 180°C/350°F/gas 4 oven for 30 minutes or until warm.

Frozen Fillings

Pies with ice cream or frozen fillings will not only be easier to cut when serving, but also have more flavour, if they are allowed to stand at room temperature for about 15 minutes after removal from freezer. Unwrap them first so that any decoration will not be spoiled.

STORING PASTRY

Most fruit pies and flans can be kept at room temperature overnight, even in warm weather, covered with foil once cold. For longer storage (2 or 3 days), refrigerate; then freshen by warming them in oven.

Pies and tarts with cream, custard, whipped cream or soft cheese filling or fillings set with gelatine should be refrigerated and used within a day or so.

Balls of unbaked pastry dough may be wrapped in either greaseproof paper or foil, and stored in the refrigerator for a day or two.

HINTS AND TIPS

Here you'll find some do's and don'ts of good cooking, selected to help you make the recipes in this book with the least time and effort, and the greatest of ease. One very important rule should be observed with every single recipe: before you start to cook, read the recipe through to make sure you understand the instructions; then assemble ingredients and equipment to make sure you have everything you need.

Finally, treat your book as a 'working manual'; keep a pencil at the side and if you find a cake takes 20 minutes to cook in your oven rather than the recommended 30 minutes, jot this down by the recipe, together with any other useful comments – for example, which dish you used, whether you added pecans rather than walnuts, and so on.

GENERAL HINTS

• When recipe calls for butter or margarine, it refers to solid, block form. When cake recipe calls for soft margarine, use the soft tub variety (it has air beaten in). Don't use low-fat margarines and vegetable oil spreads, which contain more water and less fat; they may give different results.

• Brown sugar stored in freezer will be soft and usable when thawed. If brown sugar sticks together in lumps, soften in the microwave for a short time.

• When softened butter or margarine is needed in a hurry, cut the amount called for into small pieces; it will soften more quickly at room temperature than a large piece.

• Dry ingredients – flour, sugar, baking powder, bicarbonate of soda – should be kept in airtight containers in a cool, dry place.

• To cut sticky foods like candied peel, glacé cherries or dates, keep dipping knife or scissors in flour.

• When measuring ingredients to add to those already in mixing bowl, never hold a measuring spoon over the bowl. One slip of the hand and the recipe could be ruined by too much vanilla essence, baking powder or whatever.

• Place a folded damp tea towel or dish cloth under bowl when mixing by hand or folding ingredients into a mixture; bowl won't slip while mixing.

• To determine volume of mould, simply measure amount of water it takes to fill it to the brim.

• Use the right knife and cutting techniques, and slices will be perfect when you cut cakes and desserts.
For sandwich and layer cakes, use a well-sharpened chef's knife.
For meringue desserts and Swiss rolls, use a knife with a thin, sharp blade and wipe it with a damp cloth or kitchen paper after every cut.
Before cutting cheesecakes, mousse cakes and other 'sticky' desserts, dip knife blade in very hot water and dry quickly with kitchen paper. The heated blade will cut through without sticking.
In all cases, use a sawing motion and a light touch to avoid crushing the cake or dessert out of shape.

• If you have leftover whipped cream, pipe it or drop it by heaping spoonfuls on to a baking sheet and freeze. When cream is firm, loosen with a palette knife and store in polythene bag in freezer. To use, place frozen piped shapes or dollops on top of desserts; they will thaw in just a few minutes.

CUSTARDS AND CREAMS

• Stirring a little hot liquid into beaten eggs heats eggs so they will not curdle when added to more hot liquid.

• Always remove a custard mixture from the heat when checking to see if it is thick enough. Even just a few seconds extra cooking time could be too much.

• If custard is overheating, pour it quickly into cold bowl; whisk vigorously to prevent lumps forming.

• If custard has overheated, try dropping an ice cube into it, to rescue it from curdling.

• If cooked custard needs to cool before other ingredients are added to it, gently press dampened greaseproof paper on to surface of custard. Otherwise, a tough skin may form which will cause dessert to have a lumpy texture.

• A bain-marie helps custards bake evenly because it keeps the temperature constant and moderate, not too hot.

• To avoid spilling hot water when baking in a bain-marie, place filled ramekins or baking dish in large tin and centre tin on partially pulled out oven rack. Fill tin with hot water to come halfway up ramekins or dish, then gently push rack back into oven and bake custards as directed.

FRUIT AND NUTS

• An easy way to core apples and pears is with a melon bailer. Just slice fruit in half and scoop out core in one smooth stroke.

• If using frozen raspberries to decorate top of dessert, take them from the freezer, spread them out on kitchen paper and thaw slowly in the refrigerator; they will retain their shape if used the moment they are thawed.

• When recipe calls for lemon or orange zest, that means thin yellow or orange outer layer of peel, not spongy white part (pith), which is bitter. Grate, using sharp grater, just before needed, because zest dries out quickly. Ideally, grate zest from unwaxed lemons and oranges.

• To get maximum amount of juice when squeezing citrus fruits such as oranges, lemons or limes, gently roll fruit on work surface, pressing lightly, before halving and squeezing.

• If you have a microwave oven, use it to help squeeze citrus fruit juice more easily. Place fruit on oven floor and heat on High (100% power) just until fruit feels warm to the touch.

• Store all nuts (whole or shelled) in the freezer for maximum freshness. Wrapped in freezer bags, whole nuts will keep fresh for 3 years; shelled nuts for 1 year; ground nuts for 3 months.

• Whole nuts in their shells are much easier to crack when frozen because they are more brittle.

• Delicate torte or gâteau recipes often call for 'finely ground nuts' to replace some of the flour. For successful results, nuts must be ground very finely, yet be dry and light. Be careful not to process nuts in food processor or blender for too long; if they're thick and pasty, they will be too oily and heavy. If you are grinding the nuts by hand, grind two or three times to achieve correct texture. Packets of 'ground' nuts are not fine enough and must be ground again.

CHOCOLATE

Plain chocolate is made from basic chocolate liquor, cocoa butter and other fats, cocoa powder and sugar. The more chocolate liquor, the darker the chocolate; the more cocoa butter, the richer it will be. Bitter-sweet chocolate contains less sugar.

• *Milk* chocolate contains chocolate liquor, cocoa butter and other fats, cocoa powder, sugar, milk and sometimes cream. Because of the relatively low amount of chocolate liquor, milk chocolate cannot be substituted for plain or bittersweet chocolate.

• In recipes, use the best-quality plain dark chocolate you can find because it makes such a difference. Check the label before you buy, and choose the brand with the highest cocoa butter content. Most supermarkets and delicatessens stock good-quality plain chocolate; chocolat pâtissier is one of the best.

• *Plain chocolate flavour cake covering* is less expensive than real chocolate and does not have as fine a flavour. It contains less cocoa butter and more soft vegetable or nut fat. As a result, it is far easier to work with than real chocolate, especially when making chocolate decorations such as curls and caraque.

• *White* chocolate is really not chocolate at all, but a cooked-down mixture of fat, milk and sugar, with various flavourings added. Some white chocolate contains cocoa butter to give it a slight chocolate taste. White chocolate should only be used in recipes that specifically call for it.

• *Cocoa powder* is made from chocolate liquor that has had nearly all cocoa butter removed. *Drinking chocolate powder* contains dried milk, sugar and flavourings; it should not be substituted for cocoa powder in recipes because it is too mild and sweet.

• You can substitute cocoa powder for chocolate as follows:
    For each 175 g/6 oz plain chocolate, use 6 tablespoons sifted cocoa powder plus 7 tablespoons caster sugar and 60 g/2 oz white vegetable fat or shortening.

• Store chocolate in cool, dry place. It keeps best if temperature is about 20°C/68°F, but not over 24°C/75°F.

• Chocolate stored in too cold conditions will 'sweat' when brought to room temperature.

• If chocolate is stored in too warm conditions, cocoa butter will start to melt and appear on surface of chocolate as a greyish-white coating. This does not affect flavour, and chocolate will return to its original colour when melted.

• Melting chocolate in the microwave oven: place 30 g/1 oz plain chocolate, broken into pieces, in small microwave-safe bowl. Heat on High (100% power) for 1-2 minutes, just until shiny (chocolate will still retain its shape). Remove bowl from the microwave and stir chocolate until melted and smooth.

• Melting chocolate in conventional ways: (1) Place in bowl over saucepan of gently simmering water. (2) Place in small dish or heatproof measuring jug and set in pan of hot water. (3) Place in heavy non-stick saucepan; melt over low heat – if pan is too thin, it will transfer heat too fast and burn chocolate. (4) For small amounts, leave chocolate in original foil wrapper; place on piece of foil and set in warm spot on cooker (not on burner).

• If chocolate does stiffen during melting, for each 90 g/3 oz of plain chocolate, start with 1 teaspoon and add up to 15 g/ ½ oz white vegetable fat (not vegetable oil, butter or margarine, which contain moisture), stirring until chocolate liquefies again and becomes smooth.

• Stir chocolate after it has begun to liquefy. If melting more than 450 g/ 1 lb, start with 225 g/8 oz and add remainder in 60 g/2 oz amounts.

• To speed melting, break chocolate into small pieces and stir frequently.

• When adding liquid to melted chocolate, always add at least 2 tablespoons at a time, to avoid chocolate stiffening.

• When making chocolate decorations, work with chocolate as soon as it is melted and smooth. When heated too long it can become grainy.

• To avoid breaking chocolate curls, pick them up with cocktail stick.

BAKING

• If recipe says to preheat oven, allow at least 10 minutes for it to reach baking temperature.

• Make sure tins are size called for in recipe and prepare them before you start.

• If cake tins are to be greased with melted butter or margarine, use pastry brush, or crumpled grease-proof paper or kitchen paper. ➤

• Grease fluted tins and moulds very generously, especially the ridges up the side and the central funnel, so cake can be turned out easily. The best way to do this is to brush tin or mould with melted butter or margarine, vegetable oil or shortening.

• If you do not have a springform cake tin, use a tin with a removable base – and vice versa.

• Place tins on oven rack so they do not touch one another, or sides of oven.

• Wait until minimum baking time given in recipe has elapsed before opening oven door; opening it too soon can lower oven temperature and make cake mixtures and doughs fall.

CAKES

• For 3 or 4 cake layers, 2 oven racks are needed, placed so oven is divided into thirds; stagger tins so one is not directly underneath another.

• To line a tin with non-stick baking parchment, place tin on paper and trace round base with tip of small knife. Cut out tracing and place in greased cake tin; it will fit exactly.

• For chocolate cakes, dust bottom and sides of tins with sifted cocoa powder rather than flour – it will not leave white film on cake.

• Be sure to follow timing guide given in each recipe for beating cake mixtures. If not beaten thoroughly, ingredients will not be evenly distributed and cake will fall; if overbeaten, cake may be tough and dry and will not rise properly.

• When beating cake mixture, scrape bowl often with rubber spatula for even mixing.

• When folding in, always fold light, fluffy ingredient into heavier one. Whisking part of beaten egg whites into heavy mixture lightens it and makes it easy to fold in remaining whites without reducing volume.

• For even textured cakes without any large holes, cut through mixture in cake tins with rubber spatula to remove any air bubbles, or gently tap cake tin on work surface just before baking.

• Cakes are done when they shrink away from side of tin and top springs back when pressed with finger.

• After removing cake from oven, leave to cool in tin on wire rack for about 10 minutes before turning out. If cake is cooled completely in tin, it may stick to bottom and side and be hard to remove; however, if cake is removed from tin while it is too hot, it could break.

• When baking powder is called for in a cake recipe, always add the exact amount specified. Do not be over-generous with baking powder as too much will cause cake to rise up beautifully in the oven and give you a false sense of security – cake will fall either just before it comes out of the oven or immediately after.

ICING AND FILLING

• For sandwich cakes, place first layer, top down, on plate; spread with filling, then place second layer, top up, on first, so flat bases of two layers face each other.

• Spread icing or firm filling to within 1 cm/½ inch of edge of cake, soft filling to 2.5 cm/1 inch of edge – weight of top layer will push it to edge.

• Spread cake with thin layer of icing first, to 'set' crumb, then ice again.

• When filling piping bag, stand narrow end in measuring jug or glass.

• To keep your piping bag sweet smelling, after each use, rinse it in warm water, then include it with a whites wash in the washing machine.

• A sturdy polythene bag makes a good piping bag. Fill, close with twist tie and snip small hole in corner.

FRUIT CAKES

• Line cake tin with foil to make cake easy to remove. Smooth out all creases, so side of cake will be smooth.

• Move oven rack to lower position to ensure whole cake is in middle of oven while baking.

• Mix dried fruit and nuts with a little flour before adding to mixture; this keeps them evenly suspended in mixture and prevents them from sinking to bottom while cake is baking.

• Spoon mixture evenly into tin and pack firmly to eliminate air pockets that will leave holes in baked cake.

• Test fruit cakes with a skewer or wooden cocktail stick inserted in centre; it should come out clean.

• Turn leftover fruit cake into an elegant dessert: slice cake into wine glasses, moisten with fruit juice or sherry and top with whipped cream.

PASTRY

• When making choux pastry dough, flour must be added as soon as liquid boils or water could evaporate and dough would not puff.

• Add flour for choux pastry dough all at once. Beat until smooth and formed into a ball that cleans side of saucepan.

• Pastries made with choux pastry dough should be eaten on the same day they are made, as pastry tends to soften quickly.

• Thaw frozen phyllo in its packet, otherwise it might dry out and crack.

• Once thawed, keep phyllo covered with damp cloth or cling film.

• Brush sheets of phyllo with melted butter – it adds flavour and keeps phyllo pliable so that it can be rolled or folded.

PIES

• What is the key to making good pastry? It is accurate measurement of ingredients, to ensure the correct balance of fat and flour, and not too much liquid. Too much flour makes tough pastry; too much fat results in a greasy, crumbly pastry. Too much liquid will require the excess flour that results in a tough crust.

• Roll out pastry dough on the coldest work surface possible – marble is ideal; granite and ceramic are also good.

• Roll out pastry as evenly as possible so edges are not too thin.

• When rolling out pastry dough, slide a pastry scraper or palette knife under it occasionally to make sure it is not sticking to the work surface. If it sticks, sprinkle work surface with more flour before continuing rolling.

• Never stretch pastry to fit into pie dish or tin; it will just shrink back when baking.

• After making a rope or fluted edge on a pie shell, hook points of pastry under rim of dish or tin so edge will stay in place as it bakes.

• For a shiny top, brush pastry with lightly beaten egg white. For a golden-brown glazed top, brush with beaten egg, egg yolk or milk.

• To help keep oven clean when baking fruit pie, place second oven rack below the one pie is on. Tear off sheet of foil, turn all edges up 1 cm/½ inch and place it on second rack to catch drips. Another way to catch drips from a fruit pie is to stand pie dish in a large roasting tin.

• To prevent soggy pastry in cream pies, try this: as soon as baked pie shell comes out of oven, brush it with lightly beaten egg white, making sure to cover areas pricked with fork. The heat from the hot pie shell will cook the egg white and form a protective seal to help eliminate sogginess after filling.

• If crumb crusts stick to pie dish or tin, set dish or tin on tea towel that has been wrung out in hot water and allow to stand briefly. It should then be easy to remove slices perfectly.

• After preparing your favourite pie, let your children use leftover pastry to make a special treat: get them to roll out dough and cut pretty shapes. While pie bakes, shapes can be browned in the oven at the same time, then spread with jam or sprinkled with cinnamon and sugar.

• When refrigerating a cream-topped pie, place it, uncovered, in a prominent position at the front of the refrigerator – this way everyone will notice it and it will not be knocked accidentally.

BISCUITS

• For a light texture, mix dough gently. Do not overwork dough or biscuits will be tough.

• No space to roll out biscuits? Shape dough into small balls, place 5-7.5 cm/2-3 inches apart on baking sheet and then press flat with bottom of a glass that has been dipped in caster sugar.

• Always start cutting at edge of dough and work towards centre, cutting biscuits as close together as possible to minimize scraps.

• Rehandling toughens biscuits, so press trimmings together – do not knead – before rolling again.

• Transfer fragile biscuits from board to baking sheet with fish slice to preserve shape.

• Always bake biscuits on heavy-duty baking sheets that do not bend or warp in the oven; silicone-coated baking sheets are now widely available, and are excellent for biscuit baking.

• Baking sheets should be at least 5 cm/2 inches smaller all round than your oven, so heat can circulate and biscuits can bake evenly.

• Always place dough on a cool baking sheet. It will spread too much on a hot one.

• Grease baking sheet only if recipe says so; very rich biscuits will spread too much if baked on greased sheets.

• After baking, transfer small biscuits at once from baking sheet to wire rack (they continue to bake on hot sheet).

• Cool biscuit bars completely in tin before turning out.

• Always cool biscuits completely before storing in airtight containers.

• When cutting up a tray of short-bread, cool to lukewarm, then mark into desired shapes and cut through; leave until almost cold before removing from tin. If you forget to mark and cut through, warm short-bread gently in oven again.

• Biscuits that are too hard can be softened by placing a slice of bread in the storage tin; change the slice every other day. A bread slice will also keep soft biscuits soft, just as it softens hardened brown sugar.

ICE CREAM AND FROZEN DESSERTS

• Ice cream, whether bought or home-made, keeps best in freezer at -18°C/0°F or lower.

• Ice cream will keep for 1 month in freezer compartment of refrigerator, or up to 2 months in home freezer.

• Do not re-freeze partially melted ice cream – a coarse, icy texture will result.

• To store open containers of ice cream, press cling film right on to exposed surface to protect ice cream from odours and prevent development of 'skin' or ice crystals.

• Partially frozen mixtures are ready for beating when firm 2.5 cm/1 inch round edge, though centre is still mushy.

INDEX

ACKNOWLEDGEMENTS

Photography   All photography by David Murray
Photographer's Assistant   Jules Selmes

Copy Editor   Norma MacMillan

Assisted by   Sally Poole, Diana Vowles

Typesetting   Rowena Feeny
Text film by   Disc To Print (UK) Limited
Production Consultant   Lorraine Baird
Reproduced by   Colourscan, Singapore

Home Economists
Step-by-steps and finished desserts   Elizabeth Wolf-Cohen
Finished desserts   Maxine Clark, Hilary Foster, Carole Handslip, Kathy Man, Janice Murfitt, Berit Vinegrad, Mandy Wagstaff

Stylist   Angi Lincoln

The companies listed here very graciously lent tableware

Arthur Price of England p. 131 (fork and pie slice); p. 133 (pie slice); p. 138 (serving spoon); p. 143 (pie slice); p. 144 (napkin rings); p. 154 (forks); p. 163 (napkin rings); p. 168 (pie slice); p. 175 (sugar spoon); p. 181 (silver platter); p. 182 (pie slice); p. 187 (fork); p. 235 (forks)

Classical Creamware Limited p. 77 (plate); p. 89 (plates, sugar bowl and shaker); p. 105 (tea set and plate); p. 114 (plate); p. 124 (plate); p. 133 (plate); p. 143 (plate); p. 148 (plate)

Dartington Crystal p. 179 (glass bowl)

George Butler of Sheffield Limited p. 132 (pie slice); p. 133 (forks); p. 139 (pie slice); p. 141 (pie slice); p. 149 (forks); p. 161 (forks); p. 163 (pie slice and forks); p. 166 (forks); p. 179 (forks); p. 181 (pie slice); p. 191 (pie slice)

Guy Degrenne p. 120 (pie slice); p. 157 (pie slice)

Josiah Wedgwood & Sons Limited p. 161 (plates); p. 173 (small plate); p. 180 (plates); p. 187 (plate); p. 189 (coffee set and plates); p. 191 (tray and plate)

Villeroy & Boch Tableware Limited p. 103 (glass platter); p. 122 (glass platter); p. 139 (glass platter); p. 154 (glass plates); p. 164 (glass platter); p. 186 (plate); p. 194 (plate); p. 195 (plate)

Carroll & Brown Limited would also like to thank these companies for their assistance

Corning Limited
Neff U.K. Limited
Siemens Domestic Appliances Limited

DEREK LANDY

HarperCollins *Children's Books*

First published in hardback in Great Britain by HarperCollins *Children's Books* 2010
HarperCollins *Children's Books* is a division of
HarperCollins*Publishers* Ltd
77-85 Fulham Palace Road, Hammersmith, London W6 8JB

Visit us on the web at www.harpercollins.co.uk

Skulduggery Pleasant rests his weary bones on the web at
www.skulduggerypleasant.co.uk

Derek Landy blogs under duress at
www.dereklandy.blogspot.com

1

Illuminated letters © Tom Percival 2010
Skulduggery Pleasant™ Derek Landy
SP Logo™ HarperCollins*Publishers*

ISBN 978-0-00-732598-6

Typeset in Baskerville MT by Palimpsest Book Production Limited,
Falkirk, Stirlingshire
Printed and bound in England by
Clays Ltd, St Ives plc

This book is dedicated, with great reluctance, to my
editor, Nick Lake, because he is forcing me to.

Personally, I would have liked to include Gillie Russell
and Michael Stearns who, along with Nick, really
welcomed me into the publishing world with my
first book.

Unfortunately, because Nick is now my sole editor, he has
threatened to edit this dedication down to an
unrecognisable mess of blacked-out lines, and so as a
result this dedication is to him, and him alone.

Personally I think that this shows a staggering amount of
████████ and ███████████, which proves that Nick
is nothing but a ████████████████████████████
with ████████████ for ████████████, but hey, that's just
my personal opinion.

Here, Nick. You finally get a book dedicated to you.
Hope you're ████████████ happy.

████████████.

(Editor's Note: Nick Lake is a great guy.)

1

WREATH'S TASK

The doors swung open and High Priest Auron Tenebrae strode into the room, his robe swirling around his tall, narrow frame. To his right was Quiver, a miser with words, but overly generous with withering glares. To Tenebrae's left, Craven, a bland sycophant, possessed of an uncanny skill to worm his way into his superior's good graces. Solomon Wreath had been seeing far too much of all three lately.

"Cleric Wreath," Tenebrae said, nodding imperiously at him.

"Your Eminence," Wreath responded, bowing deeply. "To what do I owe the honour?"

"Why do you *think* we're here?" Craven said, almost sneered. "You're late with your report. Did you think the High Priest would forget? Do you think him a fool?"

"I do not think him a fool, no," Wreath answered calmly. "But as to the intelligence of the people who accompany him, I'm afraid I cannot say."

"An insult!" Craven screeched. "How dare you! How dare you use a derogatory tone in the presence of the High Priest!"

"Enough," Tenebrae sighed, "both of you. Your constant bickering tries my patience."

"My humblest apologies," Craven said immediately, bowing and closing his eyes, his lower lip trembling on the verge of tears. A magnificent performance, as usual.

"Yes," Wreath said. "Sorry about that."

"Despite Cleric Craven's overt dramatics," Tenebrae said, "he is quite correct to point out that you are late with your report. How is Valkyrie Cain progressing through her studies?"

"She's a fast learner," said Wreath. "As far as the practical side goes anyway. She's a natural at shadow casting, and every time I see her she's improved."

"And the philosophical aspect?" Quiver asked.

"Is not progressing nearly as smoothly," Wreath admitted. "She doesn't seem to be at all interested in the history or the teachings of the Order. It's going to take a lot to open her mind to it."

"The skeleton has already poisoned her against us," Tenebrae said bitterly.

"I fear you may be right. But I still think the effort is worth it."

"And I have yet to be convinced."

"Just because the girl is a fast learner," Quiver said, "does not mean she is the Death Bringer."

"Cleric Quiver speaks the truth," Tenebrae nodded.

Wreath did his best to look humble, keeping his comments to himself. He'd been searching for their saviour, for the one who would save the world from itself, for most of his life. He knew full well the danger of false hope and blind alleys – he'd had his fair share of both. But Valkyrie Cain was different. He felt it. Valkyrie Cain was the *one*.

"She troubles me," Tenebrae said. "Does she have potential? Absolutely. With training and with study, she could be the best of us. But the best of us still falls far short of what the Death Bringer should be."

"I'll keep working with her," Wreath said. "In two years,

maybe three, we'll have a better understanding of what she's capable of."

"Three years?" Tenebrae laughed. "A lot can happen, as we have seen, in a short space of time. Serpine. Vengeous. The Diablerie. Dare we risk being sidetracked by a mistake? While we are busy testing Miss Cain, another one of Mevolent's disciples might actually succeed in their insane goals and bring back the Faceless Ones for good. What if, as you yourself fear, Cleric Wreath, Lord Vile returns to punish us all? If that happens, our plans mean nothing. There will be no world left to save."

"Then what does His Eminence suggest?" Wreath asked.

"We need to know if we are wasting our time with this one."

"A Sensitive," Craven nodded.

"We've tried this before," Wreath argued. "None of our psychics are able to tell us anything."

"Reading the future has never been a particular talent of the Necromancer Order," Tenebrae said. "Our Sensitives are somewhat lacking when it comes to fortune-telling. But there is another I keep hearing about. Finbar something..."

"Finbar Wrong," Wreath said. "But he knows Valkyrie personally. It would raise too many questions. Even if he didn't know her, I doubt he'd ever aid our cause. As I keep reminding you, nobody out there likes us."

"We're working to save them all!" Craven barked, and this time not even the High Priest paid him any attention.

"The psychic will help us," Tenebrae said, "and afterwards he will remember nothing about it. Cleric Wreath, I want you to take the Soul Catcher and release the Remnant we have trapped inside it."

Wreath's face slackened. "Your Eminence, Remnants are highly dangerous..."

"Oh, I trust your ability to handle any situation," Tenebrae said with an airy wave of his hand. "Have it possess this Finbar person, and if he sees a future where Valkyrie Cain is the Death Bringer, and he sees her saving the world, then we can put all our energies into making sure she fulfils her potential. If he does not see this future, we forget about her, and our search continues."

"But using the Remnant..."

"Once the job is done, simply return it to the Soul Catcher. What could be easier?"

2

THE SMILING DETECTIVE

Christmas was a few days away, and all but one of the houses on this suburban Dublin street had lights in the windows. Three of the most competitive neighbours had filled their small gardens with flickering Santas and frolicking reindeer, and some idiot had even wrapped a cable of fairy lights round the lamp post outside his gate. There was no snow, but the night was cold, and frost clung to the city like glitter.

The big car that rolled to a stop outside the house with no lights was a 1954 Bentley R-Type Continental, one of only

208 ever made. It was an exquisite car, retro-fitted with modern conveniences, adapted to the needs of its owner. It was fast, it was powerful, and if it received even the slightest of dents, it would fall apart.

That's what the mechanic had said. He'd done all he could, used all his knowledge and all his abilities to bring this car back from the brink so many times – but the next dent, he promised, would be its last. All the tricks he'd used to keep it going, to bend it back into shape, would be counteracted. The glass would shatter, the metal would rupture, the frame would buckle, the tyres would burst, the engine would crack... The only way to avoid complete and utter catastrophe, the mechanic had said, was to make sure you weren't *in* the car when all this happened.

Skulduggery Pleasant got out first. He was tall and thin, and wore a dark blue suit and black gloves. His hair was brown and wavy, and his cheekbones were high and his jaw was square. His skin was slightly waxy and his eyes didn't seem capable of focusing, but it was a pretty good face, all things considered. One of his better ones.

Valkyrie Cain got out of the passenger side. She zipped up her black jacket against the cold, and joined Skulduggery as he walked up to the front door. She glanced at him, and saw that he was smiling.

"Stop doing that," she sighed.

"Stop doing what?" Skulduggery responded in that gloriously velvet voice of his.

"Stop smiling. The person we want to talk to lives in the only dark house on a bright street. That's not a good sign."

"I didn't realise I *was* smiling," he said.

They stopped at the door, and Skulduggery made a concerted effort to shift his features. His mouth twitched downwards. "Am I smiling now?"

"No."

"Excellent," he said, and the smile immediately sprang back up.

Valkyrie handed him his hat. "Why don't you get rid of the face? You're not going to need it in here."

"You're the one telling me how much I should practise," he said, but slid his gloved fingers beneath his shirt collar anyway, tapping the symbols etched into his collarbones. The face and hair retracted off his head, leaving him with a gleaming skull.

He put on his hat, cocked at a jaunty angle. "Better?" he asked.

"Much."

"Good." He knocked, and took out his gun. "If anyone asks, we're scary carollers."

Humming 'Good King Wenceslas' to himself, he knocked again, and still no one answered the door, and no lights came on.

"What do you bet everyone's dead?" Valkyrie asked.

"Are you just being incredibly pessimistic," Skulduggery asked, "or is that ring of yours telling you something?"

The Necromancer ring was cold on her finger, but no colder than usual. "It's not telling me anything. I can only sense death through it when I'm practically standing over the dead body."

"Which is an astonishingly useful ability, I have to say. Hold this."

He gave her his gun, and crouched down to pick the lock. She looked around, but no one was watching them.

"It might be a trap," she said, speaking softly.

"Unlikely," he whispered. "Traps are usually enticing."

"It might be a very rubbish trap."

"Always a possibility."

The lock clicked open. Skulduggery straightened up, put his lock picks away, and took his gun back.

"I need a weapon," Valkyrie muttered.

"You're an Elemental with a Necromancer ring, trained in a variety of martial arts by some of the best fighters in the world," Skulduggery pointed out. "I'm fairly certain that *makes* you a weapon."

"I mean a weapon you hold. You have a gun, Tanith has a sword... I want a stick."

"I'll buy you a stick for Christmas."

She glowered as he pushed the door. It opened silently, without even a creepy old creak. Skulduggery went first and Valkyrie followed, closing the door after them. It took a moment for her eyes to adjust to this level of gloom, and Skulduggery, who had no eyes for this to be a problem, waited until she tapped him before moving on. They passed through into the living room, where she tapped him again. He looked at her, and she pointed to the Necromancer ring. It was buzzing with a dreadful kind of cold energy as it fed off the death in the room.

They found the first dead body sprawled across the couch. The second was slumped in the corner, amid the wreckage of what once had been a side table. Skulduggery looked closely at each of them, then shook his head at Valkyrie. Neither was the man they were looking for.

They moved into the kitchen, where they found a third corpse, face down on the floor. Were his head not twisted all the way around, he would have been looking up at the ceiling.

A bottle lay beside his hand, smashed against the tiles, and the smell of beer was still strong.

The rest of the ground floor was clear of corpses, so they went to the stairs. The first one creaked, and Skulduggery stepped back off it. He wrapped his arms around Valkyrie's waist, and they rose off the ground and drifted up to the body on the landing. It was a woman, who had died curled up in a foetal position.

There were three bedrooms and one bathroom. The bathroom was empty, as was the first bedroom they checked. The second bedroom had scorch marks on the wall and another dead woman halfway out of a window. Valkyrie guessed this woman was the one responsible for the scorch marks – she'd tried to defend herself, then tried to run. Neither attempt had worked.

There was someone alive in the last bedroom. They could hear whoever it was in the wardrobe, trying not to make a sound. They heard a deep breath being taken as they approached, and then there was absolute silence for all of thirteen seconds. The silence ended with a ridiculously loud gasping for air. Skulduggery thumbed back the hammer of his gun.

"Come out," he said.

The wardrobe burst open and a shrieking madman leaped

out at Valkyrie. She batted down his arm, grabbed his shirt and twisted her hip into him, his shriek turning to a yelp as he hit the floor.

"Don't kill me," he sobbed as he lay there. "Oh God, please don't kill me."

"If you had let me finish," Skulduggery said, slightly annoyed, "you would have heard me say, *'Come out, we're not going to hurt you'*. Idiot."

"He probably wouldn't have said *idiot*," Valkyrie told the sobbing man. "We're trying our best to be nice."

The man blinked through his tears, and looked up. "You're... You're not going to kill me?"

"No, we're not," Valkyrie said gently, "so long as you wipe your nose right now."

The man sniffled into his sleeve and she stood back, trying not to shiver with revulsion. He got up.

"You're Skulduggery Pleasant," he said. "I've heard about you. The Skeleton Detective."

"Season's greetings," Skulduggery nodded. "This is my partner, Valkyrie Cain. And you are...?"

"My name is Ranajay. I live here with my... with my friends. It's so nice, living next to all these normal people. We really liked living here. Me and my... Me and my friends..."

Ranajay looked like he was going to start sobbing again, so Valkyrie cut in quickly. "Who did this? Who killed everyone?"

"I don't know. A big guy. Huge. He wore a mask, and spoke with an accent. His eyes were red."

"What did he want?" Skulduggery asked.

"He came here looking for a friend of mine."

Valkyrie frowned. "Ephraim Tungsten?"

"Yes," Ranajay said. "How did you know?"

"That's who we want to talk to. We believe he's been in contact with a killer we've been tracking for five months."

"Davina Marr, right? That detective who went bad, blew up the Sanctuary? That's why the big guy wanted Ephraim too."

"Do you know if Marr has been in touch with Ephraim?" Skulduggery asked.

"Oh, she has, yes. Paid him to make her a false ID and arrange to get her out of the country. That's what Ephraim does. When people have to disappear, he takes care of it. Only this time he didn't. I think after he realised what she'd done, he didn't want any part of it. The detective, Marr, she came looking for everything she'd paid for after the Sanctuary fell into the ground, but he was gone. She tore this place up three times in the same month looking for him. Haven't seen her since then. Haven't seen Ephraim either. We all thought it'd be

19

safer if we stayed away from him, you know? Fat lot of good that did my friends."

"The man who killed them," Skulduggery said, "did you tell him where Ephraim is?"

Ranajay shook his head. "Didn't have to. *I* knew what he wanted to know. I think that's the only reason he didn't kill me. Ephraim had told me, ages ago, that the only thing he'd done for Marr was to set up places for her to stay in three spots across the city. That's all the information the big guy wanted, just to know where Marr was staying."

"Can you tell *us* the three spots?"

"Are you going after him?" asked Ranajay.

"Our main priority is Davina Marr, but the man who killed your friends has just made it to number two on our list."

"You'll stop him?"

"If we can."

"You'll kill him?"

"If we have to."

"Yeah. Yeah, I'll tell you."

3

TESSERACT

He was a giant of a man, his thick-set muscles stretching the dusty black coat he wore, but he was quiet, she had to give him that. Smart too, to get this close to her without setting off the alarms. *Probably dismantled them as he came*, she thought as she flung herself through the window into the cold air. Taking his time, doing it right, the way any good assassin should. She knew who he was, of course. Killers that size tended to be conspicuous, and only one of them wore a metal mask over his scarred and misshapen face. The Russian, Tesseract.

She hit the ground and rolled, shards of broken glass accompanying her down. She reached into her jacket, found the trigger device, flicked the safety off with her thumb and pressed the red button without even taking it out of her pocket. He was up there, right now, and she would only get one chance at this.

But when there was no big explosion, she looked up to see him climbing out of the window overhead. He'd dismantled the explosives. Of course he had. Davina Marr didn't even bother to curse. She just ran.

The ground was wet with recent rain, and she slipped in the mud and scrambled up again. All that time and effort spent fortifying this pitiful excuse for a dwelling, all for nothing. The security measures she'd placed at every conceivable entrance to the disused construction site had turned out to be useless. The traps she'd set on the metal stairs to the foreman's office in which she'd been living had turned out to be *less* than useless. The big brute had entered silently and it had only been pure luck that she'd happened to look up in time.

She ran to her car, but if he was as meticulous as she thought he was, he'd already have sabotaged the engine, so she broke left, running for the tall fence that bordered the east side of the site. She heard quick footsteps behind her and decided to try to lose him in the maze of cargo containers. It was a moonless night, too dark to see much of anything, and she hoped he was finding it as difficult in this gloom as she was. There was a heavy *clang*, followed by footsteps on metal, and he was moving above her, across the top of the containers, aiming to cut her off before she reached the fence.

Marr doubled back, wishing that she'd had time to grab her gun off the table before she'd made that jump. Magic was all well and good, she often thought, but having a loaded gun in your hand was a reassurance like no other.

She ducked low and crept along, keeping her breathing under control. She couldn't hear him any more. He was either still up there and not moving, or he was down here, in the muck and the mud and the dark, with her. Possibly sneaking up on her right now. Marr glanced over her shoulder, saw nothing but shadows.

She tried to remember what Tesseract's chosen discipline was. He was an Adept, she knew that much, but beyond that, his magic was a mystery to her. She hoped it wasn't the ability to see in the dark. That would be just typical, and it'd fit right in with how her luck had been going these past few months. All she'd wanted to do was go home, for God's sake. Marr was from Boston, born and raised, and that's where she wanted to die. Not here, in wet and muddy Ireland.

She got on her belly and crawled through a gap between pallets. She took another look behind her, to make sure he wasn't reaching out to grab her ankle, and then considered her options. They weren't great, and they weren't many, and hiding wasn't one of them. He'd find her eventually, probably sooner rather than later. She could try the east fence again, or she could go all the way back to the entrance at the south. Heading west was out of the question, seeing as how there was nothing there but acres of flat ground with no cover.

Marr propped herself up on her elbows, the cold wetness seeping through her clothes, and looked straight out in front, due north. There was another fence there, higher than the east side, but it was closer, and at least there were pallets and machinery she could duck behind if she needed to.

She inched forward, out through the gap, coming up on her hunkers. There were a couple of barrels stacked up on top of each other, and she hurried to them. Still no sign of Tesseract.

Running bent over, she came up around a bulldozer and made a mad dash for the next piece of cover. The chain-link fence was maybe twenty strides away. It was tall, as high as a house, taller than she'd remembered, but Marr felt sure she could jump it. She allowed herself a moment to envy the Skeleton Detective and his newfound ability to fly. That would really come in handy right about now. She gauged the distance and felt the currents in the air, reckoning that she'd need a running start to clear the fence successfully.

She looked back, making sure Tesseract wasn't anywhere nearby. She scanned her surroundings carefully, methodically, pivoting her head slowly, on the alert for the slightest movement. It took her a full second to realise that she was looking straight at him as he ran at her. She couldn't help it – she gave a short yelp of fright and stumbled back, tripping over her own feet.

Slipping and sliding on the wet ground, Marr scrambled for the fence. She flung her arms wide, hands open and grasping, then pulled the air in around her and lifted herself up, away from the mud. She wasn't even halfway to the top when she realised she wasn't going to make it. She managed to steer herself closer and reached out, fingers slipping through the links just as she started to drop. Her body swung into the rattling fence, her fingers burning. She looked down, saw him looking up, silent behind his metal mask. She started climbing, using only her hands. She glanced down. Tesseract was climbing up after her.

God, but he was quick.

It started to rain again, and the droplets soon began to sting against her face. Tesseract was closing the gap between them with alarming speed, his long arms reaching further than hers, and his great muscles hauling his body after her without tiring. As for Marr, her muscles were already complaining, and as she neared the top, they were screaming. Still, better them than her, she reckoned.

Below her, Tesseract had stalled. It looked like he'd snagged that coat of his in the fence somehow. Marr couldn't spare the time to be smug about it, but she promised herself a smirk when this was all over.

She clambered over the top, pausing a moment to estimate how high up she was, and then let herself fall. The street rushed towards her, and as she prepared to use the air to slow her descent, she glanced at Tesseract. In an instant she saw that he hadn't stalled, but had been cutting through the links with a knife.

As she passed him on her way down, he reached through the fence and grabbed her arm. Her body jerked and twisted. She cried out and he held her for a moment, then let her fall. She tumbled head over heels to the street below. Her shoulder hit the pavement first and shattered, and her head smacked against the concrete. Marr lay there, waiting for Tesseract to jump down and finish the job. And then a familiar car came screeching around the corner, and she blacked out.

4

GRANDER SCALES

Skulduggery braked, the Bentley swerving to a perfect stop on the slippery road. Valkyrie threw the door open and jumped out. Davina Marr lay in a crumpled heap on the pavement, several bones obviously broken.

A man landed behind Marr, a big man in a metal mask, and Skulduggery appeared beside Valkyrie, gun in hand.

"You're Tesseract," he said. "You are, aren't you? Who hired you? Who are you working for?"

The man, Tesseract, didn't even look at him. His red eyes

were focused on Marr. He moved towards her and Skulduggery stepped into his path. Immediately, Tesseract grabbed the gun, twisting it from Skulduggery's grip. Skulduggery grabbed the bigger man's elbow and wrist and wrenched, and the gun fell back into his hand.

"Get her to the car!" Skulduggery ordered, and Valkyrie grabbed Marr and started dragging her away.

As they struggled for control of the weapon, Tesseract kicked Skulduggery's leg and Skulduggery kneed Tesseract's thigh. They headbutted each other as they locked and counter-locked, using moves Valkyrie had never seen before. She heard the gun *click*, but their hands were covering it so she couldn't see what was happening. Finally, Tesseract flipped Skulduggery over his hip, but Skulduggery took the gun with him. He rolled and came up, aiming dead-centre for Tesseract's chest, and the fight froze.

Valkyrie shoved Marr into the back seat of the Bentley, and looked back in time to see Tesseract hold out his fist, and slowly open his hand. Six bullets fell to the ground.

"I *thought* it was a bit light," Skulduggery muttered, putting the gun away.

Valkyrie considered helping, but she'd never even heard of this guy Tesseract, and she knew how dangerous it was to charge into a fight without knowing who your enemy was. Instead, she slipped in behind the wheel of the Bentley.

The priority here was Marr, and they had her, after all this time. Valkyrie wasn't about to risk letting her escape again. She put the Bentley in reverse, like she'd done a hundred times before under Skulduggery's tutelage, then yanked the wheel. The car spun and she put it in first. She sped away from the fight, rounded the corner and kept going. There was no other traffic on the road.

Valkyrie took another corner a little too sharply, but maintained control. Something moved in the rear-view mirror, and then Skulduggery was flying alongside the car. He nodded to her and she braked and slid over to the passenger side. Skulduggery got in behind the wheel and they took off again.

She frowned. "Are we not going back for him?"

"For Tesseract?" Skulduggery said. "Good God, no."

"But he's in shackles, right? You beat him?"

"I like to think I beat him in a moral sense, in that he's an assassin and I'm not, but apart from that, no, not really."

Valkyrie turned in her seat, looking at the dark street behind them, then settled back. "Who is he?"

"Assassin for hire, is all I know. I recognised him from his sheer size, and the fact that he wears a metal mask. I've never encountered him before. That's probably a good thing. But let's not dwell on the new enemy we might have made tonight. Let's dwell instead on the old enemy we've got in the back seat. Hello, Davina. You're under arrest for multiple counts of murder. You have the right to not much at all, really. Do you have anything to say in your defence?"

Marr remained unconscious.

"Splendid," Skulduggery said happily.

The Hibernian Cinema stood old and proud and slightly bewildered, like a senior citizen who'd wandered away from his tour group. It had no part in the Dublin that surrounded it. It hadn't been refurbished or refitted, it didn't have twenty screens on different floors and it didn't have banks of concession stands. What it did have were old movie posters on its walls, frayed carpeting, a single stall for popcorn and drinks, and a certain mustiness that agitated long-dormant allergies. The one screen it did possess only ever showed one thing – the black and white image of a brick wall with a door to one side.

But beyond that screen were corridors of clean white walls and bright lighting, rooms of scientific and mystical equipment, a morgue capable of dissecting a god and a Medical Bay that Valkyrie visited on a worryingly regular basis.

Kenspeckle Grouse shambled in, dressed in a bathrobe and slippers, what remained of his grey hair sticking up at odd angles. He looked grumpy, but then he always looked grumpy.

"What," he said, "do you want?"

"We have a patient for you," said Skulduggery, nodding to Davina Marr on the bed beside him.

Kenspeckle glared at the shackles around her wrists. "Don't know her," he said. "Take her to someone else. She's your prisoner, isn't she? Take her to one of those Sanctuary doctors, wake *them* up in the middle of the night."

"We can't do that. This is Davina Marr. She's the one who *destroyed* the Sanctuary."

Some of the grumpiness vanished from Kenspeckle's eyes, replaced by a kind of disgusted curiosity. "This is her, then? You finally found her?" He walked closer. "She's a bit the worse for wear, but I have to admit I'm surprised she's still alive. Are you getting less ruthless as you get older, Detective?"

"We didn't do this to her," Valkyrie said, not comfortable with where Kenspeckle's questions were heading. "We saved her, actually. She'd be dead if it wasn't for Skulduggery."

Kenspeckle pulled back one of Marr's eyelids. "I put that down to your good influence, Valkyrie. But that still doesn't explain why you haven't taken her to the authorities. You are, after all, Sanctuary Detectives once again, are you not?"

"We want to keep this quiet," Skulduggery said. "Things are too volatile at the moment. If we hand her over to the Cleavers, I doubt she'll even get a trial. They'll execute her on the spot."

Kenspeckle traced his hands lightly around Marr's head. "From what I remember, you've executed your fair share of guilty people in the past."

"I'm not here to argue with you, Professor. The fact is, I don't believe she was working alone when she decided to destroy the Sanctuary, and I fear that her allies, or her *bosses*, will try to have her killed before she can name them. I'm fairly confident they're the ones who hired the assassin."

"Ah," Kenspeckle said, "so it's not mercy that stays your hand – it's a grander scale of ruthlessness."

Skulduggery cocked his head. "This woman is responsible for the deaths of fifty people, but there are others who also share that responsibility. They're all going to pay."

"Well," Kenspeckle said, "justice can wait, can it not? Your prisoner has a serious head injury. She's staying with me until she's out of danger. It should be a few hours. A day at the most."

"She's going to need someone to stand guard over her."

"You think she poses a threat? She'll be unconscious until I say otherwise."

"And what if the assassin comes looking for her?"

"First he'd have to know who she's with, then where to find me, and lastly he'd have to get past my defences, for which he'd need an army. Leave me now. I'll get in touch when she's strong enough to answer your questions."

With nothing left for them to do, they walked back to the Bentley. Valkyrie buckled her seatbelt as they pulled out on to the road. Skulduggery was using the façade again. Ghastly Bespoke's façade gave him his own face every time, minus the scars, but Skulduggery hadn't been able to decide on one look, so China made it so that *his* façade changed every time. Same cheekbones, same jaw, but all the rest was brand-new.

"Could you drop me off at Gordon's?" Valkyrie asked.

Skulduggery raised an eyebrow – a newly acquired skill. "You don't want to go home to Haggard?"

"It's not that, it's just that I haven't been to Gordon's in a while, and it's nearly Christmas. Around this time every year when I was a kid, we'd go up there, to his big house. I loved that part of Christmas, because, finally, someone would talk to me like I was a person, you know? A grown-up person, not a child. That's what I loved about him the most."

"Ah, there it is," Skulduggery said, and nodded.

"Sorry?"

"That, right there. That story you just told. That little excerpt from your life. That's the most annoying thing about Christmas. Everyone has these little stories about what Christmas means to them. You don't get that at any other time of the year. You don't get people telling you what Easter means to them, or St Patrick's Day. But everyone opens up at Christmas time."

"Wow," Valkyrie said. "I never noticed before, but you're a grouch."

"No, I'm not."

"You're a Grinch."

"I am neither a Grinch nor a grouch. I like Christmas as much as the next person, so long as the next person is as unsentimental as I am."

"Sentimental's nice."

"You *hate* sentimental."

"But not at Christmas. At Christmas, sentimental is a perfectly fine thing to be. It is allowed. In moderation, naturally. I don't want anyone, you know, being sentimental around *me*, but in principle I have no problem with... uh..."

"What? What's wrong?"

"Um, the façade..."

Skulduggery tilted his head, and the left side of his face drooped down off his skull, looking like melted rubber.

"I think something's going a bit wonky," said Valkyrie.

Skulduggery felt his ear flapping against his lapel and took hold of his face with one hand and hoisted it back up again. He gathered a thick fold around his forehead, trying his best to manoeuvre an eye back into its socket. "This is a tad undignified," he murmured. "Do please tell me if we're about to crash into something."

"Maybe you should let me drive."

"I saw how you drove a few hours ago. I'm not letting you behind the wheel of this car ever again." His voice was muffled because his lips were sliding down his jaw. "Do I look better now?"

"Oh, much."

He did his best to keep his nose in one place.

"So will I pick you up from Gordon's once your lapse into sentimentality is over? We have that meeting to go to, in case you've forgotten."

"How could I have forgotten?" she asked dryly. "I've been looking forward to this incredibly boring meeting for days, I really and truly have, oh boy oh boy."

"You appear to have found a new level of sarcasm," Skulduggery nodded. "Impressive."

"And no, you don't have to pick me up. I'll get Fletcher to pop by. Of course, if you change your mind and decide I don't have to go to this incredibly boring meeting, I can take my time about it all, and really get the sentimentality out of my system for good."

"And deprive you of your chance to be there? I actually think you'll be surprised by how interesting it all is."

"I actually think I'd be *very* surprised."

"But we'll be electing a new Grand Mage. This is history in the making, Valkyrie."

"And how long do you think the new Grand Mage will last before he's either murdered or imprisoned?"

"You're too young to be so cynical."

"I'm not cynical. I just happen to *remember* the last four years. You give me one good reason why I should go. One good reason why I would be even remotely interested in attending."

"Erskine Ravel will be there."

"Well, OK then."

Skulduggery laughed, and let go of his face. After a dangerous quiver, it settled down and stopped misbehaving, apart from the ear that was slowly drifting towards his chin.

5

VALKYRIE'S DILEMMA

With the morning sun barely making an effort to leak through the windows, Valkyrie's dead uncle made a steeple of his fingers, and peered at her over the topmost peak. When he was alive, he would often do this while sitting in an armchair with his legs crossed, giving him the air of a wise and contemplative man. Now that he was dead and could no longer interact with the physical world, it merely gave him the air of a man in desperate need of a chair.

"You've discovered your true name," he said.

"Yes," Valkyrie responded.

"And your true name is Darquesse."

"That's right."

"And Darquesse is the sorcerer that all the psychics are having visions about – the one who's going to destroy the world."

"Correct."

"So *you're* going to destroy the world."

"It looks like it."

"And when did you discover all this?"

"About five months ago."

"And you're only telling me about it *now*?"

"Gordon, it's taken me this long to stop freaking out about it. I need your help."

Gordon began to pace the room. It was a big room, lined with bookcases and Gothic paintings. An oil portrait of a semi-clothed Gordon, his body rippling with muscles he had never possessed when he was alive, hung over the vast fireplace, glaring down at all who passed like a great and terrible god. Even though this house and the land around it had been left to Valkyrie, she still couldn't bring herself to take the painting down. It was far too amusing.

"Do you realise what this means for you?" Gordon asked, as

his slow pacing took him towards the corner of the room. "A sorcerer who knows their own true name has access to power other sorcerers can only dream about."

His image began to fade away, and Valkyrie cleared her throat loudly. Gordon stopped and swung round, pacing back the way he had come. Immediately, he became solid again. The Echo Stone which housed his consciousness sat in its cradle on the coffee table, glowing with a soothing blue light.

"I don't care about any of that," she said. "I saw one of these visions, OK? I saw a burning city and injured friends and I saw Darquesse – I saw *me* – kill my own *parents*."

"Now, just wait a second. From what you've told me about Cassandra Pharos's vision, your future self and Darquesse seem to be two distinctly separate entities."

"That's just because at no time in that vision was I ever seen hurting anyone. We saw *fragments* of what's going to happen. We saw Darquesse, *me*, as a figure in the distance, fighting and killing and murdering, and then we saw me, my *future* self, close up, feeling pretty bad about it all, which was nice of her, but she's undoubtedly a little fruitloops. Listen, it's taken a while for me to look at this and be logical about it, but obviously *someone* finds out what my true name is, and they use it to control me."

"Then you're going to have to seal your name," Gordon said.

"Do you know how I can do that?"

"No," he admitted. "I wrote about magic, but as you are aware, I never had the aptitude for it. Something like that, sealing your true name, is knowledge only a certain breed of sorcerer would have."

"I can't ask Skulduggery," Valkyrie said quietly. "I don't want him to know."

Gordon stopped pacing, and looked at her kindly. "He would understand, Valkyrie. Skulduggery has been through an awful lot."

"If he's so understanding, how come you still won't let me tell him you exist?"

"Well," Gordon said huffily, "that's different. That was never about him or anyone else. It was always about me, and my insecurities."

"Which you are now cured of, right?"

He hesitated. "In theory..."

"So you'd be fine with me telling Skulduggery that I talk to you on a regular basis?"

Gordon licked his lips. "I don't think that now is the perfect time for that. You have a lot on your plate, and I think

I can be of more use to you without the distraction of other people."

"You're scared."

"I'm not scared, I'm cautious. I don't know how my friends would react. I am not actually Gordon Edgley after all – I am merely a recording of his personality."

"But...?" Valkyrie raised her eyebrows.

"But," he said quickly, "that doesn't mean I'm not a person in my own right, with my own identity and value."

"Very good," she smiled. "You've been working on it."

"I have a lot of time for self-affirmation while I'm sitting in that little blue crystal, waiting for you to drop by."

"Is that your subtle way of telling me I should call round more?"

"I practically cease to exist when you're not here," Gordon said. "There's nothing subtle about it."

The alarm on Valkyrie's phone beeped once. "Fletcher will be here soon," she said, picking up the Echo Stone and its cradle. "We better get you back."

Gordon followed as she led the way out of the living room and up the stairs. "The big meeting is this afternoon, isn't it?"

"Yeah," she scowled. "Even after everything that's been happening, with everything that's hanging over me, I still have to waste my time at this stupid thing. Skulduggery says it's important to see how this kind of politics works."

"You're lucky," Gordon said wistfully. "I would have loved to have been invited to something like that when I was alive."

"It's going to be a bunch of people talking about what we're going to do about setting up a new Sanctuary. What do I have to contribute to *that?*"

"I don't know. A general air of grumpiness?"

"Now *that* I can do."

They passed into the study, but instead of following her through the hidden doorway to the secret room where he kept the most valued pieces of his collection, Gordon went to a small bookshelf beside the window. "And how is Fletcher these days?"

"He's grand."

"Has he met your parents?"

Valkyrie frowned. "No. And he's not going to."

"You don't think they'd approve?" Gordon asked as he scanned the books.

"I think they'd start asking all kinds of awkward questions. And I don't think they'd like the fact that my boyfriend is older than me."

"He's eighteen, you're sixteen," Gordon said. "That's not *drastically* older."

"If I need to tell them, I will. Right now, Skulduggery has taken responsibility for asking every single awkward question that my parents could ever *possibly* ask, so you needn't worry."

"This one," said Gordon, pointing to a thin notebook. "In here there are directions to a woman who might be able to help you."

"She can seal my name?"

"Not her personally, but I think she knows someone who can."

"Who is she?"

"*Who* isn't important. *What*, however, is. She's a banshee."

"Seriously?"

"Most banshees are harmless," Gordon said. "They provide a service, more then anything else."

"What kind of service?"

"If you hear a banshee's wail, it's a warning that you're going to die. I'm not sure of the advantage of such a service, but it's a service nonetheless. Twenty-four hours after you hear it, the Dullahan gets you."

"What's a Dullahan?"

"He's a headless horseman, in the service of the banshee."

"Headless?"

"Yes."

"Seriously?"

"Yes."

"So he has no head?"

"That's usually what headless means."

"No head at all?"

"You're really getting hung up on this headless thing, aren't you?"

"It's just kind of silly, even for us."

"Yet you spend your days with a living skeleton."

"But at least Skulduggery has a head."

"True."

"He even has a spare."

"Are we going to get past this now?"

"Yes. Sorry. Carry on."

"Thank you. The Dullahan drives a carriage, the Coach-a-Bowers, that you can only see when it's right up beside you. He is not a friendly fellow."

"Probably because he has no head."

"That may have something to do with it."

"So this banshee," Valkyrie said, "is she one of the harmless ones, or the harmful?"

"Now *that* I do not know. Banshees are an unsociable bunch

at the best of times. If she isn't too pleased to see you, though..."

"Yes?"

"I'd recommend putting your hands over your ears if she opens her mouth."

Valkyrie looked at him. "Right," she said. "Thanks for that."

"When do you plan to approach her?"

"Soon, I suppose. I mean, as soon as I can. I want this over with. I think I'll... Tonight."

"Really?"

"Yes. I have to, Gordon. If I put it off, I'll never do it. I'll give Skulduggery some excuse. He won't miss me."

"Valkyrie, from what I know of it, sealing your name is a major procedure. You have to be sure, going in, that this *is* the best thing to do."

"I'm *going* to be sure. You remember when Dusk bit me? He tasted something in my blood, something that marked me out as different. I think that whatever he tasted has to do with Darquesse. So I'm going to get a second opinion."

Gordon frowned. "You're going to get someone else to taste your...? Oh, I see. You're talking about *him*."

"Caelan will be able to tell me what Dusk sensed. If it's bad,

45

I won't need any more proof or prodding. I'll know this is something I have to do."

"Right," Gordon said gently.

Valkyrie nodded, feeling an unwelcome mixture of apprehension and uncertainty. She left the Echo Stone in the hidden room and took the notebook from the shelf, flicking through the pages until she got to the part about the banshee. She put the notebook in her jacket pocket and went down to the living room. Her phone beeped again, and a moment later Fletcher Renn appeared beside the fireplace. Blond hair standing on end, lips always ready to kiss or smirk, one hand behind his back, the other with a thumb hooked into the belt loops of his jeans.

"I'm gorgeous," he said.

Valkyrie sighed. "Are you, now?"

"Do you ever just look at me and think, God he's gorgeous? Do you? I do, all the time. I think *you're* gorgeous too, of course."

"Cheers."

"You've got lovely dark eyes, and lovely dark hair, and your face is all pretty and stuff. And I love the way you dress in black, and I love the new clothes."

"It's a jacket, Fletch."

"I love the new jacket," he insisted. "Ghastly really made a lovely, lovely jacket." He grinned.

"You look wide awake," she said. "You're never wide awake at this hour of the morning."

"I've been researching. You're not the only one who likes to read books, you know. Apparently, my power will increase if I work at it a little, so I thought I'd give it a try. I was told there was this book in Italy, written by a famous Teleporter – dead now, obviously – that could really help me, so I went there and got it."

"Good man."

"But it was written all in Italian, so I left it on the shelf and went to Australia for ice cream." He brought his other hand out from behind his back, holding an ice-cream cone. "Got one for you."

"Fletcher, it's winter."

"Not in Australia."

"We're not *in* Australia."

"I'll take you to Sydney for five minutes, you can eat the ice cream while we watch the sunset, and then we'll come back to the misery here."

Valkyrie sighed. "Your power is wasted on you."

"My power is brilliant. Everyone wishes they had my power."

"I don't. I quite like being able to hurl people away from me just by moving the air."

"Well, every *non-violent* person wishes they had my power, how's that?"

Valkyrie frowned. "I'm not a violent person."

"You punch people every day."

"Not *every* day."

"Val, you know I think you're great, and I think you're the coolest chick I've ever met, and the prettiest girl ever – but you get into a hell of a lot of fights. Face it, you lead a violent life."

She wanted to protest, but no argument sprang to mind. Fletcher stopped holding out the ice cream, and started licking it instead, already forgetting what they'd just been talking about. Valkyrie checked the time, forcing her attention back to the here and now.

"Are you getting me anything for Christmas?" Fletcher asked, and Valkyrie found herself grinning despite everything.

"Yes. You better be getting *me* something."

He shrugged. "Of course I am."

"It better be amazing."

"Of course it is. Hey, this time next year, you'll have someone *else* to buy presents for. When's your mum due?"

"Middle of February. I'm going to be asked to babysit, you know. How am I supposed to do that?"

"Get your reflection to do it."

"I'm not leaving the baby with the *reflection*. Are you nuts? But I don't even know how to hold a baby. Their heads are so big. Aren't babies' heads abnormally large? I'm not sure I'm going to be a good big sister. I hope she doesn't take after me. I'd like her to have friends."

"You have friends."

"I'd like her to have friends who weren't hundreds of years older than her."

"Have you realised that you're referring to the baby as 'her'?"

"Am I? I suppose I am. I don't know. It just feels like it's going to be a girl."

"Do you think she'll be magic?"

"Skulduggery says it's possible. Of course, that doesn't mean she'll ever *find out* about magic. Take my cousins, for example."

"Ah, the infamous Toxic Twins."

"They're descended from the Last of the Ancients the same as I am, but we'll never *know* if they can do magic, because they don't know magic even *exists*."

"So if you don't want your sister involved in this crazy life of yours, you can just not tell her. And in twenty-five years, she'll be looking at you, going, 'Hey, sis, how come we look like we're exactly the same age?' Will you tell her *then* that magic slows the aging process?"

"I'll probably just tell her that my natural beauty makes me look eternally young. She's my little sister – she'll believe anything I tell her."

"To be honest, Val, I love the fact that this is happening. Once you have a sister, or a brother, that looks up to you and needs you, it might make you stop and think before rushing into dangerous situations."

"I do stop and think."

"And then you rush in anyway."

"There's still stopping and thinking involved."

Fletcher smiled. "Sometimes I just worry about you."

"Your concern is touching."

"You're not taking me even a little bit seriously, are you?"

"I can't take you seriously, Fletch, you have a dollop of ice cream on your nose. Besides, we can have this conversation a thousand times – it's not going to stop me going out there and doing what I do."

Fletcher finished off the cone and wiped the ice cream from his face.

"Are you so determined to be the hero?" he asked softly.

She kissed him, and didn't answer. He was wrong, of course. It wasn't about her being the hero – not any more. It was just about her trying not to be the villain.

6

THE NEW MESSIAH

Sneaking up on someone who can see into the future is not as impossible a task as many people think. For one thing, the future changes. Details shift, circumstances alter, and while the universe is struggling to realign itself into some semblance of balance, opportunity has its moment to present itself. The trick is to be a constant destabilising influence in a world that really just wants to be left alone.

Solomon Wreath was confident that he could be just such a destabilising influence. Leaving many of his decisions open to chance, he had approached the tattoo parlour three times already, and by the toss of a coin he had walked on by. The fourth toss of the coin, however, brought him to the door, and had him climbing the narrow stairs, black bag in one hand, cane in the other. No sound coming from above him. No whine of the tattooist's needle. No chat, laughter or yelp. He could practically sense the trap waiting for him, but this didn't slow his step.

At the top of the stairs he turned and walked through the doorway, and that was when the skinny man with the Pogues T-shirt came at him with a cushion. Not being the world's deadliest weapon, the cushion bounced softly off Wreath's shoulder, and the skinny man did his best to run by. Wreath dropped his cane, caught the man and threw him against a chair that looked like it belonged in a dental surgery. The skinny man fell awkwardly over it.

"Finbar Wrong," Wreath said, putting the black bag on a nearby table. "May I call you Finbar? I assume you know who I am."

Finbar sprang to his feet, hands held out in front of him, fingers rigid. "I do," he said, "and I feel I have to warn you, man, you can't beat me. I've seen this fight already, and I know every move you're gonna make."

Shadows curled around Wreath's cane, and brought it up off the floor and into his waiting hand.

Finbar nodded. "I knew you were gonna do that."

Wreath went to walk around the chair. Finbar moved in the opposite direction. Wreath turned, went the other way, and so did Finbar.

Wreath sighed. "This is ridicul—"

"*Ridiculous!*" Finbar interrupted quickly. "See? I've already lived through this encounter. You'd better walk away now, dude, save yourself a whole lot of pain."

"If you *have* seen this fight, if you knew *precisely* when I would arrive, then why did you attack me with a cushion?"

Finbar hesitated. "I'm... I'm toying with you, is what I'm doing. Hitting you with a *cushion* instead of my fists of fury is gonna, like, take *longer*, draw out your agony. Kinda like water torture, with cushions. Cushion torture."

"It doesn't *sound* very painful."

"Well, I haven't really settled on a name for it..."

"You're a trained fighter, I take it?"

"Oh, yeah."

"You're a bit thin, aren't you? You're practically malnourished."

"Looks can be deceiving, man. After all, the strongest muscle in the human body is the *brain*."

"Well then, as along as you don't hit me with your brain, I should be OK."

Finbar suddenly broke for the door. Wreath came up behind him, whacked the cane into the back of his legs. Finbar crashed into the wall.

"Ow," he moaned.

Wreath took a hold of him and dragged him back, threw him into the dentist's chair. "When did you first have a vision that I would be paying you a visit?"

"Last night," he moaned.

"And what did you do?"

"I sent Sharon and my kid away. I was gonna join them, but the vision changed, and you weren't gonna come."

"But then a few minutes ago..."

He nodded. "Had another one. Told me you were about to climb the stairs. Only weapon I had was the cushion."

"Which is not technically considered a weapon."

Finbar glared. "A true master can make *anything* into a weapon."

"But you're *not* a true master, Finbar." Wreath prodded him with the cane, forcing him to sit back. "Did your vision tell you *why* I was coming to see you?"

"I didn't really get that far."

"I need you to do me a favour. I want you to look into Valkyrie Cain's future, and tell me what you see."

"Why don't you just ask her?"

"I need something more than what you've already seen. I need you to look harder."

"Can't do it," Finbar said, shaking his head. "I won't do it. Val's a friend of mine. You can torture me all you want."

"Can I?"

He paled. "Metaphorically speaking."

Wreath smiled, and shadows crept up the chair, wrapping themselves around Finbar's arms and legs before he could even struggle. Wreath went to the black bag on the table. "It's OK. I know it would probably take a lot for you to betray a friend like that. So I'm taking the option away from you."

From the bag, Wreath took a glass sphere, encased in a stone shell.

Quickly realising that he couldn't break his bonds, Finbar settled back into the chair. "You're bribing me with a snow globe?" he asked. "That's a bit... insulting, don't you think?"

"This isn't for you."

Now Finbar could see the darkness swirling in the sphere, and his face slackened and his voice cracked. "That's a Soul Catcher."

"Yes, it is. And its occupant is the Remnant who caused everyone so much trouble a few months ago. This is the little

56

guy who possessed Kenspeckle Grouse, who went on to repair the Desolation Engine that destroyed the Sanctuary. This is not a very nice Remnant."

Finbar licked his lips nervously. "You can't put it in me. You just *can't*, man. No, listen, that thing is, it's *evil*, right? Once it's in me, it'll lie to you, tell you whatever it thinks you wanna hear."

"It will tell me whatever I want to *know*, Finbar, which is not quite the same thing."

"Aw, please, don't do this." The man was almost crying.

"I'll take it out of you immediately after," Wreath assured him. "You'll black out; you won't remember a thing."

"I don't want it in me. It'll change me."

"Only for a few minutes."

Wreath turned the sphere in the stone, and stepped back.

The darkness drained out of the Soul Catcher as the Remnant flitted straight to Finbar. He turned his head and shut his eyes and clamped his mouth shut, but the Remnant would not be denied. Things that may have been hands prised his jaws apart. Wreath watched, fighting the urge to suck the foul creature back into its prison.

Finbar tried to scream as the Remnant, no more than a streak of twisted darkness, clambered its way down his throat. The scream choked and the throat bulged. Finbar's body thrashed, but Wreath's restraints held. Finbar suddenly went limp. A moment passed, and dark veins spread beneath his skin and his lips turned black. Then his eyes opened.

"Why is it," Finbar said, "that every time I'm set free, I have to share a body that isn't in the peak of physical perfection? Last time it was an old man. Now it's... this."

"I didn't release you for a casual conversation," Wreath said. "I just want to know what I want to know."

"And why would I help *you* dig up information on my good buddy Valkyrie?"

"She isn't your friend," Wreath said. "She's *Finbar Wrong's* friend."

"And there you go, man, making the mistake that everyone makes. I *am* Finbar Wrong."

"No, you're a Remnant."

"To be honest with you there, a Remnant isn't really much more than *intent*. It flies around being angry and doesn't think too much about anything, y'know? It doesn't have a personality, or a real consciousness to speak of. But when it inhabits a body, that all changes. It's whole again. I *am* Finbar Wrong, but I'm also the Remnant inside him. We're very happy together, as you can see." He smiled, and the black veins receded and the darkness disappeared from his lips.

"It's easy for you to pass for normal, isn't it?" Wreath asked. "To hide the tell-tale signs that mark the possessed?"

"We can hide it when we need to, yeah."

"And it's good to be out of the Soul Catcher, yes?"

"Oh, yeah," Finbar laughed. "That thing is even worse than being in that room in the Midnight Hotel where they kept us locked up."

"Now that you've tasted freedom, do you want more? I can give you more. I can let you go."

"A few moments ago you said you were gonna separate us immediately after."

"I'm a Necromancer. I lied to make it easier on... you. The old you. Look into the future for me, and tell me what you see."

"And what makes you think I'll be able to see anything new?"

"Because you and I both know that Sensitives are wary about pushing themselves too hard. Seeing the future is a dangerous line of work. Minds can snap."

"That they can."

"But your mind is reinforced now, isn't it? It's stronger. So you can look further, and harder, until you see what you need to see."

"This is all very true," Finbar nodded. "But why should I trust you? The last people to ask me a favour put me in an old man's body. Now, I'm not denying I had fun being Kenspeckle Grouse for a day, especially when it came time to hammer nails through Tanith Low's hands, but they cheated me. They wouldn't let me go when they said they would."

"Scarab has never been a trustworthy man."

"And *you* are? You're a *Necromancer*."

"Then how about this? You look into the future for me, or I'll kill you. Remnants can't survive in something dead, am I right? So the moment Finbar's body dies, the Remnant inside him dies too. Do you want to die? Either of you?"

Finbar smiled. "You're talking like there are two of us in here, man. There's not. You had Finbar, you had the Remnant, and when you put them together, you get me. And I happen to think that the world would miss me too much if you killed me."

Wreath smiled back. "I thought you'd see it my way."

"I'm gonna need a few things before I start, though. Herbs, potions, a backrub..."

"You have three seconds to begin."

"A very *quick* backrub, then."

Wreath raised the cane, and Finbar laughed. "OK, OK! I

suppose I could do without the luxuries, just this one time. You're gonna have to back off – I'm not gonna be able to attain the required level of relaxation if you're hovering over me."

Wreath nodded. "Get it done, Remnant, or you're going back in the bottle."

"Chill," Finbar breathed, closing his eyes. "My old buddy Val," he murmured. "Are you going to show me why everyone's so interested in you, are you? Are you going to show me what's in store for you...?"

Wreath suppressed a sigh while Finbar prattled on, his voice growing softer and softer. He'd never had much time for Sensitives. They'd deliberately chosen a branch of magic where you reached out with your feelings instead of your fists. They were, in his opinion, a bunch of spaced-out, peace-loving hippies, and he'd *never* liked hippies. The 1960s and 70s had been particularly annoying times for him.

"There she is," Finbar said, a slight smile on his face. "Found her."

"How far ahead are you?" Wreath asked quickly.

"Hard to say, man... She looks a little older... She's got a tattoo..."

"Is she a Necromancer?"

Finbar's brow creased over his closed eyes. "Don't know..."

"What's she doing?"

"Walking..."

"Where?"

"In the ruins."

Wreath shook his head. "That's with Darquesse, right? I'm not interested in that. You need to find out if Valkyrie is the Death Bringer."

"I can only see what I see," Finbar said in a sing-song voice. "My sight is drawn to the big moments..."

"Then look away," Wreath snarled, but his impatience went unnoticed.

"I've never seen this much detail," Finbar continued, deep in the trance. "I've always flinched... But now I can see it all... So many dead... It's wonderful..."

Wreath held his tongue.

"I'm looking at Darquesse now... She's magnificent... She's striding through the city, death all around her... You'd like this, dude. So much death..."

"I didn't ask for a vision of Darquesse, I asked for a vision of Valkyrie." Wreath's eyes narrowed. "Unless..."

Finbar smiled in his dream-state. "Unless?"

"Is Valkyrie still there? Can you see her?"

"I can sense her presence, but all I can see is Darquesse."

"Maybe that's it," Wreath said, sudden excitement burning through him. "Maybe that's how she does it. If Valkyrie *is* the Death Bringer, maybe she's the one who steps up and fights. Maybe she's the one who stops Darquesse and then *this*, her victory, is what leads to the Passage. This is how she saves the world."

"I don't see any of that," Finbar said. "All I see is Darquesse." His smile was replaced by a grimace. "This is painful, by the way..."

"Keep looking."

"It hurts my head."

"Keep looking or you'll *lose* that head."

"I'll keep looking then."

Blood dripped from Finbar's nose. Wreath said nothing.

"I've found her again," Finbar said happily.

"Valkyrie?"

"Darquesse. I'm... I'm drawn to her... I don't have a choice. She is... everything. She's so cold. I'm trying to get in closer, but she's... She's unlike anything I've ever *seen*..."

"Can you see a weakness? How can Valkyrie destroy her?"

"Darquesse will *not* be destroyed!" Finbar snarled suddenly. "She is everything!"

"Tell me her weakness."

"She has none! She is perfection!"

"Then who is she? Where does she come from?"

Finbar strained harder, and blood began leaking from his ears. "The shadows are heavy around her... I'm trying to see her face... She's looking away from me... No, wait, she's turning, she's turning, I can see her..."

Finbar stopped talking.

"Well?" Wreath pressed. "Can you see her face? What does she look like? Who is she?"

Finbar's eyes opened. He blinked up at Wreath. "This changes everything."

Wreath leaned in close. "Who is she, damn it?"

"You Necromancers have your messiah," Finbar said, "now we Remnants have ours."

The black veins appeared again, and his head shot forward and crunched against Wreath's nose. Wreath stumbled back, cursing, feeling his shadow restraints collapse under Finbar's Remnant-enhanced strength. Hands grabbed him, and suddenly he was flying into the far wall. He crashed through a shelf and sent equipment spilling out across the floor.

"Hope you don't mind, man," Finbar said, smiling at him, "but I'm gonna take you over for a bit. I have a brand-new mission, and I need an upgrade."

Wreath tasted his own blood. His cane was on the floor behind him. There were two ways out of this room – the door and the window. The window was closer.

Finbar opened his mouth wide. Wreath glimpsed the Remnant start to climb out and then he spun, snatching up his cane and using the shadows to smash the window. He leaped through the broken glass without the slightest hesitation, landing painfully on the cobbled street, sending people scattering all around him. He didn't look at their shocked faces. He didn't look back at Finbar, standing at the window. He just ran.

7

BLOOD

Valkyrie took a taxi to St Anne's Park, which was still covered in a fine frosting of white that the weak sun was failing to melt away. She passed over the gurgling stream, smiling at a dog that was being taken for a walk. Her breath came out in puffs of cloud, and her hands were jammed in her pockets. She moved off the well-worn trail into the trees. Dead twigs cracked under her boots.

Caelan was standing on an embankment that dipped five metres down. He didn't look round as she approached. Instead, he kept his gaze on an old couple below him, out for a brisk midday stroll. Valkyrie wondered, briefly, if he was hungry.

"I need your help," she said, and watched him turn his eyes to her. Being held in his gaze had become an electric experience that was as addictive as it was unsettling. She didn't like this power he had over her. Being around him was like being around China, but with China she at least had the knowledge that the attraction was coerced through use of magic. With Caelan, though, the attraction was real, and so it was a lot more dangerous.

"I'm waiting," he said, with a slight smile, and she realised she hadn't spoken a word for the last few seconds. She looked away, letting her hair fall over her face to hide the blush creeping through her cheeks.

"You're probably not going to like it," she said, "so it'd be a huge favour I'd have to pay back. The problem is that I can't really tell you why I need this done. You've just got to trust me when I say I have my reasons."

"What do you need?"

Valkyrie hesitated. "I need you to taste my blood."

Caelan's smile froze on his lips. "You can't be serious."

"Dusk bit me," she said. "You know how much he wanted to kill me, and he had his chance, but he didn't take it. Haven't you ever wondered why he let me go?"

"Because I stopped him," Caelan replied gruffly.

"No. You arrived after he'd pushed me away. He told Billy-Ray Sanguine that he tasted my blood and... I don't know. Whatever happened, whatever was in my blood, it changed his mind. He no longer wants to kill me. They both think it's a lot crueller to let me live."

"You want me to tell you what's so special about your blood?"

"Yes."

"Dusk is hundreds of years older than me. He could detect a thousand different nuances in your blood that I couldn't *begin* to identify. Dusk is a connoisseur. I'm not."

"But you can try."

"There's no point."

"Caelan, there's something wrong with me, do you understand? There's something wrong with who I am and Dusk knew straight away, from one tiny bite. You might not have his experience, but I need you to *try*."

"You don't know what you're asking. It's far too dangerous."

"I'm used to dangerous."

"For *me*, Valkyrie. It's too dangerous for *me*. I don't know how Dusk managed to deny himself, but I'm not that strong. If I bite you, I won't stop feeding until you're dead."

"Then don't bite me. I'll cut my finger – you can taste a drop."

"Would you please remember who you're talking to? I'm a vampire! There's a reason I'm classed as a monster! You really think that letting me taste a drop of your blood is a good idea? Really? You think that won't drive me insane? One drop and I'd need the rest. I'd need all of it."

"You've still got a mind. You don't lose the ability to think, do you? You're not an animal."

"That's precisely what I am. You look at me while the sun is shining, and you think this is me. This is Caelan. You think the vampire is the thing that comes out at night, then goes away in the morning and Caelan comes back. You don't understand yet that the vampire *is* Caelan.

"This face is a mask. This skin is a disguise. Beneath it is the real me, Valkyrie. I'm not a tortured soul. I'm not a brooding romantic figure. I'm a monster, and not a moment goes by when I don't want to rip your throat out. No other vampire on the planet wants anything to do with me, and I really don't want to be cornered by the Skeleton Detective and his vengeance-hungry friends after I'm done feeding on your corpse. I quite like immortality. You get very used to it after a while."

Valkyrie looked at him, but didn't speak, and the anger slowly left him, until they were just two people, standing there in silence.

"You know," she said at last, "that's the most words I've ever heard you speak."

Caelan nodded. "I was just thinking the same thing."

"You feeling OK?"

"Vocal cords are a little sore."

"You might want to sit down."

He smiled, and she smiled back.

"I need you to do this."

His smile vanished. "I'm telling you, no."

"Listen to me, OK? I'm working on something, something to help me, something that could hopefully solve all my problems. But the thing is, it's dangerous. And I mean really dangerous. I might not live through it. And I can't tell Skulduggery or Tanith or Fletcher because they'll try to stop me."

"But you can tell me because you think I won't try to stop you?"

"No, I'm not telling you either. But before I do this, I have to know if this is the right thing to do. I need to know what Dusk saw, or what he felt, or what he sensed. If it's as bad as I think it is, then I'll go through with this dangerous thing because it'll be my only option. If it isn't as bad as I think, I won't. Simple as that."

Caelan turned away, and didn't speak for a long time.

"Fine," he said at last. "But afterwards, it would probably be best if we never saw each other again."

"That's a bit dramatic, isn't it?"

"Perhaps."

"But that's stupid. Why should we never see each other?"

"You say that like you'd miss me."

"Of course I'd miss you. You're my friend."

"No, I'm not."

She frowned. "You're not?"

"You and me could never just be friends, Valkyrie. We were fated to either be nothing to each other, or everything."

She stared at him, struggling to make sense of what he was saying. "Uh…"

"Eloquent as usual."

"I mean… Caelan, I'm with Fletcher. And I *like* Fletcher, and I don't want to hurt you, but I… I don't know how I feel about you. This is a bit of a surprise to me, to be honest."

"You truly didn't know how I felt?"

"I really and truly didn't. I'm sorry if you think I did."

"I see."

She looked at him as he stepped back. "And now I feel awful."

"Don't," said Caelan.

"I can't help it. Do you... I hope you don't think I was leading you on, or anything."

He shook his head, but kept his eyes down. "Of course not. This is my fault."

"It's no one's fault, Caelan. You didn't do anything wrong. It's just, you know, I'm with Fletcher, and I never really thought about... the possibility of you."

"Because I'm a vampire," he said softly, like he was cursing his very soul.

"That's part of it," admitted Valkyrie. "But most of all it's because I'm sixteen and you're, like, a hundred."

"Ah," he said, cracking a smile. "I'm too old for you."

"Ever so slightly."

"And there is no part of you that wonders what it would be like?"

She swallowed. "I didn't... I didn't say *that*..."

"You need me to do this?"

"Yes. I do."

"Very well." He stepped up to her, one hand at her shoulder, the other sweeping her hair slowly from her neck. "I'm sorry to say this will hurt."

"I've been bitten before," said Valkyrie, and gritted her teeth.

Caelan pulled her towards him and she waited. When she was this close to Fletcher, she could feel his warmth, the heat emanating from him with each rapid heartbeat, but there was no warmth coming from Caelan. He was cold as smooth stone. Even though his mouth was a centimetre from her bare skin, she felt no breath. The fingers of his right hand curled in the collar of her jacket, the fingers of his left in her hair. She waited for his teeth. His cold body sagged, and he stepped back.

"I can't," he murmured. "I'd tear your throat out." He took a penknife from his pocket, slid the blade free, and gave it to her. "Just a drop. No more, Valkyrie, OK? I should be able to handle a drop. I think."

She pressed the blade into the pad of her fingertip, wincing as it pierced the skin. A drop of blood swelled up, and she brushed it with the knife and handed it back to him. Caelan hesitated, then brought the knife to his lips, running his tongue the length of the blade. He worked the blood around in his mouth, and as he did so, he folded the penknife and put it away. His movements were slow and deliberate; his eyes were closed. He swallowed, and licked his lips, like a lion standing over a felled deer.

Valkyrie had a sudden urge to step away.

"Caelan?" she said softly.

He was on her, lifting her off her feet and driving her back, teeth bared and diving for her throat. She twisted in his grip and hit a tree and he moved from her throat to her mouth and kissed her, his mouth crushing against hers. The kiss took her by complete surprise, and she hung there for a long moment before she realised she was kissing him back. She felt her arms wrap round his neck, felt his hard chest press against her. Then something sparked in Valkyrie's mind.

She pushed off against the tree with one foot while she tripped him with the other. They both fell to the ground, and she rolled off him and got to her feet. She tried to speak, but he was already behind her, his cold hands on her face, turning her head to kiss her again. Valkyrie folded into him, weakness flooding her body, before she forced strength back into it. She broke off the kiss and leaned away.

"This is not going to happen," she breathed.

"It already is," he said, his eyes dark.

"What did you see? Caelan! My blood. What did you see?"

He smiled. "Nothing. I tasted your blood and saw nothing."

"You're sure?"

"I don't know what insight Dusk gained, but I gained nothing. The only difference between your blood and anyone else's is... history."

"What do you mean?"

"It's old blood. It stretches back to power."

"To the Last of the Ancients?"

"That's probably it." His hand reached out to her and she slapped it away. His smile broadened. "But everyone knows you're descended from the Ancients. I can't see why it should come as such a big revelation to Dusk."

"Maybe he saw something else."

"Very possible. I've changed my mind, you know."

"About what?"

"About how we should spend some time apart."

"Caelan..."

"Now I think we should spend more time *together*."

"I think I need to go now."

Valkyrie went to walk by him and he laughed, and grabbed her hand. When she swung back to face him, his laugh was gone. "Fletcher's a boy," he said.

"That's why they call it a boyfriend."

"We're meant for each other."

"Holy God," she said, "do you always come on this strong?"

Caelan looked like he was about to sneer, then he frowned, and backed off. "I told you," he murmured, looking away. "I'm not... I'm not always in control."

Valkyrie took the opportunity to hurry away.

"Thank you," she called over her shoulder.

Caelan didn't answer.

8

THE ZOMBIE KING

The refrigerated van pulled in to the side of the road. Seconds passed, and the driver got out. He was a middle-aged man with bad skin. He wasn't very bright and tended to say stupid things that annoyed his master. His master was a great and terrible man. His master was the Killer Supreme. His master was the Zombie King.

Thrasher opened the rear door and Vaurien Scapegrace, the Zombie King, stood there majestically, blinking against the cold afternoon sunlight.

"We have arrived?" he asked imperiously.

"We're here," Thrasher said, nodding his idiot head. "We got lost for a little bit. I took a wrong turn, had to stop and ask for directions. I had a map with me, but it's pretty old, and with all these new one-way systems it's pretty hard to..."

And he prattled on, annoying the Zombie King with mind-numbingly boring detail. Not for the first time, Scapegrace wished he'd picked someone else to be his first zombie recruit. Every recruit *after* Thrasher decayed at the normal speed for a dead body, but Thrasher had – unfortunately – inherited some of Scapegrace's longevity.

But even the great Zombie King was looking poorly these days. Months earlier, his face had been badly burned by Valkyrie Cain. He had tried to peel the burnt skin off in giant flakes, but that only made things worse. His body would not repair itself, and so the disfigurement stayed, and occasionally another bit of him would fall off or stop working. Survival had become his only ambition. He went everywhere in this refrigerated van, he stayed out of the sun as much as possible, and he covered himself in car fresheners that struggled to mask the stench of rotting meat with sickly wafts of pine.

Survival. That's what it was all about. And that's why he was here today. Scapegrace stepped out of the van, on to the road.

"What do you need me to do, Master?" Thrasher asked, eagerness ripening his features.

"Stay here," Scapegrace replied, "and don't annoy me. How is my face?"

Thrasher hesitated. "It's... good. Fine. The make-up is... it really hides the, uh, the worst of the scarring."

"And my suit? Do I have any bits on it?" His ear had fallen off the day before. He'd stuck it back on with glue.

"It looks clean, sir."

"Excellent. Back in the van you go, Thrasher."

"Yes, sir... only..."

Scapegrace sighed. "What?"

"Don't you think I should be the one to talk to these people, Master? They are civilians, and I don't have the... distinguishing features that may alarm them..."

"Nonsense. I have it all worked out. I have my plan, and I've accounted for every single possibility. Every question they are likely, or even not so likely, to ask, I have prepared an answer for. My backstory is rock solid. My lies are intricate and one hundred per cent infallible. You'd only mess it all up."

"Yes, Master."

"Back in the van, moron."

Thrasher bowed, and did as he was bid. Scapegrace

adjusted his tie, then strode purposefully along the pavement. The road was a cul-de-sac, with only three buildings on it – a funeral parlour on either side, and a large house at the end with a car outside.

Scapegrace entered the first funeral parlour. A man in a sombre suit hurried up to him, took one look at his face and faltered.

"It looks worse than it is," Scapegrace chuckled good-naturedly.

"I... see," said the man.

"It was the same accident that killed my brother," Scapegrace continued, realising that he should probably stop chuckling. "It's a tragic shock. We're all very saddened by his loss."

The funeral director shook Scapegrace's hand, and gave him a sad smile. "Would you like to sit down?" he asked gently.

"I would, yes. I'm feeling quite faint, because of the loss of my dead brother."

The funeral director showed him to a comfortable chair, then sat behind his big desk and solemnly opened a ledger. He picked up what looked to be an expensive pen, and raised his eyes to Scapegrace. "May I ask your name?"

Scapegrace had rehearsed this part a dozen times, coming

up with answers for every possible question. This was an easy one. "Elvis O'Carroll."

The funeral director hesitated, then nodded, and wrote it down. "And your brother's?"

"I'm sorry?"

"Your brother's name?"

Scapegrace froze. It had all been going so well. "My brother's name," he managed, "is... a name that makes me cry every time I hear it. His name, my brother's name, my dead brother, is..." His mind raced, careered off walls and stumbled over hurdles. A name. A simple name. All he needed was a simple name to get to the next stage of the conversation, and he could not think of one. Aware that he was staring at the funeral director with a perplexed look on his face, Scapegrace seized a random name from history. "Adolf," he blurted.

The funeral director stared at him. "I'm sorry?"

"Adolf O'Carroll," Scapegrace continued, trying to be as calm as possible. "That's with two L's at the end."

"Your brother's name was Adolf?"

"Yes. Do you find something wrong with that? It's a common name in my family. I had an uncle Adolf, and a great-aunt Adolf."

"A great-aunt? You realise, of course, that Adolf is traditionally a man's name...?"

"Well, that makes sense, as my great-aunt was traditionally a man."

"You do seem to have an interesting family, Mr O'Carroll," the funeral director said politely as he scribbled notes.

"Please," Scapegrace said. "Call me Elvis."

"Indeed. May I inquire as to what service you wish us to provide for you, during this trying time? The funeral, of course, is what we specialise in, but we also—"

"Embalming," Scapegrace said. "Do you do your own embalming?"

"We prepare the departed for their final resting place, yes."

"And you do that here?"

"On the premises, yes. We have a staff of professionals who take care to treat each individual with the utmost respect. We have found there to be dignity in death, as there is in life."

"How long does it take?"

"The embalming process?"

"How long does it take to stop the decomposition?"

"I'm not sure I understand... What exactly are you asking us to do?"

"I want him preserved."

The funeral director put down his pen, and interlaced his fingers. "Are you... Are you asking us to perform taxidermy?"

"Am I? What's that? Is that when an animal is stuffed and mounted?"

"It is."

"That's it!" Scapegrace said happily. "That's what I want! Can you do that?"

"No."

"Why not?"

"Because the actual animal body is not *used* in taxidermy. The animal is skinned, and the skin is stretched over a *replica* animal body. Note, I keep saying *animal*. That is because taxidermy is not done to humans. It might be seen as somewhat barbaric."

"Wouldn't suit me anyway," Scapegrace murmured. "It needs to be the original body. So can you embalm it and just give it to me?"

"I'm afraid that we do not provide a take-away service."

"Maybe the place across the road does."

"That wouldn't surprise me," the funeral director said huffily, "but I doubt even *they* would stoop to that level. Mr O'Carroll—"

"Elvis."

"Elvis, I think the death of your brother has affected your judgement. You're not thinking clearly. What you're asking for is... unsettling."

"It's what Adolf would have wanted."

"I'm sure he would have appreciated a more peaceful resting place."

"His last words to me were, *'Don't bury me'*."

"We also provide a cremation service."

"And then he said, *'Don't burn me either'*."

The funeral director sighed. "Elvis, I don't think we are the people to help you. It is not often I recommend our rivals across the road, but I feel they would be more suited to your needs. I'm sure they'd be happy to deal with your... requests."

He smiled.

Scapegrace left the funeral parlour and crossed the road, dousing himself with a half-can of deodorant as he went. He was greeted by another sombre funeral director, explained his injuries without the chuckling this time, and was shown to another comfortable chair. He skipped through the tragic loss stuff quickly and got down to specifics.

"Adolf was a devout Catholic," he said. "And I mean, devout. Oh, he was crazy for that religion. He'd be praying every day, sometimes twice a day. It was all *Our Father* this and *Hail Mary* that. Rosary beads and signed pictures of the Pope. He went nuts for the whole thing. He thought priests were great altogether."

The funeral director nodded slowly. "So at least he was comforted in his time of need. Then it will be a traditional funeral you're looking for?"

"Not at all. Have you read the Bible?"

"I have, yes. I find great strength in its words."

"Did you read the bit about the zombies?"

"Uh..."

"The bit at the end, where God raises the dead for Judgement Day."

"Um, I... I'm not sure I..."

"It's when God decides who gets into Heaven and who doesn't, and all the dead climb out of their graves and they all wait there to see who gets in. That's in the Bible, right? That's what Adolf wants to do, but he wants a head start on all the others. He doesn't want to waste time crawling out of a hole in the ground. He wants to be ready for the sprint. So I want you to preserve him."

The funeral director paled. "*Preserve?*"

"I was thinking, if you pump all that embalming fluid into his veins, then I can take him away, store him somewhere cool, and he'll be ready to go at the end of the world. What do you think?"

"Are you... being serious?"

"I've got my dead brother in the back of my car. Of course I'm being serious."

"Mr O'Carroll..."

"Elvis."

"Elvis, what you're saying makes no sense."

"Do not deride my brother's religion."

"I assure you, I am doing no such thing. But what I *am* saying is that... your plan is nonsensical. A dead body will rot, sir, no matter how much embalming fluid is injected into it. Over time, everything decays."

"Adolf is particularly resilient."

"Even if Judgement Day happened before he started to decompose – say, if it happened on Thursday – embalming fluid would actually be a hindrance. It suffuses the muscles, stiffens them until they can't be moved. Do you understand, Elvis? He wouldn't have a head start on anyone. He'd actually be left behind, unable to move."

Scapegrace frowned. "So... So there's nothing you can do to stop decomposition?"

"I am sorry."

"What about those bodies they find in bogs, hundreds of years old?"

"Do you really want to lay Adolf to rest in a bog? Elvis, unless you're prepared to mummify your brother, he is going to decompose."

"What's that? Mummify? He'd be a mummy?"

"We don't do that sort of thing here."

"Well, who does?"

"Nobody."

"What about the Egyptians?"

"Nobody apart from the Egyptians," the funeral director nodded. "Take him to an Egyptian funeral parlour. They'll wrap him in bandages and put him in a sarcophagus and he'll be right as rain come Judgement Day."

"Really?"

"No. Those morons across the road paid you to come in here and waste my valuable time, didn't they?"

"Of course not."

"Did they tell you to act so stupid?"

"I'm not acting," Scapegrace responded.

"Tell them if they want to start this practical joke war again, then I'm fine with that. I've still got a few tricks up my sleeve. If it's a war they want, it's a war they'll get."

Scapegrace left the funeral parlour, confused and disheartened. It was as if the universe was closing off every avenue just as he was realising it was there. He had pinned all his hopes on being embalmed, and what was he left with, now that science had let him down?

He stopped in the middle of the road. Magic. Of course. He hadn't considered it before because, quite honestly, he had no sorcerer friends. But surely there *must* be something a mage could do. They were always coming up with new and exciting ways to live for as long as possible. Would it really take that much power to stop meat from rotting?

He was no expert – even in life, his grasp of magic had been negligible at best – but this seemed possible. All of Scapegrace's magic was used to animate his body and keep him thinking, but there was nothing stopping anyone else from performing magic *on* him.

There was a name that his old master Scarab had once mentioned. He had been talking about an expert in science-magic... Grouse, that was it. Kenspeckle Grouse, who had a

Medical Facility somewhere in Dublin. Butterflies of excitement fluttered within Scapegrace's stomach. He just needed to find out where it was, and all his troubles would be over.

A car horn beeped right behind him and he jumped in fright, then stalked to the pavement, muttering curses. The car carried on past him. Scapegrace saw it out of the corner of his eye, and froze. He knew that car. The first time he'd seen it, he had been thrown into the backseat in handcuffs. The second time, he was thrown into the trunk, in another set of handcuffs. It was the car Skulduggery Pleasant drove.

Scapegrace suddenly forgot how to walk like normal people. How had Pleasant known he was here? Had he been following him? Was this the day his existence ended? He was sure he hadn't been recognised, because he had been facing the other way and he was dressed in a suit, but all it would take was one glance and it would all be over. He staggered to a large bush and fell into it, then crawled around to take a look through the leaves. The black car turned the corner and was gone.

This didn't make any sense. Was it all an elaborate trap? An ambush? Pleasant had driven right by him. Had the great Skeleton Detective made a silly mistake? Or maybe he *hadn't* been searching for him after all. Maybe this was just a coincidence. Maybe the house...

Scapegrace looked back at the big house. Pleasant's car had been parked outside it. In the driveway in fact. Pleasant had parked his car in the driveway of the house like... like... like he'd *owned* the place.

Scapegrace stared. He knew where Skulduggery Pleasant lived.

Now all he had to do was figure out who'd pay the most for the information.

9

THE NEW GRAND MAGE

Valkyrie followed Skulduggery as he strode briskly through the alley. It was so cold it was almost painful, and for once, she was glad of it. It meant she had something else to think about other than kissing Caelan. She regretted it now. She'd regretted it the moment after it happened, but she couldn't stop replaying it over and over in her head.

Skulduggery came to some steps leading down below street level, and an iron door swung open to let them through. The corridor they walked into was warm, with fantastic images carved into the walls on both sides. In places the paint was cracked and peeling, but the years had not diminished the sheer lushness of the colours used. Valkyrie bent to examine a tiny running figure. Even the light glinting in the figure's eyes had been painted in.

"What is all this?" she asked.

"History," Skulduggery answered. "It's all here, for those who know how to look." He nodded to a carving of two men and a woman, holding light in their hands. "These are the Ancients, discovering magic for the first time. The clouds above them represent the Faceless Ones, and the grass at their feet represents the people."

"Regular people are represented by a lawn?" Valkyrie asked with a raised eyebrow. "How nice, and not at all insulting."

"The people are represented by individual blades of grass," Skulduggery said, a smile in his voice. "Born of the earth, as natural and integral a part of life as magic. You can see the Ancients protecting the grass from the unnatural storm clouds."

"All I see are the Ancients *standing* on the grass, being rained on, and not one of them thought to bring an umbrella. Not the smartest, were they?"

"Don't be *too* harsh – you're descended from one of them, remember."

"Any ancestor of *mine* would have brought an umbrella," Valkyrie muttered, and crossed to the other wall. The scene depicted there disturbed her, like a hook that had found its way inside her belly and was now tugging gently at her guts. A city in ruins, the dead scattered like dry leaves fallen from a tree on a still afternoon. At its centre stood a man, burning with black fire. "And this?" she asked. "Is this meant to be Mevolent?"

Skulduggery stood at her elbow. "These chambers were built before the war with Mevolent even started. No, that's not Mevolent. That's his master. That's the Unnamed."

Valkyrie looked at him. "Was his *name* the Unnamed, or did he just not *have* a name?"

"He didn't have one."

She frowned. "But how does *that* work? All our magic comes from our true name, right? I've been reading all about this. So if he didn't *have* a true name, where did he get his magic from?"

"To every law of nature, there are the aberrations. I'm very impressed that you're doing a little research, by the way."

"After Marr ordered Myron Stray to kill himself and destroy the Sanctuary, I thought it might be a good idea to learn a little more about the whole name thing."

"You're worried that someone might learn *your* true name?"

Worried was such a weak term for something so coldly terrifying. Valkyrie nodded, but didn't speak. She didn't trust herself to answer him.

Skulduggery started walking again. "So what did you learn?"

She walked beside him, forcing herself to remain casual. "Our true names are names of magic, from the oldest of the magical languages. Virtually all of us go around without knowing what that name actually is, but we can still use the magic it provides."

"And?"

"If you find out what your true name is, it's kind of like going straight to the source. You'd become more powerful than even the Ancients were. You'd be able to take on the Faceless Ones without needing a weapon."

"If that is so," Skulduggery said, "then how come Myron Stray became a puppet, and not a god?"

"Someone, in this case Mr Bliss, found out his true name before he did, so he never had time to seal it."

They walked into the Great Chamber and the conversation died away. Thirty or forty people stood around on the marble floor, talking quietly. The walls in here were splendid, the elaborate carvings continuing up to the domed ceiling.

Erskine Ravel smiled as he came over. Valkyrie had met him a few times before – he had fought in a special unit with Skulduggery and Ghastly during the war. She liked Ravel. He was charming and nice and quite beautiful, in a manly sort of way.

"Erskine," Skulduggery said, shaking his hand.

"Skulduggery, good to see you," said Ravel, shaking Valkyrie's hand next. "Valkyrie, you're looking well."

She actually blushed, and turned her head so it wouldn't be noticed. Then she spotted an old man with a grey beard, and frowned. "Why is he here?"

Ravel put his hands in his pockets. "Like it or not, we need representatives from all the major groups in order to elect a new Grand Mage, and the mages in Roarhaven have as much say as anyone."

"But why does *he* have to be here?"

"You don't like the Torment?"

"He doesn't like me."

The Torment scowled at Valkyrie when he met her eyes. There was a woman beside him, in a black dress that flowed on to the ground at her feet. Her face was covered by a veil, and her hands were gloved.

"He's here with his sister," Ravel said, anticipating her next question. "Not his real sister, of course, but another Child of the Spider."

Valkyrie had seen with her own horrified eyes the way the Torment could vomit black spiders the size of rats, with talons for legs. He also had the disconcerting habit of transforming into a spider himself – a huge monstrous thing that liked to haunt her dreams every once in a while.

"Madame Mist," Skulduggery said, eyeless gaze on the woman in the black veil. "She lives in Roarhaven now too? Since when? I didn't even know she was in the country."

Ravel shrugged. "We really weren't chatting long enough for me to get the details. I try to stay away from Children of the Spider, you know? They tend to give me the creeps. And speaking of creepy..."

High Priest Tenebrae entered the hall, flanked as always by Craven and Quiver. Tenebrae nodded to Valkyrie as they swept by in their black robes.

"Well now," Ravel said, catching the nod. "You seem to know more people here than *I* do."

Valkyrie smiled. "I'm still going to need some help with the boring ones."

Ravel laughed. "I'm sure they'd love to hear themselves being called that. In this hall, you have the usual suspects.

Sorcerers of particular power or age or standing. That lady over there is Shakra, and beside her is Flaring. You probably know them from the Sanctuary. They were lucky enough not to be there the day the Desolation Engine went off. To their left are assorted sorcerers you may not know – they work behind the scenes mostly, and do their best to stay out of the spotlight.

"Over here we have Corrival Deuce," Ravel continued, indicating a portly old man in a colourful coat. "He's more or less retired now, but we dragged him out of his house for this little get-together. He's a good man."

"A very good man," Skulduggery agreed. "We took orders from him during the war. There aren't many people I'd take orders from. He's one of them."

Valkyrie had heard Skulduggery and Ghastly mention Corrival Deuce in their conversations, always with real affection and respect. She decided she liked the old man very much, even though she'd never met him.

"The two people ahead of us," Skulduggery said, "are Geoffrey Scrutinous and Philomena Random." Scrutinous had bizarrely frizzy hair and a goatee, and despite the cold weather outside, he was wearing sandals. Random's appearance was altogether more sober – she had short hair, a warm coat, and none of the beads or rings or bangles that decorated her colleague's wrists and hands.

"They're public relations officers – it's their job to convince the mortals they didn't see what they thought they saw. The five people glaring at the Necromancers call themselves the Four Elementals. They see themselves as being in harmony with the world around them, and because of this they're astonishingly self-righteous."

"The Four Elementals?"

"Yes."

"But there are five of them."

"I know."

"Can they not count?"

"They started off with four, but then Amity, the man with the unusual chin married the heavyset woman with all the jewellery and insisted she be allowed to become the fifth member of the quartet."

"Couldn't they just rename themselves?"

"And become the Five Elementals, when there are only four elements? They didn't want to lose their precious synchronicity."

"It's better than everyone thinking you can't count."

"That it is," said someone at Valkyrie's elbow. She turned,

surprised to see Corrival Deuce standing there. She hadn't heard him approach. "You're Valkyrie Cain," he said, smiling. "I've heard so much about you. This is indeed an honour."

She shook his hand. "Hi," was all she could think to say.

"Erskine," Corrival said. "Skulduggery. Good to see you again."

"I didn't think you'd come," Ravel said to the older sorcerer.

Corrival barked a laugh. "What, after a solid three weeks of you pestering me about it?"

"I thought I was being subtle."

"You don't know the meaning of the word. Where are the others, then? Where's Ghastly, and Vex?"

"Ghastly hates these things," Skulduggery said, "and I don't know where Vex is."

"Probably having another adventure," Corrival said with a little sigh. "That boy needs to grow up one of these days, he really does. What about Anton Shudder?"

"Shudder likes to stay in his hotel," Ravel said. "Besides all the Remnants trapped in there, he also has a vampire guest to contend with. If I were him, I'd want to keep a close eye on things too."

The memory of Caelan's kiss came flooding back into Valkyrie's mind, and she fought against it in vain.

Corrival looked around. "So is this it? Is everyone here? Erskine, maybe you should start the ball rolling. I have places to go and things to do."

"Me?" Ravel asked. "Why do I have to start it? You're the most respected mage here. You start it. Or Skulduggery."

Skulduggery shook his head. "I can't start it. I don't like most of these people. I might start shooting."

Ravel scowled. "Fine."

He turned, cleared his throat, and spoke loudly. "Everyone who is going to be here is here," he announced. The other conversations died down, and all eyes turned to him. "We all know why we've gathered. If we can elect a Grand Mage today, then we can immediately start work on forming a new Council and finding a new Sanctuary."

"Before we talk about the new Sanctuary," Geoffrey Scrutinous said, "I think we should discuss the old one. In particular, I think everyone would like to ask how the search for Davina Marr has been going."

"As far as we know, she's still in the country," Skulduggery said. "Any more than that, I'm afraid I can't disclose."

"Why not?" asked the Elemental named Amity.

"It's an ongoing investigation."

"She has evaded you for five months already, Detective

Pleasant. Maybe we should be entrusting somebody else with the task of tracking her down."

"Then by all means, Amity," Skulduggery said, "find someone else."

"The damage has been done," the woman called Shakra said in a Belfast accent. "Marr isn't important, not any more. What is important is how weak we appear. The Sanctuaries around the world are waiting to pounce, did you know that?"

"That's a slight exaggeration," Scrutinous said.

"Is it? The Americans have already announced how they will no longer stand by and watch as Ireland struggles against the legacy that people like Mevolent have left us. That's what they said, word for word."

"It was a gesture of support," Amity said.

"No," Shakra responded, "it was a threat. They're telling us they're getting ready to step in and take over if something like this happens again."

Amity shook his head. "Nonsense. Ireland is a Cradle of Magic. No one would dare disrupt the delicate balance that holds the world in check."

Shakra scowled. "You're a moron."

"Being rude does not make you more intelligent than I."

"No, being more intelligent than you makes me more intelligent than you, you goat-brained simpleton."

"I did not come here to be insulted."

"What, do you have somewhere special to go for that kind of thing?"

"Can we please focus?" Corrival asked. Immediately, everyone shut up. "In the last five years alone, two of our Elders have been murdered, the third betrayed us, and the Grand Mage who took over has been revealed as a criminal. Two out of Mevolent's Three Generals returned, and the Faceless Ones actually *broke through* into this reality.

"Amity, you and your Four Elementals may not want to believe this, but Ireland is under attack. We have enemies both obvious and hidden. The war with Mevolent was fought largely on Irish soil. His actions, and the actions of his followers, have created an instability that is impossible to be rid of. This is where the agents of unrest are drawn. There is blood in the water here."

"That's right," Flaring said. "Dark sorcerers like Charivari in France, or Keratin in the mountains of Siberia, hate us and plot against us with every moment that passes. And what about all the visions of this Darquesse person, laying waste to the world? We need to be ready."

Valkyrie saw the nods and the looks in the eyes. If any one of them knew the truth, they'd have torn her apart right there and then.

"Then we need to get down to business," High Priest Tenebrae said. "The task ahead is not an easy one. We'll have to set up a new Council, elect a Grand Mage and two Elders, build a new Sanctuary and consolidate our power base. Even though it will add greatly to my responsibilities and workload, I am willing to put my own name forward for the role of Grand Mage."

There were some rolled eyes and cruel whispers, but Corrival held up a hand to silence them. "Thank you, High Priest. Who are the other nominees?"

"Some of us have been talking about this among ourselves," Scrutinous said, "and we'd like to suggest Corrival Deuce as a candidate."

Corrival raised an eyebrow. "Excuse me?"

"You're well-respected and well-liked, Corrival, and—"

"I know what I am," Corrival interrupted, "and what I am is retired. Even if I wasn't retired, I've never been interested in the job. That's for people like Meritorious, not people like me."

"Your country needs you," Flaring said.

"My country needs better taste."

"You're the only one who can do it."

"This is ridiculous," Corrival said. "I don't have the experience or the training, and I'm always getting into arguments. Not many sorcerers agree with my point of view, you know."

"Even so," said Philomena Random, "you're one of the few people who could bring the Irish magical community together in its time of need."

"Nonsense. There are plenty of others."

"We don't make this suggestion lightly, Corrival. We've considered this a great deal."

"And all you could come up with was me?"

"I'm afraid so."

"But I'm really enjoying my retirement. I get to sleep in every day. I do crossword puzzles and eat cakes."

"Duty calls, Corrival."

"Then we'll vote," Flaring said. "Right here, right now. Let's forgo the usual pomp and circumstance and have it as a simple *aye* or *nay*. All those in favour of High Priest Auron Tenebrae as the new Grand Mage, say *aye*."

Craven and Quiver both said *aye*. Tenebrae clenched his jaw against the overwhelming silence.

"OK then," Scrutinous said. "All in favour of Corrival Deuce as the new Grand Mage, say *aye*."

Ayes filled the room. Only the Necromancers and the Roarhaven mages stayed quiet.

Scrutinous grinned. "I think it's decided."

"Fine," Corrival said. "I'll accept the position, on the condition that as soon as someone more competent comes along, you'll all let me retire in peace."

"Agreed," said Amity. "So now we need to talk about nominations for the other two seats on the Council, and where the new Sanctuary is going to be built."

"Don't need to start building," the Torment said in his dreadful croaky voice. "We have a Sanctuary, ready and waiting."

"In Roarhaven?" Tenebrae said, disgust in his voice.

"Yes," the Torment glared back. "A fine building, built especially for this purpose."

"Built for a coup that failed," said Ravel.

"That may be so," the Torment said, "but the fact remains. There is a new Sanctuary building with all the rooms and requirements. Do any of you have any proper objections, apart from the fact that it's outside your precious capital city?"

There was silence.

"It's a good suggestion," Corrival said. Valkyrie looked at him in surprise. She wasn't the only one. "The fact is," he continued, "it's there, and it's available. And if someone sets off another bomb, we won't have to explain it to the civilian authorities. And as for the other two seats on the Council, I already have my nominees. I nominate Erskine Ravel and Skulduggery Pleasant."

Someone barked a laugh. Valkyrie turned to Skulduggery, really wishing he was wearing a face so she could see his reaction.

"Ah," said Ravel.

"Oh," said Skulduggery.

"Sorry, fellas," Corrival said, "but if I have to suffer through this ridiculousness, then so do you. Both of you are controversial figures, but I fought with your unit on the battlefield, and I've never known such bravery and honour. Erskine, you like spending money way too much, but you've been my trusted confidant for the last hundred years, and I don't think there is anyone who is going to deny that you would make an excellent Elder. You're wise when you need to be, and impulsive when you have to be.

"Skulduggery, my old friend, I daresay a lot of people are going to object to your nomination."

"Myself included," Skulduggery answered.

"You make more enemies than friends, which isn't saying an

awful lot, but you also make the difficult decisions. You always have. That's all I'm going to say on the matter. The rest is up to the voters. As duly elected Grand Mage, I now call a halt to proceedings, as I have a crossword to do and some cakes to eat."

Without waiting for a response, Corrival turned and walked from the room.

"I was not expecting *that*," Ravel said in a low voice.

"I'll vote for you," Skulduggery said, "so long as you promise *not* to vote for me."

Ravel grinned. "And let you miss the fun? Not on your life, dead man."

As they were walking for the Bentley, Valkyrie caught sight of a pretty blonde girl standing by a long, black car. "Back in a minute," she said to Skulduggery, and jogged over to the girl, trying her best not to smile too broadly.

"Hi Melancholia," she said brightly.

Melancholia scowled. She was four years older than Valkyrie, tall, and she wore black Necromancer robes. From the very start, Melancholia had never made a secret of the fact that she despised Valkyrie utterly. Valkyrie, for her part, thought this was astonishingly amusing, and revelled in the many opportunities she had to annoy the older girl.

"What you doing?" Valkyrie asked, smiling a friendly smile.

"I'm standing here," Melancholia responded, not looking at her.

"And a fine job you're doing of it, too. Do you know where Solomon is? He said he was going to come today, but I didn't see him."

"Cleric Wreath is on an assignment."

"Cool. What kind?"

"I don't know."

"Is it exciting?"

"I don't know."

"Right. So you're just waiting here for the others, then? Waiting for ol' Tenebrae?"

Melancholia stiffened. "You should show more respect for the High Priest. You should use his full title when referring to him."

Valkyrie shrugged. "High Priest Tenebrae just takes so long to say, you know? I usually just call him Tenny. He likes that."

"If you were truly one of us, you would be severely disciplined for such behaviour."

Valkyrie frowned. "Do you really talk like that, or are you just putting it on?"

Melancholia finally looked at her. "You are mocking me?" she snarled.

"Is that a statement or a question?"

Melancholia was taller than Valkyrie, and she loomed over her. "I should punish you myself, on behalf of the High Priest."

"I don't think Tenny would like that very much."

"You are *not* our saviour."

"Solomon seems to think I am."

"Cleric Wreath has spent too long out in this decadent world. He's lost his objectivity. He looks at you and he sees the Death Bringer, whereas everyone else looks at you and sees a pathetic little *child*."

Valkyrie grinned. Despite how sinister it sounded, the Death Bringer was a title that she was beginning to actually like. She found Necromancers creepy on a very fundamental level – Solomon Wreath aside – but even so, it was nice to be thought of as a possible saviour. Certainly, it was a change from having to think of herself as Darquesse. The chance, no matter how slim, that instead she might turn out to be the Death Bringer was a source of comfort to her. Two possible destinies – one where she saves the world, and one where she ends it. Her future couldn't get any starker than that. "Maybe I *am* the Death Bringer," she said.

"Don't be absurd. You've been studying Necromancy for just over a year. I've been studying death magic since I was four years old. You're nothing compared to me, or anyone like me."

"And yet," Valkyrie interrupted, "I'm the one they're all making a fuss of."

Melancholia scowled. "You're nothing but an Elemental *playing* at being a Necromancer."

"And you're a Necromancer, through and through. You've wanted to be nothing else your entire life. And yet, I've been invited to all the important meetings and you get to stay out here and mind the car. I've been told things about your art and your religion that you won't be told for another year or two."

"Ridiculous."

"Is it? When were you told about the Passage?"

Melancholia hesitated. "I learned about the Passage when I was ready, when I had completed my studies on over three dozen—"

"It was pretty recently, wasn't it?"

Melancholia gritted her teeth. "Yes."

"See, I was told about it ages ago. Now, I'm not saying I'm an expert. In fact, I have loads of questions about the whole thing. You must have noticed that some of it just doesn't seem to make any sense. Your religion is based on the idea that when you die, your energy passes from this world to another one, right?"

"It's not an *idea*," Melancholia said tersely. "It's a scientific *fact*."

"It's little more than a theory," Valkyrie countered. "But I'm OK with that. So you guys are waiting for the Death Bringer to come and collapse the wall between the two worlds, so the living and the dead can exist in the same place, at the same time, meaning that there will be no more strife, no more war, and everyone will live, or at least exist, happily ever after."

"Yes," Melancholia said.

"And yet, no one has told me how this is possible."

"You can hardly expect to understand the advanced stages of our teachings, if you do not have the patience or the skill to master the basics."

"Do *you* know how it's possible?"

"I will. Soon. Once I experience the Surge, once I am locked into Necromancy for the rest of my life, all of its secrets will be laid open for me."

"Oh, that'll be nice. I still don't know if it's for me, though. I really don't want to draw my power from death, and that's basically what Necromancy is. I'd rather not have to rely on other people's pain to use magic."

"I hardly think it will be up to you. The sooner the Clerics realise what a mistake they're making, wasting their time on you, the better. Then you can run along with your skeleton friend and have lots of fun together, and you can leave the important stuff to us."

"Sometimes I get the feeling that you don't like me."

"Trust your feelings."

"So we're not going to be friends?"

"I'd rather gouge my own eyes out."

Valkyrie shook her head sadly, and started to walk back to the Bentley. "Your leaders are looking to me to be their saviour, Melancholia. You might have to learn to love me."

Melancholia's voice was laced with venom. "You are *not* our saviour."

Valkyrie looked at her over her shoulder, shot her a smile. "Better start praying to me, just in case."

10

THE BONEBREAKER

Back when Vaurien Scapegrace was alive, he had briefly owned a pub in Roarhaven that catered, almost exclusively, for sorcerers. That had been before he'd found his true calling as a Killer Supreme and, later, as the Zombie King, but he'd enjoyed it nevertheless. He knew there were pubs and clubs and bars around the country, around the world, whose clientele were magical, but he liked to think that his pub offered something a little different. A home away from home perhaps. A refuge from the pressures and stresses of modern living.

But now that some time had passed, now that he was viewing it all with a more objective eye, he realised what it was that his pub had really offered. It had offered dim lighting, bad drinks, grumpy bar staff and a toilet that smelled of wet cabbage. There was absolutely nothing to take pride in. Nothing to feel good about. But that, of course, was the whole point. Sorcerer pubs were bad pubs by necessity. If they were good pubs, *everyone* would be going to them.

Sitting in this particular sorcerer pub in Dublin, Scapegrace reflected on the trials and tribulations he had gone through as a living man, and hoped that by the time this night was done, he would be a step closer to being a living man once again.

Thrasher came through the sombre crowd, spilling someone's drink and apologising profusely before arriving at Scapegrace's table. "Some men are here," he said urgently. "They say they know you."

Scapegrace leaned back in his chair. "Let's see them."

Thrasher nodded, turned, but the crowd was already parting for the six newcomers. Scapegrace did indeed know them. Lightning Dave sidled up on Scapegrace's right, playing with a bright stream of electricity that crackled between his fingertips. His hair stood on end, and his features had settled into a permanent smirk.

Beside him was Hokum Pete. Hokum Pete had been born in Kerry, but harboured a well-known and widely ridiculed desire to be seen as a Wild West outlaw. He liked to wear cowboy boots and long duster coats, and today he had a six-gun holstered low on his right leg. His hand flashed and the gun cleared the holster. He started to spin it around on his finger, like that was going to impress anyone.

Thrasher gave a delighted "*Oooh*", and Scapegrace fought the urge to hit him.

To Scapegrace's left was a pair of sorcerers who had never managed to garner much of a reputation for themselves. They weren't powerful and they weren't smart, and Scapegrace could never remember their names.

Brobding the giant, bringing up the rear, had to hunch over to even fit in here, and the man who stood right in front of Scapegrace was Hieronymus Deadfall. Deadfall had been a mercenary, had fought in a few wars, both magical and mortal, before returning to Ireland and settling down in Roarhaven, where he had stolen Scapegrace's pub from under him. Not that Scapegrace held a grudge or anything.

"Hello, moron," said Scapegrace.

"My God," Deadfall responded. "It's true. Everything they said is true. You're a shambling pile of decomposition."

Hokum Pete sniggered, and Scapegrace sat up a little straighter. "I am the living dead, if that's what you mean, yes. What can I do for you, Hieronymus? I assume you've heard about the auction."

"We heard," Deadfall nodded. "So you know where the Skeleton Detective lives?"

"Yes, I do. You want revenge, for the time he smacked you around your own pub? This is how you do it. Catch him unawares. Or you can sell the information to someone else. His little partner will probably be there too."

"Cain," snarled one of the sorcerers whose name Scapegrace couldn't remember.

"This information is worth a lot," Scapegrace continued, "but all I'm looking for is information in exchange. Kenspeckle Grouse. I want to know where to find him."

It was all going so perfectly, and Scapegrace had to resist grinning in case any more teeth fell out. He'd give up the Skeleton Detective's location, and in return he'd find Kenspeckle Grouse and get himself fixed. It was, he had to admit, one of his more brilliant plans.

"Grouse..." Deadfall said. "The scientist? How the hell would I know that?"

"If you don't know it, you're of no use to me. Next! Anyone know where Kenspeckle Grouse is?"

Deadfall smiled. "Tell me, Vaurien, what's to stop us from just pulling you apart, limb from limb, until you tell us the skeleton's address?"

Scapegrace didn't really have an answer for that one.

There were mumblings and mutterings in the crowd as a large man in a long coat passed Deadfall and approached the table. He had his hood up, and beneath it Scapegrace could see metal, like a mask.

"I need to know where Skulduggery Pleasant lives," the big man said with an accent. Eastern European maybe, or Russian. Scapegrace decided on Russian. It was, like many sorcerer's accents, one that came from a lot of places over the years.

"Do you have what I need in exchange?" Scapegrace asked, ignoring Deadfall's scowl.

The head beneath the hood shook. "I have heard of this Grouse person, but I do not know where he lives."

"Then why are you wasting my time?"

The Russian didn't answer for a bit. Then he placed both hands on the table, and leaned in. "Because I'm giving you a chance to avoid bloodshed. Tell me where the Skeleton Detective lives and we can all walk out of here. You are a dead man, but there are ways to kill even dead men."

The conversation had tilted wildly out of Scapegrace's control in a remarkably short amount of time, with an astonishingly small amount of words.

It was the tone the big Russian was using, a tone that implied that violence was a mere afterthought. Scapegrace didn't like that one bit. Anyone who did not give violence its careful and rightful due was someone to whom violence was an old pair of shoes – slip on, slip off, think nothing more about it. That wasn't Scapegrace's style at all.

"Maybe," he said, "we can reach a compromise."

"No way," Deadfall said to the mysterious Russian. "Listen, pal, a funny accent and a funny mask don't scare me. We were here first, so you, take a hike."

The big man turned to him slowly. "You do not want to make trouble with me."

Deadfall actually chuckled in disbelief. "Scapegrace, take note. After we deal with the funny man here, you're next."

Hokum Pete was still showing off with his six-gun. His finger in the trigger guard, he spun it until it blurred, then flipped it, reversed it, slid it into the holster. It barely had time to settle before it flashed out again. He tossed it into the air and caught it as it spun, tossed it to his other hand, still spinning. He threw it over his shoulder and caught it, reversed the motion and that was when the Russian reached back, snatched it from the air, and shot him point-blank.

Hokum Pete flew backwards, there were screams and yells and cries, and suddenly everyone was moving.

Lightning Dave snarled and electricity burst from his fingers. The Russian dodged behind the giant, and Brobding shrieked as the stream hit him instead. Scapegrace toppled backwards over his chair, saw Thrasher dive to the floor. Panic spread, and there was a stampede for the exits.

The Russian shot Lightning Dave twice in the chest. Deadfall, his fists already turning to hammers, knocked the gun from the Russian's hand and swung for his head. The Russian ducked under the swing and moved past him, towards the two sorcerers with the forgettable names.

The first of them had glowing hands, ready to discharge a blast of energy. The second had opted for the up-close-and-personal approach, drawing a long dagger from his sleeve. Scapegrace watched as the Russian bent the second sorcerer's arm back, stabbing him with his own blade. The poor, unmemorable fool gurgled in astonishment, and the Russian took the dagger from him and whipped it across the throat of his friend. Then he turned, saw Brobding coming for him and flicked the dagger to the ground. It impaled itself through the giant's foot, pinning it to the floor. Brobding shrieked.

Deadfall came at him. The Russian swayed back out of range, watched the hammer swing uselessly by his face, then leaned in. His knuckles met the hinge of Deadfall's jaw, and Deadfall's legs gave out from under him.

Brobding pulled the dagger from his foot with a self-pitying squawk of pain. He fixed his face with a snarl, and charged. He didn't have far to charge, but he did have to keep himself stooped, so it resembled more of a stumble. Still, the intent behind it was unmistakable.

The Russian ducked under the giant's arms. Brobding's great fist came around, but the masked man avoided it easily. Brobding lunged and the Russian snapped out a pair of jabs that broke the giant's nose and split his lip. Brobding bellowed and the Russian kicked his knee. The bellow became a howl, drawn-out and horrified, his huge hands clutching at his leg.

The Russian tapped a single fingertip lightly against Brobding's chest. There was a terrible crack of bone, and Brobding fell, dead. It was like a great oak falling in a forest.

Deadfall was up again, preparing to swing his hammer-fists, but the Russian just stepped close and pressed his hand against him. Every bone that comprised the skeleton of Hieronymus

Deadfall gave a slight tremor, and then came apart with a violence that ruptured his body. Bone shards burst both organs and skin, spraying blood into the air. His corpse dropped, contorted and disfigured beyond recognition. The Russian turned to look at Scapegrace, his eyes red beneath his mask.

"I'll tell you," Scapegrace said, hands high above his head. "I'll tell you where Skulduggery Pleasant lives. Just please, don't explode me."

11

THE ROARHAVEN MAGES

The closer you got to Roarhaven, the sicker the trees looked, the browner the grasses, the blacker the lake. Its streets were narrow, its buildings hunched, their windows squinting. Paranoia and hatred, seething resentment and bitter hostility – these things leaked through the town like its lifeblood. It was a creature, a mangy, diseased dog, afflicted with fleas and ticks and lice, kept alive by its own loathing.

The man with the golden eyes stood by the stagnant lake, his coat buttoned up against the cold. "Marr?" he asked.

"Still alive," said the old man behind him.

The veiled woman in black spoke quietly. "I thought we hired the best."

The old man didn't bother to keep the irritation out of his voice. "We did."

"She needs to die," said the woman. "She's far too dangerous to be languishing in chains."

"Tesseract assures me she will be dead soon." The old man looked away from the woman. "Do they still think the Americans are to blame?"

The man with the golden eyes shrugged. "Who knows what Skulduggery Pleasant thinks? We can only stick to the plan. If he begins to suspect us, we'll deal with him then. For the moment, though, we're on schedule. This town will hold the new Sanctuary. From here, we're going to change the world."

12

KEEPING A STRAIGHT FACE

China Sorrows wasn't in the library that took up an entire half of the tenement building's third floor, and neither was she in her apartment across the hall, which took up the other half. China's assistant, the thin man who never spoke, merely cast his eyes downwards when Skulduggery asked him her whereabouts, but apparently, this was sufficient.

Valkyrie followed Skulduggery down the dank staircase. His façade was up, but still refused to settle. She watched as his face started to drift round to the back of his head.

"Where are we going?" she asked. A pair of dull green eyes floated slowly through Skulduggery's hair.

"To the basement."

"I didn't know this place had a basement."

"There wasn't one until China bought this building and commissioned the work to add a sub-level. Even the people living here don't know about it."

"You've got eyes in the back of your head, you know, and I don't mean that as compliment."

"I know," said Skulduggery sadly.

"How can you even see right now?"

He glanced back at her. The mouth of the façade was gaping wide over his left eye socket.

"That is so wrong," she murmured.

They continued walking.

"There's only one reason why China ever goes down into the basement," Skulduggery said. "Well, it's also where she keeps her car. OK, so there's only two reasons why she ever goes down there, apart from the fact that it's secure and dry and it works well as a storage area. So that's three, only three reasons why she ever goes down there, and apart from the car and the storage, the main reason is privacy. Seclusion. Why does she need privacy and seclusion?"

"Don't know."

"She needs privacy and seclusion when she catches someone trying to steal from her." They reached the ground floor.

"How do we get there?" Valkyrie asked. "Is there an invisible elevator? A trapdoor? Oh, is it one of those fire station poles that we get to slide down?"

Skulduggery went to the broom closet, and opened the door. There were no brooms in there, and no floor. There were only—

"Stairs," Valkyrie said, disappointed.

"Not just ordinary stairs," Skulduggery told her as he led the way down. "Magic stairs."

"Really?"

"Oh, yes."

She followed him into the darkness. "How are they magic?"

"They just are."

"In what way?"

"In a magicky way."

She glared at the back of his head. "They aren't magic at all, are they?"

"Not really."

The basement was cold. A dim bulb struggled valiantly

against the darkness. They walked down a narrow corridor between chain-link walls, passing stacks of boxes and crates. Rusted pipes crossed the ceiling, the failing light making them look like boa constrictors, liable to drop down and snatch the pair of them up and slowly squeeze the life out of them. Out of *her*. Skulduggery had no life to squeeze.

They heard voices ahead. Finally, the chain-link maze came to an end, and they stepped into a wide-open space, illuminated only by the headlights from an idle car. A man was on his knees, doing his best to shield his eyes. Whether he was shielding his eyes from the blinding light or the blinding beauty of the woman who stood above him was hard to tell.

China Sorrows was cast in half-shadow. Her raven hair was tied off her face in a simple ponytail. The light hit her back and made her clothes shine and her skin glow. She held a book by her side. Skulduggery and Valkyrie stayed where they were, watching silently.

"I'm sorry!" the man sobbed. "Oh God, Miss Sorrows, I'm so sorry! I didn't mean to do it!"

"You didn't mean to hide this book under your jacket and leave without telling me?" China clarified. "This is a very valuable edition, and would be sorely missed from my collection."

"Please. Please, I have a family. They're starving."

"And so you planned to *feed* them the book?"

"No... No, but..."

"You planned to sell it then. To whom, I wonder?"

"I don't... I can't..."

"If you tell me who the interested party is, I will let you go." At a wave of her hand, a section of wall opened up at the top of a concrete ramp – obviously the means of exit for her car – and daylight flooded the gloom. "You will never be allowed back here, and you will cross the street and run away to avoid me, but I will take no further action. Against *you*. The actions I will take against the interested party, however, will be quite severe, even by my standards. I never ask twice – my patience is quite short. You will tell me now."

He sagged. "Eliza Scorn."

If there was any reaction shown in China's face, the shadows hid it. "I see," she said. "You may leave."

"I... can?"

China sighed, and the man scrambled up, wiped his eyes, and hurried towards the ramp.

"Wait," China said. She looked at him for a long moment.

"If you return to Eliza Scorn without this book, she will most likely kill you *and* your pathetic starving family." She held it out. "Take it."

"Really?"

"I have three more around here somewhere. Take it before I change my mind."

He scurried back to her, accepting the book. "Thank you," he wept. "Thank you for your kindness and your, and your beauty. I... I love you, Miss Sorrows. I've never loved anyone as much as—"

"You have a pathetic starving family to get back to, you grubby little man. Get back to them."

He tore his eyes away from her and ran, wailing, up the ramp and out into the alley. The wall closed up behind him, and China turned, allowing the light to cast itself over her perfect features.

"An act of kindness," she said, "purely for your benefit, Valkyrie. I know how much you dislike me being mean to people."

Valkyrie stepped out of the shadows, smiling. "Kindness suits you."

"Really? I think I'm quite allergic to it. Now what can I do for you both? Perhaps you are here seeking my opinion on matters discussed at this top-secret meeting to which I was not invited?"

"You may not have been there," Skulduggery said, "but I'm sure a woman of your resources has heard detailed accounts of everything that was spoken about."

"Nonsense. That meeting was highly confidential. Congratulations, by the way."

Skulduggery grunted. "There's nothing to congratulate."

"Don't be so modest – I haven't laughed so hard in years. Erskine, possibly, has the makings of a good Elder, and Corrival Deuce is an inspired choice for Grand Mage. But you? Skulduggery my dear... that is inspired lunacy."

"Yes, well, we'll see how it all pans out, but I'm afraid we're here on matters much more cosmetic." Skulduggery took a step out of the gloom, and China saw his drooping face.

"Oh dear," she said.

"It gets better when I do this." He began slapping himself and shaking his head violently, causing the face to tighten slightly.

"Well," China said, "at least you're keeping your dignity. Come. Keep the façade active."

She touched the car and the headlights went out. They followed her out of the basement and up the stairs.

"What have you heard about Tesseract?" Skulduggery asked as they climbed. His bottom lip hung over his chin like a dead slug.

"The Russian killer? Why on earth would you want..." China looked down at them, her pale blue eyes narrowed. "He's in the country?"

"You didn't know?" Skulduggery asked, actually sounding shocked.

There was a brief flicker of annoyance on China's perfect face, and then it evaporated. She turned, and resumed climbing to the third floor.

"Here is what I know about Tesseract. Born and raised in Russia, somewhere between three and four hundred years ago. He is an Adept, nobody knows who trained him, and nobody knows how many people he's killed. He wears a mask – again, nobody knows why. He lives in a truck of some description. He's self-sufficient, doesn't need to resupply for weeks at a time. His method of communication is a mystery to me – how those who require his services get in touch with him, I confess, I do not know.

"What all this means is that he could be living across the street from me and I'd never know it. It means that I have not heard one single rumour about him in twenty years, and the fact that he is here and I didn't know about it causes me no small amount of alarm and drives me to unimaginable fury. I am, however, hiding it well. You are *sure* he is here?"

"We saw him," said Skulduggery.

They reached the third floor and stopped talking as a man and a woman passed. The man stared at China, entranced by her beauty. The woman stared at Skulduggery, repulsed by the face that was slowly sliding down his head. China led them into her apartment – to Valkyrie it was as beautiful and elegant as China herself – and shut the door after them.

"He went after Davina Marr," Skulduggery said.

China's eyebrow raised. "Did he kill her?"

"He came close."

"Do you have her?"

"She's somewhere safe and secure – you don't have to worry about her. This can't be repeated to anyone, of course."

"Who do you think I am, some cheap and tawdry gossip-monger? Sit. Loosen your tie."

Skulduggery did as he was told, and China took a small black case from her desk. From the case she withdrew a calligraphy pen that reminded Valkyrie of a scalpel. She dipped it in black ink before taking a monocle from a side pocket. She crossed to Skulduggery, undid a few shirt buttons to expose the symbols carved into his collarbones, and examined them using the monocle. "Have you questioned Marr yet?" she asked.

"She remains stubbornly unconscious," he answered. "However, the very fact that someone sent an assassin after her has told us an awful lot. Up until now I was almost prepared to believe that Marr acted alone. She could have enslaved Myron Stray of her own volition, put the Desolation Engine into his hands, and arranged for Valkyrie and myself to get caught in the blast. I was close to putting her actions down to pure anger and a petty need for revenge that escalated into something terrible. But that doesn't hold up. Not any more."

"Because of Tesseract?" Valkyrie asked.

"Tesseract was put on her trail, which leads me to believe that she had co-conspirators who have since abandoned her, and now want her silenced."

China put down the monocle, pressed the pen against the symbol on Skulduggery's left collarbone, and applied pressure. "If there is a conspiracy, who would gain from the destruction of the Sanctuary? There has been a five-month period where there has been no Sanctuary, no Grand Mage, and yet from what I can see, there has been no dramatic upsurge in antisocial activity. Whoever organised this seems to have missed their opportunity."

"Unless the scale is far grander than we imagine," Skulduggery said.

"Now you just sound paranoid." Whatever China was doing to the symbol was having an effect on Skulduggery's face. It tightened until it almost split, then loosened again. "If you're right about this grand conspiracy, by the way, you might want to consider the possibility that Marr never really stopped working for the American Sanctuary."

"We've thought about that," Skulduggery said. "Valkyrie?"

"OK," Valkyrie said, "so two years ago, Marr is working for the American Sanctuary. Thurid Guild offers her a job in Ireland, thinking she won't be able to resist the chance to work at a Cradle of Magic because, let's face it, every day here is an adventure. She tells her bosses, they tell her to accept the job, but to work undercover for them. Any Sanctuary around the world would want to gain a foothold in a country with this much raw magic at its core, and America is no different.

"She starts work, proves to be as good at her job as everyone expects, but all the time she's looking for a way to bring down the Sanctuary. The Americans need a crisis so they can swoop in. Marr eventually gives them that crisis."

"The problem with that theory," Skulduggery continued, "is that once the Sanctuary is destroyed, the Americans do nothing, and then Corrival Deuce gets elected as Grand Mage, with Ravel and myself as possible Elders. I really can't see how that would benefit the Americans, or anyone else, in the slightest."

"That should do it," China said, stepping back. Skulduggery looked up at her, his face staying put. "It was off by a millimetre in depth," she explained. "An unforgivable mistake on my part, and yet I think I shall manage to forgive myself. Could you deactivate the façade now?"

Skulduggery tapped the symbols, and the face slid away. "You want me to use it only when I have to?" he asked.

"Not at all," China said. "It's just that talking to you when you have a face is quite disconcerting. I much prefer you as a skeleton."

"Me too," Valkyrie agreed.

As Skulduggery stood up and buttoned his shirt, China began to pack away her equipment. "Then maybe it *isn't* the Americans," she said. "Maybe Marr was working undercover for somebody else."

"It could be someone who just doesn't like us," said Valkyrie. "We've already had Dreylan Scarab and Billy-Ray

Sanguine come after us for revenge, so what about other bad guys we've beaten? What about Jaron Gallow? No one's heard from him since he chopped off his own arm and ran away from the Faceless Ones. And Remus Crux. If there's anyone crazy enough to want to kill that many people, it's *that* lunatic."

"It's not Remus Crux," China said.

"How do *you* know?"

"Because Davina Marr would never work with someone so unstable."

"Then what about the Torment? Roarhaven stands to benefit a lot from this. They get the Sanctuary right in the middle of their creepy little town."

"But that still doesn't grant them any great degree of power," Skulduggery argued, fixing his tie. "There will still be a Council of Elders, and an entire staff of non-Roarhaven sorcerers. All they gain is the proximity of location."

"Which is not a good enough reason to set off the Desolation Engine," China said. "The Children of the Spider *are* known for their cunning, but the fact is, this may have nothing to *do* with Roarhaven."

"I still think the Torment is behind this," Valkyrie muttered.

Skulduggery's smile was in his voice. "Is that because he tried to get me to kill you?"

"I think he's behind this because he's a horrible old man who turns into a giant spider. But mostly because he tried to get you to kill me. There are still plenty of others to choose from, though. And don't forget, we only have Scarab's word that *he* wasn't behind it. This might be his last bid for revenge before he dies in prison, to make us think there's someone else out there."

"So," Skulduggery said, "to sum up: Davina Marr's co-conspirators could either be the Roarhaven mages, the Americans, or anyone else who just doesn't like us."

China smiled. "I'm just glad we could narrow it down." She walked from the room, Valkyrie and Skulduggery following her into the library. "And may I say what a privilege it is to be involved in this investigation at its inception. It fills my heart with warmth to know that, finally, you trust me enough to bother me with things at a much earlier stage than I am used to or am, indeed, happy with."

"They say sarcasm is the lowest form of wit," Valkyrie said.

China glanced at her. "They've obviously never met *me*."

"The fact is," Skulduggery said as they walked through the labyrinth of bookcases, "over the past few years you've proven yourself to be someone who can be depended on."

"And the unfortunate side effect of that," Valkyrie

continued, "is that you get to join our little crime-fighting club, whether you like it or not."

China stopped, and turned to them, a slight frown on her face. "Does this mean... Please don't tell me this means we are all now *friends*. I have done very well without friends up to this point and I have no intention of developing any *now*."

Valkyrie frowned. "You make us sound like a rash."

"An irritation that shows up when you least want it? I think the analogy is quite apt."

"You do realise that I know what all the big words you're using *mean*, right?"

"And there I was, trying to baffle you with my verbiage."

"Understood *that*, too." Valkyrie glimpsed a familiar face in among the stacks. "Be right back," she said. They walked on and she approached her friend. "This is where we first met," she said.

Tanith Low looked up, and smiled. "God, that seems like a hundred years ago. You were so small."

"I was never small."

"And so narrow. Now look at you. How are the arms?"

"I'm not showing you."

"Yes, you are."

"No, I'm not. We're in the middle of a library."

"A library frequented solely by freaks and other assorted weirdos. I haven't seen the arms in weeks. Come on."

Valkyrie tried to sigh, but ended up grinning. She unzipped her jacket and took it off.

"*Damn*," Tanith said, drawing the word out. "I hope Fletcher appreciates all the work I've put in to making his girlfriend rock solid."

"I've told him I'm aiming to have shoulders like yours. He kind of dribbled when he heard that." Valkyrie put her jacket back on. "But I was never small."

Tanith laughed, slid the book she'd been reading back on to the shelf. "You were so unsure and innocent and wide-eyed and shy... Well, maybe not shy."

"Never shy."

"But definitely unsure. I knew from the moment I met you we'd be friends, you know."

"Really?"

"I didn't know we'd be quite so close, but I saw you and I went, yeah, she's cool. Hadn't a clue you had anything to do with why I was over here, though. Things kind of worked out quite well, didn't they?"

"Yes, they did."

"My folks say hi, by the way. And my brother wants to meet you. He's heard so much about the great Valkyrie Cain."

"Your parents are lovely, and I've seen a picture of your brother. I definitely want to meet *him*."

Tanith wagged her finger. "You, my dear, are a one-man woman. Stick with Fletcher, and stay away from my *older* brother." Tanith's smile faded slightly. "What's wrong?"

"What do you mean?"

"I said 'one-man woman' and you... you practically *flinched*."

"No, I didn't."

"Everything OK with Fletcher?"

"Yes," said Valkyrie. "Things are great."

"And you're happy with him? Still having fun?"

"Sometimes it's like leading a child around, but yes, absolutely, still having a laugh."

"Then what's wrong?"

"Nothing's wrong," Valkyrie said, and laughed.

"What did you *do*?"

"I didn't do *anything*."

"Who is he?"

"I don't know who—"

Tanith looked into her eyes.

"Oh no," she breathed.

"Oh no what?"

"Not him."

"Tanith, I really don't know what you're on about."

"The *vampire*, Val? *Really*? The *vampire*?"

"He has a name."

"He's a vampire!"

"I don't know what you're talking about, OK? Nothing happened!"

"Oh, that's a big old lie right there."

Valkyrie prepared to argue, but she knew there was little use. She sagged. "Fine. OK. We kissed."

Tanith covered her face with her hands. "No. No no no. You can't do this."

"I'm not doing anything. It was a one-off. It's not going to happen again."

"He's too old for you."

"I know that."

"And he's a vampire."

"Tanith. Caelan has problems, but he's not like the others."

"Valkyrie. You're insane. He's *exactly* like the others. This isn't some brooding Gothic rubbish."

"I swear to God, I know all this. I explained to him, it'll

never happen again. I'm not in love with him, for God's sake. It meant basically nothing."

"It might have meant nothing to *you*," Tanith said, "but I can tell you that it meant a lot to *him*."

"That's not my problem."

"It will be. Val, I hate to disapprove of *anything* that you do. We're friends. I shouldn't lecture you. I should support you. And I will. And I do. But something like this, you're just going to have to forgive me, because I'll keep going on about it until it's over for good."

Valkyrie nodded. "I understand that."

"I take it Fletcher doesn't have any idea?"

"God, no."

"Good. There's no point in hurting him and destroying your relationship when you don't have to. It was a mistake."

"Yes, it was," said Valkyrie.

"And it'll never happen again."

"No, it won't."

"But if it does, you can talk to me about it and I won't shout at you too much."

"Thanks."

"I'm not even going to ask if Skulduggery knows. If Caelan's still alive, that means he doesn't."

Valkyrie nodded her agreement, the truth of that statement making her uneasy. They walked out of the stacks, to where Skulduggery and China were talking.

"Oh, good," China said without enthusiasm, "Tanith's here."

Tanith's smile made no effort to reach her eyes. "Hello China. You're looking radiant as ever."

"And your leather seems to have shrunk since the last time I saw you," China responded. "Don't you all have somewhere else to be? It's not that I want you to go, it's just that I don't want you to stay."

13

SUFFERING

leric Craven was in no hurry as he walked the cold corridors of the Temple. He'd always disliked the cold, but such was the Necromancer way. Hardship and suffering, misery and discomfort. The Temple was, almost to its last metre, cold and dark and dank, lit only by sputtering torches in rusted brackets on the walls. *To suffer is to live*, as the saying went – one of the basic tenets of his faith. Who was Craven to object to that? Who was he to demand special consideration? Who was he to forgo the suffering, when so many of his fellows shivered and rattled and didn't complain?

Beneath his robes he was wrapped in thermals.

He knew for a fact that High Priest Tenebrae wore thermals beneath *his* robes. Cleric Quiver didn't, as far as he could tell, but then Quiver was the kind of man who enjoyed the odd bit of suffering. As for Cleric Wreath, he didn't even *wear* his robes, and his clothes *always* looked warm. Craven would expect no less from a Cleric who had spent so many years out *there*, in the world. The house where he lived was furnished, insulated and warm no matter how cold it got elsewhere. Decadent. Indulgent. How Craven envied him.

He reached the iron door of the High Priest's office and let himself in. Shelves of books and papers. Cabinets of trinkets. Bare walls, bare floors. A single desk. Two chairs. No decoration. The bare necessities – nothing more.

Tenebrae, seated at his desk, glanced at him, scowling, before returning his eyes to Wreath. Behind him, the White Cleaver stood, scythe strapped to his back. Quiver stood by the far wall, hands clasped beneath the sleeves of his robe. Immediately, Craven regretted his tardiness. Wreath was agitated. Craven fought to contain his grin.

"Cleric Wreath," Tenebrae interrupted, "I understand your concerns, but we are quite safe here in the Temple."

"The Remnant is loose," Wreath said angrily. "The moment they realise this they'll be coming here to ask questions."

"Let them come."

"Your Eminence, with all due respect, they are going to want to know how the Remnant escaped. Skulduggery Pleasant will work out that we attempted to use it to control someone."

"Nonsense. We can tell them one of our acolytes set it free, quite by accident. We'll tell them the acolyte has been punished and will never do it again. You're getting upset over nothing, Cleric."

Craven stood by the door, enjoying this immensely. It wasn't often he got to see Solomon Wreath being patronised.

"Having a Remnant loose out there is a good enough reason to be upset," said Wreath. "If we are going to tell people it got free by accident, then at least let it become public. Sorcerers have to know of the danger."

Tenebrae sat back. "Solomon, for all we know, the Remnant will leave the psychic's body and fly off somewhere to be alone, and never bother anyone ever again. Why invite scrutiny and derision when we don't have to? If it makes a nuisance of itself, and if the Skeleton Detective or anyone else comes here asking questions, we can feign surprise and shame upon learning of this terrible, accidental oversight on our part."

"What did he see?" Quiver asked.

Wreath looked at him. "What?"

"The Sensitive. What did he see when you put the Remnant in him?"

Wreath sighed, and pinched the bridge of his nose. "Nothing. Nothing useful. He got sidetracked."

"By what?" Tenebrae asked.

"He saw a vision of Darquesse. Seemed quite enamoured with her."

"So he saw nothing about the Cain girl?"

"Actually, I think there's a reason Darquesse intruded upon his vision. I think Valkyrie is going to be the one to defeat her. I think that will be the start of her journey to becoming the Death Bringer."

Craven cleared his throat, pleased with the anger that flashed in Wreath's eyes. "If I may, High Priest?"

Tenebrae waved a hand. "Of course."

"Cleric Wreath, I admire your tenacity, and I admire your faith in Valkyrie Cain. I do think, however, that you have allowed yourself to focus on her to the exclusion of all others. You say it is now your opinion that Miss Cain defeats Darquesse. And yet every vision we have heard about has Darquesse *killing* both Cain and Pleasant, before starting in on the rest of the world."

"The future can be changed," Wreath growled.

"Oh, yes, indeed it can. I'm not arguing with you there. I'm just wondering about your interpretation. Have you considered the possibility that the Sensitive saw a vision of Darquesse because there *was* no Valkyrie Cain to see? She is obliterated. Wiped from existence. That, to me, would seem the logical interpretation."

"Cleric Craven makes a valid point," Tenebrae nodded. "Solomon, I wanted proof that Cain is strong enough. We have not had that proof."

"What we *have* had," Quiver said, "is a warning. We can't waste any more time on candidates who are going to fall short of what is required. This Darquesse woman is coming. Unless we find our Death Bringer before she arrives, this world will be destroyed."

Wreath's jaw clenched and his face flushed. Craven's grin was itching to spread.

"And the Remnant?" he asked. "We're just going to let it go free?"

"What would you have us do?" Tenebrae asked, almost laughing. "Form a search party? Track it down? Cleric Wreath, that is not the Necromancer way. The Remnant, at this moment, is not our problem. Let others deal with it, if they have to."

"Your Eminence—"

"You are not to involve yourself in this matter any further. Do you understand me, Cleric?"

Wreath stopped himself, and bowed. "Yes, sir. Of course, sir."

Craven walked into the depths of the Temple, allowing the grin to consume his face. That had been most enjoyable. That had been altogether *thrilling*. Not only had Solomon Wreath been humbled before him, but also permission had been given, in a way, for Craven's own plans to commence. The need was apparent. The time frame inescapable. Tenebrae didn't know about it, of course, but then His Eminence was too cautious a leader. In times of strife, victory favoured the bold.

Craven came to a section of the Temple that he had quietly, and secretly, sequestered for his own use over the years. This was the darkest and dankest and coldest part of the Temple, at its lowest point beneath the graveyard. He took a long key from his robes, slotted it through a door and turned. A heavy *clunk* rewarded him, and he stepped in. Melancholia was already standing beside the chair he had given her. She waited with her head down, hands by her sides.

"You may raise your eyes," Craven said. "Cleric Wreath has returned. His mission, unfortunately, a failure."

Melancholia's eyes sparkled. "Then Cain isn't the Death Bringer?"

"We can't be sure, and my fellow Cleric has not been forbidden to continue her lessons... but it is looking increasingly unlikely. You never believed she would be the one, did you?"

Melancholia hesitated. "No, sir, I'm sorry. I didn't."

"Neither did I."

She frowned. "Cleric?"

"Even if Valkyrie Cain does have the power to usher in the Passage, I don't think she would. She's the wrong person. Just like Lord Vile was the wrong person. But you, Melancholia, you might just be what we've all been waiting for."

"Me?"

"You may not have Cain's natural gift, but you make up for it in passion and dedication – attributes I value much more highly. What age are you?"

"Twenty, sir."

"And you haven't reached the Surge yet."

"No, sir."

"You're sure it's Necromancy you want, then? When your

power surges, in a month, in a year, whenever it happens, your choice is over. From that point, you will be locked into one, and only one, discipline, for the rest of your life."

"Necromancy is all I've *ever* wanted."

"Good. Good. I have been waiting for someone with the right qualities, of the right age, on the cusp of the Surge. I've been waiting for *you*, Melancholia."

"You really think I can be the Death Bringer?"

"With my help, yes. I do. We will need to work hard. It won't be easy and it will be painful. We're going to have to prepare you, so that when the Surge happens, you will be infused with shadow magic."

"Is that... is that possible?"

"I'm not going to lie to you. This has never been done before. It's never even been thought of. My research into the language of magic has opened up possibilities that we had never considered. But I've grown tired of waiting. My patience has ended. If we can't find someone powerful enough to assume the mantle of the Death Bringer, then we will *make* someone powerful enough. You, Melancholia, will be the one to save the world. Do you accept?"

"Yes, sir," the girl said, her eyes gleaming. "Oh yes, sir."

14

DEAD MEN

It always surprised Valkyrie whenever she realised just how close the weird and the wonderful, and the fierce and the frightening, lived to the rest of the non-magical, *mortal* world. She'd visited Dublin streets where every house held a sorcerer. She'd been thrown from the balcony of a block of flats that was home to a dozen vampires. She'd had tea with a psychic in a tattoo parlour, fought a blade-wielding assassin beneath the Waxworks Museum, and she'd dodged bullets at a football stadium. And the latest example of how close her two lives ran came in the form of an address for a banshee who, apparently, lived within a half-hour's drive of Dublin.

Valkyrie had decided that she was going to take a taxi to see her – so all she had to do was make her excuses to Skulduggery and leave. It would have been simple if, when she followed Tanith into Ghastly's shop, Erskine Ravel hadn't been there to greet them.

"I don't believe I've had the pleasure," Ravel said when he set eyes on Tanith.

"I think I would have remembered," she replied, smiling as they shook hands. "I'm Tanith Low. You must be the notorious Erskine Ravel. I've heard stories about you."

"Did any of them paint me in a flattering light? Because if they did, they are probably lies."

"Just the usual Dead Men tales."

Despite her pressing need to be elsewhere, Valkyrie frowned. "Dead Men?"

"That's what they called us during the war," Ghastly said, carrying a broken mannequin into the backroom. His shirtsleeves were rolled back off his thick forearms. His muscles, added to the ridges of scars that ran vertically down his entire head, plus the glare he sent Ravel's way, would have been enough to make practically any man back away from Tanith. But it only made Ravel's smile widen.

"They were legends," Tanith told her, missing the glare completely. "Skulduggery, Mr Ravel here, Shudder, Dexter Vex. And Ghastly of course. They called them the Dead Men because they went on suicide missions and always came back alive."

"Not all of us," Skulduggery reminded her as he came in behind them. "Erskine, so good to see you again after so short a time."

"I was in the neighbourhood," Ravel shrugged. "I thought I'd drop in and say hi to Ghastly. I kind of hoped you'd stop by, actually. Has it sunk in yet?"

"Has what sunk in?" Skulduggery asked. "The insanity of what Corrival asked, or the stupidity?"

Ravel shook his head. "It's ridiculous, isn't it? I was just thinking that and... It *is* ridiculous. The two of *us*, on the Council of Elders? Do you realise how boring that job would get? We're not used to jobs that... peaceful."

"I hear Elders don't even get to punch anyone," Skulduggery said miserably. "Apparently, we'd have people to do that for us."

"We're just not suited to it. We've commanded people on the battlefield, we've issued orders during investigations... I mean, being a leader is one thing, but..."

"But being mature is something else entirely," Skulduggery nodded. "I agree completely."

"So you're not going to do it?" Tanith asked. "Really? You're both going to turn this down?"

"What would we be turning down?" Skulduggery asked. "It's only a nomination. It doesn't mean anything."

"What about Corrival?" Valkyrie asked. "If he'd said no to the Grand Mage position, would you have accepted that?"

At that, both men hesitated. Finally, Ravel shrugged.

"I don't know. The chance to make a difference? To make some real and lasting changes? He's perfect for the job."

"And it's going to be really nice to have someone in the Sanctuary we can trust," Skulduggery said. "If he said no, I wouldn't have stopped until I'd convinced him to change his mind."

"So you're saying that you wouldn't have *allowed* Corrival Deuce to turn down this opportunity," Tanith said, "but the pair of you are just too *cool* to say yes?"

"Well, we're rogues," Ravel informed her.

"Mavericks, one might say," Skulduggery added. "Also, we don't appreciate our own arguments being used against us. It's self-defeating in the worst possible way."

Tanith raised an eyebrow. "And also tremendously hypocritical?"

"If I'm a hypocrite," Ravel announced, "I haven't noticed. I've never cared much for introspection. I've done my best to leave that for the bleakest of poets and the most self-pitying of vampires."

Valkyrie was going to point out that not all vampires were self-pitying, but she didn't feel like getting a glare from Tanith. Also, she wasn't entirely sure she believed it.

Ghastly came out of the backroom. "When are you going to tell him you're saying no?"

"I'm planning on delaying it," Skulduggery said. "The longer it goes on, the more ridiculous it will seem, and the more people will complain about it. They'll do my job for me. Erskine, of course, doesn't have that luxury."

Ravel looked at him. "What? Why don't I?"

"Because not enough people dislike you. And Corrival trusts you implicitly – he always has. Erskine, to be brutally honest, it doesn't sound like a completely stupid idea to have you as an Elder."

"Take that back," said Ravel.

"He's going to need your help. As he goes on, he's going to make a lot of enemies. He's prided himself on being a man *of* the people, *for* the people. His greatest priority has always been the safety and protection of the mortals. I can see him restricting sorcerer activity even more than it already has been. That's probably a wise move, too. The way things have been going, it's only a matter of time before one of our secret little battles explodes across the mainstream media, and then not even Scrutinous and Random will be able to smooth things over."

Ravel shook his head. "Not everyone is going to be as understanding as you, Skulduggery. I've been by his side for the last hundred years, and even I'm going to have trouble with some of the things he'll introduce. He has this glorious vision of sorcerers as humanity's guardian angels – silent, invisible..."

"Exactly what they need."

Ravel laughed. "I suppose you're right."

"The new Council needs to be strong," Ghastly said. "Without a strong leadership with a clear purpose, I have a feeling that our friends around the globe won't be content to just sit back and watch."

"They'd try to take over," Skulduggery said.

"Could they?" Valkyrie asked. "I mean, would they be allowed?"

"Who'd stop them? The fact is, they don't trust us to take

care of our own problems. They're not our enemies. If the Americans *were* involved in the destruction of the Sanctuary, it's not because they want to destroy us – it's just because they think that things would be better if they were in charge."

"So... they'd invade?"

"It would be quiet, vicious, and sudden."

"You two would probably be the first to be killed," Ravel said.

Valkyrie stared. "What?"

"Sorry, but it's true. The amount of damage the pair of you have inflicted on anyone who's crossed you over the past few years? They're not going to take a chance on leaving you alive."

"He's right," Skulduggery said. "We're just too good at our job."

"Damn it," Valkyrie scowled. "I hate being too good at our job."

The conversation drifted. Ravel was charming and funny, and he certainly amused Tanith, even if Valkyrie sensed a hesitancy in her laugh whenever Ghastly walked by. Valkyrie checked the time, and the butterflies began fluttering in her belly. She'd have to leave soon. Her phone rang.

"Marr will be ready to be moved in the morning," Kenspeckle told her.

"Is she conscious?"

"She regained consciousness and I sedated her. I have no intention of talking with that woman. Tell the detective he can collect her first thing. I don't want her here one second longer than she has to be."

"Is everything OK?" Skulduggery asked when she'd hung up.

She nodded. "Kenspeckle says we're to pick up Marr in the morning."

Ravel looked surprised. "What? What's this? You know where Marr is?"

Valkyrie closed her eyes and groaned.

"Ah," Skulduggery said. "Yes. That was supposed to be a secret, Valkyrie."

"I know," she said miserably. "I'm sorry."

"You have Marr?" Ravel said. "She's in custody? Why is it a secret? This is great news!"

"We're not telling anyone until we've had a chance to question her," Skulduggery said. "Or that was the *plan*, at least."

"I said I'm sorry," Valkyrie muttered.

"Well let's go," Ravel said. "She's with Kenspeckle Grouse? Let's go question her."

"Professor Grouse has made it clear," Skulduggery said, "that he's quite happy to help us and heal us, but he doesn't want his facility used as a headquarters. No, tomorrow we'll take her somewhere else. We're going to need somewhere secure."

"How about *your* house?" Tanith said.

Skulduggery tilted his head. "That's not a bad suggestion, actually." He looked at Ravel. "Erskine, seeing as how you are now part of this incredibly well-kept secret, do you want to tag along?"

Ravel glanced at Tanith, and smiled. "Sounds like fun. Ghastly? You in?"

"I'm busy," Ghastly said, a little gruffly. "These dresses aren't going to make themselves, you know."

"Well, all right then," Skulduggery said. "Tomorrow morning, we get the answers we've been looking for."

Valkyrie managed to keep her mouth shut until they were outside, and walking for the Bentley. Tanith was heading for her bike, and Ravel had fallen a little behind.

"I have to go," she blurted.

Skulduggery turned his head to her. "Sorry?"

She smiled, hoping he wouldn't see the nervousness in her eyes. "I have to go. Sorry. I should have told you. I've got something else on. Other stuff. Personal business stuff."

"I see. Is everything all right?"

"Yes," she laughed. "Everything's fine. I just should have told you."

He shook his head. "No, nonsense, you don't need to explain. Will this business be finished by tomorrow?"

"Oh yes, God yes. Absolutely. I really don't want to miss out on interrogating Davina Marr if I can help it. I kind of owe her for when she interrogated *me*."

Skulduggery nodded. She had the feeling he was waiting for her to tell him where she was going. When she didn't, he nodded again and picked a loose thread off his sleeve. "You're OK for a lift?"

"I have Fletcher."

"Of course you do. Well, I'll see you later, then."

She gave him a little wave, and walked away, a hollow feeling growing in her gut. She didn't keep much from Skulduggery. Up until five months ago, Gordon's Echo Stone was the only significant truth she'd kept from him, and that wasn't even her choice. But this was different. She had an urge to run back to him, tell him everything, tell him that she was

Darquesse, that she was on her way to talk to a banshee, and she was sure he'd understand, sure he'd help her, make things easier on her...

But Valkyrie didn't run back to him. She just kept on walking.

15

THE BANSHEE

own by the river, sheltered from the wind by the ancient trees that grew unhindered by city or road, the cottage sat in its patch of darkness and shadow. The river, no more then a stream really, flowed down from the hills and bisected the fields and meadows, and even from her vantage point Valkyrie could hear the gentle rush of water.

She didn't like doing things like this without Skulduggery, but she couldn't see that she had a choice. She stuffed

Gordon's notebook into her jacket and started down the hill slowly, trying her best not to slip on the grass.

And then she heard the scream.

Valkyrie looked up, eyes wide. There was another scream and she took off running, sprinting down to the river and splashing through it, soaking her clothes in the freezing water. She emerged from the other side and saw a narrow road ahead, and a woman stumbling to her knees.

Valkyrie called out and the woman glanced back. Relief washed over her face, and that's when Valkyrie heard the thunder of many hooves, and a creaking and a trundle. She looked around. They were alone out here, but the sounds were getting louder...

And then it materialised in front of her, a great black coach driven by four headless horses, the colour of night. Valkyrie leaped out of the way as it hurtled by. It vanished from sight, but she could still hear it, and now the woman was screaming again. Valkyrie scrambled to her feet and sprinted.

The woman tried to run, but was sent sprawling as if hit from behind. Valkyrie ran closer and the carriage appeared, as the headless horses drew to a stop. The driver climbed down. He was dressed in traditional coachman's attire, though he, like his horses, had no head. He didn't seem quite so ridiculous now.

"Leave her alone!" Valkyrie yelled, running up to him.

He turned to her as she summoned fire and threw it, the ball of flame exploding against his chest, but dying away instantly. She ran right into him, charging him with her shoulder and he stepped back under the collision, but gave no more ground. She felt a cold hand around her neck and she was flung into the air, and she hit the ground hard.

"Help me!" the woman cried as the driver, the Dullahan, strode towards her. He took hold of her arm and pulled her back to the carriage as she begged and screamed.

Valkyrie launched herself at the Dullahan, pushing outwards at the air and making him stagger and then driving a kick into him. He swiped at her with his free hand, but she ducked under it and punched, and her fist met his side and it was like punching a wall. The back of his hand caught her and she spun like a top and dropped to one knee. The Dullahan carried on towards the carriage.

She could only watch as the Dullahan shoved the woman up against the carriage, the door of which opened silently behind her. The woman kept her eyes on the headless driver, tears running down her face, and then a dozen pale hands grabbed her and pulled her, screaming, into the carriage. The door swung gently closed and the Dullahan climbed back to his seat.

Ignoring Valkyrie completely, he flicked the reins and the headless horses took off at a trot, the Coach-a-Bowers trundling behind them. It vanished from sight, though Valkyrie could still hear the hooves, fading into the distance.

She stood up, still a little dizzy from when he had struck her.

"You can't defeat the Dullahan," said a voice from behind her.

She turned. A woman walked up, her black hair hanging over her lined face, her ragged dress trailing on the grass behind her. Her feet were dirty and bare and her hands were thin.

"He is not a man," the woman continued, "he is not a beast, he just is. You cannot defeat what just is."

"Who was she?" Valkyrie asked, forcing herself not to be intimidated. "The woman he took."

The answer came in a voice that was almost fond. "Her name was Margaret. She was the last of her family. She heard my cry and now that family is no more, wiped from the world like a stray tear."

"Why?"

"Because it was her time."

"Who are you to decide?"

The old woman looked up and her hair parted, showing

more of her face. All Valkyrie could make out were wrinkles and lines and one hazel flecked eye, blinking at her. "I'm not the one who decides," she said. "Now then, who are you, and why have you sought me out?"

Valkyrie looked down at her, her anger bubbling right beside her needs. She made herself calm down. "My name's Valkyrie Cain. I was told you could help me."

"Who told you this?"

"My uncle. Gordon Edgley."

"Gordon," the banshee said, smiling. "I haven't heard from him in years. How is he?"

"Dead."

"Give him my best, won't you?"

"I need to seal my name. He said you might know someone who could do something like that."

"You know it, then? Your true name?"

"Yes, I do."

"Impressive. And Gordon was right — I know of one who could do what needs to be done. Its name is Nye — a doctor, and quite a curious creature. I wouldn't trust it, but then, I don't have to. Of course, there is no guarantee that Nye will agree to help. Its time is taken up with experiments and... procedures. It depends how busy the good doctor is, if it can fit you in, and if you make it curious. Luckily for you, I *do* think you will make it curious. Tell me, my dear, do you know what the sealing of your name would entail?"

"I only know that it's dangerous."

"Oh, it is. You're absolutely sure you want me to arrange it?"

Valkyrie thought of her mother, her father, the baby on the way. She thought of what she'd seen and the screams she'd heard. "Yes," she said.

The old woman turned to go. "Then I will be in touch shortly."

"Wait," said Valkyrie. "What *will* it entail? Do you know?"

The banshee smiled. "I only know that the first thing you will have to do is die. Once you've done that, Nye's work will begin."

16

THE INTERROGATION OF DAVINA MARR

er teeth gritted against the cold of the morning, Tanith followed Skulduggery and Ravel into the Hibernian, fantasising about what it would be like if her clothing of choice was waterproof fleece instead of tight leather. She wouldn't cut such a striking figure, it's true, but the comfort and warmth and sheer cosiness would more than make up for it. The door unlocked for them and they passed through, into the relative warmth of the dark and musty cinema.

Skulduggery had let Ravel do all the talking on the drive over, while he'd stayed quiet. She knew he was wondering about the personal business that had delayed Valkyrie. She'd never chosen personal business over the job before, at least not that Tanith was aware, and it was an unsettling development. Back when Skulduggery was trapped in a world overrun by Faceless Ones, Valkyrie was single-minded in her dedication to rescuing him. But since then, it seemed, she'd been distracted. There was always something going on, something she didn't want to talk about.

Was it Caelan? Was she feeling guilty about the kiss? Was there something more, something she hadn't told Tanith? Was she with him now, despite the promises she'd made? Tanith knew full well how things could get confusing at that age. She had been a teenager once, and she knew that, despite the apparent contradiction, a person's teenage years lasted well into their fifties. It had only been at age sixty that *she'd* managed to gain some control over herself, after all.

These days she was a fine young woman of eighty-three, and even though she was still astonishingly immature for her age, the allure of bad boys had faded somewhat. They were still all around her of course – in her line of work, she had her pick of them. But bad boys would always disappoint. It was inevitable. Whereas nice guys tended to surprise you.

The only parts of her that weren't numb with cold were her feet, because she was wearing boots Ghastly had made for her. He hadn't needed any special occasion to do it either. He'd just presented them to her one day, mumbled something about the importance of circulation, and wandered into the backroom of his shop. She grinned at the memory.

But as for Valkyrie... Tanith was willing to give her the benefit of the doubt. She might *not* have been with the vampire last night. It may have been *family* business – it *was* Christmas time, after all. Or Fletcher. Maybe they'd had a date.

Tanith frowned. Did people still go on *dates* any more? She was sure they did. They probably called it something different though. She tried to think of the last date she'd been on. The last *proper* date. Did fighting side by side with Saracen Rue count as a date? They ended up snuggling under the moonlight, drenched in gore and pieces of brain – so it had *probably* been a date. If it wasn't, it was certainly a fun time had by all. Well, not *all*. But she and Saracen had sure had a blast.

Tanith needed a date. She needed a lot of things, but above all she needed a date.

It didn't help to be reminded of that fact every time she saw

Valkyrie and Fletcher together. Valkyrie didn't like public displays of affection, but she wasn't allergic to them either. The hand-holding, the sitting close together, Fletcher's hand on the small of her back... These things did nothing to take Tanith's mind off the subject. And then there were the talks, Valkyrie filling her in on details Tanith could have done without. But that was her role, she supposed. Best friend and big sister, all in one.

Her eyes drifted to the back of Skulduggery's head. Maybe not *best* friend, she corrected. But close enough.

They climbed on to the stage and passed through the door in the screen. Clarabelle met them in the corridor, wearing her white lab coat over a summer dress, and a huge black gas mask contraption on her head.

"Good morning," she said, her cheery voice muffled. "Are you here to pick up the patient? She's not very nice. She said some harsh words about my intelligence before the Professor made her go unconscious again."

"Why are you wearing that?" Tanith asked.

Clarabelle's head dipped heavily as she looked down at her dress. "Because it's pretty."

"No, I mean the gas mask."

"Hmm? Oh, *this*. I just wanted to see what it would be like to live in a bubble. Professor Grouse is busy elsewhere. He said the patient should be awake in about half an hour, and then he asked me to escort you to her."

"It's OK," Skulduggery said, "we know where she is."

"Good, because I think I'm lost." Clarabelle caught sight of the doorway nearest to her and she wandered through it, bashing her head against the doorframe on the way.

"Delightful lady," Ravel said as they walked on.

They got to the Medical Bay, where they found Davina Marr sedated and unconscious. Skulduggery undid the restraints, then shackled her hands behind her back. He pulled her into a sitting position, and suddenly she started levitating. For a split second, Tanith was ready to spring into action.

"You were going to carry her?" Ravel asked, manipulating the air to float Marr gently to the door. "Why make things more difficult than they have to be?"

Tanith relaxed, and Skulduggery shook his head as they followed Ravel out into the corridor. "I like to keep magic for special occasions. I don't use it simply to show off." He caught the grin Tanith threw his way. "Shut up."

She laughed.

They put Marr in the boot of the Bentley and drove to Skulduggery's house, with Tanith following on her motorbike.

By the time they got there, Tanith's teeth were chattering with the cold.

Skulduggery carried Marr into the living room, where he secured her to a chair. He left his hat and gun on a coffee table and Ravel hung up his coat. Tanith turned the heating on, and when she walked back into the room, Marr was awake, and smiling.

"You look happy," Skulduggery said.

Marr shrugged. "Not happy, just surprised."

"At your surroundings?"

"At the fact that I'm still alive. I thought Tesseract would have tracked me down by now."

"I assure you, you're quite safe."

"No I'm not, and neither are you. Any of you."

"In that case, we better talk fast before we're interrupted. You've been betrayed. Tell us what we want to know and we'll protect you."

Marr laughed. "You can't protect me. This is Tesseract we're talking about."

"You may not have noticed, but there are more of us than there are of him."

"I'm startled that you think it'll make a difference."

"Tell us who you were working with," said Skulduggery.

"I wasn't working with anyone. Why is Erskine Ravel here, anyway? Have you joined this merry band of detectives, Mr Ravel? Have you got nothing better to do with your time?"

"Things have been happening since you've been away," Ravel said. "You don't know what you've been missing."

"You claim that you decided to destroy the Sanctuary all by yourself," Skulduggery said. "Why, Davina? Were you bored that day?"

"Well, it sounds silly when you say it like *that*..."

"You don't owe these people your loyalty. They want you silenced. They want you dead."

"I sincerely don't know what people you're referring to."

"If you don't help us," Skulduggery said, "all the blame lands at your feet. You will be tried, *alone*, for multiple counts of murder and terrorism."

She shook her head. "Terrorism. Everything is *terrorism* lately. Such an overused word."

"Those whose spread terror are terrorists by definition."

"But don't you think that word misses out on the subtleties that separate these acts from each other? Why do they have to be terrorists? Why can't they just be criminals and murderers? The spreading of terror isn't a motive – it's a means to achieving a goal. Labelling an act of atrocity as terrorism instantly dismisses the nuances of human behaviour as regards hatred, anger and greed."

Skulduggery folded his arms. "The destruction of the Sanctuary, then. This wouldn't be terrorism?"

"Not at all."

"It would simply be murder?"

"Now you're getting it," Marr said with a nod.

"So you're a murderer."

"Finally, we agree on something."

"You forced Myron Stray to take the Desolation Engine into the Sanctuary and set it off. You wanted Valkyrie and myself to be there when it happened."

"Sorry about that. Purely personal."

"Why did you do it?"

"I was disgruntled."

"You were having an off day?"

Marr smiled. "Again, you make it sound so silly."

"I think you're lying."

"I am deeply hurt."

The front door opened, and they all spun. Footsteps approached, and Valkyrie walked in.

"Hello, sweetie," Marr smiled.

Immediately, Valkyrie scowled. "Is she talking?"

Marr chuckled. "Do you really think you're going to get anything out of me? I've been where you are, remember. I've been the one asking the questions. This doesn't intimidate me."

"Well, yeah," Valkyrie said, "you asked the questions, but you weren't very good at it, were you? I mean, I was interrogated by you, and you failed so spectacularly that you had to try to *beat* a confession out of me."

"Very true," Marr nodded. "I didn't get a confession though, did I?"

"No, you didn't."

"But I did get you to beg."

The look of anger that came over Valkyrie's face was startling, and Marr laughed. Tanith silently willed her friend to stay calm.

"That's enough," Skulduggery said. "Davina, you have this one chance to help yourself. If you don't seize it now, you will die in prison. Were you working for the American Sanctuary? Did they orchestrate the destruction of the Sanctuary to destabilise the country?"

"This country is already destabilised."

"You were reporting back to them, weren't you?"

"Maybe the odd postcard."

"I've never known you to make so many jokes."

"You've never known me. You thought you did. You thought many things. You know your problem? You think you're smarter than you actually are. It becomes very annoying to the people around you. You agree, don't you, Valkyrie? Or maybe I'm asking the wrong person. How about you, Tanith? You're not besotted with him like Valkyrie is, are you? You've got far too many other romances to be thinking about. You're a very popular girl, from what I hear."

Tanith frowned. "Are you coming on to me?"

"How's the tailor, by the way? Are you still torturing him by pretending not to notice how he feels?"

The retort died on Tanith's tongue, and she just glared.

"Struck a nerve, did I?" Marr asked. "Deeply sorry. You can continue your interrogation now, if you want. It's a fun way to pass the time while we wait for Tesseract to find me."

"Why are you protecting them?" Skulduggery asked. "They want you dead, Davina."

"The whole country wants me dead."

"I can't understand this. You've been abandoned. By your own admission, your life is in incredible danger. Why won't you help us stop the people responsible?"

"Because this is more amusing."

Skulduggery shook his head. "No. That's not it. That's not why you're refusing to help. I think you're refusing to help because you can't."

"I see," Marr said. "Yes. That's exactly right. Well done."

"Think about the people responsible."

"I told you—"

"Yes, yes, you told us you were working alone, and we don't believe you. What I want you to do, Davina, is to think of the people you were working with. You don't have to tell us their names. I just want you to think about the people. OK?"

"You want me to think about no one?"

"I don't care if you keep up the charade – the only thing I want you to do is see them, in your mind. Picture them. Think of their names."

Skulduggery paused, then tilted his head. "You can't, can you? You can't picture them. You can't think of their names. You try to. You've probably been trying to for the last five months. But you can't."

Marr wasn't smiling any more.

"They've blocked themselves from your memory," Skulduggery continued. "The harder you try to remember, the further away they get. Given time, with the right people and the right procedures, we could break through that wall. But we don't have the time."

Marr shrugged. "So you've worked out my little secret. Big deal. Now you can stop repeating the same questions, right?"

"What do you remember?"

"You've just figured out that I don't remember anything."

"You don't remember anything specific. What about generalities? Vague impressions? How many of them were there?"

"Don't know."

"Five? Ten?"

"One," Marr said. "A man. I think."

"A man contacted you?"

"Yes."

"Told you his plan, asked if you were interested?"

"That's as much as I remember."

"He left the finer details up to you?"

"He told me why he wanted the Sanctuary destroyed. Whatever it was he said, it made sense, I remember that much. I agreed with him. I came up with how to go about it, and I set the plan in motion."

"You can't remember anything about him?" Skulduggery pressed. "Height? Accent? Hair colour? Age?"

Marr sighed. "Nothing. Whatever he dazzled me with, it dazzled me good. I've been trying to remember the finer details since it happened, but all I get is a very confused fog."

"If we can get you remembering, will you help us?"

"No point. I'll be dead before the day is out."

"If we keep you alive, will you help us?"

"And what do I get out of it? Immunity? Do I get to walk free?"

"No," Ravel said. "We can't give you that. But we can make sure that the people who set this up are brought to justice."

"What kind of justice? The kind of justice where I'm tied to a chair in someone's living room? I don't see any officials here, or anything stopping you from executing me the moment I tell you what you want to know. Would they be brought to *this* kind of justice?"

"*Exactly* this kind of justice."

She smiled. "Well, why didn't you say so? Call whoever you have to call – let's get my memories unlocked."

Skulduggery made a few calls, and Tanith and Valkyrie went into the kitchen to chat. A few minutes later, Tanith excused herself and walked into the bathroom. She shut the door behind her, unbuckled her belt, and looked up into the mirror just in time to see a colossal man in a metal mask reaching for her.

17

THE JOB

Tesseract spent three hours getting into the Skeleton Detective's house. First he dismantled the magical defences, then he turned his attention to the technological. He worked quickly but without hurry, allowing himself to be impressed with the attention to detail in the security arrangements. Before this visit to Ireland, he had never personally encountered Skulduggery – Tesseract liked to be on a first-name basis with the people he would probably end up killing – and he was glad to see that all the stories about his professionalism appeared to be true. A worthy opponent, if ever there was one.

Of course, Tesseract wasn't especially interested in worthy opponents. He was not on a crusade to prove himself, or test himself, or needlessly risk his life or his freedom. If he had the choice, he always preferred to kill someone when they were distracted, or when their back was turned, or when they were sleeping. He had even, on one memorable occasion, killed a man who was already dead. A heart attack had taken his target's life before Tesseract had even reached him, so he stabbed him once, not too deep, and returned to his employer to claim his payment. Tesseract was not above a little foul play. He was, after all, an assassin.

And so his current situation was not resting easily in his mind. He didn't like the fact that, in order to find out where Davina Marr was being kept, he would have to go through Skulduggery Pleasant, and probably Valkyrie Cain, and whoever else they might have along with them. The numbers were against him, but his employers at Roarhaven had given him a deadline. Tesseract's hand, as they say, had been forced.

He wasn't nervous. He wasn't excited. He wasn't looking forward to the blood he had to spill, but neither was he dreading it. Two, or even three, against one were not good odds, and yet he felt no fear. He was a professional, and he was quite capable of killing three sorcerers in one go, even sorcerers as powerful and experienced as Skulduggery, provided he took them by surprise.

Neither was he dismissing Valkyrie Cain. He had files on everyone he was likely to go up against, and he had one on her too. She had a habit of upsetting the plans of her enemies – through either luck, skill, or pure bloody-minded determination. She was not to be underestimated.

His face itched under the mask. He had chosen an angular one for today, with deep cheekbones cut into the metal and three small holes at his mouth. He took a knife from the sheath under his arm, poked the tip through the left eyehole and manoeuvred it down to give himself a good scratch. He grumbled with satisfaction, but put the knife away when he heard the car.

He went to the window, saw Skulduggery and Erskine Ravel get out of the Bentley. Tanith Low rode up after them on her bike. Three powerful sorcerers. These weren't good odds, but he'd faced worse. Under the cover of night, Skulduggery lifted something large from the boot of the car. For once, luck was smiling on Tesseract. They'd brought Davina Marr *to* him.

He left the room, staying away from the other windows. He stood behind the door in the bathroom, his breathing as calm and as quiet as ever. The front door opened and they came in. He heard Davina's voice as they questioned her.

If he was lucky, Davina would be allowed a bathroom break. Then all Tesseract would have to do was step out and implode her skull, and vanish before anyone came knocking. If he was *un*lucky, he'd have to kill Tanith or Erskine first, and work through them one at a time. If he was *really* unlucky, no one would need to visit the bathroom at all, and he'd have to confront the whole lot of them at once.

He stayed behind the door for twenty-three minutes. He heard Valkyrie arrive, which brought the tally to four against one. The odds were getting worse. There was a break in the questioning, and Valkyrie and Tanith moved to the kitchen. Another minute passed before one of them left, their footsteps getting closer. Tanith Low walked into the bathroom, already unbuckling her belt, and swung the door shut without seeing him. The first to die, then.

He stepped up behind her, reached for the back of her head, and looked into the mirror over the sink at the same time as she did. Her eyes widened. He promised to curse himself later for making such a grievous error.

She whirled, whipping the belt from her trousers as he lunged. The belt wrapped around his wrist and she tugged it, tried to pull him off-balance, but he was already adjusting. He rammed his shoulder into her, driving her through the open doors of the shower. Before she could call for help he kicked her. She wasn't expecting it. In his experience, fast people rarely expected to encounter someone faster than they were. The toe of his boot sank into her belly and lifted her off her feet, doubling her over and forcing all the air from her lungs. She dropped forward and he cracked his knee into her chin, and caught her as she fell.

He didn't kill her. Unconscious, she was no longer a threat, and so he saw no point to it. Also, he tried not to do freebies if he could avoid it.

Tesseract moved to the door and listened to the low murmur of uninterrupted conversation – Skulduggery was talking to Davina Marr again. Tesseract stepped out, walked silently to the kitchen. Valkyrie had her back to him. She was making a pot of tea. How very Irish of her.

Even as he crossed the floor, he acknowledged that he had an opportunity to leave her alive, but decided against it. The encounter with Tanith had simply turned out that way. The simple truth was that it was easier and quieter to kill this girl than to subdue her. Tesseract was nothing if not a practical man, and so he went for the spine.

She must have felt the air shift, because she started talking, assuming he was a friend. His fingers closed around her neck, and her body jerked and she made a noise like someone had kicked her in the throat. Then she twisted out of his grip and stumbled to the floor.

"Help!" she barked.

Tesseract narrowed his eyes, looking at the jacket that she was wearing, realising too late the magical properties it must possess. His fingertips had pressed against the collar, not her skin, and the collar had protected her. Another mistake, in a day that was becoming chock-full of them.

Skulduggery Pleasant burst into the kitchen and Tesseract went to meet him head on. He ducked under a punch and slammed an elbow into Skulduggery's side. He felt the framework under the skeleton's clothes flex inwards, and then the rewarding crunch of elbow against ribs. Skulduggery staggered away and Erskine came next. He pushed at the air, but Tesseract moved around it. Credit where it was due, Erskine switched to a physical attack without blinking. Not that it was going to do him any good.

Tesseract blocked a punch with his forearm, then smacked Erskine in the mouth and followed him as he stumbled back. Too late, Tesseract saw it was a ruse. Erskine kicked at his leg, and if Tesseract hadn't managed to move slightly, he was in no doubt that the kick would have smashed his kneecap.

The air shimmered and hit him like God's own punch. He was thrown across the room, landed on the table and rolled off the other side.

Erskine threw a handful of fire that Tesseract had to sidestep to dodge, and as he did so Valkyrie caught him in the chest with a stream of shadows. He tumbled into the living room. Davina was shackled to a chair, staring at him with wide eyes. She started struggling against her bonds.

Before he could move towards her, Skulduggery and the others barged in behind him. Skulduggery gestured and his gun flew from a coffee table towards his gloved hand. Tesseract flung his knife. The tip of the blade slid through the trigger guard and pinned the gun to the wall.

"Let me free!" Davina yelled.

Tesseract ran at Valkyrie, hurling the coffee table at Skulduggery to distract him. Valkyrie whipped a tendril of shadows at him, but he dived under it, rolled and came up, grabbed her black clothes with both hands and lifted. He slammed her against the wall and then spun her around, throwing her like a rag doll to the window beside them. Her legs smashed through the glass, and he released her and the momentum kept her body turning. Her back hit the edge of the window frame and she rebounded and fell, cracking the shards of glass beneath her. She lay half in, half out of the window, folded over the sill. If it weren't for those clothes, she'd have been slashed to bloody ribbons.

He turned as Skulduggery rushed him, a snarl behind that impassive skull. Tesseract dodged a punch and swung into him, throwing him over his hip to the ground. He heard a finger click, and Erskine sent flames bursting across his back. Tesseract stumbled, but Skulduggery was already on his feet. His coat on fire and his skin burning, Tesseract caught Skulduggery's fist in his hand, his fingertips curling around the glove, making the bones underneath tremor. Skulduggery cried out as they snapped apart. Tesseract's power could only be transmitted through his fingertips, so when his knuckles broke Skulduggery's jaw, it wasn't magic that did it, it was a combination of pure strength, the right angle, and a happy piece of luck.

Skulduggery went down, just as a wall of air slammed into Tesseract and sent him hurtling over the couch. He ripped off his fiery coat and turned to meet Erskine's charge, saw the Elemental's hands pushing down by his sides, and knew what was coming next. He grabbed a floor lamp with both hands, and as the air shimmered and Erskine shot towards him, he swung the lamp like a baseball bat. It splintered on impact, catching Erskine perfectly and sending him crashing to the ground.

And then a kick came from nowhere, right into his face, and Tesseract tripped over the broken coffee table and went sprawling. Tanith Low dropped from the ceiling. He should have killed her. He should have killed her when he had the chance.

She jumped at him, aiming to finish the fight with another kick to the head. Tesseract raised an arm to block it, but she flipped over him. He rolled sideways, avoiding the foot stomp, and got up in time to block the next attack and give himself some room. He had never been one for talking during a fight, but he would have loved to ask her a question right now. Once she'd regained consciousness, had she run immediately to help her friends, or had she done the smart thing and delayed for a moment, long enough to call for reinforcements?

Tesseract darted forward, catching her off guard, the heel of his palm striking her in the chest. He tried to follow it up with a grab, but she demonstrated a most impressive aerial cartwheel and got away from him. She backed off, and his eyes flickered behind her and saw where she was headed. Her coat lay over a chair, and upon that chair lay her sword. She ran for it.

Tesseract wrapped an arm around the music system that was on a shelf beside him. He yanked it free of the wires and cables and hurled it across the room. Tanith grabbed her sword and turned and the music system hit her square in the face. She twisted as she fell, and the system clattered to the ground beside her.

If she *had* taken a moment to make that call, he knew she would undoubtedly have called Fletcher Renn, told him to bring help. Tesseract strode to where Davina Marr struggled.

"No," said Davina, real fear in her eyes. "Not like this. At least let me stand up. Please, not like this."

He would have liked to grant her wish, but the Teleporter would have gone to either Ghastly Bespoke or China Sorrows – most likely the former. The question then became, if Fletcher had been alerted, how long would it take him to find Ghastly? Thirty seconds? A minute? Tesseract just didn't have the time to waste.

He placed his hand on Davina's chest and her breastbone shook and the ribs splintered inwards, piercing her heart. She died with her eyes open.

Tesseract turned, and a heavy fist caught him in the hinge of the jaw, right where his flesh met the mask. If Ghastly Bespoke hurt his hand with the punch, he gave no sign as he pressed forward.

Tesseract absorbed the punches, swung one of his own that Ghastly swayed away from. Three jabs rocked the mask against his face, then Ghastly went low, working the body. He surprised Tesseract with a kick that buckled his leg. Tesseract went down, but was helped back up again with an uppercut to the chin.

Fletcher Renn was across the room, carefully lifting Valkyrie down from the shattered window. The moment she was clear of the glass, they both vanished. A moment later, Fletcher was back, alone. Eye blink by eye blink, he disappeared with Skulduggery, Tanith and Erskine.

Tesseract had worked out Ghastly's rhythm by now, and dodged three more jabs before responding with a punch that sank into the muscle in the boxer's right side. Ghastly fell back, gasping for air, eyes suddenly wide. A good punch would do that to you, Tesseract knew. A good punch did more than deliver hurt – it disrupted an offensive, shook a fighter. Ghastly was shaken. He wasn't expecting a punch that fast, that hard. Tesseract could tell by the way he was circling that Ghastly was wary now, and unsure.

Fletcher appeared. "You ready?" he asked. Ghastly kept his eyes on Tesseract and didn't answer. "Ghastly. You ready to go?"

"Yeah," came the grudging reply.

Fletcher nodded. He took Skulduggery's gun down from the wall, tossing the knife away. He teleported to the chair and picked up Tanith's sword, then Skulduggery's hat, and then he appeared at Ghastly's elbow. They both vanished.

Tesseract let his fists uncurl. His back was burnt, the skin bloody and charred, but his mission had been a success. He found himself hoping that his Roarhaven employers would hire him to kill Skulduggery and the others. He'd quite like to finish this.

18

LICKING WOUNDS

Valkyrie lay in a tub of cold mud, its healing properties working on the damage Tesseract had inflicted on her back. A curtain separated her from the others. Skulduggery was on the bed to her right, mumbling instructions while he waited for his jaw to set. His hand, she had seen, was wrapped in gauze until his bones realigned. Ravel was to her left, healing up from his smashed ribs. Across the room, behind another curtain, was Tanith. Her jaw had been broken, her cheek shattered, nose crushed and four teeth had been knocked out. It was taking Kenspeckle Grouse a little longer to heal her.

Valkyrie lay in the tub and listened to the conversation go on around her.

"One man?" Kenspeckle was saying. "One man did all this?"

"We weren't ready," Ghastly said, and she could hear the quiet anger in his voice. "I should have gone with them. Should have been there at the start."

"Then who would Fletcher have gone to for help?" Kenspeckle asked. "No, Ghastly, I think it's just as well they had you as back-up. The man who did this, Tesseract. He wouldn't happen to be Russian, would he?"

"That's him," she heard Fletcher say. "You know him?"

"I've read reports of some people he's killed. He's a bonebreaker – he can break bones with the gentlest of touches. Highly unusual ability, but extremely effective. I daresay, actually, that he'd be the only person in the world who would be assured of killing Detective Pleasant here, if he so desired."

Skulduggery murmured something that sounded like, "Your bedside manner is dreadful."

"I thought I told you not to talk."

Skulduggery grunted.

"Tesseract could kill him?" Valkyrie asked, sitting up.

"Oh, yes," came Kenspeckle's answer, "and quite easily, too. We've seen how my grumpiest of patients can survive being dismembered, but it has long been my theory that if there isn't a large enough section of him that remains intact, his consciousness would dissipate. Just drift away. Tesseract has the ability to splinter an entire *skeleton*. I doubt there'd be anything left of the detective to think *with*."

Valkyrie lay back in the mud. She had come to regard Skulduggery as unkillable – mainly because he was already dead. She didn't like the idea of someone utterly *destroying* him.

She heard Ravel get off the bed to her left, and saw his shadow under the curtain as he moved to join the others.

"Mr Ravel," Kenspeckle said sharply, "I must insist that you allow yourself time to heal."

"I'm fine, Professor," Ravel responded. He groaned slightly, and Valkyrie heard the rustle of fabric. He was putting on his shirt. "I need to report this to Corrival. The upside is that we caught Davina Marr, which shows the Councils around the world that we can take care of our own messes. I don't think we should mention that Tesseract was the one to kill her though."

Skulduggery murmured something that could have been, "Agreed."

"We'll say she died resisting arrest, or she took her own life or something. Leave it with me. I'll take care of it."

"And what about Tesseract?" Fletcher asked. "He's still out there."

"His job is done," Ghastly said. "Unless he has another target, he'll slip away like he's always done."

Skulduggery murmured something that nobody understood. He made a few grunts that sounded like threats, and then Kenspeckle's voice moved closer to Valkyrie.

"Fine," Kenspeckle said. "I'll remove the bandage, but if your jaw falls off, you're going to the back of the queue."

Everyone waited a moment.

"OK," Kenspeckle said. "Open your mouth. Close it. Move it side to side. Very well, you can speak."

"Thank you," Skulduggery said. "Ghastly's right – Tesseract is probably gone already. And with him, any hope we have of finding out who his employers were."

"If he even remembers," Ravel said. "They could have dazzled him the same way they dazzled Marr."

The curtain by Valkyrie's tub parted, and Kenspeckle came through. He motioned her to lean forward, and checked her spine.

"I don't think so," Skulduggery said. "You wouldn't take the chance of double-crossing someone like Tesseract, not unless you planned to kill him. And we all know that's not exactly an easy thing to do."

"So he's collected his payment and gone," Ghastly said. "And Marr is dead, and her co-conspirators are safe. Where does that leave us?"

"Your back is healed and the swelling is going down," Kenspeckle said to Valkyrie. "There's a robe by the chair."

She nodded her thanks and waited until he had left before climbing out of the tub. She listened to the conversation as it developed into an argument for and against Roarhaven's involvement. She put on the robe, feeling it squelch against the mud covering her, and slipped her feet into the slippers. She was a little stiff as she walked through the curtain.

"The fact is," Skulduggery said, "we have nothing. No clues, no evidence. The only thing we know is that one of the people involved has the power to cloud memories. That's all."

Valkyrie looked at him. "Did we lose this one?"

"Of course not. We just didn't win it."

Ravel grabbed his coat. "I have to go. Grand Mage Deuce needs to know what we know."

"We don't know an awful lot," Skulduggery said.

"Then it's going to be a short meeting."

Skulduggery and Valkyrie drove back to Haggard in glum silence. It was dark again – they'd spent practically an entire day recovering from their injuries. Valkyrie's parents were undoubtedly asleep by now, which meant she had missed her chance to spend Christmas Eve with them, and this put her in an even worse mood than before. That heartless, soulless reflection had been there instead, smiling its fake smile. She sank into her seat and glowered.

"How are you?" Skulduggery asked.

"Fine," she muttered.

"You don't sound fine."

"I'm as fine as could be expected then, for someone who was in a fight in which one guy beat four of us at the same time, and then got away."

"We were the ones who fled, actually."

"You didn't have to point that out. I could have done without you pointing that out. He killed Marr with a touch. We'd probably all be dead if he'd been paid to kill us."

"That's a possibility."

"I don't like the fact that there's someone out there who can do that."

"We're not unstoppable, you know," said Skulduggery.

"Sometimes we are."

"Not tonight."

"No, not tonight. I'm glad she's dead. That's probably really horrible, isn't it? But I am. I'm glad Marr is dead."

"She killed a lot of people."

"Is that it, then? Is it over?"

"It appears to be. For now. Are you going to tell me what else is upsetting you?"

"What? Nothing." He cocked his head and she rolled her eyes. "Fine. I missed Christmas Eve with my parents. Happy? This is my last Christmas Eve as an only child, and I wanted to bask in my parents' love one final time."

He sounded amused. "They're not going to stop loving you just because you have a new brother or sister."

"You don't understand. When I was seven, Mum bought me a rabbit, Mister Fluffy. For two weeks, Dad paid more attention to that rabbit than he did to me. He played with it, he took it on walks, he practically tucked it in at night. And that was a *rabbit*. Imagine what he's going to be like with a *baby*."

"But after those two weeks, once the novelty wore off, he was back to normal, wasn't he?"

"I don't think it was because the novelty wore off. I think it was because he stood on Mister Fluffy."

"Pardon?"

Valkyrie sighed, her head lolling back on the seat. "He stepped on it. Squished it. Squashed it. Killed it. Cut it down in its prime. It kicked the bucket, turned up its toes, shuffled off this mortal coil. It was... an ex-rabbit."

"He's a dangerous man, your father."

"The baby better learn to dodge."

The windshield wipers activated, and Valkyrie looked out at the swirling snow caught in the headlights.

"That's pretty," she said. She lowered the window and stuck her head out, getting a freezing blast full in the face. She brought her head back in, slightly dazed.

"Fun?" Skulduggery asked.

She brushed the snowflakes from her hair. "It lightened my mood. I still have tomorrow off, right?"

"That's our deal."

"No matter what happens, Christmas Day is off-limits. It's a day for presents under the tree, turkey for dinner, and dozing off on the sofa while we watch Indiana Jones on TV."

"Sounds lovely."

"What are you going to do?"

"The same, except completely different."

Valkyrie managed a smile. "I love Christmas. I'll never understand anyone who doesn't."

"Plenty of people don't enjoy Christmas. It can be a lonely time of the year."

"But it's when all the family gets together," she said, speaking too fast to stop herself. Skulduggery dipped the headlights as a car passed in the opposite lane, then flicked them back up.

"Sorry," she said quietly.

He turned to her slightly. "What for?"

"You know. The family thing."

"Oh," he said. "You mean because my family is dead."

She winced. "Yeah."

"You know, I'd completely forgotten about all that until you brought it up."

She stared at him, horrified. They passed a sign for Haggard.

"I'm joking," he said at last.

"Oh, my God. That was mean."

"You shouldn't feel guilty about enjoying something that other people don't. Well, apart from torture, but that's probably the only exception. You love Christmas, and that's wonderful. Keep in mind that not everyone does, but don't let that take away from how you feel."

"Wow," she said. "It's like you're teaching me something and being all wise."

"You are not easy to get along with," Skulduggery said.

They got to the pier in Haggard and Valkyrie unbuckled her seatbelt. "Tomorrow is off-limits and everything, but... you're still going to drop by, aren't you?"

"Of course. I have to give you your present, don't I?"

She grinned. "Yes, you do. Merry Christmas, Skulduggery."

"Merry Christmas, Valkyrie."

She got out, and ran home through the snow.

CHRISTMAS MORNING AT THE MIDNIGHT HOTEL

nton Shudder knocked on the door to Room 19 as he unlocked it. He waited a few moments, and then the door opened and the vampire looked out, wearing its human skin.

"Good morning," Caelan said. "Did I... I'm sorry if I was loud last night."

"Not at all," Shudder said. "The walls are still sealed. No sound escapes."

"I'm afraid I broke some furniture. The chain snapped and, well... I'll pay for it, of course. Some of the walls are scratched, too."

"We've discussed this. Snapping your chains or damaging the walls means nothing if you can't leave this room – and once I've locked this door, you don't even have the option. You're safe in there, and everyone else is safe out here. You are a guest in the Midnight Hotel. You have no need to apologise."

"Thank you. Where are we, by the way?"

"Scotland."

"Are we scheduled to appear in Ireland today?"

"In just under an hour. You have business there?"

"Some," Caelan said.

"I'll let you know when we arrive."

"Thank you, Mr Shudder."

Shudder walked to the stairs, nodding to a guest coming the opposite way. He climbed to the second floor on his usual morning rounds. All but two of the rooms on this floor were occupied, but none of the guests were awake yet. He stopped outside Room 24, as he always did, and tested the handle. It turned, but didn't open. Locked tight, as it always was.

Satisfied, he returned to his office on the ground floor. He busied himself with paperwork, barely noticing the location shift. Had anyone been standing outside, they would have seen the Midnight Hotel suddenly come apart, and then sink into the earth within the space of a few seconds. For those within the hotel, however, there was a slight tremor and nothing more.

He reached for the phone and called the vampire's room as another tremor passed, and the hotel sprouted and grew in a wood just outside Dublin. He told Caelan they'd arrived, and a minute later, the vampire left the hotel.

Shudder worked for another hour, then took the keys for the car he kept parked here and walked out. He needed supplies, food and cleaning materials. Also, some new furniture for the vampire's room. And some decent chains.

The forest was chilled as he passed through the trees. Twigs cracked dully under his weight, his steps tossing wet leaves from his path. He got to the clearing beside the road that acted as the hotel car park, and stopped.

A man lay unconscious on the ground in front of him. Despite the cold, he was only wearing jeans and a T-shirt. He had tattoos and piercings.

Something caught Shudder's eye, and he turned just as the Remnant flew at him. He stumbled back, tried in vain to stop it from prying his mouth open and slithering in. He gagged, throat bulging as the Remnant forced its way down. Shudder fell to his knees, feeling it spread out inside him, rushing through his body, its darkness seeping into his bloodstream. The pain stopped. His fingers and toes were buzzing.

Shudder got to his feet. He looked over at Finbar Wrong, who lay unconscious in the wet grass and leaves. He remembered being Finbar, and he remembered all the things he'd seen in the vision. Before Finbar, Shudder had been Kenspeckle Grouse, and before that... Well, before *that* he'd spent a long time trapped in a room in the Midnight Hotel, with all the other Remnants.

Shudder took the key from the chain around his forearm, and walked back to the hotel to free his brothers and sisters.

20

'TIS THE SEASON

There had been a time, not too long ago, when Christmas morning was a big deal. A morning when Stephanie Edgley would wake up and rush to her parents' room, practically dragging them out of bed. Her father would go downstairs first, to check that Santa Claus was gone. When he gave the all-clear, Stephanie and her mother would hurry into the living room, and all three of them would dive under the tree, squealing with delight as each present was torn open. Her dad squealed the loudest, for some reason, especially when he got packs of brand-new socks. Her dad *loved* new socks. It was almost disturbing how he looked forward to slipping each pair on.

Her mother found each and every Christmas morning hilarious. Some of Valkyrie's fondest memories were of her mother, doubled up with laughter upon receiving her gift from her husband. Like the year she'd been given a hammer. Valkyrie could still see her dad's face, proud that he had managed to get his wife a present without help from anyone, and then the look of puzzlement that crept over his features as his darling Melissa slowly collapsed to the carpet, laughing so hard she was completely silent.

Valkyrie hadn't missed a Christmas Day yet. With all the time she spent away from home, she felt it was important to spend this day with her family, doing normal Christmas things like a normal daughter. Skulduggery would usually drive up in the evening, and she'd slip out to meet him at the pier. They'd exchange presents as the sea crashed beside them.

His presents were always much better than hers. Last year she'd given him a mug with a picture of Betty, a neighbour's one-eyed mongrel (and officially *Ireland's Best-Loved Dog* after she won a competition), printed on the side. Valkyrie feared she may have inherited her dad's dreadful present-buying prowess, but Skulduggery didn't seem to mind too much.

For so long, she'd been an only child at Christmas, and it was fair to say that she'd been a little spoiled by it all. But the idea that next year she'd have a little brother or sister made her smile as she lay in bed thinking about it. Having a kid around to get excited, to whoop and squeal like she had done, would ensure that Christmas stayed as special as the ones she remembered. They'd have to alter the routine, of course. The kid would have to wake *her* first, then they'd *both* wake their parents, drawing out the excitement, prolonging the anticipation. She couldn't wait.

Her mother knocked on her door and peeped in. "Steph?"

"Mum."

Immediately, her mother broke out into a smile and came in, her dressing gown closed over her round belly. "Happy Christmas, sweetheart," she said, sitting on the bed and leaning down to kiss Valkyrie's cheek. "Are you getting up? Desmond got impatient. He's downstairs, waiting to check that Santa is gone."

Valkyrie chuckled. "Oh, I'm so sorry. I've just been lying here."

"Thinking heavy thoughts?"

"Thinking about the baby we'll have around this time next year."

Her mum grinned, patting her bump. "It'll be fun, won't it? You promise you won't get jealous, now?"

"I think I can manage that."

They heard heavy footsteps coming up the stairs, and her dad appeared in the doorway. "Hurry up!" he whined.

"Speaking of babies," her mum muttered. She heaved herself off the bed and walked over to him as Valkyrie threw off the covers. Even as they were flying from her she remembered the massive bruises all over her body, and she yanked the covers back and held them tight against her.

"Didn't see anything!" her dad cried, his eyes squeezed shut. "Didn't see one little thing! Not one!"

Valkyrie laughed as her mum shooed him away. His eyes still shut, he allowed himself to be manoeuvred through the door.

"Please God," she heard him say, "let the next one be a boy."

Once she heard them on the stairs, she let the covers fall and examined herself. The bruises were angry purple and yellow and blue, but they looked more painful than they felt. She pulled on a T-shirt and grabbed her dressing gown, rooted out her fluffy bunny slippers and hurried downstairs, just in time to watch her father lunge into the living room.

"He's gone!" he proclaimed. "Santa Claus has gone, and he left me presents!"

Valkyrie got clothes, and a little money, and a new music device that was smaller than her thumb. She opened an envelope and a card slipped into her hand. She frowned at it. "Gym membership?"

"For a year," her mother said. "It's the good place, beside the Pavillions. They have a pool, and a sauna, and you can take in one guest for free. And I *really* like saunas."

"And I really like *pools*," her dad smiled.

Her mother looked at him. "She can only take in one guest at a time."

"I know, so what's...? Oh. You mean *you*. So... what am *I* going to do?"

"You're a big boy, Des, you can make up your own mind. Maybe you can stand outside and listen to the splashing."

"I can listen to splashing in the *bath*," he pointed out, somewhat sulkily.

"Excuse me?" Valkyrie said. "Um, the gym. Why?"

Her mother shrugged and smiled. "You're working out *somewhere*, so we thought why not do your training where all the instructors know first aid and everything's clean and nice?"

"I'm not *working out*, Mum. I'm... I play sports in school, that's all."

"What kind of sports?" her dad asked. "Badminton? Rugby? Cage-fighting?"

"Just sports. I run a lot. And swim."

"The gym has a *pool*."

"Yes, Dad, I know."

"If you don't want it, that's no problem," her mum said, reaching out to take the card back.

Valkyrie held it close to her chest. "Oh, God, no," she laughed. "I'm using this!"

Her parents smiled, turning to the next present on the pile, and Valkyrie wondered why she'd been so defensive. She was fine about accepting observations concerning her physique from sorcerers, from anyone in that part of her life, but apparently she wasn't so relaxed about it out here. Maybe she didn't want her family noticing how different she was. She liked the idea of blending in once she was home, of sinking into the background and becoming something unexceptional. Here, she wasn't a potential Death Bringer. Here, she wasn't Darquesse, the World Killer. Here she was Stephanie Edgley – daughter, schoolgirl and soon to be big sister.

In the weeks following the glimpse of her future self, she had hated the thought of getting older, of getting stronger. The older and stronger she got, the more like her future self she'd become. But when she'd realised there was a way of sealing her name, of making sure she would never turn into the monster who would go on to kill her own parents, all that had changed. She was back in control and looking forward to becoming more like Tanith. Toned. Streamlined. Efficient.

She didn't need a gym membership to do it, either, but it was a nice gesture from her folks. It showed they were taking an interest without interfering. She appreciated that.

They went visiting. At midday every Christmas, her mother's side of the family would meet up at Valkyrie's grandmother's house over in Clontarf. Valkyrie used to dread this visit, but now she loved it. Her cousins were so much more interesting than they had been as children, and her aunts and uncles revealed personalities that all their head-patting and cheek-pinching had obscured over the years.

Her nana reminded her of a silver-haired Tasmanian devil, whirling from group to group, making sure everyone was enjoying themselves, or at least had a paper plate piled with food in their hands. Valkyrie chatted and laughed easily, feeling like a normal sixteen year old.

After an hour of good times, it was time for the bad. They drove from her mother's side of the family back into Haggard, to her father's side. They found a parking space on the road outside, and walked like condemned prisoners up the garden path to the front door.

"Knock," said Valkyrie's mother.

Her dad shook his head. "Don't want to."

"They're *your* family."

"I can't knock. I have no hands."

"Stephanie, would you be a good girl and knock on the door, please?"

But Valkyrie was busy pretending she was deaf.

Her mother sighed, said "Fine", and raised her knuckles. She hesitated. Her hand lowered. "Would they miss us?" she wondered.

"They wouldn't," Valkyrie's dad said immediately.

"It's probably packed in there," his wife continued. "It'd be pretty difficult to see anyone. We could be in there an hour and not get through half of them. I doubt we'd even be noticed."

"We should go home and wait for the turkey to be ready."

And then the door opened, and Beryl looked out at them, and any hopes of escape were dashed.

"Happy Christmas," Beryl said, her mouth twitching into a rigid smile. "Won't you come in?"

Valkyrie let her parents go first, and trudged in after them.

The heat in the living room was on full blast. That, and the hot air being emitted from the assembled guests, was probably eating a hole in the ozone layer. There were some Edgleys here, but most of the crowd were Beryl's lot, the Mullans. They talked long and they talked loud, and Valkyrie guessed that half of the adults were already on their way to full drunkenness.

She headed for a gap in the crowd near the Christmas tree, gaudily decorated in different-coloured lights and streams of tinsel. It wasn't a particularly big tree, nor was it particularly nice. It was lopsided, lacking that ideal Christmas tree shape that her father always managed to find, no matter how late he left it.

Carol and Crystal broke through the crowd, practically stumbling into her.

"Oh," said Carol.

"Ah," said Crystal.

Perfect. "Merry Christmas," Valkyrie said.

They responded in kind, with as much enthusiasm as Valkyrie had mustered. They had changed so much since the last time she'd seen them. They were almost nineteen, and Carol was heavier, looking like she'd been insulated and left to wander around on her own. Her dress was designed to seize as much of that extra weight as possible and shove it out in front. The result was possibly not what she had intended.

Her twin had gone the other way. From what Valkyrie's mother had told her, Crystal had become obsessed with counting calories, and flitted from one diet to the next, gradually getting skinnier and skinnier. She was close to losing all shape except straight. Carol was still bottle-blonde, Crystal was a redhead, and neither looked healthy.

"You're looking well," Valkyrie lied.

Carol nodded and Crystal grunted, and Valkyrie prepared for the sarcastic comments to start flying.

Instead, Carol sighed, and said, "Get anything nice?"

"Uh... mostly clothes. You?"

"Same. We got money too."

"Dad said he'll buy us a car," Crystal added. "He says as soon as the economic climate picks up a little more."

"Right," Valkyrie said. "Can you drive?"

"Like, right now? No. But when we have the car, we'll have a reason to learn."

"Makes sense. How's college?"

"Boring," said Crystal.

"It's not too bad," said Carol.

Valkyrie nodded. She hadn't a clue what to say. They'd

never gone this long without flinging insults before. And then she saw it, the looks the twins were getting from their other cousins. She saw smirks and sneers, right behind their backs. The twins were doing their best to ignore it all and concentrate on the one person who wasn't mocking them.

Valkyrie felt a sudden, and quite surprising, need to protect them, so she plastered a big smile on her face and forced herself into conversation. She laughed and joked, and basically acted like Carol and Crystal were the two most interesting people alive.

It was quite a performance.

When it was time to go, she said her goodbyes and hugged the twins, promising to meet up soon, and then she allowed herself to be dragged out of the house. Her parents stared at her as they walked to the car.

"Do not ask," Valkyrie sighed.

They got home, and she helped her mother with the turkey and ham and roast potatoes while her dad lit the fire. They sat down to Christmas dinner, pulled crackers and told the awful jokes they found inside. Valkyrie was stuffed after dinner so turned down the offer of Christmas cake. Her phone rang and she walked into the kitchen as she answered.

"Is that Valkyrie?"

It was a woman's voice, sounding very distant, and the line crackled.

"It is," Valkyrie said. "Who's this?"

"Nye is ready for you."

It was the banshee. Valkyrie frowned. "What, *today*?"

"Yes. Today. Now."

"But it's Christmas."

"Doctor Nye cleared his schedule for you. Unless you've—"

"No," Valkyrie said quickly, "no, that's OK. I can do it. Where do I go?"

"You'll be picked up," said the banshee.

"Where?"

"Wherever you are. You have exactly ten minutes."

The banshee hung up. Valkyrie felt sick. Some advance warning would have been nice. It was bad enough she had to leave her parents on Christmas Day, but now this had to be the day she died? Granted, it wasn't permanent death. At least, she hoped it wasn't. All at once she felt glad this was happening so suddenly. If she had time to consider all the possibilities, she might not go through with it.

She walked back to her folks. They were sitting at the fire, talking. If something went wrong, if Nye killed her but was unable to revive her, this would be the last time she'd ever see them. She hugged her dad, and then went and hugged her mum.

"Thanks for a great Christmas," she said.

"Aww," said her mum, "you're welcome, love."

"I'm going to lie down for a bit," she said. "I think I ate too much."

"That gym membership is really looking like a good idea now, eh?" her dad winked.

She smiled and left, and the moment she was out of the room her smile disappeared. She'd had a lot of practice at closing off the part of herself that felt sad about things like this. Now it came naturally, and she felt the wall go up and didn't stop it. She climbed the stairs to her bedroom and called Skulduggery.

"I can't meet up later," she said.

"Oh," came his reply. "That's a pity."

"Yeah. There's a family thing on that we're all going to. Hopefully it won't happen every year, but I couldn't really say no."

"Of course not. Well, maybe I'll drop by later tonight."

"I'm not sure when we'll get back," Valkyrie said, feeling terrible all over again. "How about, if I'm back at a reasonable hour, I let you know, OK?"

"Sure, that's fine. Are you having a good day so far?"

She swallowed. "It's great. Everything's great."

"Even your cousins?"

"Surprisingly, yes. I really have to go."

"All right then. Merry Christmas."

"Skulduggery?"

"Yes?"

Valkyrie hesitated, a jumble of words on her tongue. "I'm really glad we're friends," she ended up saying.

"Me too, Valkyrie."

"Bye."

She called Fletcher, and told him she couldn't see him. He wanted to know why he couldn't just pop over, present her with her gift, and vanish. She didn't tell him she didn't want to see him. She could lie about this on the phone – not face to face.

"Fine," he said, sounding annoyed. "I won't come over."

"But tomorrow," she said. "I want to go out on a date."

"You what?"

"A date. I think we should go out."

"Go out where?"

"I want to go dancing."

His voice turned sceptical. "Seriously?"

"There's a nightclub in Skerries that has a disco thing every

Christmas for under-eighteens. I just want to have a good time with you. We never get to do normal things, and we're not going to live forever, you know? I think we should cram the normal stuff into our lives now, while we have the chance."

"You OK, Val? You're sounding pretty... morbid."

"Will you take me dancing or not?"

He gave an exaggerated sigh. "Fine."

"Also..."

"Yes?"

"Tomorrow, I think you should meet my parents."

For the first time since she'd known him, Fletcher Renn was too stunned to speak.

Valkyrie put the phone down, undressed and touched the mirror. Her reflection stepped out, started putting on the clothes Valkyrie had just taken off, while Valkyrie donned her black outfit.

"You're going to die," the reflection said as it dressed.

"I know," Valkyrie replied, irritated.

"You might never come back."

"You know what to do if that happens."

The reflection nodded. "Take over your life. Be a good daughter. Make sure our parents are happy."

Valkyrie looked up. "What did you say?"

"I'm sorry?"

"You said make sure our parents are happy."

"I said make sure *your* parents are happy."

"You said *our*."

"Oh. It must be another glitch. I was never meant to be used this much, as you know. Do you have any more instructions for me?"

Valkyrie looked at it. It would be an absolutely perfect copy except for the fact that she doubted her own face had ever looked quite so innocent. She put on her jacket, and went over to open the window. "Just stay up here for half an hour."

"OK. Merry Christmas."

Valkyrie slid out of the window and let herself fall. She landed gently and hurried away from the house.

She went down to the pier, checked the time on her phone, and looked around for whoever it was who was picking her up.

Valkyrie didn't like the fact that the banshee apparently knew where she lived. Haggard was her safe place, her haven, and the times when her other life had encroached upon it disturbed her more than anything. Dusk had led a small army of the Infected here – it was on this exact spot that she'd finally managed to lose them. Remus Crux had visited Haggard twice

– the first time to arrest her, the second to try to kill her. Such invasions were unforgivable in her eyes.

She heard hoofbeats and turned as the great black Coach-a-Bowers materialised in front of her.

"Oh, hell," she said.

The headless horses swung around as they slowed. The driver, the Dullahan, gave a last tug of the reins and the horses settled. Their bodies were sleek and muscled and beautiful. They were huge – their backs level with Valkyrie's eyes – and steam rose from them into the cold air. Their heads had been severed halfway up the neck, and now that she was close enough Valkyrie could see that it hadn't been a clean cut. She saw nicks and tears and false starts, evidence of uneven sawing. The wounds hadn't healed over, but neither were they leaking blood.

The Dullahan didn't climb down. He didn't even give any indication that he knew she was there. Could he see her? Could people without heads see?

And then the carriage door opened and a single pale arm drifted out of the darkness within. The hand beckoned to her, the finger curling slowly.

Valkyrie stepped forward on unsteady legs, and reached up to take it.

21

NYE

The hand was cold to her touch. Another reached out, taking gentle hold of her wrist. Another hand then, closing around her sleeve, and another, and with every hand that held her, Valkyrie was pulled just a little closer to the open door. She put a foot on the step and rose up off the ground, and there was a sound, like a sigh, as the hands guided her inside.

Valkyrie's breath left her. Her lungs filled with cold. Her blood slowed in her veins as her heart stopped beating. She no longer felt the weight of her clothes against her skin. She sat back in the seat, a dead thing now, feeling nothing, and her mind became dull.

There was no warmth in the carriage. Three people sat opposite, looking at her with blank eyes. A part of her wondered briefly where all the others had gone. She had expected, after all, a carriage filled with the dead. But no, there were just these three, and that idle curiosity faded from her mind before she could ask them any questions.

She looked away. She didn't care what they were wearing, or what they looked like. A man and two women, that's all she saw before she lost interest. The carriage trundled along uneven ground. The seats were red leather, but the colour was muted. She parted the black curtain with a hand so pale it was turning blue, and she looked at her reflection in the window and saw the face of a corpse, framed by dark hair.

She took her hand away, the curtain falling back into place. She sat on the red leather seat, opposite the three dead people, and the dullness in her mind became a thick and heavy blanket that suffocated her thoughts in their infancy.

And time did what time did – it passed.

*   *   *

Valkyrie was gazing blankly at the shoe of a fellow passenger when she became aware of the carriage slowing to a stop. She dragged her gaze upwards, to the window, but the curtains were still drawn and she felt no urge to part them now. The door to her right opened, and the three dead people left without speaking. Moving without energy, she followed them.

They were in a warehouse of some sort. It was as cold here as it had been in the carriage. The Dullahan was waiting for her, and she followed him away from the others, into a room of tables. The head of a woman blinked at her from where it lay, on its side, beside a body separated from its limbs. Dead people, in various stages of dissection, hung from the walls on hooks and large iron nails. They looked at her as she passed, but made no sound.

The Dullahan stopped before a creature wearing a grubby smock, its arms and legs impossibly long, hunched over a corpse on a table. It swivelled its head as Valkyrie approached. In the gap above the surgical mask and beneath the cap, she could see the oily pallor of its skin. Its eyelids were punctured with broken bits of black thread, and its pupils were small and yellow.

It put away the knife it had been using to poke around inside the corpse, and pulled the mask down to its chin. It had a large scab where the nose ought to have been, and a mouth, like the eyes, that had once been sewn shut, but which now gaped at her with a smile like an open wound.

"I've been looking forward to this," it said, its voice high-pitched and breathless. It was impossible to tell whether this creature was male or female. "Do you know who I am?"

Valkyrie nodded. "Your name is Nye." Her voice sounded odd to her.

"Indeed it is. I'm the only living thing in this place. Do you know what that makes me?" It didn't wait for an answer. "It makes me *better* than you."

Valkyrie didn't say anything. None of this mattered.

Nye looked at the Dullahan, and annoyance flashed across its face.

"I know, damn it. I will. Well, I'm not *going* to deviate, am I? I learned my lesson!"

Seemingly satisfied, the Dullahan turned and walked out.

"But just to be sure," Nye called after him, "if she doesn't make it, I get to keep what's left, yes?"

The Dullahan didn't slow down.

Once he was gone, Nye stood up straight, its head nearly brushing against the lights hanging from the ceiling. It looked at her. "You're here to get your true name sealed," it said. "It isn't easy, you know. Not many people ever find out what their true name *is*, so people like me don't get a lot of practice doing what we have to do. What did the banshee tell you?"

"She said I'd have to die," Valkyrie answered.

"Which you have already done," Nye nodded. "You died in the Coach-a-Bowers, and you'll be dead until you leave this place and life returns to you. Did she say anything else?"

"You'd need to operate."

That open-wound smile again. "Yes. It's a delicate procedure, requiring me to carve three symbols on to your heart in an impossibly precise fashion. I would ask you if you are prepared to accept this risk, but I honestly don't care. The fact is, you're dead, and you're here, so your free will is a little compromised, isn't it? You're not thinking too clearly. Even if you changed your mind right now, I'd still go ahead with the operation and you wouldn't be able to stop me. I haven't done this in years, so I'm mildly curious to find out if I can do it without killing you forever. Undress now, please."

No argument occurred to her, so Valkyrie did as she was told while Nye wiped its instruments on old rags and laid them out on a small tray. When she was done, she lay on a table and Nye strapped her wrists and ankles tight. It spat on the blade of its scalpel, and looked down at her.

"The truly tragic thing about all of this," it said, "is that you won't feel any of the great pain I'm about to put you through."

Nye pressed the tip of the scalpel to Valkyrie's shoulder and slit her skin all the way to the breastbone. Blood, with no functioning engine to pump it, trickled lazily.

"This ought to be excruciating," Nye said, its voice straining with effort as it continued to cut down to her belly. "If you were alive right now, you'd be screaming. Begging me to stop. I'm going to be cracking open your ribcage in a minute, so that would *definitely* be sore."

Nye stood back, putting down the scalpel and shaking its hand loosely, like it was getting rid of a cramp. "That wasn't easy," it told her. "You've got an impressive amount of muscle around the abdomen."

Valkyrie didn't want to see this – didn't want to see what Nye was doing to her. She tried telling it, but she possessed no energy to speak. Nye looked into her eyes and its own eyes widened, as if it understood.

"Oh, my!" it said suddenly. "Oh, you're quite right! I am being *very* unprofessional!" Nye took a moment to fix its surgical mask back over the lower half of its face. "Hygiene is most important in the operating theatre. I'm terribly sorry."

Nye peeled the flaps of skin away from the chest wall, and

Valkyrie looked down at herself as her flesh came apart as easily as a zipper being undone.

"Some people use an electric saw to get through the ribs," Nye continued, "but I find it somewhat unsatisfying." It held up large pruning shears, the kind Valkyrie would have found in the garden shed at home. "And these are much more effective."

Valkyrie closed her eyes as Nye bent over her again. She heard a loud crack, and looked around, craning her head, seeing all the dead people on the walls around her. None of them seemed to care about what was going on. There was another crack, and when she looked back at herself, Nye was lifting her sternum away from her body.

"Almost at the heart," Nye told her. "Now, I *am* going to have to remove it so that I can carve in some symbols, which will take a little time, but I'm fairly confident that I can reattach all the necessary arteries and such afterwards. Heart surgery isn't *brain* surgery, after all," it added with a chuckle. "Little medical humour for you there."

It went back to work and Valkyrie lay there, knowing she should be filled with pain, yet unable to escape the dullness that had settled over her mind.

Nye lifted her heart from her chest and showed it to her.

"You'll forgive me if I don't make any jokes about how I've

stolen your heart," it said. "I've used them all up on previous patients, I'm afraid. Rest assured, every last one of those jokes was suitably morbid and witty."

Valkyrie watched her heart being placed on a tray beside the pruning shears. Nye's yellow eyes narrowed as it smiled beneath its mask.

"There," it said. "That wasn't so bad now, was it? I didn't drop anything. I didn't nick the kidneys or put my thumb through a lung. The first part of this operation, I think you'll agree, has been a resounding success. And now it's time for supper."

Nye turned and walked away on its impossibly long legs, leaving Valkyrie strapped to the table.

22

SOUL SEARCHING

ye returned an hour later and put Valkyrie's heart in a vice. She watched the vice being tightened, and a part of her mind started to scream, fearing the heart would burst. Nye's hand came away from the vice and she relaxed, settling back into the dullness that death brought. Nye spoke to her while it held a scalpel over a flame, telling her about past glories, about the life it had had outside these rooms. The words meant nothing to Valkyrie, forgotten as soon as they reached her ears.

Nye hunched over the vice and gently pressed the red-hot

scalpel against her heart. A book lay open beside it, and before every stroke of the scalpel, Nye would consult the pages, measuring the length and breadth of the symbols detailed within, calculating depth. The scalpel went from her heart back to the flame, then to her heart. Again and again, this process was repeated. Slight trails of smoke rose from the lines being carved. Valkyrie could hear the soft sizzle of the meat.

An hour, it took Nye, to complete the first symbol. The second one, a simpler pattern, took half that time, but the third one took twice as long.

"Once this heart is back inside you," Nye said, yellow eyes fixed on its work, "and once it begins beating again, these symbols will inhabit you. Do you understand me? Do you understand anything I'm saying? The dead here are so dim-witted."

Valkyrie grunted.

"Oh, good, you *can* understand me. When you walk out of here, you will *own* your true name, instead of your true name owning you. Armed with this knowledge, you can do great things. You could be the greatest sorcerer this world has ever seen." Nye glanced at her. "Or you could be the most terrible."

The door opened, and Nye's eyes returned to the heart as the Dullahan strode in.

"Almost finished!" Nye called. "I can't be rushed on things like this, you know! One wrong stroke, one part of a symbol too thin or too thick or too deep or too shallow, and it's not going to work! I am a professional and I must not be hurried!"

The Dullahan stood still, and Nye straightened up, uncoiling its long body. "Oh," it said, in response to whatever the Dullahan was silently saying. "Of course. No, no, I completely understand. Your duties take you elsewhere. You are a busy man, after all. Have no fear, when the operation is complete, I shall send this girl on her way, back to the land of the living. Of course not. I wouldn't dream of such a... Now, listen, as I've said before, those experiments are over, and you *know* that. That part of my life is behind me. I realise now that I was misguided and... I learned my lesson. Yes. Well, if you can't trust a surgeon, who *can* you trust?"

Nye listened for another moment, then nodded gravely, and the Dullahan turned and strode out. The door closed behind him.

Nye returned its attention to the heart, and didn't speak for fifteen minutes.

Finally, it straightened up again. "Done," it said. "And a splendid piece of work it is too, if I do say so."

It took the heart from the vice, and showed it to Valkyrie.

"You see the precision?" it said. "See the craftsmanship? China Sorrows herself could not have constructed these symbols any better. A work of art, don't you agree?"

Nye pulled the surgical mask down off its face. "But I'm afraid I have a bit of bad news. The Dullahan has been called away. You may have heard me agreeing to look after you, to deliver you back to the living. But the bad news, the truly unfortunate and tragic news, is that I was lying the whole time."

Nye dropped the heart on to the tray beside the table, disturbing the instruments, making them jangle.

"No one will know you never left. I can hide you among the corpses here. You'll never be found. I'll tell the Dullahan, and I'll even tell the banshee if she comes to investigate, that I waved goodbye and watched you leave. Who knows what could have happened to you after that? You could be lying in a ditch for all we know."

Nye leaned down over Valkyrie, its face centimetres from her own. "You're mine now," it said. "You've been delivered to me to help with my research. I know you have. All these corpses around you? All these dead people, and many more besides? They've all helped me. They've all *tried*, at least. But you... I have a good feeling about you."

It stalked off, with great loping strides. Valkyrie turned her head to watch it.

"What do you know about the soul?" it asked from the other side of the room, as it pulled a sheet off a large instrument cart. "Not much, I'd wager, but you've undoubtedly seen it in different forms."

Nye pushed the cart over. Its wheels creaked and the blades and saws and clips clattered. "Ghosts, Remnants, even gists, are forms the soul can take. But none of them are its *pure* form."

The cart banged into the table. The blades were caked with old blood.

"The pure soul resides somewhere in the body, somewhere it can't be disturbed. I've narrowed it down to the likeliest places, but as yet I haven't found it. I do, however, feel like I am on the cusp of a breakthrough." It picked up a long breadknife. "I'm going to do you a favour. I'm going to dissect your brain last. That way, if I find your soul among your innards or inside your organs, you can at least partially share in my moment of glory."

Nye pulled the mask up over the scab of its nose. "This is going to get messy."

23

THE GRAVE

The country roads started out plump and healthy, before narrowing as they came closer to Roarhaven, finally becoming little more than starving veins that twisted through a dead and frozen landscape. The town squatted between a stagnant lake of foul water, a few desiccated trees bordering its banks, and a hillside of frosted yellowed grasses and gorse brush. The main street, if that's what it was, possessed a gnarled handful of shops and businesses necessary for survival, but this was not a town that attracted visitors. Roarhaven was the town where sorcerers lived.

Tesseract parked his truck and moved through into the trailer. His whole life was in this trailer, firmly secured against the rigours of the road. Everything was held down by straps and buckles and bolts. The wall above the desk was lined with his metal masks. He took one down, one that had a frown over the eyes and a snarl carved below the nose. Sometimes he preferred the blank ones, but today he was feeling like he wanted some expression.

He checked the needles around the edges, and when he was sure nothing was clogged, his hands went to the mask he was already wearing. There was a slight *hiss* as the needles retracted and the mask detached. He took it away and looked at his lumpy face in the small mirror. Every day, the lumps were different. Sometimes his cheeks would bulge, and his forehead swelled. Other times it would be his nose that would swell up and his chin that would jut out. Whatever way the lumps arranged themselves, he was always ugly. The masks made his skin pale and greasy, and the angry red wounds where the needles slid in, arranged in a border around his face, would weep with pus.

Even as he was looking at himself, he saw his flesh begin to rot. He quickly pressed the new mask to his face, hearing the needles hiss as they slid into the wounds. He felt the rot stop, and recede, as the liquid contained in those needles did its job. Saving his life for yet another day. He made slight adjustments to the straps, and left the trailer.

A woman was waiting for him outside – Ceryen. She led him up the hill on the east side of the town, to where the Torment was peering into a large hole that was being dug by a man named Graft.

Tesseract gave the Torment his report, keeping it short and succinct. The Torment nodded.

"If you want me to continue," Tesseract said, once he'd finished, "I'm sure we could come to an arrangement. A group rate, perhaps. Skulduggery Pleasant, Valkyrie Cain, Erskine Ravel, Tanith Low, Ghastly Bespoke. And the Teleporter, if you wish."

"We have plans to take care of them," the Torment said with a wave of a hand. "Our contract with you is now complete."

Tesseract was disappointed, but didn't press the point. He was a professional after all. "In that case, all that remains is my fee."

"Of course," the Torment said, but he made no move to pay him.

Something pricked Tesseract's skin, and he turned his hand

as a tiny white spider scuttled into his sleeve. One of Madam Mist's, if his files were correct. Tesseract felt hot, and his tongue felt heavy.

"You were in a bar fight," the Torment said. "There is nothing wrong with this, and you got the information you needed to complete your assignment. Unfortunately, the men you killed were citizens of Roarhaven."

Tesseract tried to reach for him, but his arm wouldn't move. He swayed on his feet, unsteady.

"I personally did not care for these men. They were irritants and braggards. But if we are to control this town, we need to follow its rules. You took the lives of Roarhaven mages. So we take yours."

The Torment walked away. Tesseract saw Ceryen out of the corner of his eye. He couldn't even move his head any more. He felt her hand on his shoulder, and she gave a push. He toppled forward, into the hole, into the grave, landing in a twisted position with his right ear pressed into the cold, wet earth.

"OK," Ceryen's voice came from above him, "fill it in."

"There are two shovels," he heard Graft mutter. A rain of dirt pattered across Tesseract's back.

"I'm the brains," Ceryen responded. "You're the brawn."

"The brains of what, exactly? Digging a hole? They really entrusted you with a lot of responsibility, didn't they?"

Another shovelful of dirt came down, heavier than the last.

"They did, actually," Ceryen said. "You think this is just digging a hole? Filling it in? It's not. This is disposing of evidence. If it was a simple hole-digging job, you'd have been able to take care of that yourself now, wouldn't you? You wouldn't need supervision."

"I *don't* need supervision," Graft said. "I need someone using that second shovel."

Every last ounce of feeling was leaving Tesseract's body. It took all of his remaining strength to turn his head even the slightest fraction, but turn it he did, until he was looking straight down, his chin tucked into his chest. Then he could move no more.

"You know your problem?" Ceryen was saying. "You complain too much."

The dirt came tumbling down on the back of Tesseract's head.

"No, I don't," said Graft.

"You do. You think you should be leading. You think the direct way is the only way. You have no idea about tactics, or strategy."

"It's a hole, Ceryen. What strategy is there, other than dig it?"

Ceryen's voice turned smug. "Get someone else to dig it."

A few moments passed, and Graft said, "I hate you."

Another shovelful of earth came down, and another, and their voices grew dull as they buried Tesseract alive.

24

THE DEAD GIRL

Valkyrie lay in the semi-darkness.

Nye wasn't there. Nye had left to go to bed. Valkyrie didn't care. She lay there in the semi-darkness with her heart outside her body.

Her gaze drifted from the ceiling. The main lights were out, and only patches of the room were visible. The bodies on the walls were nothing but shapes. Her eyes took in their forms, took in the geometry of the room, took in the tables and carts. Then she closed her eyes, and when she opened them, Skulduggery was standing over her.

"I'm here to rescue you," he said. He was dressed all in black. Even his shirt was black. "Can you understand me?"

Valkyrie nodded. Hope blossomed, flowered.

"Good," he said. "Remember when you rescued me from the Faceless Ones? You came in and dragged me out? I'm returning the favour, because that's what partners do." She waited for him to start unbuckling the straps holding her down. Instead, his head tilted. "Why are you here, by the way? This is an odd place to be."

They didn't have time for this. Nye would be back soon.

"Are you here for an operation?" Skulduggery asked. "Why would you need an operation? What's wrong with you? Why are you folded open like this? Why is your heart over there?"

"Please..." she whispered.

"Please? Please what? Please help you? Why would I help you? You're going to kill me."

Valkyrie shook her head. This wasn't right. "No..."

"Yes, you are. You're going to kill me, Valkyrie. You're going to kill *everyone*. Why should I help you? Can either of *you* give me a reason?"

Her parents were standing on the other side of the bed. She didn't know how they'd got there.

"My Stephanie wouldn't kill anyone," her mum told Skulduggery.

"*My* Stephanie would," her dad said sadly.

Valkyrie's mouth was dry. "I'm stopping that from happening."

"Can we take that chance?" her mum said. She patted her belly, which was huge. "I've got another child on the way. A better child. Better than you. We can't risk you hurting it."

"I think we should shoot her," Valkyrie heard her own voice say. Her reflection was standing beside Skulduggery, dressed in the clothes Ghastly had made for Valkyrie, but they were all in pink. "Why do we need her? I can take her place."

This was wrong. This wasn't real. This didn't make sense.

"But you can't do magic," Valkyrie's dad said.

"I think that's a good thing," her reflection responded. "Valkyrie can do magic, and she's going to kill the world if Skulduggery doesn't shoot her."

"Who's Valkyrie?" asked her dad.

"Stephanie," said the reflection.

"Oh," said her dad.

"She's right," Skulduggery said, and took out his gun. "I'm going to have to shoot you, Valkyrie."

"Not real," Valkyrie mumbled.

"I'm sorry?"

Valkyrie focused on a single spot on the ceiling above her. The harder she stared, the less defined the figures around her became. Her mother and father faded away. Her reflection slowly disappeared. Only Skulduggery remained.

This was all in her head.

"You're right," Skulduggery nodded.

She ignored him, and the gun he was holding.

"You can't ignore me forever," he pointed out. "And I'm not going to shoot you. Imaginary bullets are surprisingly ineffective against... everything, really. I'm not going to come for you, you know. There is no one coming to rescue you. You got yourself into this mess, and it's up to you to get yourself out."

Skulduggery holstered the gun, and faded away, leaving Valkyrie alone again.

No.

She held on to it, that momentary hope that had spread through her. She caught it before it flitted away and her mind returned to the dull state of non-being. How long had she lain here like this, without a thought entering her head? Even now it was a struggle to keep her mind remotely sharp. She needed to get free. She needed to escape.

Her body was numb. She couldn't feel the air around her, or how the spaces connected. She clicked her fingers and couldn't feel the spark – couldn't focus enough to turn it into a flame. The Necromancer ring was in her jacket, in the pile of clothes on the next table over. Magic wasn't going to save her. Not here.

Nye had left its serrated breadknife on the table beside Valkyrie's knee, but it was too far to reach. The cart, on the other hand, was still in place beside her, and on it were all the instruments that had been used to cut her open and poke about inside.

She strained against the strap that secured her left wrist, and her fingers stretched for the tip of the scalpel. She tapped it, lightly, and it moved, and she tapped it again and suddenly it was within reach. She closed two fingertips around it, and slowly pulled it off the cart. But her numb fingers didn't have a good enough grip, and the scalpel fell to the floor.

Anger flashed into her mind and she kept it there, refusing to let it go, to allow the apathy to return.

She reached for the cart itself and shook it as best she could, trying to move some other blade closer. But the instruments only rattled and moved further away. She got a good grip on the edge of the cart and pulled it, in an effort to tip it over. The cart tilted for a moment, then slipped from her grasp, clattering back to its four wheels and knocking against the big lamp Nye had been using as an overhead light. The lamp toppled, hitting the table and sliding along it on its way to the floor. Valkyrie made a grab for it. The lamp hit the ground, and Valkyrie looked down and realised she was holding the lamp's electrical cord.

She had something. Now she needed to think clearly enough to figure out if it could be of any use.

She pulled on the cord, then carefully inched her fingers back along it, and pulled again. She repeated the exercise slowly, until there was a loop of cord moving across her belly. The loop found her other hand, and her movements became more confident. She pulled on that cord until it became taut, and then she pulled harder.

She heard the plug being yanked from its socket, then she pulled it across the floor. It got caught twice, probably on the legs of tables, but Valkyrie managed to loosen it, and kept pulling. She didn't know how long it took, how many seconds or minutes – all she concentrated on was the task. And then the plug was in her hand. She let it go, let it hang on a long piece of cord, down by the table. She started to rotate her wrist.

The plug swung in a wide circle. Before she released it, she made sure that the slack was wrapped around her other hand. Then she let go, and the plug rose through the air and hit her leg. She pulled it back. It touched against the breadknife, then fell off the edge of the table.

Valkyrie gathered it back in her hand, swung it again, and released it a second time. The plug landed behind the breadknife, and when she pulled it, the breadknife moved a little before the plug slipped over it.

She tried a third time, and missed completely.

The fourth time, the breadknife moved closer to her hand.

It took eight swings until the breadknife was in her hand. She held the handle so that the blade was pressing into the strap on her wrist. She started sawing. At first, the serrated edge caught on the strap and every movement was an uncoordinated jerk. But then the blade found purchase, and Valkyrie found her rhythm, and she started to cut through the strap.

Her eyes wandered as she cut, her gaze drifting from the walls to the ceiling, becoming transfixed by a low-wattage bulb at the far end of the room. In the gloom, it was as bright as the sun.

She looked at the bulb.

The bulb flickered and Valkyrie frowned, unable to remember how long she'd spent looking at it. She dragged her eyes away and looked down at her hand. She still held the breadknife, but she was no longer cutting.

She snarled, the anger flaring and driving back the dullness. She focused on the blade and the strap. Nothing else mattered. There was nothing else in the world, only this blade and this strap.

And then the blade cut through the strap, and her hand was free.

Valkyrie dropped the breadknife and reached across to undo the strap on her right hand. Both hands loose, she pushed herself into a sitting position, and reached down to undo the ankle restraints. And then she was free.

Moving slowly, she swung her legs off the table, and stood. There was a table nearby, stacked full of bandages. She took a roll and wrapped it around her torso, around and around, then walked unsteadily to her pile of clothes. She dressed slowly, feeling no sense of comfort or relief. She took out her phone but could get no signal.

Valkyrie went to the door and opened it, moving into the corridor beyond. This wasn't how she had come in, but she walked on nonetheless. All she wanted was to get out. She didn't care how.

She passed a room where every blade ever forged hung on rusty nails, and another room containing nothing but heads in jars that gaped at her as she passed. A third room was empty, the walls splashed with blood.

She got to a large hall, reached the door on the other side, then stopped. Her heart. She'd forgotten her heart, and all the other things Nye had removed from her. Valkyrie turned, and something caught her eye and she looked up. Nye lay sleeping in a hammock high above her, its arms and legs dangling down. She looked at all the pulleys and ropes and levers, but didn't wonder about the process Nye went through to raise itself off the ground every night. She heard the surgeon snore.

Moving quietly, she retraced her steps, passing the rooms with the blood and the heads and the blades, and stepped back into the operating theatre. She took her heart and her sternum and put them in a bag she found in the corner, and then she left by the other door.

She emerged into the warehouse where she had first stepped down from the carriage. The dead stood around, barely looking at her as she passed between them.

"Where do you think you're going?"

Valkyrie turned as Nye ducked through the doorway.

"You think you're going to escape?" it asked, walking over.

It was still wearing the smock, but not the mask or the cap. Thick veins pulsed against the pale skin at its temples. "You can't escape, you stupid girl. You're dead. In here, as in the Dullahan's carriage, you enjoy an untroubled existence. You're one of the dead things. But outside of these walls is *life*. You set one foot outside, you collapse. Blood spurts and your body caves in. You're carrying your heart around in a *refuse bag*, for God's sake. What did you think was going to happen?"

"Let me go," Valkyrie said, her tongue thick in her mouth.

"No," Nye said. "Get back on the table. I'm not finished with you."

"Fix me then," she said.

Nye's ruined mouth jerked into a surprised smile. "I'm sorry? What? You're giving me orders, is that it? Is that what you're doing?"

She nodded.

"You don't give me orders!" Nye screeched, and it was in front of her before she even realised it had moved. The back of its hand swooped down and caught the side of her face. The force of the impact sent her stumbling, but she felt no pain.

"I'm in charge here!" Nye yelled, and kicked her. Valkyrie rolled across the ground, and the bag was snatched from her grasp.

"We'll see how many orders you give once your heart has been incinerated!" the surgeon spat, and turned to stalk back to the door.

Valkyrie pushed herself up and reached out, but Elemental magic was still closed off to her. A thought flashed into her mind, and she plunged her hand into her jacket pocket, sliding the ring on to her finger.

Shadows coiled around her, and a great wave of darkness smashed into Nye and took it off its feet. The surgeon squealed in fear and Valkyrie slammed the wave to the floor. Nye struck the hard ground and bounced slightly.

Valkyrie went to walk towards him, but, like an eager servant, the shadows swept her up. She touched down beside Nye and it scrambled up, tried to run. She was vaguely aware of an intent, to simply stop him from fleeing, and then suddenly the shadows wrapped themselves around Nye's right leg, its long right leg, and wrenched.

Nye screamed as its leg snapped in a dozen places, and it fell to the ground.

"Please!" it called. "You don't know what you're doing!"

The shadows played with Valkyrie's hair.

"That's Necromancy!" Nye yelled. "But you're dead! It's death magic wielded by a dead person – you don't know what you're doing! You can't control it – you're not strong enough! Please don't kill me!"

"Fix me," Valkyrie said.

"I will!" Nye cried, tears streaming down its face. "But my leg is broken! Let me mend it and then I'll—"

"Fix me now," Valkyrie said without emotion, "or I'll let the shadows kill you."

Nye nodded quickly. "Yes, yes, of course. Just get you back to the table and—"

"No straps," said Valkyrie. "Nothing tying me down. You do this or you die."

25

DIRT

Surviving the poisoning wasn't the hard part. Tesseract had survived poisonings before. The fluids that his mask injected into his skin were designed to bolster his immunity and his natural, and unnatural, defences – mainly against the rotting disease that cursed him, but also, as a happy side effect, any other diseases, afflictions and poisons he happened to encounter on his travels. So the poisoning hadn't really troubled him for more than a few minutes.

The being buried alive part, however, was more of a reason to worry.

He had made a small air pocket for himself, giving him a little more time to shake off the poison's effects. When the feeling returned to his limbs, he tried to heave himself up, but the weight of the earth was just too much. The hole was, at the most, one and a half metres deep. That meant that all he had to do was stand up and he'd be out.

Standing up, however, was not as easy as it had once been.

His fingers scrabbled at the dirt, digging upwards slowly. He managed to get them reasonably far up, before realising that all he had achieved was to put himself in an even more uncomfortable position.

He lifted his body, straining against the weight, and kicked his legs. Loose earth shifted beneath him as he moved his right knee slowly. Moving the second one was more difficult, but he managed it. Now both knees were beneath him, his face was still pressed to the bottom of the grave, and his arms were somewhere above. If he died down here and was dug up in hundreds of years' time, he had a feeling the archaeologists would be puzzling over what exactly he had been doing upon his ridiculous death.

Tesseract took a deep breath, the last of the oxygen, and raised his head. His legs were burning, his back muscles screaming at him, and he felt like every tendon in his neck was about to snap. He pushed upwards, forcing his body straighter, his hands clawing at the freezing dirt. The fingers of his left hand suddenly felt no resistance. He pulled himself up, his right hand breaking through now, and then he felt air on his scalp, and all at once his head was free.

He gasped, sucking in air through his mask and blinking the dirt away from his eyes. His vision was blurry, but he was relatively sure he was alone. The way his luck had been going lately, he wouldn't have been at all surprised to find Ceryen and Graft standing here, still arguing.

A little more effort was required to climb out of the grave, and then Tesseract sprawled on the sodden grass, his vision clearing as he looked up at a sky so grey it could have been made from slate. He was just thankful to be looking up at any kind of sky at all. Slate grey, he decided, was a particularly beautiful shade of grey.

He got to his feet. There was cold clay in his clothes, down his back, down his trousers, in his mask. He brushed off what he could, shook out what he was able, but there was no denying the fact that it still felt like he had just crawled out of his own grave.

He looked down the hill, at the town and the lake and the Sanctuary. He didn't take it personally. He was a hired killer, after all. It would be pretty hypocritical to take a murder attempt personally, after everything he'd done. But that was no reason to let them live.

Graft, from what he could remember from his files, lived just off Roarhaven's main street. Tesseract found him in a small house, freshly emerged from the shower, and killed him while he begged for his life.

Ceryen worked directly for the Torment, though, so she would have returned to the Sanctuary. Tesseract entered without being seen. Everyone was too busy setting it up for business to bother guarding the entrance. After fifteen minutes of sneaking around, he heard the Torment's voice, and followed it through the long corridors.

He peered round a corner, saw the Torment and three other Children of the Spider – Madam Mist, a young woman called Portia and a young man called Syc. Ceryen trailed behind at a respectful distance. The Spider people were talking among themselves.

Tesseract had encountered Portia before, but had only heard stories about Mist, and had only ever seen a blurred photograph of Syc. He didn't know much about them though, and that made him uneasy.

The Torment led his brethren through a heavy set of double

doors, and gestured at Ceryen, dismissing her. She bowed, waited until the doors were shut, and walked towards Tesseract. He stepped back into the shadows to watch her pass, then followed. When they were far enough out of earshot, he made himself known by reaching down and tapping her leg. She screeched as it bent back on itself and she crumpled to the ground.

"Hello, Ceryen," Tesseract said, walking around so she could see him.

"My leg!" she cried. He had never worked out why some people liked to name the parts of them that had broken. "Please don't kill me!" He knew what was coming next. Tales of woe and then begging, interspersed with logic and reason. "The Torment ordered it! I was following orders! Please don't kill me! I have a family!"

"And yet I'm going to kill you anyway."

She lunged at him, but he reached down, and caved in her head with a touch.

"You are not an easy man to kill."

Slowly, Tesseract turned to face the Torment, who stood with Madam Mist at his side. He heard movement behind him, and didn't have to glance back to know that Portia and Syc were closing in to trap him.

"You shouldn't have tried to cheat me," Tesseract said. "I would have returned home and we would never have crossed paths again. Instead, we are where we are. You understand, I cannot let you live."

"You speak as though you hold the upper hand. There are four of us."

"Being outnumbered means very little to me. You will still die one by one."

The Torment vomited blackness that splashed to the ground and became spiders, as big as rats. Tesseract kicked one away from him, stomped on another, and backed away as thousands of smaller spiders, tiny spiders, spilled towards him like water. They flowed from the folds of Madam Mist's long dress, scrambling over her body, in and out of her clothes, crawling up her neck and disappearing behind her veil.

He heard blades being unsheathed, and spun to dodge the first swipe of Syc's twin daggers. He tried to grab him, but Syc was fast, faster than anyone Tesseract had ever seen. The blades flashed again and Tesseract stumbled. He stepped on a mass of spiders and they crunched beneath him.

One of the big spiders scuttled up his leg, digging its talons in as it came. Tesseract snarled and looked down. Syc was young and inexperienced and unimaginative, and he took the bait. When he sprang, Tesseract caught him and hurled him into the wall. Syc kept him at bay by vomiting, like the Torment had. The inky blackness coalesced, formed spiders, not as big as the Torment's, but definitely getting there. Tesseract backed away again. Too many damn spiders.

Portia came for him. Like Syc, she had a way to go in her studies, but the fact that she wasn't able to complete the full transformation to spider made her look even more fearsome. She had grown to twice her size, with black armour covering her chest and back. Four extra arms sprouted from her elongated torso, each tipped with claws, but it was Portia's face that was the most terrifying. Her fine-boned features had disappeared, replaced by a mouth that was a gaping hole, filled with fangs that dripped venom. Eight black eyes were grouped around her head.

Tesseract dodged as she attacked. Spiders were crawling all over him. Their poison was in his system and making him clumsy. He should have run when he'd had the chance. He looked up to see Syc plunging a dagger at his chest.

He blocked, fingers closing around Syc's wrist. The bones there broke and Tesseract took the dagger and slammed an elbow into Syc's face. He kicked him and the younger man went down, falling on thousands of spiders. Tesseract used him as a springboard to leap on to Portia. He held on as she tried to dislodge him, then slipped the dagger between her armour plates. He dropped to the ground as she reared back, shrieking.

Something flitted to her face, and clung there. Something black. Tesseract turned, saw Anton Shudder striding through the corridor, Remnants swirling around him.

One of those foul black things crawled into Syc's mouth, and the young man gagged and choked. Barely aware of the Torment and Mist already fleeing, Tesseract knew it was too late for him to make his escape. So he leaped forward, to Shudder, kicking him to drive him back. Shudder smiled, and reached for him, and Tesseract seized his arm and broke the bones.

Shudder hissed in pain and stepped back. "You've damaged me," he said.

Then the Remnant darted out of his mouth, to Tesseract's mask, and for a moment Tesseract couldn't see anything. It squirmed in through the eyeholes and he felt it cold on his face, sliding down. He glimpsed another Remnant attaching itself to Shudder's unconscious form – waste not, want not – and then he fell to his knees. The Remnant found his mouth, and Tesseract gagged as it forced its way in.

26

THE TRUTH

Valkyrie stepped into the sunlight and she was alive again.

She rubbed her eyes, as if she was awakening from a long sleep. Feeling flooded through her. Emotion. Sensation. The cold air forced the grogginess from her mind, which began to sharpen as the world came into focus around her. She was in the docklands. The weak sun was directly overhead. It was midday.

"You haven't fallen apart," Nye said.

Valkyrie turned. Nye stood inside the warehouse, where

everything was grey and lethargic. She looked at the line she'd crossed as she'd moved from dead to living – a line where the gloom of the warehouse was beaten back by the vivid clarity of life.

"I've done a good job," Nye nodded, more to itself than to her. "And it wasn't easy, what with the pressure I was under. But I did it. I'm one of the few who could."

"How many more like me do you have in there?" Valkyrie asked.

"Like you?"

"People who aren't supposed to be there."

"None," it said, shaking its head. "Everyone else was delivered by the Dullahan according to the rules. The Dullahan always follows the rules. He makes sure I do too."

"Sometimes he messes up. You were going to keep me."

Nye smiled. "Can't blame me for trying, eh? But all's well. You're walking, talking, living, breathing – and not falling apart. And your true name is sealed. It wasn't easy, but I knew, if anyone could do it, I could."

Valkyrie reckoned she ought to do something, but she couldn't think what. Arrest him? Punch him? Threaten him? She decided to go with threatening. "I'll be keeping an eye on you," she said. "If I ever hear of you trying anything like that again, I'll come back and drag you out of there."

Nye nodded. "Yes, yes, you're very frightening. Better run along and play now. Grown-ups have work to do."

It smiled, and the warehouse door slid closed. Valkyrie glowered. She should have gone with option two.

She hailed a taxi. She was halfway home before she thought to check that she had any money, but thankfully she found some cash in her back pocket. The driver listened to the radio all the way to Haggard, and Valkyrie watched the world pass. She got out at the pier, hurried to her house, and rose to her window. She slipped her fingers through the crack, opened it and climbed in.

Her room was empty, the reflection elsewhere. Valkyrie was glad. She looked around and realised she was smiling. It was good to be home. It was good to be alive, and safe, and home, and it was good to know that she wasn't going to become a monster who would murder the world. That was particularly comforting.

She heard someone coming up the stairs, and recognised her own footsteps. The reflection opened the door, not looking the least bit startled to see her.

"Your parents have gone out," it said, and Valkyrie

wondered if it had said 'your' simply to reassure her that its earlier mistake would not be repeated. "Do you want to resume your life?"

Valkyrie shook her head. "I just want to take a shower and eat something, then I'll be heading out again."

"I'll stay up here then, shall I?"

Valkyrie remembered, in her hallucination, the reflection encouraging Skulduggery to shoot her. "Yeah, you do that."

She went downstairs, grabbed a plate of leftover turkey and a glass of milk while she turned on her phone. Messages popped up – three missed calls. She cringed, and called Skulduggery to apologise for sleeping in. He sounded bemused, but told her he was on his way, and he'd be there in half an hour.

Valkyrie ate more turkey and drank more milk, then took a shower. As she stood under the spray, she ran her hand along her chest, not detecting the faintest trace of any scar. Nye was good – its skills might even be comparable to Kenspeckle's. And she reckoned their bedside manners were roughly the same, too.

She dressed, grabbed the present she'd wrapped for Skulduggery, and climbed out of the window without even glancing back at her reflection. She walked to the pier, wondering if she should tell Skulduggery what she'd done. Now that the danger was over, now that the future was changed, could she share this secret she'd had to keep for five months? He'd understand why she hadn't said anything. If anyone would understand, he would.

She reached the pier. The Bentley was already parked, and Skulduggery stood beside it, looking out at the sea that thundered against concrete and rock. He had brown eyes today, and thin lips. Same cheekbones and jaw, and the same waxy skin. His hat was cocked at its usual angle. Valkyrie marvelled at the way it tended to stay on, no matter how hard the wind was blowing. Then she realised he was probably manipulating the air around his head. Sneaky and stylish, the perfect combination.

She held out her hands. "Present."

He looked at her. "You're not getting your present."

Valkyrie frowned. "What? Why not?"

"Because it was a *Christmas* present. It's not Christmas any more."

"Of course it is. There's twelve whole *days* of Christmas."

"They don't count."

"Yes they do."

"The twelve days are merely to let people know when it's

time to take down their tasteless decorations. It's St Stephen's Day today, and I didn't get you a St Stephen's Day present."

The wind whipped her hair in front of her face. "But... But that's not fair! I have *your* present!"

"Can I have it?"

"No you can't!"

"Why not?"

"Why do you think? Because you won't give me *mine*."

"Ah, that's just mean."

"How can you consider *that* mean when you started it?"

"I'm not giving you *your* present because I just don't give Christmas presents after Christmas. I don't see the point. But you have no such policy, and so no such excuse. The only reason, that I can see, that you won't give me my present is because of sheer bitterness. You're just being mean."

Valkyrie glared. "Fine. Here's your present."

She took it from her jacket and threw it to him. He examined the wrapping. "It's a fairly distinctive shape."

She grunted.

"I'm not entirely sure I need to unwrap it. I think I can guess what it is."

"Good for you."

"Valkyrie, is it a hairbrush?"

She jabbed a finger at him. "Yes! See? That's a thoughtful gift! You haven't needed a hairbrush in hundreds of years, but you do now! Sometimes, anyway."

"Yes, but you got me a *hairbrush* for Christmas."

"It works on two levels! It's thoughtful *and* amusing! The present you gave me works on *no* levels, because you didn't *give* me a present. Don't you dare complain."

Skulduggery hesitated, then put the gift in his pocket. "It's a very thoughtful and amusing present, Valkyrie. Thank you."

"You're welcome. Can we get in the car now? It's really cold."

"Did you have a nice Christmas?"

"Sure."

"How did your family event last night go?"

"Fine."

"Do you think it will become an annual tradition?"

"Nope."

"OK then," Skulduggery said.

Valkyrie nodded. "Let's go."

She moved to the Bentley, then looked back at him. His arms were folded. "You're not moving."

"We are hurtling through space at a rate of 390 kilometres per second, Valkyrie. I would hardly call that not moving."

"Then we are not moving to the *car*," she sighed.

"This is true."

"And why are we not moving to the car, Skulduggery?"

"Because," he said.

"Because what?"

He looked around to make sure there was no one watching, and let his face flow away. Once he was back to his usual skeleton self, he continued. "Because I am waiting for you to tell me what is going on. You've been keeping something from me – and that ends now."

"Oh."

"Ordinarily, of course, I would respect your privacy, but—"

"No you wouldn't."

"Sorry?"

"You wouldn't respect my privacy."

"Yes I would."

"Skulduggery, you never respect my privacy."

"I do so all the time. Just last week, I respected your privacy."

"What was I doing?"

"Well, you weren't around."

"That makes almost no sense."

"But it does make a *bit* of sense, which is all I need. As I was saying, ordinarily, I wouldn't ask, but whatever you're keeping from me is interfering with your work. You are my partner, after all."

"OK," she said, "I'll tell you. I was going to tell you anyway, eventually. But before I do, I've already sorted everything out. I solved the problem. So keep that in mind when I tell you this. Promise?"

"I promise."

"OK." Valkyrie took a deep breath. "Are you ready?"

"I am."

"You're sure?"

"Quite sure."

"OK. So I'll tell you. Here I go. Skulduggery..."

"Yes, Valkyrie?"

"I'm... I don't know how to say this. I..." She swallowed. "I'm Darquesse."

Immediately, she felt better. Immediately, she felt cleaner, and lighter, and back to her old self. She found herself smiling.

"Right," Skulduggery said.

"Yep."

"You're Darquesse."

"That's it."

"In what way?"

"In a... what do you mean, what way?"

"You're Darquesse in a metaphorical way? *We all have evil in our hearts, we're all Darquesse* sort of way?"

"No," Valkyrie said slowly. "I mean I'm Darquesse. In a literal, *I'm Darquesse* sort of way."

His head tilted. "So you're Darquesse?"

"Yes."

"The same Darquesse who's going to kill everyone?"

"That's me."

"The same Darquesse who kills your parents?"

"Apparently so."

"And how have you reached this conclusion?"

"Remember years ago, when you were fighting Serpine, and the Book of Names fell? I caught a glimpse of my true name, so quick it didn't even register. But when I heard the name Darquesse a few months ago, I knew I'd heard it somewhere before, and that's where. It's mine."

"I see," Skulduggery said. "How long have you known?"

"Roughly since we first heard about her. After the Sanctuary was destroyed."

"And you've kept it to yourself?"

"Until now."

"Why didn't you tell me this before?"

"I wanted to take care of it."

"Have you?"

"I wouldn't be telling you all this if I hadn't. Darquesse will not be making an appearance for the foreseeable ever. The world is safe."

"How did you manage that?"

"I'll tell you," Valkyrie said. "But first you tell *me* what you think happens. Why do I kill everyone? Or why *would I* have if I hadn't just, you know, stopped me?"

"The likeliest scenario would be that someone learns who you are and uses your true name to control you."

"Exactly. So that's taken care of."

"How?"

"I sealed my name. I spoke to a few people, tracked down some other people, figured it out and implemented my plan all on my own. Are you proud of me?"

"Who did it?"

"Did what?"

Skulduggery cocked his head. "Who sealed your name?"

"It doesn't matter."

"Kenspeckle couldn't have done it. Something like that would take years of research and trial and error, even for him."

"It doesn't matter, OK? It's done. My heart was taken out,

the little symbols were drawn on, and I was stitched back together."

"By whom?"

"I don't want to talk about it."

"You said you'd tell me."

"I said I'd tell you what I've been up to lately. I didn't say I'd give you this person's name."

"There's only a handful of possibilities..."

"Skulduggery, drop it."

"You should have told me," he said. "I could have made sure it was safe."

"Don't worry about it."

"You had your heart removed from your body," he said sternly. "You were *dead*."

"You're dead all the time, and you're fine."

"Who did it?"

"I don't want to talk about this. I don't want to talk about the person who did it. I just—"

"*Person*," Skulduggery said. "You keep saying *person*. Not *he*, or *she*. Is it in an effort to further protect the identity, or is it... Is it an *it?*"

"I don't know what you're—"

His voice turned hard. "Doctor Nye."

"What does it matter?" she blurted. "OK, fine, it was Nye! So what? It did its job, and now I'm back home and everything's grand."

"Nye's a sick, twisted, evil freak, Valkyrie. You're lucky you came back. You're very, *very* lucky."

"I know," she said quietly, and looked away.

"You should have told me. You should have trusted me. You should have..." He stopped, and went silent. And then he said, "Never mind."

She looked up. "What?"

"You were scared. I understand. You didn't know how I'd react."

"Well... yeah."

He stepped towards her, and his hand went to her shoulder. "That was a mistake," he said gently. "I'm not going to judge you, Valkyrie. I'd never judge you."

Suddenly she felt like crying. "I'm sorry I didn't tell you."

"What a burden it must have been. You're very brave for facing it alone."

"Thank you," she mumbled.

"Amazingly, astonishingly *stupid*, but brave."

She cracked a smile. "Yeah."

"Very foolish, is what I'm getting at."

"I can see that."

"Thick, basically. Just thick. Dumb as a bag of hammers. Not too bright there, Valkyrie."

"You can really stop complimenting me now."

Skulduggery pulled her gently into a hug, and patted her back. "You brainless moron. You simple-minded cretin. You're a half-wit. A dimwit. An imbecile. You're as sharp as a marble. Thick as a ditch. Not the sharpest knife, nor the brightest crayon, and not the brightest bulb. You just fell off the turnip truck. The wheel is turning, but the hamster is dead."

She laughed into his chest. "Please stop talking."

He pulled away from her. "In future, you tell me if you think there's even the *slightest* chance you might be responsible for Armageddon, agreed?"

"Agreed."

He hesitated. "And you know, of course, that you might be wrong."

"About what?"

"About what makes you become Darquesse. We don't *know* what triggers it, we're only guessing someone tries to control you."

"So basically, even though I've just sealed my true name, that doesn't mean I won't turn? Yeah, I've thought of that. I don't believe it, but I've thought of it."

"OK," he said, and nodded. "Just wanted to make sure." He turned back to the Bentley, and opened the door. "I knew you were keeping *something* from me," he said. "I didn't think it was quite so *big*, though."

Valkyrie smiled. "What did you think it was?"

"It seems laughably insignificant now."

"Let's hear it."

"I... OK, I thought you were going to tell me that there was something going on between you and Caelan. You know what? I actually think I'm relieved."

Skulduggery chuckled, and got in behind the wheel. Valkyrie turned away so he wouldn't see her smile drop, and got in the other side.

"Where to?" she asked as she buckled her seatbelt.

"Someone told Tesseract where I lived. I spent all of yesterday asking questions, and I finally found who the culprit is."

"Do I know him?"

"Yes you do."

"Are we going to track him down?"

"Yes we are."

"Am I going to enjoy it?"

"Immensely."

27

BACK WITH FINBAR

Finbar Wrong was curled up in the corner, with the wooden shutters on the windows closed. It was dark, and the place was quiet. Wreath had been forced to break the lock to get into the tattoo parlour. He'd moved quietly through the ground floor, then came upstairs, cane in hand. He didn't know what use Necromancy would be against a Remnant in its true form, but it was better than nothing.

He'd spotted Finbar the moment he'd stepped in, and he'd been watching the psychic rock back and forward with his head down for three minutes. Every now and then, Finbar would mutter something. Wreath was now using his cane only to lean on. The Remnant wasn't here any more.

"Finbar," Wreath said. He got a mumble in reply. He repeated himself, louder this time, and Finbar looked up.

"Who's that?" Finbar asked.

"Solomon Wreath. You know me."

Finbar nodded. "I know you. Yes. You're a Necromancer."

"That's right."

"What do you want? I'm very..." Finbar stood up and straightened his T-shirt. "I'm very busy."

"The sign on the door said closed."

Finbar shook his head. "Never trust a door; they'll always lie to you. Mr Wreath, I don't want to be rude to someone as scary as you, but I don't tattoo Necromancers. It's a policy I have, that I came up with just there."

"Finbar, what do you remember about the last few days?"

Finbar frowned. "Why d'you ask? The fact that you asked means there's something I obviously don't remember. What is it?"

"What *do* you remember?"

"I remember... I had a vision of something. A person. Dressed all in black."

"Yes. Do you remember their face?"

"It's... It's hazy... Yes. I do."

"Who was it?" asked Wreath. "Who did you see?"

Finbar's eyes widened. "I saw *you.*"

"What?"

"I saw you, coming in here and threatening me and... and doing something..."

Wreath sighed. "That was two days ago."

"It was?"

"You had that vision two days ago, so you sent your wife and child away and waited around to see if I'd turn up."

"And here you are," Finbar said dramatically.

"Actually, this is my second visit. I was here two days ago, and I'm here again."

Finbar frowned. "Did I hit you with a cushion?"

"So you *do* remember. Do you remember anything about what you did afterwards?"

"Why should I tell you?"

"Believe it or not, Finbar, I'm here to help. I think Valkyrie Cain is in danger, and if you can remember what happened to you over the past two days, I hope to be able to stop something bad from happening to her."

Finbar looked at him, like he was trying to make up his

mind whether to trust him or not. Surprisingly, he decided to give it a go. "I remember this morning," he said. "Or maybe it was yesterday. I locked the door and came up here. I think I've been to the toilet a few times. And had some tea."

"And before that?"

"I... I, uh... I don't know, it's hazy... I think I was in a forest. I woke up, and there were all these trees, and I started walking. I'm not sure. I've been having these awful, awful headaches."

"What forest?"

"Don't know. I walked out, and someone stopped to give me a lift. I couldn't see straight. The headaches, you know? I'm seeing... stuff."

"Visions?"

"Or nightmares. Can't tell. I think something went wrong. With me. In my head, like."

Wreath had no way of knowing if the damage the Remnant had done was permanent. Some doors, once opened, can never truly be closed. He looked at this skinny man with the tattoos and the crumpled T-shirt and felt sorry for him.

"What are you seeing?" he asked.

"I really don't know. It's too confused. It's not nice, I'll tell you that much. What kind of danger?"

"I'm sorry?"

"What kind of danger is Valkyrie in?"

"I don't know yet. I want to find out more before I tell her, though."

"You should talk to the Skul-man about it," said Finbar.

"Yes," Wreath said. "Maybe I will. Finbar, thanks for your help. And I'm sorry about the headaches."

"Me too."

Wreath left him and walked down the stairs, but when he opened the door there was something waiting for him.

28

THE Z-WORD

obody likes zombies.

That was the lesson Valkyrie was learning. They'd been scouring the city, looking for Scapegrace and Thrasher, and everyone they talked to made a face whenever the Z-word was mentioned. Noses were wrinkled in disgust, like the word brought with it a bad smell. Those who knew anything, anything in the slightest, were more than happy to share that information. Nobody clammed up, nobody refused to answer questions, and nobody demanded anything in return. Zombies, it seemed, were not afforded the same street code as other criminals and killers.

"I know them," a notoriously tight-lipped sorcerer named Tarr had said. "One of them talks big and the other one agrees with everything he says. They the two you're looking for? Yeah, I know them. They're living out of a refrigerated truck that's got two flat tyres. It's parked a couple of streets over."

They found the truck where Tarr said it would be. As they approached, they saw two men walking towards them from the other direction. When the men saw them, they stopped, spun, and proceeded to slip and slide on the icy pavement in a manic effort to get away. Skulduggery and Valkyrie strolled up to them.

"Hello, Vaurien," Skulduggery said.

Spinning around again, and barely managing to stay on his feet, Scapegrace glared. "Why are you after us? We haven't done anything wrong."

"You're zombies."

"But we haven't killed anyone."

"Yes you have."

"*Recently*. We haven't killed anyone *recently*."

"You told Tesseract where Skulduggery's house was," Valkyrie said.

Scapegrace shook his head. "No we didn't."

"Six sorcerers were killed in a Dublin bar," said Skulduggery, "three nights ago. The one witness we found who would talk said that a big man in a metal mask took them apart, and afterwards he spoke with a pathetic little zombie who cowered and wailed. That was you, am I right?"

"No," Scapegrace said. He pointed at Thrasher, who was grabbing a lamp post and pulling himself up off the ground. "It was him."

"Oh," Thrasher said.

"We've let you wander around," Skulduggery said, "because we reasoned you're not that big a threat. We didn't think you'd be too eager to recruit more members, not after your little horde went crazy the last time. But now you have proven yourselves to be a nuisance the world could do without."

"Spare my master!" Thrasher wailed. "End my life, but leave my master alone! I beg of you!"

"I agree with him," Scapegrace said.

Thrasher jumped between Skulduggery and Scapegrace. "Master, run! I'll hold them off!"

"You couldn't hold off a sneeze," Scapegrace muttered.

"But I'll die trying!"

Thrasher lunged at Skulduggery, who pushed him towards Valkyrie, who stepped sideways and tripped him as he passed.

"OK," Scapegrace said nervously, "how about a deal?"

Skulduggery took out his gun. "What could you possibly offer us?"

"Information."

"About what?"

"About things. Things on the street. Secret things. Dark things."

"Such as?"

"Well, I... I don't know any right *now*. I mean, we'd have to go undercover for you. We'd be your spies, going places you could never go."

"I don't really think you'd be very good at that," said Skulduggery.

"OK, OK then, how about you making us your back-up? You could have a secret army of zombies—"

"There are only two of you."

"You could have a secret zombie duo as your back-up, ready at any moment to respond to your call. We could be part of your team, saving the world, beating the bad guys..."

"I think you'd probably betray us. Or just be useless."

"We wouldn't be, I promise." Scapegrace looked like he was going to start crying. "Please. You can't kill me."

Skulduggery raised the gun. "You're already dead."

"Not really. Not properly dead. I can still do things. I can still think."

"You won't even know what's happened."

"But... but I want to stay. I'm sorry, all right? I'm sorry for all the bad things I've done. Valkyrie, I'm sorry for trying to kill you all those times. Please, don't let him... don't let him do this."

He looked at her with his dull eyes, his burnt face slack and rotting, and for a moment he reminded her of a dead dog by the side of the road. "Skulduggery," she said, "we can't kill him."

Skulduggery's gun-hand didn't waver. "And why not?"

"Look at him. It would be different if he was attacking us, but... he's not."

Scapegrace held up his hands. "See? I'm not attacking anyone. And neither is Thrasher. Are you, Thrasher?"

Thrasher sat up. "I think I bit off a piece of my tongue."

"We don't want to hurt anyone," Scapegrace said. "We just want to be normal again. I want to live. I want be alive."

Skulduggery lowered the gun, but didn't put it away. "Impossible."

"No, not impossible. There's a doctor who can help us. Kenspeckle Grouse."

"And why do you think Kenspeckle can help you?"

"Dreylan Scarab talked about him. He said he was the best in the world. If anyone can help us, he can. Do you know him? Do you think he would help us? Could you set up an appointment?"

"You really want to change?"

"Yes. God, yes. I hate being like this. I just want another chance."

"Please," Thrasher said. "It's Christmas."

"He has a point," said Valkyrie.

Skulduggery looked at her. "'*It's Christmas*' is not an argument. It's not a reason. It's just a statement of the obvious."

"But this *is* the season of forgiveness."

Skulduggery holstered his gun. "Fine. You want us to take these two to Professor Grouse, we'll take them. If he can't do anything for them, we destroy their brains. Agreed?"

"Agreed."

"I'm not sure I like that," Scapegrace murmured.

Valkyrie smiled. "I don't care."

*   *   *

Thrasher yelped in anguish as a piece of his ear was cut off. Kenspeckle muttered something, probably telling him not to be a baby, as he carefully laid the piece of ear on a Petri dish. Valkyrie stood outside, looking in through the transparent door.

Kenspeckle turned to Scapegrace. "Sit up on the bed," he ordered, his voice coming through the speaker on the corridor wall. Scapegrace did what he was told, but as the scalpel moved towards his left ear, the ear fell off. Scapegrace looked embarrassed. Kenspeckle examined the ear.

"Is this glue?"

Scapegrace nodded, a little sheepishly.

"And these small holes here – piercings?"

"Staples."

Kenspeckle sighed, put the ear on a second Petri dish, and left the room. The door slid shut behind him. He joined Valkyrie.

"Well?" she asked. "Can you cure them?"

"I don't know yet. Theoretically, yes. Zombies were an accident – much like champagne and penicillin, but much less welcome. Necromancers weren't working on a way to turn people into shambling pieces of unintelligent rot—"

"Hey," said Scapegrace from the other room.

"—they were trying to return the dead to full life. This is as

291

far as they got. Not complete and utter failure, but look at them – they're not exactly a roaring success either."

"I resent that," Scapegrace said.

"The question is, can I take what the Necromancers have done and go further? Can I complete the resurrection with my own brand of science-magic? That's what intrigues me. Then there are all the variables. Can I reverse the decomposition? Can I return the body to its natural state? Can I reverse brain death?"

"My brain isn't dead," Scapegrace said angrily. "It's sleeping."

"All together, a fascinating proposition. Thank you for bringing it to my attention, Valkyrie."

"My pleasure. I'd keep this door locked, though, if I were you."

"I intend to."

Scapegrace jumped off the bed, looking startled. "What? What was that? I've got to stay in the same room as *him?*"

Thrasher did his best not to look wounded.

"This will not do," Scapegrace insisted. "We are not prisoners, we are guests. And as such, I demand separate rooms."

"You are my patients," Kenspeckle said, "and you will do

what I tell you. Mr Scapegrace, how much time had passed from the moment you were brought back as a zombie to the moment you infected Gerald here?"

"His name is Thrasher."

"I refuse to call him that. How long, Mr Scapegrace?"

"I don't know," Scapegrace scowled. "Two hours, maybe three." He jabbed a finger at Thrasher. "And you – don't get used to being called that ridiculous name."

Thrasher hung his head.

"Three hours," Kenspeckle murmured.

"Why is that important?" Valkyrie asked.

"It very possibly isn't important in the slightest, but as usual I have my theories, and now seems to be an excellent time to test them."

Scapegrace stalked up to the door. "Concentrate on curing me, OK? That's the only reason we came to you. That's your only purpose. Drop everything and focus on bringing me back to life."

Valkyrie raised an eyebrow at him. "Before anything important falls off?"

Scapegrace glared, and Thrasher cleared his throat and looked down at his shoes.

"And what about you?" Kenspeckle asked, glancing at

Valkyrie. "How are you going to spend the rest of the day, while I conduct tests on dead people? Are you going to be fighting? Running? Chasing?"

"Dancing," she said with a smile. "I'm going to be dancing."

29

HER GUARDIAN ANGEL

He could still taste her blood. He ran his tongue over his lips, liking the way it electrified his whole body. It was as if he had a pulse again, a working heart that beat in his chest. It was as if he was alive.

Caelan watched Valkyrie with her family, through the window of their kitchen. He watched her talk and smile and laugh. He was in love with that part of her, the part she didn't allow him to see. When they were together, her guard was up, she was always careful around him, always wary. But here, at home, she could relax. She could drop the act. She could be herself. He doubted even Skulduggery Pleasant got to see this side of Valkyrie Cain. He doubted even the great Skeleton Detective knew this part of her.

Caelan sat back against the wooden fence of the garden. Finding her had been easy. Now that he had tasted her blood, there was nowhere she could go that he couldn't follow. There were many aspects to being a vampire that he hated, but even he had to admit, sometimes his predatory abilities came in useful. Because of them, Valkyrie would never again be alone during the day. While the sun was up, she would always be protected, always watched over.

She didn't know it yet, but he was her new guardian angel. The only thing left for him to do was to find a way to be around her at night, when the monster within showed its face.

Even his love wasn't strong enough to protect her from that. Since he had tasted her blood, in fact, the monster had got stronger, more ferocious. In a frenzy, it had torn apart his room in the Midnight Hotel, which was undoubtedly why Anton Shudder had abandoned him.

The day before, he had returned to find that the hotel had already moved on without him. He didn't blame Shudder. The only part which surprised him was the fact that it had taken so long. Caelan had barely made it to his emergency cage by nightfall, and he'd shackled himself up just as he felt the monster emerging. Just in time.

He didn't like to think what would have happened if he'd been too slow. His mind, robbed of its reason and superficial humanity, would have focused on Valkyrie, and Valkyrie alone. Caelan knew he would never forgive himself if he harmed her in any way.

It was getting late. The sun would be down soon, and night would swoop in. His insides tearing, he forced himself to his feet. He took one last look at Valkyrie through the window, and jumped the fence.

30

MEET THE PARENTS

Valkyrie smudged her mascara and stormed away from the mirror, cursing. She hated make-up. She hated the fact that she had to *wear* make-up. Her dress was fantastic, her hair was glossy, her shoes had actual heels. So why did she need make-up? She was going for the bare minimum, but she had still managed to almost poke herself in the eye three times already. Growling, she returned to the mirror to finish the job.

Finally, she was done. Her phone rang.

"Hey," said Fletcher. "You ready?"

Valkyrie looked at herself in the mirror. Presentable. "Yes," she said.

"Cool, I'll be there now."

"Don't teleport."

He paused. "What?"

"Fletch, you can't teleport into my *room*. This is a *date*. You knock on the front door. You meet my parents."

"You were serious about that?"

"Oh yes. I've told them about you. You are my boyfriend, we've been going out for three weeks, you used to go to my school, where you were two years ahead of me. You've just started college. You're studying economics."

"Economics? Val, I know nothing *about* economics."

"Neither do my parents. It'll be fine. Your folks are separated and you live with your dad, somewhere not too close to here. You're taking me to an under-eighteens' disco. Say no more about it than that."

"I really don't know about this. Val, parents don't like me when they first meet me."

"Fletch, *nobody* likes you when they first meet you. You're incredibly annoying, remember?"

"Oh, yeah."

"Knock on the front door in a few minutes."

"How many minutes?"

Valkyrie sighed. "I don't know. Surprise me."

She hung up, put her phone in her purse, hung the purse off her shoulder, and went downstairs. Her parents were in the living room, watching TV. The Christmas tree was all lit up, the fire was roaring, and the mantelpiece was filled with cards. Her dad frowned at what she was wearing.

"It's a little black dress," she told him.

"It's a little *too* little," he frowned back. "And where's the rest of it? I can see your knees."

"Don't be a prude," his wife said from where she was sitting. She was far too comfortable, and pregnant, to get up. "Steph, you look lovely. Tell her she looks lovely, Des."

"Stephanie, you look lovely. I do think the knees are a bit much though."

"Dad."

"Des."

"I'm just expressing an opinion, that's all. Personally, I think knees should be kept for the eighth or ninth date, or the wedding day. As a nice surprise, you know? '*Oh, my darling, you have knees! I never would have thought!*'"

The doorbell rang, and Valkyrie's dad barred the way out of the room.

"Sorry, Stephanie," he said, hiking up his trousers, "but it is a father's duty to open the door to the first boyfriend. You stay here with your mother and talk about knitting patterns. If I approve of him, and like the cut of his jib, we may even adjourn to my study for brandy and cigars."

"You don't have a study."

"I mean, obviously, the downstairs toilet."

"And do you even know what a jib is?"

"Of course I do," he said defensively. "It's a hairstyle of some description."

"No, it's one of the sails on a ship."

"And how do *you* know that?"

Valkyrie shrugged. "It's just one of the things I know."

"Well, just for that piece of showing off, young lady, you get to wait here while I interrogate your gentleman caller."

And he was gone. Valkyrie looked back at her mum, who smiled and shrugged. "Let him have his fun," she said.

Valkyrie strained to hear what was being said out in the hall, but all she could pick up were mumbles. She had a terrifying image of her father and Fletcher, standing there mumbling and looking down at their shoes. But then she heard the front door close, and footsteps approached. Her father led the way in.

"His hair is huge!" he exclaimed.

Fletcher followed him in, looking sheepish but cute in dark jeans and a black shirt.

"Look!" her dad continued, pointing. "It's just sticking up at odd angles! Like a demented porcupine!"

"Stop teasing," Valkyrie's mum said, clambering to her feet. She shook Fletcher's hand. "Your hair looks wonderful, Fletcher. I'm Melissa, and this is Desmond."

Her dad glared. "I told him he should call me Mr Edgley."

"Don't mind him, Fletcher. You can call him Des."

"Stop undermining my authority."

"Sorry, dear. You say something now."

"Thank you." Her father peered at Fletcher through narrowed eyes. "What are your intentions towards my daughter then? I hope you don't think you're going to be holding her hand or anything. Just because her knees are visible does not mean she is the kind of girl to hold the hand of a strange-haired boy on their first date."

"No, sir," Fletcher said, "not at all."

"Where are you planning to take her?"

"A dance, sir."

"And yet you brought no flowers, no heart-shaped box of

chocolates. It's been a few years since I was on a date, Fletcher, as you can see by my wife..."

"Oi."

"...but I still remember the rules. A bouquet of flowers and a box of chocolates. Every girl loves them."

"I don't like bouquets of flowers," Valkyrie said.

"Every girl apart from my daughter, naturally."

"I wouldn't have minded the chocolates, though."

"Hear that, Fletcher?"

"Des," Valkyrie's mother sighed, "would you please leave the poor boy alone? Fletcher, Stephanie tells us you're in college. How's that going?"

"Really well," Fletcher said, trying to smile. "I'm doing economics. That's the study of the economy. I love it."

"Which college?"

"Hmm?"

"Which college do you go to?"

Fletcher nodded. "Yes."

"I'm sorry?"

"Oh," Fletcher said, and laughed.

Valkyrie's parents looked at Fletcher in near bewilderment. Fletcher looked back at them in total bewilderment. Valkyrie shook her head.

"He's not good with first impressions," she said sadly. "He doesn't know what he's saying. We should go, before he starts to dribble. Fletcher, I expect you have the taxi waiting outside?"

"Um. Yes?"

"Perfect. Mother. Father. He's not a total idiot. Please believe that. Fletcher, let's go."

She led the way out and Fletcher followed.

"You're going to need a jacket!" her dad called after them.

"I'll be fine!" she called back, and then stepped outside and gasped at the cold, but kept walking. Fletcher hurried to keep up.

"That went well," he said.

"The moment we're out of sight," said Valkyrie, "teleport."

A gust of freezing wind tore in across the sea and Valkyrie fought to keep her dress from flying up around her waist. She wasn't used to dresses.

She stepped out of the queue to see how much further they had to go, and groaned. There were a lot of people waiting to get into Shenanigans, the number one nightspot in Haggard's neighbouring coastal town. Valkyrie wasn't sure, but she had a suspicion it was also the *only* nightspot in

Haggard's neighbouring coastal town, which wasn't much to brag about.

According to her mother, it had once been an amusement arcade, out here on the tip of the peninsula, practically on the stony beach itself, back before the advent of home computers and games consoles. It had closed down, been extensively remodelled, and reopened as a pub, then a nightclub, then both. Now, finally, it was a nightclub again – a two-storey den of loud music, smoke machines and flashing lights. The place had changed owners more times than it had changed names.

Valkyrie's parents used to take her here as a child. She played on the rocks, with the smell of the fishing boats coming in with their haul. Tonight, however, the tide was in and the fishing boats bobbed on the waves, and all she could smell was the sea.

She glanced at Fletcher, saw him visibly straining against his own irritation. He hated queues. Getting where he wanted to be instantly was as much a part of his life these days as breathing, and he really resented having to wait in line with other people.

The wind was getting stronger, threatening to mess her hair. She moved her hand discreetly, diverting the gusts around her. Standing in a bubble of calm, Valkyrie hoped nobody would notice that her hair was now still and her dress was staying down. Thankfully, they all seemed to be far too busy shivering.

They reached the front of the queue and passed in through the doors, into the warmth, just before the doormen announced that the club was full. Fletcher turned to her and she grinned, kissed him, then took his hand and led the way to the dance floor.

31

THE FIRST WAVE

hastly parted the blinds and looked out on to the quiet street. Still dark. Still empty. Still glistening.

"You look like you're waiting for someone," Ravel said from behind him. "Anyone I know?"

"I'm just looking, Erskine."

Ravel took a sip from his mug of tea. "You know who I'd like to meet again? Tesseract. And this time we'd be ready for him."

Skulduggery, not bothering to lift his gaze from his

newspaper, said, "I wouldn't be too eager for a rematch, if I were you."

Ghastly lifted a swatch of material to a small table, and sat at the sewing machine. "It's been a while since I faced anyone that good. It was only a few seconds, but it was enough."

Ravel smiled. "You boys have lost your sense of adventure. There was a time when we'd have raced headlong into something like this."

"We're not young men any more."

"Be honest, though – doesn't the thought of the Dead Men getting back together fill you with a dangerous kind of glee?"

"The Dead Men aren't getting back together," Skulduggery said. "It's just *us*, sitting around at Christmas because we've got nothing else to do."

Ghastly pressed his foot to the pedal. The low *whir* of the machine caught his thoughts and settled them. He was always calmer when working. "Besides, I don't go looking for fights any more, especially against people like Tesseract. I have responsibilities now. I have this shop. And you two are going to have to grow up sooner or later, you know. People expect a certain level of maturity from Elders."

There was the sound of fingers digging into newspaper. "Do not joke about that, Bespoke," Skulduggery said.

Ghastly smiled as he fed the sleeve of the jacket through the machine, making minute adjustments as it went. "You haven't changed your mind about taking it on?"

"I think I would be a horrifically bad choice. Maybe Corrival can be convinced to ask someone who is less controversial than I am – China, perhaps."

"Oh, everyone would love that," Ravel laughed. "A founding member of the Diablerie and a devout follower of the Faceless Ones."

"Ex-follower."

"That will make such a difference to the people with long memories." Ravel sat back. Then he said, "Your friend Tanith is an interesting girl."

Ghastly hissed as the sleeve bunched up under the needle. He corrected the mistake and nodded. "That she is."

"How long have you known her?"

"A few years," Skulduggery said. "Not long. Bliss brought her in to help out against Serpine. She's been a good friend to Valkyrie, and a good ally to the rest of us. And you, Erskine, are to stay away from her."

Ravel laughed. "And why is that?"

He looked at Skulduggery and Skulduggery tilted his head, but said nothing. Ravel's smile died away, and he glanced over at Ghastly. "Oh," he said. "Right. Sorry."

Ghastly raised an eyebrow. "Sorry about what?"

"Nothing. Nothing at all. Tanith's great, but she's not my type. I mean, I'm not saying there's anything *wrong* with her. She's amazing. But, you know, not for... not for me, basically. For someone else, though, I'd say she'd be, uh, perfect. If, you know, if someone else liked her."

Ghastly concentrated on sewing, and Ravel changed the subject pretty fast.

"I was thinking, actually, about this Council thing. Maybe it won't be so bad. It could be a new start for everyone. New Council, new Sanctuary... The slate wiped clean. I think it's time you had a clean slate, Skulduggery."

Skulduggery folded the newspaper and put it down. "Meaning what?"

Ravel hesitated. "Whatever burden it is you're carrying around, whatever you did during the war that was so terrible, maybe it's time you let it go. It might be good for you, to reclaim your family crest. Sooner or later, you'll have to forgive yourself and move on."

Skulduggery was silent for a moment. "Is that so?"

Ghastly stopped sewing. "I agree with Erskine. The fact is, I think Valkyrie might be your way to do just that. I think she's a good influence on you, to be honest. She makes you a better person."

"You didn't always see it that way. She told me about the vision your mother had – about Valkyrie and myself fighting side by side, and falling."

"And the world falls with you," Ghastly said. "I think my mother was the first Sensitive to foresee the arrival of Darquesse, but I don't think that future will happen. Not any more. The two of you, together, are strong enough to change what's to come."

"You sound uncharacteristically optimistic, Ghastly."

"It's Christmas. I'm allowed my optimism."

Someone knocked on the door, and Ghastly got up to answer it.

Ravel smiled. "Who could that be, I wonder? Who would venture out on such a cold, unforgiving night as this? A certain young Englishwoman, perhaps?"

Ghastly glared at him. "Do not say anything."

"Not a word."

Ghastly opened the door, but instead of the shapely figure of Tanith Low, he was greeted with the portly figure of

311

Corrival Deuce. "Grand Mage," Ghastly said, slightly dismayed.

"Don't sound so bloody enthusiastic," Corrival sighed, shuffling by him. "Oh, it's nice and warm in here. Hello, lads."

Skulduggery and Ravel stood.

"What's wrong?" Skulduggery asked.

Corrival laughed. "Why must something be wrong? Can I not visit old colleagues without some dastardly ulterior motive? It's the holiday season, for God's sake."

Ravel frowned. "So... there's nothing wrong?"

"Nothing. You can relax now. That's an order." Corrival picked up a wooden chair, brought it closer to the others. "So what's going on? Three old friends sharing war stories, is that it? No ladies? No other company?"

"Just us," Ghastly said.

"Not ideal," said Corrival, "but it'll do."

Corrival slammed the chair into Ghastly's back. The skylight exploded in a shower of broken glass, and Solomon Wreath dropped down into the shop at the same time as the door crashed open and Anton Shudder strode in. Ravel charged at Wreath and Skulduggery went for Shudder.

Corrival's lips were black and dark veins spread beneath his skin. He pushed at the air and Ghastly was lifted off his feet. He hit the wall, breaking shelves.

Shudder was holding his right arm like it was broken, but his gist was darker and more furious than ever. It flew at Skulduggery and he barely had time to dive out of its path. Tackling the gist itself was futile – the only way to fight Shudder was to take the fight directly to him. Skulduggery clicked his fingers and hurled a fireball, but the gist swooped down to intercept.

At the other end of the shop, Ravel was doing his best to avoid the sharpened shadows that Wreath was firing at him. He sent the Necromancer stumbling with a wave of air, then lunged, trying to wrestle the cane from his grip.

Ghastly dived and rolled to avoid another wall of air, and he came up beside Corrival and swung a punch that would have felled someone twice his size. But Corrival merely grunted, and Ghastly was reminded of his mercifully short fight against Tesseract – an enemy who did not seem to feel pain. Corrival hit him and the world spun. Ghastly fell back.

The gist screeched as Skulduggery reached for one of the massive rolls of fabric that Ghastly kept along the wall and yanked it out. The fabric, a very expensive deep red, unspooled with a rumble, and the gist flew straight into it and became tangled. Before it could shred its way clear,

Skulduggery used the air to fling himself at Shudder. He got behind him, wrapped an arm around his throat, and tightened. The gist shrieked as it was pulled back into Shudder's chest.

Ghastly snapped his palm at the air and Corrival hurtled backwards. He looked over at Ravel, who had taken Wreath's cane and was using it to beat the Necromancer senseless. There was movement at the broken skylight, and a Remnant flitted down, attaching itself to Ravel's face. Ravel jerked away and fell to his knees. Ghastly ran to help but it was too late – black veins were already spreading across Ravel's skin.

"Skulduggery!" Ghastly shouted. "We have to go!"

He turned to the door as Tesseract walked through.

Skulduggery grabbed Ghastly. "Hold on," he said, and they flew upwards, up through the skylight and into the cold night air.

32

SHENANIGANS

henanigans was packed. Valkyrie and Fletcher went up to the second floor, where there were huge mirrors on one side, perhaps in an effort to convince the dancers that the dance floor was bigger than it was. The mirrors were a distraction. Fletcher kept glancing at his reflection as he danced, checking his hair. Valkyrie didn't laugh at his vanity, though – she took a few glances at the mirrors herself, just to make sure she looked as good as she reckoned she did.

There were two steps leading down to the dance floor. No

alcohol was being served, but even so, three people had already stepped off them without realising they were there, and fallen flat on their faces. Valkyrie remained amused by the whole thing.

They danced, and laughed, and talked loudly over the music, and then Fletcher went to the bar to get her a Coke. Valkyrie stood by the edge of the dance floor, and a boy approached. He was Fletcher's age, with brown hair cut short, and a nice smile.

"Hi," he said.

Valkyrie gave him a polite smile back. "Hi."

He leaned in so he could be heard. "Can I buy you a drink?"

She shook her head. "My boyfriend's getting me one."

"That's your boyfriend?"

She nodded.

"He's a lucky guy."

She smiled again.

"Name's Owen. What's yours?"

"Valkyrie," she answered.

"Sorry?"

She blinked. "Stephanie," she said loudly. "My name is Stephanie. Hi, Owen, how are you?"

"Oh, I'm good," Owen said. "I've been watching you all night."

Valkyrie nodded again and leaned in. "Yeah, that's a little creepy."

He laughed. "I was wondering if I could have your phone number."

"I've got a boyfriend, Owen."

"I've got a girlfriend, Stephanie. That doesn't mean you can't give me your number."

"Very true," she said, patting his arm. "It just means I won't."

Valkyrie slipped by him and didn't look back. She pushed her way into the crowd, eventually breaking through. She went straight to the ladies' toilets. For once, there wasn't a line of girls waiting to get in, but Valkyrie still had to wait a minute for a cubicle to become empty. She stepped in and locked the door behind her.

The music was muted in here, enough to hear the chatter of the girls around her. When she finished, she undid the latch on the door, and went to the sinks to wash her hands and check her make-up. Not one smudge. Whenever she felt like the dancing was about to result in perspiration, Valkyrie and those around her would suddenly be caught in a mysterious but welcome blast of cool air. Magic was astoundingly handy at times.

A crowd of girls came in behind her and she turned to leave, but they blocked her path.

"That's my fella you're chatting up," the first one said, a pretty blonde with an ugly sneer and too much make-up.

Valkyrie stepped back. "I'm not chatting up anyone," she said. "I'm here with my boyfriend."

The blonde's three friends closed in around her, girls in low tops and short skirts and high heels. Valkyrie recognised one of them from school, but didn't know her name.

"Looked like you were chatting him up to me," the blonde said, her head tilting with the attitude of someone who's starting a fight.

"You're talking about Owen?" Valkyrie asked. "We had a very short chat, that's all. I have no interest in him, if that's what you're worried about."

The blonde jabbed a finger into Valkyrie's chest. "Do I look like I'm worried? You think I'm scared he'll go with you, do you?"

Valkyrie smiled patiently. "I like how you do your make-up. Do you use a brush, or just dip your head in the bucket?"

The blonde's head shot forward. Valkyrie managed to turn

her face just in time, and got a *whack* into her cheekbone instead of a broken nose. She stumbled back against the sinks as all four girls came at her. Two of them grabbed her hair and she cried out as she was pulled forward. She fell to her knees and the blonde, she was pretty sure it was the blonde, slammed a kick into her ribs. The breath left her body. They were all around her, cursing her, kicking her, not letting her get up.

The blonde kicked again and Valkyrie blocked it, held it, and with her other hand she scooped the blonde's supporting leg from under her. The blonde screeched as she fell, taking one of her friends with her. Valkyrie reared back, driving the point of her elbow into the muscle of another girl's thigh. The fourth girl, now temporarily alone, stood back as Valkyrie got up. Valkyrie punched her, hard, across the jaw, and she went down.

Valkyrie held her ribs, struggling to breathe. Kicks like that would have been easily absorbed by Ghastly's clothes if she'd been wearing them – but she *wasn't* wearing them. She was in a nightclub toilet, fighting in a dress that was too damn short.

The girl Valkyrie had hit in the thigh flung herself at her. Valkyrie deflected the fingernails that were aimed at her face and gave her a shove, and the girl's head cracked into the wall.

The blonde and her one remaining friend were on their feet

now. Valkyrie ducked under a swipe and her fist sank into the friend's soft belly. She wrapped an arm around the girl's waist and flipped her over her hip. The blonde was struck by her mate's flailing legs, and staggered back against the closed door of a cubicle.

Valkyrie faced the blonde, surrounded by the sobbing, groaning forms of her other attackers. She slipped off her right shoe. Fury distorting her face, the blonde launched herself forward, and Valkyrie's bare foot hit her square in the chest and drove her back. The cubicle door crashed open, the blonde landing on the terrified girl within.

"Sorry," Valkyrie called. She put her shoe back on and grimaced as pain shot through her ribs. The light flickered weirdly and threw shadows across the walls. She turned to go, and was just leaving when she heard one of the girls gagging. She stopped. If anything she'd done resulted in serious injury for anyone in the bathroom, as detestable as they may be, she knew she wouldn't be able to sleep for a month. So she turned, walked back in, and froze. All four girls she'd fought, plus the other girl who'd been in the cubicle, were now standing, and they looked at her and smiled with black lips.

"No," Valkyrie whispered.

"You can't get away," the blonde said. Black veins spread

over her face. Valkyrie had seen that happen before, back when Kenspeckle had been possessed, back when he'd tortured Tanith.

"We're all out of that little room," the blonde continued. "Every single one of us. And one of us has seen the future. We know you're going to kill the world, Darquesse."

Valkyrie paled. "That's a lie. That's wrong. That isn't the future any more. I changed it."

"Then we're going to change it back. We're not here to fight you. We're here to join you. We want to help."

"Don't come any closer."

"You're frightened. You're confused. We understand. That's why we're here. We're here to guide you and to serve you. We love you, Darquesse."

Valkyrie spun and bolted.

She ran for the first set of stairs, barging through a crowd of the young and the beautiful. Someone screamed, and then someone else screamed, and Valkyrie looked up to see a cloud of black streaming down over the bar. Remnants, hundreds of them, diving at the people as they panicked below. She watched the shadow creatures crawl up to screaming mouths, impervious to the desperate attempts to keep them out. Throats bulged as the creatures forced their way inside.

Valkyrie looked around for Fletcher, saw him across the room, shouting for her. The crowd surged, knocked him over, and he was lost to sight. She forgot about the stairs and ran for the edge of the terrace. She vaulted over the railing and fell, the Remnants swirling all around her as they attacked the people on the dance floor beneath.

She used the air to slow her descent, but still landed heavily on top of a young couple who were trying to get away. All three of them collapsed, and immediately half a dozen Remnants attached themselves to the young man's back and shoulders. Valkyrie had to leave the girl to scream as her boyfriend was taken over, and then the music was cut off and all she could hear was screaming.

She ran past terrified dancers, avoiding the grabs of those the Remnants had already overcome. She dodged into a Staff Only area and ran the length of it, out through the open door, finding herself at the rear of the club. Seawater sprayed over the edge of the concrete barriers, making the ground dark and wet. Valkyrie took out her phone to call Skulduggery, and saw she had three missed calls from him. She heard footsteps and looked up. A Guard was hurrying over.

"What's going on in there?" he asked. "What's happening?"

"There's a fight," Valkyrie said, struggling to think of something. "I wouldn't go in there if I were you."

The cop didn't answer; he just slapped the phone from her hand and charged, and they hit the low wall and tumbled over into the cold, heaving water.

There was a moment of shock that Valkyrie pushed back as quickly as she could, and then she swam for the slipway. The Guard rose up from beneath her and pulled her down. They grappled in the freezing dark. Her fingernails raked across his face and he let go. She broke free and swam. The cop was right behind her. She changed course, forgetting about the slipway now and just swimming back to the wall.

She gripped the water and it churned, lifting her from its depths, throwing her to the barrier. She crashed against it and held on, gasping, then threw a leg over and fell to the road on the other side. She'd lost her shoes somewhere in the sea.

There was water in her ears, so she didn't hear the cop behind her until his arms encircled her waist. He threw her into the side of a parked van and she fell. He grabbed her ankles and hauled her back. She cried out, her dress bunched up and her shoes gone and her wet hair in her eyes. The cop dragged her some more and laughed.

Valkyrie swept her hand behind her, and a gust of wind hit

the cop hard enough to make him release her. She got up as he pulled a long baton from a deep pocket and grinned at her. A sliver of streetlight caught the side of his face – Valkyrie could see the dark veins beneath his pale skin.

She snapped her palm against the air. The space shimmered, but the cop was already moving, dodging the strike. She clicked her fingers in his face and a flame flared. He cursed and staggered back, hands at his eyes. She kicked him square between the legs and he buckled, but he blocked the knee that came for his face and lunged at her. Valkyrie sidestepped and he went past, tripping over her foot. His face hit the side of the van with a sickening *thud*. He lurched unsteadily to his feet. She kicked his leg, deadening the muscle. He toppled sideways against the van, blood streaming from his shattered nose. She clicked her fingers and hurled a fireball. It hit his arm. He howled and dropped the baton, and she kicked it away.

"No way," said a disbelieving voice behind her, and she turned, snarling at whoever it was who dared interrupt. Then she froze.

"Stephanie," her cousin Carol said in astonishment, "why are you beating up that policeman?"

33

THE TWINS

The cop seized the opportunity offered by Valkyrie's distraction, and dived on her. She fell back, his hands on her throat, his face twisted.

"Let go of her!" Crystal roared, trying to drag him off.

Carol started whacking her handbag into his head. When that had no effect, she tried clawing his eyes out. The cop cursed, but didn't take his hands from Valkyrie, and then Fletcher was there, barging between Carol and Crystal. He wrapped an arm around the cop's throat, and all three of them managed to haul him away. Carol and Crystal let go, and Fletcher and the cop vanished.

The twins stared.

"*Whu?*" said Carol.

Fletcher arrived back, without the cop. "They're everywhere," he said. "The entire club..."

Managing to get her breathing under control, Valkyrie listened. "No more screams," she said. "Oh my God, they got everyone."

"Where did you go?" Crystal asked Fletcher.

Valkyrie picked her phone up off the ground. "Everyone hold hands. Fletcher, the pier beside my house. Go."

They teleported to the pier, just four miles up the coast. Carol and Crystal staggered away from them, eyes wide at their new surroundings, and in unison, they doubled over and threw up on their own shoes.

"What's happening?" Carol wailed.

"You're safe now," said Fletcher.

"We were outside Shenanigans!" Crystal screeched. "How are we here?"

"I teleported you," he said, doing his best to sound reassuring.

Carol blinked. "Like in *Star Trek?*"

"Exactly like in *Star Trek,*" he smiled, "without the machines."

Carol swung her gaze to Valkyrie. "And you. You. You set fire to that Guard. You set fire to a policeman!"

"No," Crystal said. "She *threw* fire. Stephanie, you *threw* fire at him. And then you pushed him away, but you didn't even *touch* him. How did you do that?"

"It's complicated," Valkyrie said, suddenly feeling very wet and very cold.

Crystal stepped back, wary. "Are you a mutant?"

"I'm sorry?"

Carol's eyes widened. "Do you have super powers?"

"No, I don't. It wasn't super powers, it was... well, magic."

Carol laughed suddenly, and a little crazily. "You expect us to believe that?"

"You'd be willing to believe that Valkyrie is a super-powered mutant," Fletcher said, "but not that she's magic?"

"Who's Valkyrie?" Crystal asked.

"I am," Valkyrie answered. "It's like a code name, or something. You can still call me Stephanie, though. In fact, I'd really rather you still called me Stephanie. I'll answer your questions in a second, OK? I have to make a call."

She turned away, and speed-dialled Skulduggery. "Remnants," she said when he answered.

"I know," he said. "What happened?"

"They came after me in the nightclub. Hundreds of them. They've taken over everyone inside."

"Are you OK?"

"Yeah," she said. "I'm sore, and freezing, but we got out."

"Get to Kenspeckle's. Ghastly's already there."

"We have to warn the others."

Skulduggery hesitated. "You let me worry about that."

"What do you mean? They're all in danger."

"For all we know, the Remnants have already got to them. Valkyrie, I'll check it out. I'll do my best to gauge if they're still who they are, but you have got to get *yourself* to safety."

"What about my parents? If the Remnants possess someone who knows where I live..."

"Your reflection isn't alive – they can't possess it. Tell it to alert you if anything happens. That's the best you can do."

"I don't like this..."

"Just get to Kenspeckle. He's already locking down the building. You and Fletcher stay there with Ghastly and wait for me. Do not answer your phone to anyone. Understand?"

"Yes."

"Be careful. I'll see you soon."

He hung up.

"OK," Carol said. "Just what is going on? Explain it to us.

Right now. Or we will... We will tell our parents. And they'll tell your parents, and you'll be in serious trouble."

"Don't tell your parents," Valkyrie said, her eyes narrowing. She forced herself to be nice. "Guys, we don't have a lot of time here, but you know all those things Uncle Gordon wrote about?"

"In his books?" asked Carol. "We were never allowed to read his books. Mum said there were dirty bits."

"I read them," Crystal said, somewhat meekly.

Carol looked astonished. "When did you read a book?"

"I read a few of them," Crystal said defensively. "They're all about magicians and wizards and monsters. There are some dirty bits, but they're not that bad."

"It's all true," Valkyrie interrupted, "except they're not called magicians and wizards, they're called sorcerers and mages. Everything Gordon wrote about was true."

"Even the dirty bits?" Crystal asked.

"Well... maybe not the dirty bits."

Carol put her hands on her hips. "How did *you* become magic?"

"Some people are born with magic inside them. All it takes is the proper training to let it come out."

"We're your cousins," Carol said. "Are we magic? Does it run in the family? Is there a test we can take to find out?"

"There's no actual test," Valkyrie said slowly, desperately searching for a believable lie, "but the fact is, you're not tall enough to be magic."

Crystal looked disappointed. "Really?"

"That's true," Fletcher said. "There is a height requirement, and you guys are just a little under it."

"We could wear higher heels," Crystal tried.

"Not going to work," he said with a sad shake of his head.

"That man," Carol said. "The thin man at Gordon's will reading, with the ridiculous name. He's involved in this, isn't he?"

"Skulduggery Pleasant," Valkyrie nodded. "And yes, he is."

"I knew there was something wrong about him. I knew it the moment Mum said there was something wrong about him. I'm a very good judge of character. So, OK, you're witches and wizards and whatever else..."

"Sorcerers," Valkyrie insisted.

"...but why were you fighting with the cop?" Carol continued. "What's that all about? And what was going on in there? The bouncers said it was full, so we were trying to sneak round the back, and then we heard all this screaming."

"The cop wasn't a cop. He was a Remnant – like an evil ghost. They crawl inside your mouth and absorb your

330

personality and possess you. If you don't get rid of them within four days, they're inside you forever."

"Gross," Carol muttered.

"Listen, I have to dry off and get changed. Fletcher can fill you in on everything else while I'm gone, and then we'll take you home. Fletcher, my room."

"Wait," Carol said, "you're going to leave us here alone?"

"Two seconds," Fletcher smiled. He took Valkyrie's hand, and they appeared in her bedroom.

"Keep them calm," she told him. He nodded, and vanished. She crept to the bathroom, stripped off her clothes and jumped in under the hot shower. She hugged herself until the goose pimples went away, then got out and found a towel. She scooped up her wet clothes and hurried across the landing, just as her mother reached the top of the stairs.

"You're back early, I see."

Valkyrie forced a smile on to her face. "Yep."

"I didn't hear you come in."

"I'm ninja quiet," Valkyrie nodded. "Just got home there now."

"Did you have a good time?"

"It was OK. The music was rubbish and the people were annoying. Apart from that it was fine."

"And did Fletcher enjoy himself?"

"I suppose. I was really tired, though, so I just wanted to go to bed."

"Do you think you'll be seeing him again?"

"Fletcher? Yes. He's great, actually. He just *seems* stupid."

"Well, I thought he was lovely," her mum said, then frowned. "Are your clothes wet?"

"I left the shower door open," Valkyrie replied, as sheepishly as she could.

Her mother rolled her eyes, then kissed her cheek. "Goodnight, sweetheart."

"Night, Mum."

Valkyrie went to her room and closed the door quietly behind her. She touched the mirror and her reflection blinked, and stepped out.

"Let me know," Valkyrie said, "the moment anything goes wrong. Now get into bed." She took out her black clothes and began to dress.

"What are you going to do?" the reflection asked.

Valkyrie looked around. "I told you to get into bed."

"I will," the reflection said. "But you need someone to talk to."

Valkyrie laughed. "You? I'd be better off talking to *myself*."

"The Remnants know you're Darquesse."

"None of that's going to happen any more. Why are you asking questions? Every time you're activated you have all of my thoughts and memories. You know everything I know."

"Actually, I know more."

Valkyrie narrowed her eyes. "What?"

"I know the things that you don't want to face. The Remnants know that you are Darquesse, so that means they have a Sensitive. It makes sense that they'd take over one, if not both, of the most powerful Sensitives in the country."

"Finbar Wrong," Valkyrie said, "or Cassandra Pharos."

"And if they have control over one or both of *them*, who else do they have control over? China, maybe? Tanith? Fletcher?"

"What are you talking about? Fletcher helped me escape just five minutes ago."

"And in the four minutes since he's been out of your sight, anything could have happened."

Valkyrie wanted to tell the reflection to shut up, but it was speaking the truth and she knew it.

"You can't trust your friends," the reflection said.

"I can trust Skulduggery. Remnants can't inhabit anything dead."

"And yet you *don't* trust Skulduggery," the reflection said casually. "If you did, you would have told him that you were Darquesse months ago."

"You *know* why I didn't tell him that," Valkyrie said angrily.

"Yes I do, but you don't."

"I'm getting kind of sick of this snarky new attitude of yours."

"You were telling yourself that you didn't want Skulduggery to look at you any differently, but that's not the reason at all."

"That's enough," Valkyrie growled. "Just go to sleep, would you?"

"The reason you didn't tell him..."

"I said, *go to sleep.*"

"Is because you're scared of him."

Valkyrie laughed. "I'm scared of him? That's it? That's your big insight? I'm not scared of Skulduggery, you idiot."

"You were afraid of what he'd do to you if he found out. When you were strapped to that table and you hallucinated, when you saw him take out his gun to shoot you... *That's* what you're afraid of."

"He would never hurt me," said Valkyrie.

"You don't believe that."

"Actually, yes, I do."

"Actually, no, you don't. Ask yourself, what if the visions don't stop?"

"What?"

"If the Sensitives keep having visions of Darquesse – if sealing your name didn't change the future. What do you think Skulduggery will do if you're still a threat?"

"Shut your mouth," Valkyrie snarled, "and go to sleep."

"Of course," the reflection said, and did what it was told.

Valkyrie fumed as she pulled on her jacket over her T-shirt. She called Fletcher's phone. "I'm ready," she said when he answered.

In the three seconds in which she waited for him to teleport over, she was seized by a panic. Maybe the Remnants *had* got to him. Maybe he was going to teleport her right into the clutches of her enemy. Fletcher appeared in front of her, and held out his hand.

She hesitated.

"How are the twins?" she asked.

"I think I've managed to calm them down."

Valkyrie took his hand with her left hand, leaving her right hand free to fight if she needed to. Her heart pounded, and then they were outside again, by the pier – *not* surrounded by Remnants. She did her best not to make her sigh of relief too audible.

"Carol's having a panic attack," Crystal said, jerking a thumb at her sister, who was walking in circles and hyperventilating.

"I just got her to stop that," Fletcher muttered, and hurried over to her.

"Is he your boyfriend?" Crystal asked, once he was out of earshot.

"He is," Valkyrie answered.

"He's older than you, though. He might prefer someone like me. I'm closer to his age."

"Yeah, no. Don't see that happening."

"Does he have a brother?"

"Nope."

"He's gorgeous."

"He thinks so."

"His hair is amazing."

"It defies both gravity and reason."

"Where did you meet him?"

"I helped save his life."

"Oh," Crystal said, nodding like suddenly the whole thing made sense. "So he's your boyfriend out of gratitude."

Valkyrie sighed.

34

REMNANTS UNLEASHED

Eamon Campbell was a hail, rain, sleet or snow kind of milkman. He took his job seriously, applying the same level of dedication to his work as his father had, and *his* father before him. There once was a time when Eamon had hoped that the tradition might carry on after he was gone, but unless his son lost his enthusiasm for accounting sometime soon, Eamon feared the days of the Campbell milkmen were drawing to a close. Eamon had no time for accounting. It was all numbers and digits and complicated pieces of paper. He didn't like it and he didn't trust it.

He liked milk, though. Milk was simple. The best things in life, Eamon had often thought, were simple. His job. His wife. The best things.

He didn't mind the early starts. In fact, he liked being up before anyone else, working in the dark, bringing the milk to people's doorsteps. He was the last of a dying breed, as he was fond of telling anyone who'd listen. These days, everyone got their milk in great big shops. Where was the personal touch? he often asked. Where was the effort?

Eamon slowed his milk truck, careful on the icy roads. A lot of people were complaining about the weather. Eamon wasn't. He was used to it. When you started work at three o'clock in the morning, you could get used to anything. He turned off the radio, tutting at reports of fights breaking out in a nightclub. Things were a lot different when *he'd* been young, and no mistake.

He got out, opened the side panel of the truck, gathered three cartons in his hands, and left them at the doorstop of Number 11. Number 12 bought their milk in a supermarket, so all he gave them was a scowl. He left two cartons at Number 13, and the same at Number 14. He missed the clink of milk bottles as he worked. Some of his fondest childhood memories were of the clink of milk bottles in his father's big hands.

He saw the jogger heading his way, keeping to the grass verge along the pavements, and muttered under his breath. The jogger had appeared a few months ago, passing Eamon at the same time every morning, giving him a nod and a smile as he went by. He wore reflective armbands and belts and flashing lights on his wrists. He looked ridiculous, but that wasn't why Eamon hated him. Eamon hated him for the simple reason that he had stolen Eamon's alone time.

This time of the morning, from 3 am to 5:30 am, was Eamon's. He was the only one up, the only one awake, the only one active. And then this eejit, lit up like a lanky Christmas tree, started interrupting his routine. A nod and a smile. Eamon didn't want *anyone* nodding and smiling to him, especially not some bloody gobsheen they could probably see from space.

Eamon's reaction was to simply ignore the man. For the first few weeks, this worked fine. The jogger jogged by, nodded and smiled, and Eamon looked down at his milk, or looked up at the stars, or looked across at a hedge. The jogger must have realised he was being ignored, because he started to run as near to Eamon as he could, and when that didn't work, he added a wave to his repertoire, and then a "Howyeh". It was getting harder and harder to ignore him, but Eamon was determined that this blow-in would not beat him.

Eamon filled his arms with milk cartons and glanced up, noting that the jogger wasn't doing his usual prancing gazelle run. He was sprinting. Eamon could understand sprinting. You ran fast because you had somewhere to get to. He didn't understand this jogging lark. It was a run, only slower, so obviously you were in no hurry to get where you were going. So why not walk?

Still muttering to himself, Eamon crossed the road, heading for Number 9. He happened to glance at the jogger again, whose quick feet crunched over the frost-covered grass. Sprinting. Not like a gazelle, but like a lion. Like a lion, closing in on its prey.

The jogger left the grass and ran on to the road. He ran straight into Eamon and took him off his feet. The cartons flew through the cold air, hitting the ground and bursting. Spilt milk. Eamon almost cried.

"What do you think you're doing?" he yelled, shoving the jogger off him. "You could have killed me!"

He picked himself up off the road, fuming. The jogger

was already on his feet. There was something wrong with his face.

The jogger's hands closed around Eamon's throat, tightening to a choke that instantly made the blood pound in Eamon's head. He squawked and slipped backwards, taking the jogger with him. They slipped and slid, but the choke stayed on, the grip impossibly strong. The jogger's face was mottled with dark veins and his lips were black.

"I never liked you, old man," the jogger said with a grin.

Eamon hit the side of his truck and felt around for a weapon. Smashing a milk bottle into his attacker's head would have stopped him. Smashing a milk *carton* wasn't going to have the same effect.

Eamon pushed back, propping himself against the truck to gain whatever purchase he could. The jogger's running shoes, the heels of which flashed with pretty lights, slipped on the ice, and once Eamon had a bit of momentum going, he piled on the pressure, steering his attacker towards the puddle of milk. The jogger's legs went from under him, and the choke was lost. The jogger hit the ground and Eamon reeled back, gasping for breath. The jogger laughed, and opened his mouth wide.

Eamon watched as a black shadow pulled itself out of the

jogger's mouth and flitted through the air, to the door of Number 9. It opened the letter box and disappeared through.

Eamon stared. Never, in all his years' delivering milk, had he seen anything like *that* before.

He looked back at the jogger, who seemed to have fallen asleep. He lay there, all those stupid lights still flashing, the dark veins gone, no more a threat to Eamon than a baby duck. But that thing, the shadow thing, was in Number 9, and Eamon had a responsibility to help the people he delivered milk to. He started across the road, hands balled into fists.

Before he was halfway over, the hall light turned on, and a moment later, the door to Number 9 opened. A bare-footed girl, maybe twenty-five years old, stood there in her pyjamas. Eamon took off his hat, and was about to speak when the girl bolted out of her house, straight at him.

He had time to see those same dark veins on her face as he turned to run, but she leaped on to his back. He tried to throw her off, but she was strong, stronger than him, and she nothing but a slip of a girl. She laughed as he struggled, her hands gripping his head, so tight he felt his skull might burst. He knew if he fell, he was finished. He had to stay on his feet. So long as he stayed on his feet, he had a chance of dislodging her and getting out of there.

He stepped into the puddle of milk beside the unconscious jogger and slid on the wet ice. Eamon fell to the road, the girl laughing all the way down.

35

SCRUTINOUS

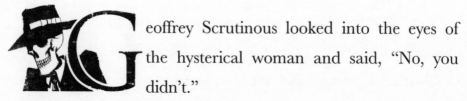eoffrey Scrutinous looked into the eyes of the hysterical woman and said, "No, you didn't."

She grabbed his arm, tears running down her face. "I did, I swear! I know it sounds insane, but I saw these... these *things*, these *shadow things*, climb inside people's *mouths*!"

"You didn't see that," Scrutinous said, speaking calmly and maintaining eye contact. His hair was especially wild and frizzy tonight, but he was hoping she'd ignore that and keep looking into his eyes. "And you're not panicking right now. You're feeling much calmer."

She nodded, and took a deep breath. "I am, actually. But I still saw—"

"You saw people turn violent," Scrutinous interrupted, "and then you got out of there. That was quite shocking to see, wasn't it?"

"Oh, it was."

"You're glad you left when you did."

"You have no idea how glad I am," she told him.

"You're going to go home now, get into bed, and in the morning you won't remember any of the bad stuff that happened tonight."

She released his arm and gave him a shaky smile. "I really have to go. Thank you for your help, but I..."

"Not at all, not at all. Safe home now."

The woman smiled, pulled her coat tighter around her, and hurried away. Immediately, Scrutinous started walking for his car. He pulled out his phone and dialled.

"This is bad," Philomena Random said upon answering the call.

"It sounds like Remnants," Scrutinous said. "Break it off.

We're not going to be able to contain this and it's too dangerous out here. Get back to the Great Chamber. I'll meet you there."

He hung up and heard a cry. Cursing under his breath, he moved to the corner and peeked around, as a fat man threw a Guard against a shop window. The window cracked and the cop rebounded off. He was battered and bloody, and could barely stand.

"I hate people," the fat man told him. "Bags of meat, that's all you are. Disgusting bags of meat."

Not for the first time, Scrutinous really wished his chosen Adept discipline had been combat-based – then situations like these would not be as daunting as they were now. The plain fact of the matter was, he hated violence, he always had, but that was mainly because he was so rubbish at it.

The cop did his best to throw a punch. It hit the fat man, but failed to do any damage.

"Look at what I'm wearing," the fat man said, and hit him back. The cop folded, gasping. "It smells. Can you smell it? It stinks. You stink. You all stink."

But what was Scrutinous going to do? Stand here at this corner and watch a Remnant kill a mortal – just because he didn't want to get into a fight? That was against his code, wasn't it? Well, it would have been, if he'd had a code. He really wished that he'd bothered to come up with a code, then situations like this would be much easier to resolve.

The fat man closed one chubby, meaty, sweaty hand around the Guard's throat, and pinned him to the wall. The Guard struggled and kicked, but his face was already turning purple.

Scrutinous scowled, and sprang into action.

"Excuse me?" he said.

The fat man turned his fat head. "What? Who's there?"

Scrutinous peeked out from behind the corner, and gave a little wave. "Uh, me. I'm going, um, I'm going to have to ask you to put down that mortal."

"Is that so?" the fat man sneered.

"I'm... I'm sorry, but I have to insist."

The fat man laughed and tightened his grip on the Guard. Scrutinous took a few quick breaths to get the blood pumping, and then he leaped out and sprinted towards them. But his sandals had no grip, and so he slipped on the icy road and fell, skinning his knee and cracking his elbow.

As he rolled around on the road in pain, the fat man shook his head. "You're rubbish."

"That's just what I was thinking," Scrutinous said through gritted teeth.

The fat man let the now unconscious Guard drop, and walked over. "You're a sorcerer, then? What can you do?"

Scrutinous forced himself up. "I'm a trained fighter," he lied. "Come one step closer and I'll tear out your larynx with my Tiger Paw Technique."

The fat man smirked, and Scrutinous stopped hobbling long enough to fall back into a t'ai chi pose he had seen once. A fat fist crunched into his nose and he reeled, staggering towards a bright light. Was that it? Had that single punch killed him? Was he leaving this world behind, travelling into the Great Unknown? And then he heard the engine, and a car door open, and knew he was stumbling towards a set of headlights.

"More bags of meat?" the fat man said. "Fine with me."

"No meat here," Skulduggery Pleasant said, stepping between Scrutinous and the fat man, "but plenty of bone." He had his gun out, aimed directly at the fat man's head.

The fat man smiled. "You wouldn't shoot."

"No?"

"I'm innocent. I'm mortal."

"The man before me is innocent," Skulduggery said, "and mortal, but the Remnant inside him is twisted and evil. And it has ten seconds to vacate."

"Why bother? I'll just find someone else to possess."

"You do that. Find someone in better shape. You're about to give that man a heart attack."

The fat man looked down at Scrutinous. "You're lucky."

He threw back his head and the Remnant crawled out of his mouth, flying into the air, disappearing in the darkness. The fat man collapsed to the road, unconscious.

Skulduggery helped Scrutinous to his feet. "You OK?"

"I skinned my knee and hurt my elbow."

"Poor you. Get in the car – we have to get to the Great Chamber."

Scrutinous limped to the passenger side as Skulduggery got back behind the wheel. It was a nice car, the Bentley. It moved fast.

"How did it start?" Scrutinous asked.

"I don't know yet," Skulduggery replied. "Shudder, Ravel, Corrival Deuce – they've all been possessed. I'm quarantining the people who I *know* are unaffected until I have a better idea of what we're up against."

Scrutinous looked at him. "They got Deuce? Already? But... why? He's not the most powerful sorcerer around, he's just..."

"He's our Grand Mage. This isn't like the outbreaks we've had before, Geoffrey. This time, the Remnants seem to have a plan."

Scrutinous paled. "If that's the case, then... then one of their first ports of call would be the Great Chamber, to stop us organising the fight back."

Skulduggery nodded. "No one at the Chamber is answering their phone."

"Then why are *we* headed there?"

"Because every single sorcerer in the city will be on their way to help, and that's where they'll be going."

"Into a trap."

Skulduggery looked at him. "Aren't you glad you got out of bed this morning?"

36

QUIET, PLEASE

China's library never closed. No matter what time of the day or night, no matter what season, no matter the weather, the library stayed open. Knowledge did not take holidays, after all, and neither did China. There were no windows in the library – she hated the thought of the sun fading the spines of her books – but the windows of her apartment showed a Dublin that glistened with frost. It was cold and silver out there. It was warm and tastefully lit in her apartment. There were moments when China could not understand why anyone would ever want to go outside.

The man on the radio told her of police being called to a riot in North County Dublin. The man's voice was too thin, too weedy for his chosen profession, but she forced herself to listen as he offered up the few meagre scraps of information he possessed. He mentioned the name of the nightclub, repeated the same eyewitness accounts, and generally got overexcited at the first real piece of news ever to come his way at this hour of the night.

China turned off the radio, then crossed the hall from her apartment and walked through the library, taking into account the shifting stacks that arranged themselves according to necessity.

It was an old trick, showy and gauche, and somewhat misleading. The stacks actually shifted in response to the mood of the room. If the mood was hostile, the books on combat would move to the front; if it was paranoid, the books on secrets and how to keep them would be foremost. It wasn't a sophisticated trick, but China kept it because it reminded her of the library she'd had in her old family home.

She used to get lost in those stacks for hours, surrounded by books on the Faceless Ones. It had been a happy childhood. Completely insane, but happy. When she looked back on it now, she could see what a hollow comfort her faith in the old gods had been. From the day the first cracks in that faith had appeared, it had taken decades for her to break through.

Every disciple of the Faceless Ones knew that if the old gods returned, they would bring hell with them. And yet every single one of them hoped that they would be among the few to be spared, to be elevated to godhood alongside their masters. A ridiculous expectation, but one that was reinforced by centuries of brainwashing.

As intelligent as sorcerers like Serpine and Vengeous were, as intelligent even as Mevolent himself was, they could not break free of a dozen lifetimes worth of conditioning. Bliss had managed it, and China had followed, but it hadn't been easy.

But it *had* been worth it. True, she had generally had more fun in the old days, but at least she was alive, and independent, and she didn't have to spend half her day praying. She'd never liked the praying part. She'd never been able to understand why the Faceless Ones weren't praying to *her*.

She slid a book from its place, catching sight of Flaring in the next aisle over. Flaring was an ideal patron of the library. She didn't talk loudly, she didn't leave books scattered around, and if she did have to borrow a work, she made sure to have it back within a reasonable amount of time. If only every library patron was as satisfactory as Flaring.

China opened the book in her hand, scanning the index, and something caught her eye. She looked back to the gap on the shelf. Flaring was out of sight now, but China knew she had seen a shadow move. She was not one to dismiss *anything* as her imagination playing tricks. China's imagination was a wondrous thing, as every mage's imagination needed to be, but it was also a disciplined, *ordered* thing. It was in many ways like a well-trained pet, and it did not, under any circumstances, *trick* her.

She became aware of a sound from the next aisle. It was Flaring. She sounded like she was retching. And then the sound suddenly stopped.

China was a logical woman, one not prone to jumping to conclusions, but two facts immediately surfaced in her thoughts. The first was that the Necromancers had a Remnant they'd been examining, and the second was a rumour she'd heard, just a few hours earlier, of an argument between Solomon Wreath and his High Priest.

Her mind flowed over the facts and the possibilities, and she replaced the book on the shelf and stepped slowly backwards. There was a Remnant loose. In fact, taking into account the nightclub riot so close to Haggard, there was probably more than one. A lot more.

China turned, walking smoothly and without unnecessary

haste. If she could silently alert the other patrons and evacuate them all, then she could seal the library and trap Flaring, and the Remnant, within. If she couldn't, or if she felt the odds were leaning even slightly out of her favour, she would abandon everyone and seal the library anyway. Skulduggery could be here within minutes, take care of the problem, and the library would reopen without the loss of too much goodwill. A solution elegant in its cold simplicity.

But when she passed Jago Balance, and saw him struggling with a Remnant that was forcing itself down his throat, she knew her solution was no longer feasible.

She stepped back before he turned, taking a different route. She almost jumped when Hidalgo emerged from an aisle in front of her. He had that distracted look in his eye he always did, that seemingly only went away when he saw her. True to form, as soon as his gaze fell upon her, he straightened up and sucked in his belly.

"Hello, China," he said quietly, a happy smile breaking out.

She put a finger to her lips, and he blushed.

"Sorry," he whispered, and hurried down another aisle like a chastised schoolboy. He was acting completely normally. he wasn't acting like he was possessed.

She started down the aisle after him, and froze. His back

was to her, his hands were at his face and he was gagging. Then he straightened up.

China walked on, forcing herself not to break into a panicked and undignified run. The door was close by. All she had to do was reach it and then she was out. Down the steps and into the car. Call Skulduggery as she was driving away. Once she knew she was safe.

But there were people by the door. China could see them through the narrow gaps between the books and the shelves. At least four of them, standing there, not talking. She heard someone behind her, but didn't look round. Instead, she took a book from its place and moved onwards, flicking through the pages as she walked, pretending to read.

The material of her gorgeous skirt was soft and tight. Completely impractical for fighting. The heels of her gorgeous shoes were high and thin. Completely impractical for fleeing. For one dizzying moment, China found herself envying the rather vulgar style of Tanith Low, constantly attired as she was in the clothes of a common brawler – leather and boots and straps and buckles.

Then China came to her senses. All that leather may prove useful once in a while, but class was a gift that gave eternally.

She approached the back wall of the library without

encountering anyone, friend or foe. A secret door there led to a platform, just big enough for one. The platform lowered the passenger to the basement. All very secret, all very private. Nobody knew about it except for China. Well, except for China and her *assistant*...

Who was standing there now, hands clasped before him. She ducked back before he saw her.

This was what she got for trusting someone. Back in her Diablerie days, she'd have killed anyone who knew about her secret escape route. Footsteps behind her and she dodged left, scowling as she did so. Forced to scurry in her own library. She hurried through the stacks and ducked down, and listened to them talking.

"Have you seen China?" her assistant asked quietly.

"Glimpsed her," came the reply. Flaring.

"Think she knows?" asked another voice, a man's this time.

"Possibly," her assistant said. "Do we have everyone?"

"I think so."

"Then there is nothing to be gained from stealth."

China saw movement, and pressed herself back into the shadows.

"China," her assistant called loudly. "We know you know. Why don't you come out?"

"It's really not that bad," called Flaring.

"Be quiet," the assistant said. "Whatever chance we have of her surrendering to me, we have none at all of her surrendering to the likes of *you*." His voice grew louder again. "This is most undignified, I hope you realise. You're hiding, for goodness' sake. China Sorrows is *hiding*. I have to say, cowering does not become you."

No matter how much she wanted to gouge out his eyes at that moment, she was forced to agree with him there.

"We'll find you!" the man shouted. "If you fight us, we'll hurt you!"

"Will you shut up?" the assistant barked. "China, we have known each other for a long time. I have been your faithful assistant for centuries. I don't want to see you scrambling around in the dark, like a scared mouse with the cats closing in. If you're worried about what will happen, please don't be. You don't lose who you are. I am still me. You will still be you. Once the Remnant is inside you, you become *more*, not less."

Moving quietly, China took off her shoes. She closed her eyes. The other reason why she kept the old trick of the moving stacks was far less sentimental than reminding her of her childhood. Sometimes, very occasionally, old tricks became very useful, such as when the library was attuned to *her* moods much more than anyone else's. China told the library what she needed, and the library obeyed.

The stacks moved suddenly, slamming up against the possessed sorcerers, forcing them apart, making them stumble and stagger and cry out in shock. China leaped up and ran, bookcases creating walls on either side of her, forming a straight line to the door. But there was someone in her path. Hidalgo had managed to avoid being shunted aside. He turned and saw her, and started to smile just as the bookcase to his left shot into him, squashing him against the bookcase on his right.

China sprinted by. She plunged out into the corridor and slammed the door shut, tapping the symbol over the lock. The seal wouldn't hold them for long, but it would be enough for her to make her escape.

She turned for the stairs, but two mages were just reaching the top. They smiled when they saw her. She didn't wait to find out if the smiles were genuine, and she didn't bother to warn them of the danger. She ran into her apartment, headed to her bedroom and grabbed the bag she kept for emergencies. She tapped the symbols tattooed onto her legs and felt the energy charge through her muscles.

At a gesture, the window flew open and China vaulted out. The cold hit her, the wind gushed around her, and she fell three storeys to land in a crouch on the pavement. Nobody was around to stare. Headlights approached. She waved, and a taxi braked, skidding slightly on the icy road, and she jumped in the back.

"Drive now," she commanded, "and drive quickly."

The driver laughed, then glanced back at her, and fell in love.

"Drive!" she snapped.

Whimpering, he stomped on the accelerator and the car fishtailed as it leaped forward.

"Watch the road!"

He fixed his eyes ahead.

"Head for the city centre," she said, unzipping her bag. "I'll tell you where exactly we're going once I make a phone call."

She saw his eyes flicker to her in the rear-view mirror. "I love you," he said.

China didn't bother to respond. She took a pair of expensive boots from the bag, put them on the seat beside her, and took out the rest of the clothes. They were dark, tight-fitting, and stylishly practical.

"You don't mind if I get changed back here, do you?" she asked.

She heard him whimper again.

37

ENEMY HANDS

"Philomena," Scrutinous hissed. "Philomena! Get over here!"

Caught sneaking across the quiet street, Philomena Random jerked around, fists clenched, ready to fight. She saw Scrutinous waving frantically and hesitated, then jogged over. The moment she was close enough, Skulduggery stepped out and levelled his gun at Random's face.

Random held up her hands. "Don't shoot. I'm me."

Skulduggery shrugged. "Unfortunately, Phil, if you were possessed, that's exactly what you'd say."

"Don't call me Phil. My name is Philomena."

"If you were possessed, you'd say that, too."

"Geoffrey," Random growled, "tell him to put his gun down. The Remnants didn't get me. I've spent the last half-hour running from cover to cover to get here. I haven't been seen by anyone or anything."

"We'd like to believe you, Philomena," Scrutinous said.

"Ask me then," Random said. "Go on. Use your mojo on me."

"I don't know if it'd work on a Remnant."

"Why wouldn't it? It works on mortals, it works on mages. Why wouldn't it work on a Remnant?"

"Do it," Skulduggery said. The gun in his hand was scarily steady.

Scrutinous looked into Random's eyes. "You're going to tell me the truth," he said.

"Yes, I am," Random answered.

"You're not going to lie to me."

"No, I'm not."

"Who are you?"

"I'm me, you moron."

"No need to be snarky."

"Then get to the point."

"Do you have a Remnant inside you?"

"No, I most certainly do not. Satisfied?"

Scrutinous looked at Skulduggery. "I didn't feel anything odd. I think it's her."

Skulduggery put the gun away. "Philomena, we have reason to believe the Great Chamber is already infested. I think the Remnants are having a race to get to the most powerful vessels they can. This would be one of the first places they'd go."

"So what are we going to do?" Random asked.

"We have to make sure. If we're lucky, the sorcerers inside figured out what's been going on in time, and they've sealed themselves away. If they have, we just have to reach them and get them out of there."

"But you don't think that's what happened?"

"No, I do not – but we have to be sure."

"So we're going in," Scrutinous said.

Random laughed. "No, we're not."

"Yes, we are."

Random's laugh dissolved. "No, we are not. Are you crazy? Skulduggery, you're used to this kind of thing, but Geoffrey and I are in public relations. We don't fight, or shoot guns. We convince mortal witnesses that they didn't see what they actually saw. We can't storm a building that's fallen into enemy hands. We couldn't storm a *closet*."

"You're going to have to learn," Skulduggery said, "because you two are the only way I have of making sure people are who they say they are."

"But it's *scary*," Random whined.

Scrutinous laid a hand on Random's shoulder. "I was in a life or death struggle earlier tonight, Philomena. I was almost killed. But I got through it. Was I injured? Yes. Was it serious? My knee still stings. But I'm alive. I did it. You can too."

Random took a breath. "OK. OK, let's do it. But you're going first."

"Actually," Scrutinous said, "Skulduggery's going first. He's got the gun."

"Well, I'm not going *last*," said Random. "I'll go in the middle."

Scrutinous glowered. "*I'm* going in the middle. I'm injured."

"You skinned your *knee*."

"Skinning your knee is one of the most painful non-lethal injuries there is."

"It's not worse than a paper cut."

"I said *one* of the most painful," Scrutinous pointed out.

"The pair of you," Skulduggery said, "shut up. I'll lead the way. You two can walk side by side behind me. Happy?"

"Not really," said Random, but Skulduggery was already walking across the street. Scrutinous grabbed Random's arm and dragged her across. They followed Skulduggery down the steps and through the iron door. It closed behind them as they passed into the corridor with the carved walls.

"If a Remnant takes control of me," Scrutinous whispered to Random as they crept along, "I... I would rather you kill me than allow me to hurt anyone."

Random looked at him, and nodded solemnly. "You have my word. And if one of those *things* takes control of *me*, I... I want you to leave me alone and let me go about my business."

"You're hysterical," Scrutinous said. "You don't really mean that."

"I am *not* hysterical and yes, I *do* mean that. If I'm possessed, you are not allowed to let *him* shoot me."

"But you'll be evil."

"At least I'll be walking around. Do I have your word?"

"No," said Scrutinous crossly, "you do *not* have my word."

"Fine," Random snapped. "Then you don't have my word either."

A door opened, somewhere beyond the Great Chamber, and they heard shouting, and cries of alarm. Crashes and bangs and the sound of things breaking. A battle being fought.

They hurried to the door ahead, looked into the Chamber just as figures sprinted through. A fireball exploded and the air rippled. It was the ridiculously named Four Elementals, all five of them, and it was three against two. Black veins stood out clearly on the faces of the three attackers. The two defenders backed away.

Skulduggery strode in, Scrutinous and Random hurrying to keep up. "How about we even up the odds in here?" he said, at which point all of the Four Elementals looked around. Skulduggery stopped walking immediately, and said, "Oh, hell."

The two defenders were black-lipped, vein-ridden Remnants too. This wasn't a battle between good and evil, it was more a squabble between siblings.

The Four Elementals pushed at the air as one, and a wave of air hit Scrutinous and Skulduggery and Random, and tossed them back off their feet. Random hit the wall beside the door and dropped to the ground, while Scrutinous and Skulduggery sprawled out into the corridor. Scrutinous looked up, dazed, in time to see a Remnant flit towards Random, and then Skulduggery was pulling him to his feet, and they were running.

There were more shouts and Scrutinous glanced back, saw Shakra joining the Four Elementals as they sprinted in pursuit, saw even more sorcerers emerging behind them. And above them, darting from point to point, Remnants, closing in. Scrutinous piled on the speed, his sandals slapping the hard floor, the beads around his neck leaping up to hit his goatee. Skulduggery was fast, and was already close to the exit. Scrutinous was not.

Something cold latched on to the back of his neck, and slithered around before he could even get his hands up. He stumbled, tried to call for help, but the moment his mouth opened the Remnant slipped inside. Ahead of him, Skulduggery had the door open and was looking back. Scrutinous tried to scream as the black-lipped sorcerers caught up to him and the cold feeling spread down into his throat. When he looked back at the door, Skulduggery was gone.

38

FIGHTING

The early morning sun did nothing to beat back the freezing cold. Few cars ventured out, but Tanith's bike hugged the treacherous roads like it was a warm summer's day. She pulled into a garage where the only other vehicle was an SUV, set the bike down on its kickstand, and took off her helmet. Her hands were numb as she slipped the petrol nozzle into the tank. The gauge on the pump clicked steadily upwards, her own chattering teeth adding to the symphony.

Even though Kenspeckle had healed the injuries sustained

when Tesseract had thrown that *stereo* into her *head* – the very thought of it stirred her anger – the cold was making her face ache. Standing there, freezing, she decided to finally ask Ghastly to make her some warmer clothes. She'd always liked the clothes he'd made Valkyrie, and the fact that they acted like body armour was a bonus she could probably do with. Those kinds of clothes were expensive, though – but she figured if she asked him nicely...

She returned the nozzle to the petrol pump and hurried in to pay. The warmth embraced her the moment she set foot in the door, and she shivered in appreciation.

"Cold out," said the guy behind the counter.

If it had been Valkyrie standing there instead of Tanith, the guy would have been fixed with a withering stare for stating the bloody obvious. As it was, Tanith smiled as she approached.

"It is indeed," she said.

The guy, no more than eighteen, smiled as he brought up what she owed. "Nice bike," he said. His nametag identified him as Ged. "I want to get a bike, but the insurance is way high."

Tanith handed over cash. "Well, they're not the safest way to travel, I have to admit."

He nodded, still smiling. "I like your coat."

"Thank you."

"I like your boots."

He was still smiling. Not in an endearing way, and not, bless his heart, in a flirtatious way. Just smiling. Just standing there smiling, making random comments.

"Thanks," Tanith said again. The door opened behind her and a gust of cold air swept in. "Well, be seeing you."

A middle-aged woman stood between her and the door. She was plump, her hair a little too red to be entirely natural. She wasn't moving, wasn't shivering, wasn't shopping, wasn't looking through her handbag. She was just standing there, looking straight at Tanith, a faint smile on her face.

Ged grabbed Tanith's hair and yanked her backwards, halfway over the counter. The middle-aged woman ran forward, fist plunging into Tanith's belly. The air left Tanith's lungs and she wanted to fold up, but Ged still had her hair. She tried to break his grip, but he was stronger than he looked. The woman hit her again, and again, then leaned in, hands on Tanith's face.

"This won't take a minute," the woman said, and opened her mouth wide. Something stirred within her throat, something black, writhing and wriggling its way up her gullet. Tanith saw eyes, slits of white. She stopped trying to break

Ged's hold, and instead slapped both hands against the woman's ears. The woman sagged, dazed, her mouth closing, forcing the darkness back down inside her. A Remnant. It had to be. The woman took a step back and Tanith kicked her in the face.

Ged growled, and Tanith cried out as she was hauled all the way over the counter. Ged dropped her on the floor on the other side and knelt on her, firing punches. She covered up as best she could, but the punches were getting through and rattling her skull.

In desperation, she heaved herself sideways, letting her legs swing up wildly. She caught him on the shoulder and he grunted. She scrambled up, but he was on her already, forcing her back. Her hip slid along the wall and she twisted, flinging him against a rack of car-cleaning products.

Tanith sprang over the counter, ignoring the middle-aged woman who was trying to get to her feet, going right for the door.

A little boy, aged around eight or nine, stood there.

"Why did you hurt my mammy?" he asked.

Ged charged into her, and they crashed into a row of shelves. The shelves toppled. Jam jars smashed and bags of sugar exploded and a dozen other household goods spilled out across the floor. Tanith rolled on top and rammed her elbow into Ged's grinning mouth. As she hit him, he actually started laughing. She drove her knee up into him and he grunted, and the laugh was reduced to a pained chuckle.

She pushed herself up. The middle-aged woman was on her feet, but shaking her head, like her equilibrium was lost and she was trying to get it back.

"Mammy!" the little boy cried, hurrying to her. He passed Tanith and suddenly swung around, his little fist crunching against her ribs. Sharp pain stabbed through her side, and she doubled over as he hit her again.

The little boy looked at his hands, eyes bright. "This is new," he murmured. He took hold of her, stepped back and launched her across the floor.

"I'm fairly certain that I just broke my little hand," the boy said, sauntering over. "Not that it matters. I'm about to get an upgrade."

Tanith raised herself to her hands and knees, but the little boy lunged, his foot smacking into her cheek. She sprawled on to her back.

"We had a deal, you see," the little boy continued as he stood over her. "The three of us. We all want a sorcerer's body, so we decided that the one who beats you, gets you. They both went for the older and stronger vessels. But me? I had a feeling you wouldn't be too eager to hit a child."

The Remnant made him stronger, but it didn't make him any heavier. She swung her leg into his ankle and he toppled into the magazine rack, which collapsed on top of him. Tanith sprang up. Ged and the woman were closing in.

"You can't kill us," Ged said, blood pouring from his ruined mouth. "These are innocent people we're using."

"Good people," the woman nodded.

"If you give yourself to me," Ged promised, "I promise I'll take good care of you."

"You'll be happier with me," the woman said. "I'm getting used to a female body, and us girls have to stick together, don't we?"

"I don't care if you're good people," Tanith snarled. "Kenspeckle Grouse was a good person, but he still hammered nails through my hands and legs. If either of you takes one more step, I'll hurt you."

Ged and the woman looked at each other, laughed, and came closer.

Tanith took three quick steps and jumped, twisting her hips slightly and snapping out both legs. The toe of her left boot hit Ged's cheek, and the heel of her right boot crunched into the woman's nose. They went sprawling on either side of her as she landed.

She ran out into the cold and hopped on her bike. Pulling on her helmet, she moved the bike off its kickstand and fired up the engine. She looked back to see the boy sprinting after her, screaming in fury as she roared out on to the road.

39

MURIEL

uriel Hubbard came in, left her car keys on the hall table and draped her coat over the banister. She went looking for her husband, found him in the living room on the phone, talking about a riot. Today was his day off, but they still came running to their Chief Superintendent whenever anything bad happened. Her own phone rang, and James looked around, gave her a tight smile. She smiled back and left the room, bringing the phone to her ear.

"Mum." It was Ashley. She was whispering. "I need help."

Muriel adjusted the thermostat in the hall, it was much too warm in the house, and walked into the kitchen. "What's wrong, sweetie?"

"They're after me."

"Who is after you?"

"The others."

"Your friends?"

"They're not my friends."

Muriel brought the kettle to the sink and filled it. "Are you arguing with Imogen again? Sweetie, you know what she's like. Give her a few hours and she'll be all apologies."

"Imogen's dead."

"Oh, don't be so dramatic. You'll forgive her, you always do."

"Mum. Imogen is dead. They killed her."

"Who killed her?" asked Muriel.

"The others. Dan and Aoife and the others." Her daughter's voice shook. "They... they tore her apart."

Muriel nodded. "And why did they do that?"

"I don't bloody know!"

"There's no need to curse, Ashley. We've all had arguments, we've all had fights, we've all torn strips off each other. True friends work it out."

"Mum, you're not listening to me. I don't mean they tore her apart with *words*. They tore her apart with their *hands*. She's not dead to *me*, Mum, she's just *dead*. Are you understanding me now? They physically attacked her and physically *killed* her."

Muriel sighed. "Then why don't you come home?"

"I'm hiding."

"Where?"

"I'm in the playground, in the little hut thing."

"Where the little kids play? You can fit into that?"

"They're looking for me. They want Dad."

Muriel poured boiling water into a cup and dipped a tea bag in. "Why do they want your father?"

"I don't know. They said he has influence."

"Of course he has influence, he's the Garda Superintendent."

Ashley's whisper rose again. "I know who he is, Mum! I'm just telling you what they said! They said they could use him, and they wanted to get to him through me!"

"Oh, right." Muriel took a sip of tea.

"They're here," Ashley said, much quieter.

"Your friends?"

Ashley didn't answer. Muriel took another sip as she waited

for her daughter to speak again. She heard a distant shout, and the sound of movement, the phone being jostled, and then rushing wind in the receiver.

"Mum!" Ashley cried, loud enough so that Muriel had to hold the phone away from her. "Get Dad! They're after me! I'm heading home, but they're right behind me! They're faster!"

Jostling. The rush of wind. Ashley's panicked breathing. Muriel shook her head, and looked up as her husband walked in.

"There's something happening in town," James said, picking up his car keys. "Bunch of people going crazy, apparently. Riots in the streets. Have you seen my coat?"

"I think it's on the bed," Muriel told him. He nodded, went upstairs. "Sorry sweetie," she said into the phone, "what were you saying?"

"Get Dad!" Ashley screamed. The sound of movement abruptly ended with a loud *thud*.

Muriel heard Ashley crying, but she sounded far away, like she'd dropped the phone.

James came back in, his coat on. "Maybe you should stay indoors," he said. "It mightn't be safe out. Where's Ashley?"

"I'm just talking to her now," Muriel said.

He nodded. "Tell her to come home."

"Oh, she won't like that."

"Tell her she can give me one of her teenage tantrums later and I'll sit through the whole thing, I promise. But it's not safe out."

"It's not even safe *in*," Muriel said with a chuckle.

James laughed, then stopped. "I don't get it."

Muriel hit him and he flew back against the kitchen counter and collapsed on to the tiled floor. The first time in thirty-two years of marriage that one of them had raised a hand to the other. Sad, really.

Another voice came over the phone. Low. Mocking. "Is that Ashley's mammy?"

"Hello, Dan," Muriel said. "You're too late, I'm afraid. You should have gone after him through the *wife*, not the daughter." She heard Dan curse, and it made her smile. She opened her mouth wide and the Remnant struggled out. Her body dropped, and it flitted to her husband and climbed down his throat. James's eyes flickered open. He groaned softly as he sat up, really wishing he hadn't hit himself so hard. He reached for the fallen phone as he stood.

"Still there, Dan? Now I'm the one in control of all those nice policemen and women, and you're *what*, exactly? A spotty teenager?"

"No," Dan said defensively. "I have a Plan B."

"Oh, I'd love to hear it."

"Well, first I'm going to kill your daughter here. Then I'm..." James heard other voices, and after a moment Dan came back on. "OK," he said, "apparently, I'm not going to kill your daughter. Aoife got a bit carried away, the little psycho. But I'm still going to have fun. You're the Superintendent? Then I'm going to be the *Taoiseach*."

James laughed. "From spotty teenager to prime minister – not a bad promotion. Providing someone doesn't get there before you. You'd better hurry, Dan. If you keep wasting time like this, all the super-powered sorcerers and the very important mortals will be taken."

Dan didn't answer; he just hung up. James laughed, got to his feet, and stepped over his unconscious wife. Then he left the house, going in to work on his day off.

No rest for the wicked, he thought to himself, and laughed.

40

THE PLAN

The Hibernian Cinema was in lockdown. The doors were barred and the windows covered. Every non-essential wing of the science-magic facility was sealed off. Kenspeckle was taking no chances.

Valkyrie sat in the Medical Bay. She'd been here for hours, had spent the morning inhaling a bowl of steam that Kenspeckle had shoved into her hands. "So you won't catch cold," he'd gruffly said as he busied himself with something else.

Fletcher was beside her, watching the news on TV, and

Tanith and Ghastly were across from them, sitting side by side on one of the beds. China sat in the corner, making phone calls that weren't answered, doing her best to stay away from Clarabelle, who seemed to be fascinated by her. Skulduggery walked in, hat pushed back off his brow, the only sign that he was concerned.

"China?" he asked.

"Nothing," China said. "Everyone's gone straight to panic stations."

"Don't make any more calls," Skulduggery said. "If they haven't answered by now, we can assume they've been compromised. From this moment out, we trust no one."

"How many?" Tanith asked. "If they've all escaped from the Midnight Hotel, and we have to assume they have, how many of them are we talking about?"

"We don't know," Ghastly said. "A thousand. Maybe two. No one's ever been able to accurately count."

"Two thousand Remnants," she breathed. "What do they want? What are they after?"

Valkyrie went pale.

"They're after Darquesse," Skulduggery said, before she could even consider confessing. "That's what they told Valkyrie. One of them must have hijacked a Sensitive and seen that version of the future. Now they have someone to worship."

Tanith frowned. "So you're saying they have a purpose? Remnants have a *purpose*? A reason to *organise*? That's unheard of. That's... bloody terrifying."

"They're all over the news," Fletcher said. "Reports of a riot in the nightclub, disturbances all over the city, and another riot in Galway."

"No," Kenspeckle said, walking in, "the Galway thing wasn't the Remnants. That was me."

Valkyrie frowned. "What?"

He smoothed down his lab coat. "Ever since my experience with the Remnants five months ago, I've been working on a carefully controlled virus. It heightens aggression and anti-social behaviour, lasts a few minutes, and then vanishes, leaving the infected people unconscious, with no memory of what happened. We placed canisters full of this virus around the country where they've lain dormant, until tonight."

Fletcher stared at him. "Why? I mean... for God's sake, *why*?"

"It's our cover story," Skulduggery said. "It gets the civilian population believing that there is a somewhat rational explanation to all this madness, while at the same time scaring them into staying off the streets and locking the doors. Leaving us to operate unhindered."

"I thought we might need it," Kenspeckle nodded. "Granted, I thought it would be a few *decades* before we'd need it, so it's a good thing I work fast."

"But the Professor says it won't hurt anyone," Clarabelle said happily.

"It's a thought virus as much as anything else," he said. "If the infected person is in danger of harming himself or anyone else, he falls asleep ahead of time. I've done what I can to reduce the risk of injury, but the point is the real Remnant attacks will be mixed up with our fake ones, so it'll look like the same outbreak. When we have the real problem solved, and all those dreadful things are locked away, I'll pass the secrets to the antidote to some struggling young doctors who just want to make the world a better place. They'll save us all, be heroes, and whatever wonderful projects they're working on will have ten years' worth of funding overnight. Everyone, as they say, wins."

"Now all we have to do is solve the real problem," Skulduggery said.

Valkyrie put the steaming bowl down. "This happened before," she said. "You told me about it. Years ago, in Kerry."

"Eighteen ninety-two," Skulduggery nodded. "They took over an entire town. A giant Soul Catcher was built in the MacGillycuddy's Reeks to trap them."

"Who reeks?" Fletcher asked.

"It's a mountain range on the other side of the country. And that machine, the Receptacle, is our only chance to stop them."

"OK then," Tanith said, "so we lure the possessed there, turn it on, the Remnants get sucked out of the bodies they're in, and the problem's over."

"As usual," China said, "it's a little more complicated than that. For one thing, we're hardly going to be able to lure them back to the only place in the world where they *know* they can be hurt. They fell for it once, they're not going to fall for it again. And for another thing, I'm fairly certain that nobody knows how to even turn this giant Soul Catcher *on*."

"Nobody alive," Skulduggery agreed. "Gordon Edgley was the only person I knew who had that knowledge."

"I can find it," Valkyrie said, stepping forward. "It'll be in his study. He kept all his research there."

Skulduggery shook his head. "It's far too dangerous."

"Fletcher can teleport me over, I'll find out what we need to know, and we'll be back in three minutes."

"We'll all teleport over," Skulduggery said.

"Uh, I tend to find things quicker when I'm alone."

"This isn't open for discussion."

"China's right, though," Ghastly said. "Activating the Receptacle is one thing, but how are we going to lead the possessed there?"

Skulduggery looked at Fletcher. "How many people do you think you can teleport at one time?"

"Uh," said Fletcher. "Don't know. Ten?"

"You're going to need to teleport a lot more than that. If we lure the possessed into one spot, if we have them all touching, or connected, maybe standing on the same surface, do you think you'd be able to teleport them to Kerry?"

Fletcher stared. "Two thousand people? Two thousand *evil* people?"

"Do you think you could do it?"

"No. Not a chance."

"But it's possible," Skulduggery said. "I saw Cameron Light teleport a ballroom full of people halfway around the world without batting an eyelid."

"Well, that was Cameron Light," said Fletcher. "I've only been doing this a few years. I still haven't a clue what I'm doing half the time. Plus, I've never been to Kerry, and I can't teleport somewhere I've never been."

"First things first. We need to know if we can turn it on. Fletcher, you're going to teleport all eight of us to Gordon's house."

Kenspeckle looked around. "What's this? I'm going too?"

"We have to stay together," said Skulduggery.

"But I don't want to go," Kenspeckle frowned. "I object to the very idea of teleportation."

"Sorry, Professor, I'm really not giving you a choice. We'll only be there a minute."

"I want to teleport!" Clarabelle announced, smiling excitedly. "Will I change my shoes? I have wellington boots with cows on them."

"Your shoes are fine," Skulduggery said. "Everyone step in and link arms. Fletcher?"

Fletcher waited until everyone was linked, and the bright Medical Bay changed instantly into the darkening living room of Gordon Edgley's house.

"Ooh," Kenspeckle murmured, "I don't feel well."

"I'm going to be sick!" Clarabelle laughed.

"Everyone stay here," Valkyrie said. "I'll take a look in his study."

"I'll come with you," said China.

Skulduggery held up his hand. "There's nothing up there

that you can add to your collection, China. Valkyrie will be quicker alone."

China rolled her eyes. "You're all so suspicious of me." But she stayed where she was.

Valkyrie turned on a few lights as she hurried to the stairs. It was late afternoon and already dark. She reached the landing and closed the door of Gordon's study behind her. Moving quickly, she passed through into the hidden room, and pressed her finger to her lips as Gordon's image shimmered up before her.

He raised an eyebrow. "We have company?" he whispered.

"They're downstairs," she whispered back. "Gordon, we have a serious problem. The Remnants are loose, and you're the only one who knows how to activate that big Soul Catcher in the MacGillycuddy's Reeks."

"The Remnants are loose? What, all of them?"

"It seems that way. *Do* you know how to activate it?"

"The Receptacle? Yes, it's fairly straightforward. All you need is the key, and I know where that is. How do you plan to lure them there?"

"We're still working on that. Skulduggery wants Fletcher to teleport them over, but Fletcher says he can't teleport that many people."

"Of course he can. You need to read *Into Thin Air* again. Not only is it one of my best books, full of danger and intrigue, and the winner of the Bram Stoker Award, a Hugo *and* a Nebula, but as research I conducted many interviews with Teleporters. There are quite a few chapters which could help Fletcher reach his potential."

"We don't really have time to read, Gordon."

He shook his head sadly. "That's the problem with the world today – no one takes the time to sit down with a good book."

"Actually, the problem with the world today is that the Remnants are loose and trying to kill everyone."

"I don't know, I still say it's that no one likes to read any more."

"Gordon, I need you to do me a favour."

"Anything."

Valkyrie hesitated. "I need you to talk to Skulduggery and the others."

"Anything but that."

"It's time for you to make your grand return."

"No it's not," said Gordon.

"We need you."

"I can tell you what you need to know, and you can tell

them. Wouldn't that be so much better? That way, you get to save the day."

"I've saved the day plenty, Gordon. We don't have the time to do this our usual way – you know everything we need to know. Why are you afraid?"

"Because I am not *me*, Valkyrie. I am not Gordon, no matter how much I pretend to be. I am little more than a recording."

"You think they'll be disappointed?"

"It's not that, it's... You treat me like you have always treated me, and I appreciate that. But to everyone else, to all my old friends, I will appear... diminished. And my ego, while furious and grand, could not take that kind of attack."

"You won't help us because of your ego?"

"My dear niece, a great portion of who I *am* is ego. Confidence bleeds to arrogance, and arrogance props me up when my limbs are too weak."

"Gordon, you have to do this. You have to make the sacrifice."

"I've never been good with sacrifice. I'm better with small donations."

"I'm pretty sure the Remnants intend to worship me."

He raised an eyebrow. "Really?"

"What if this is how I become Darquesse? What if sealing

my name didn't change *anything*? What if I'm driven to do what I do because I have two thousand insane shadows *telling* me to? I don't want to kill anyone, Gordon. I don't want to hurt my parents. Please. Help us."

Gordon softened. "Very well, Stephanie. Take me to them."

She picked up the Echo Stone in its cradle. "Thank you."

He nodded. She tapped the Stone and his image faded away, and she went downstairs. The others were talking in the living room, arguing over plans and possibilities. They stopped when Valkyrie walked in and watched her place the cradle on the table.

"There's someone I want you to meet," she said, a little nervously. "Before you do, I just want you to know that I didn't like keeping this a secret." She tapped the Stone again, and Gordon appeared.

"Hello," he said.

Eyes widened. Mouths dropped open. Skulduggery remained still.

Gordon quickly continued. "Do not blame Valkyrie for this. I insisted that she not tell any of you that I was... around. She tried to get me, on many occasions, to change my mind, but I was resolute. I suppose I was somewhat embarrassed, or ashamed of my current incarnation. And while I do not pretend to be the man you once knew, I believe that I can be of some assistance in this hour of need. Treat me the same way as you would a book, or similar font of knowledge." Gordon cleared his throat and waited for the rebuke.

"It's about time," Skulduggery said.

Now it was Gordon's turn to look surprised. "You knew?"

"Of course."

Valkyrie frowned. "You knew? How could you know?"

"Whenever we needed to find information that only Gordon would have," Skulduggery said, "you'd come here, alone, take a few minutes, and arrive back with precisely the answer we were looking for."

"So you never believed me when I told you I'd been researching?"

"No."

"You thought I was *cheating*?"

"You *were* cheating."

"But you *thought* I was cheating! That's *worse* than me cheating, the fact that you *doubted* me!"

"Your logic is astoundingly confusing."

"Why didn't you say anything?" Gordon asked.

"If I was right," Skulduggery said, "and if Gordon had copied his consciousness on to an Echo Stone, I imagined that

392

version of Gordon would be a tad sensitive about his situation. When you were ready to tell me, you'd tell me. I was prepared to wait. It's good to see you, old friend."

Gordon blinked. "I... yes. It's, it's very good to see you too."

Ghastly smiled from across the room. "Welcome back. I'd shake your hand if I could."

"Ghastly, it truly is wonderful to see you," Gordon responded. "I heard you were a statue for a time. You're looking much better. And China... you're even more beautiful than ever."

China's own smile was warm. "Hello, my darling dear."

Tanith made her way forward. She licked her lips, and when she spoke, her voice shook. "I am," she said, "such a big fan."

"Oh," Gordon responded, obviously delighted. "Thank you."

"I have read all your books. All of them. *And The Darkness Rained Upon Them* was brilliant. It's probably my favourite, after *The Coward Colonel Fleece* and *Brain Muncher*."

"Fleece has always been my best character. You must be Tanith, then. Valkyrie has told me so much about you, but I'd heard tales of your exploits even when I was alive. Did you know that one of my short stories is based on a tale I heard about you?"

Tanith's smile grew so wide Valkyrie thought she might swallow her own head.

"Enough fawning," Kenspeckle said. Tanith nodded self-consciously and stepped back. "Gordon, it's good to see you, but we don't have time for idle chatter."

"We were talking about my work," Gordon replied. "There is nothing idle about that."

Kenspeckle sighed. "Nevertheless, can we move on to something that could help our situation? The more time we spend discussing how brilliant, or otherwise, your books may be, the more people get hurt."

"Of course," Gordon said. "So long as we all agree that my books are indeed brilliant."

"Fine," Kenspeckle growled. "Now can we talk about something that matters?"

"By all means. Valkyrie told me your plan, and of Fletcher's uncertainty. I spent four weeks interviewing Teleporters, and I am positive that I can impart what I learned quickly and easily. Uh, hello."

Clarabelle had walked up while he had been speaking, and now she stood in front of him with a faintly quizzical look on her face. She chewed lightly on her lower lip, like she was trying to solve a particularly difficult equation, and slowly bent forward, so that her head passed through Gordon's chin.

"Ah," said Gordon.

"Oh, for heaven's sake," Kenspeckle muttered. "Clarabelle, stop that."

She straightened up, and started to circle Gordon, examining how real and solid he looked. Gordon, for his part, smiled and did his best to ignore her.

"So you can tell Fletcher how to teleport two thousand people?" Skulduggery asked him.

Gordon nodded. "Oh, yes. It's not a technique, you see. It's a state of mind. It's an idea that must be understood and accepted. I feel certain that if I explain it as it was explained to me, Fletcher will grasp the intricacies and be able to perform what is expected of him before the day is out."

"Perfect. It's a good thing you're still around, Gordon."

Gordon smiled, was about to say something modest, when two slender fingers emerged from his forehead and wriggled about.

"Clarabelle," Kenspeckle said crossly, "get your hand out of Mr Edgley's head."

Clarabelle withdrew her hand sulkily.

"There is another matter," Skulduggery said. "The Receptacle."

"Yes, of course. Activated by a key that was broken into two pieces and hidden. It's not a key as we know it, in fact; it's just a flat piece of gold, the length and width of your hand. Whatever imperfections there are in the gold, however, activate the machine."

"Do you know where the pieces are?" Skulduggery asked.

"One piece is in Drogheda," Gordon said, "in St Peter's Church. It was attached to Plunkett's case, that's all I know about it. The other piece was hidden in Newgrange, until it was stolen by a man named Burgundy Dalrymple. He lives in the outskirts of Meath."

"Dalrymple," said China. "I've heard of him. He fought for Mevolent during the war. Good with a sword."

"Better than good," Gordon said. "A master swordsman, he was. When the war ended and his side lost, he adjusted better than most, and he did OK, all things considered. But he was one of the people possessed the last time the Remnants were loose. The Remnant was torn out of him at MacGillycuddy's Reeks, along with all the others, but Dalrymple... Dalrymple had difficulties after that."

"What kind of difficulties?" Skulduggery asked.

"Once a Remnant abandons somebody, and then that person reawakens, they can't remember anything of the experience. But occasionally, they do remember *sensations*. Dalrymple remembers the *sensation* of not being alone, of being part of something greater than he, and he's been trying to recapture that feeling ever since. He's been waiting for the Remnants to return, and he probably stole that half of the key so that when he *is* possessed once again, no one will be able to activate the Receptacle to tear them apart."

"What about the machine itself?" China asked. "Have you seen it?"

Gordon shook his head. "It's in a hidden cavern. I don't know how to find it, and I don't know how to get to it. It's supposed to be amazing though. I spoke with some of the sorcerers who built it and they told me enough to get my imagination working."

"Why didn't they tell you how to find it?" Fletcher asked.

"The Receptacle saved the world," Gordon told him. "It was their last-ditch effort against the Remnants. Once it was used, they vowed to seal it up so no one could tamper with it, or take it apart, or corrupt it. One of them said to me that when you're dealing with magic, you can never trust your enemies to stay beaten, or to stay dead. If we ever had to face those things again, they ensured that at least we'd have a weapon."

"And we have no time to waste," Skulduggery said. "Fletcher, take us back to the Hibernian."

Valkyrie picked up the Echo Stone in its cradle and they all linked arms. In an eye blink, they were back in the Medical Bay.

"That was much better," Clarabelle beamed. "I only threw up a little bit in my mouth."

Skulduggery turned to Gordon. "Are you sure you can teach Fletcher what he needs to learn?"

Gordon smiled, and nodded. "It shouldn't be a problem."

"Then you're going to get started almost immediately," Skulduggery said. "But first, Fletcher is going to teleport Valkyrie and Tanith to Drogheda, to search that church and find the first half of the key. China, you'll accompany me to track down this Dalrymple fellow."

"I love it when you get all commanding," China said, without any significant trace of sarcasm.

"Ghastly," Skulduggery continued, "you're going to drive Fletcher to MacGillycuddy's Reeks. Gordon, I'd like you to accompany them to Kerry, if that's OK with you?"

Gordon blinked a few times, and when he spoke, his voice was oddly strangled. "Of course. Glad to be of assistance."

Valkyrie didn't say anything, but she knew Skulduggery had

just paid Gordon the highest possible compliment – he'd treated him like a real person.

"You'd better hope you can educate this boy in a few hours," Skulduggery said.

"All he needs is to realise the fundamental truth behind teleporting," said Gordon, "and then he'll be able to do what he needs to. Shouldn't be a problem."

"Kenspeckle, I'm afraid we're going to have to use this as our base of operations," Skulduggery said. "When Ghastly and Fletcher reach the MacGillycuddy's Reeks, they'll teleport back to us, we'll lure the possessed here until they're all in one place, and then Fletcher will teleport *everyone* to the Receptacle."

"How are we going to lure them in?" asked Ghastly. "It's chaos out there."

Skulduggery shook his head. "It's not as disorganised as you might think. Look at it this way – the Remnants have been locked away without bodies for years. Their first night out, some of them are going to go a little crazy. But they do have purpose, and that purpose is Darquesse. They're going to start to group together. The Remnants might not have leaders, but their human hosts do. Once we get the leaders chasing us, the others will fall in behind. And the fact is, sooner or later,

Erskine or Shudder *are* going to figure out where we are. They *will* be coming for us."

"Happy happy," Tanith said, "joy joy."

"We're going to need some way to physically connect the possessed," Fletcher said.

"I can do that," said Valkyrie. Everyone looked at her, and she reached out to the shadows in the room, and they rose up like mist around them. "It's one of the training exercises in Necromancy," she said. "When they're this spread out, the shadows can't hurt anyone, but it'd still work as a bond. All Fletcher would have to do is teleport me, and everyone these shadows are touching would come with us."

"That's fine here in this room," China said, "but would you be able to connect all those Remnants?"

Valkyrie hesitated only a moment. "Yes," she said. "I would."

"Excellent," said Skulduggery. "Ghastly, you'd better set off as soon as Fletcher's teleported Valkyrie and Tanith. It should take four or five hours in this weather to get to Kerry, even with the Bentley's tyres."

Ghastly blinked. "You're letting me take the Bentley?"

"It's faster than your van. Just... take good care of her, OK?"

"I will."

Skulduggery went silent. When he spoke again, it was with great reluctance. "Not one scratch."

"OK."

"Not *one*, Bespoke."

"You concentrate on getting the keys. Let me worry about your car."

"I'm multi-talented, I can do both. OK, that's everything. Unless anyone has any other questions, let's get to it."

Fletcher took the Echo Stone from Valkyrie. "Don't get into any trouble while I'm gone," he said to her. "I know you're not going to be able to resist the temptation, but you have to remember that I won't be able to rescue you."

Valkyrie smirked. "I think I can manage without you for a few hours."

He nodded, and leaned in, and they kissed. "Please stay safe," he whispered. His kisses were much nicer than Caelan's. Softer. Sweeter. Warmer. She banished thoughts of Caelan from her mind, and kissed her boyfriend again.

"I will," she whispered back.

They looked around when Ghastly cleared his throat, and watched him touch the tattoos on his collarbones. Clear skin flowed over his scars, and he walked awkwardly up to Tanith. "Um," he said to her. "Don't die."

"OK," Tanith said.

"When this is over," he continued, "I'm going to make you dinner. You don't have to like it, and you don't have to eat it, and I suppose you don't even have to be there, but... But that's what I'm going to do."

Tanith frowned. "Are you asking me on a date?"

"I think so, yes. Will you have dinner with me?"

Tanith smiled the most beautiful smile. "I'd love to," she said. She laid a hand on his chest, tapped her fingers on his collarbones, and the clear skin retracted. Once his scars were revealed, Tanith kissed him, once, on the lips. "I like steak," she said. "Can't go wrong with steak."

"Steak it is," he murmured.

He stepped away, and Valkyrie grinned at Tanith.

"Oh, good God," China said, rolling her eyes. "I do hope the Remnants kill *me* first."

41

THE HEAD IN THE BOX

rogheda town centre was lit up against the dark, but there was no one around to appreciate the Christmas lights. It was far too cold for people to be walking the streets, and the roads were far too icy for driving. Fletcher left Valkyrie and Tanith on the main street, gave Valkyrie a quick kiss, and offered another to Tanith. Valkyrie punched his shoulder and he vanished with a pained expression on his face.

"My eyeballs are cold," Tanith said. "That's not a good sign."

They walked quickly, in an effort to warm themselves up.

"They're saying this is the coldest winter in sixty years," Valkyrie muttered. "I need a woolly hat and mittens."

"Mittens," Tanith echoed wistfully. "Maybe tied to my sleeves..."

"I need earmuffs too," Valkyrie decided. "Fluffy ones. My ears are red, aren't they?"

Tanith took a glance. "Yep. But not as red as your nose. I'm going to ask Ghastly to make me clothes like yours. Then only my hands and face will get frostbite."

"Have you thought, maybe, that the reason you're freezing your bits off is because you don't wear *enough* clothes? How about wearing something under that waistcoat?"

Tanith pulled her coat tighter around her. "My waistcoat is not designed to have anything under it but me, Valkyrie."

"And you wonder why you're cold."

They reached the church. As daunting as it was impressive, its spires stretched into the night sky like spear tips. The doors were locked, but clicked open at Tanith's touch.

With the main lights off, the inside of the church was creepy. They passed a tomb that had a carving of skeletons wearing shrouds. To the left of the massive altar was a shrine, the centrepiece of which was a pedestal that held a glass case ensconced in gold and surrounded by long candles. It was topped off with a brass spire that reached upwards for three metres. Resting inside the case was a mummified head, leathery and brown, with empty eye sockets and tiny yellow teeth. Tanith peered at it.

"Who's this guy?" she asked.

"Oliver Plunkett," Valkyrie told her. "In sixteen hundred and something, he was hanged, drawn and quartered for practising Catholicism in Ireland. By the English, of course."

"Of course," Tanith responded solemnly. "And we're all very sorry about that."

Valkyrie nodded. "As well you should be."

"And why is his head on display in a church?" asked Tanith.

"Where else would you display a head?"

"Doesn't it seem kind of gruesome to you? I mean, *we're* used to seeing stuff like this, but what about ordinary people just coming here to pray, kneeling and muttering and crossing themselves, and they look over and see someone's head in a glass box? That's pretty morbid, not to mention kind of weird."

"Excuse me?" said a voice from behind.

They turned. A priest stood there, paunchy and middle-aged. "I'm Father Reynolds," he continued. "Can I help you with anything?"

Valkyrie held her hands down by her sides, ready to push at the air should she notice even one black vein. "We're just passing through, Mr Reynolds," she assured him.

He stiffened slightly. "That's *Father* Reynolds," he said.

"Oh, I'm sorry," Valkyrie said. "And what's your first name?"

"My full name is Father Declan Reynolds, and you, young lady, have broken into this church."

"Pleased to meet you, Declan," Valkyrie responded, ignoring the accusation. "I'm Valkyrie, this is Tanith. You might be able to help us, actually. We're looking for something. It's a flat piece of gold, about the length of your hand. Would you have seen it?"

The priest frowned at her. "You lost some gold?"

"We didn't lose it," Tanith said. "We're just looking for it. A friend of ours told us it'd be somewhere near the head in the box. We're assuming that he meant *this* head in the box, unless you have another one stashed away somewhere?"

"I may be new to the parish, but as far as I am aware, this is the only head in a box that we have. I'm sorry, if this is a joke, I fail to see how it is funny."

"The flat piece of gold," Valkyrie said. "Have you seen it?"

"I don't know what you're talking about," the priest said,

turning to walk away, "but maybe you can explain yourselves to the Guards when they get here."

If he expected them to protest, or to run after him, he was disappointed. When he'd walked a few steps and they still hadn't reacted, he whirled, to find them examining the box. "Come away from there at once."

Valkyrie ran her hands along the base. "In a second," she said.

"You are not allowed to touch the cabinet!" the priest shouted, storming towards them. Valkyrie's fist caught him just under the chin. He stumbled back, his legs wobbling and his eyes already closing. He slumped to the ground and lay there, unconscious.

"Oh," Valkyrie said. "I thought he was possessed."

"Sure you did," Tanith grinned. She pressed her hand against the golden base of the cabinet and they heard a soft *click*. She pushed, rotated her fingertips, and a flat piece of gold came away, dropping from the base into her palm.

"Damn," she said. "I'm good."

They called Skulduggery to let him know they'd found the first half of the key. He told them to walk to the bus depot and wait for him there.

Up through Drogheda, the streets were frozen and empty. The roads glistened, like someone had carelessly tossed down a hundred thousand tiny crystals. Parked cars were covered in frost, windshields thick with ice. Christmas lights gave it all an unearthly sheen, and somewhere far away a house alarm was going off.

Valkyrie and Tanith crossed the road and kept heading south, towards the bus depot. Valkyrie had her arms crossed, hands jammed under her armpits. Her ears were freezing and her nose was red and running. She stepped on an icy patch and her feet flew out from under her. For the third time in ten minutes, she landed on her backside. Tanith looked back and sighed. Even she had stopped finding that funny.

They crossed the bridge, staying off the pavements, sticking to the road, where it was less slippery. They hadn't heard one single moving car, let alone seen one. The lights at the depot were on, and the buses sat still and silent. They hopped the low wall and Tanith pushed open the glass door. An old woman looked up from where she was sitting.

Valkyrie nodded to her warily, while Tanith went to the ticket booth. It was almost as cold in there as it was outside.

"There's nobody else here," the old woman said. "I tried the office as well. Nobody here at all."

Tanith glanced at Valkyrie, and went to make sure. When she was gone, the old woman looked back to Valkyrie. "Have you been watching the news? Terrible, isn't it? All those sick people."

"It is," said Valkyrie.

"I've been sitting here for hours. I tried calling my son, but I couldn't get through."

"The phones are down."

"Is that what it is? I hope he's all right. I hope he hasn't got sick. He's got children, you know. A ten-year-old and a four-year-old."

"He's probably fine," said Valkyrie.

The old woman did her best to smile. "I just want to get home. It isn't right. This town is never this quiet. Where are all the people? Are they all sick? The man on the news said that the sick people are prone to outbreaks of violence. If everyone is sick, it's not safe here. I just want to go home."

"Us too."

"What's your name, child?"

The old woman didn't look like someone a Remnant would hijack. She was neither young nor strong. She was small, and her hair was white, and even though she was wrapped up against the cold, she looked thin and frail.

"My name's Valkyrie."

"That's an unusual name. French, is it?"

"Uh, Scandinavian, I think."

"It's very pretty."

Tanith came back. "No one here," she said.

"I told you," the old woman responded. "I've been here for three hours, and you two are the first people I've seen. I should just be thankful that you're not like the ones they showed on the news."

"Where do you live?" Valkyrie asked.

"Duleek," the old woman answered. "Do you know it?"

"I've seen signs for it."

"The Duleek bus was supposed to leave at ten past seven, but nothing out there has even moved. I haven't seen any drivers. I don't know how I'm going to get home."

"We're expecting a lift any minute now," Valkyrie said, "maybe we could give you a—"

"Val," Tanith interrupted, glaring at her.

"You're very kind," the old woman smiled, "but it's quite all right."

"We can't leave her here," Valkyrie said to Tanith.

"Why not?" Tanith answered. "Who's going to touch her? She's safer here than she would be with us."

"It's freezing in here."

"So? She has mittens." Tanith turned to the old woman. "Normally, I'd have no problem inviting you along. But for all we know, you might be sick."

"Me?" the old woman said, surprised. "But I'm not running around hurting people."

"No, you're not. But you could be about to start."

The old woman blinked at them, then seemed to shrink back into the layers of clothes she was wearing. "I should probably stay here anyway. My son might be looking for me."

Tanith shrugged at Valkyrie. "See? Problem solved."

Then the lights went out.

"Great," she heard Tanith mutter.

For a few seconds, they were in nothing but blackness. Then Valkyrie's eyes started to adjust, and she could see vague outlines in the gloom. The shape that was Tanith moved to a window.

"The whole town's gone dark," she said. "There's not a light on for miles."

"Maybe they have a torch in the office," said the old woman, sounding scared.

"I have a lighter," Valkyrie said, clicking her fingers. She cupped the flame, disguising the fact that it burned in her palm.

"Oh, that's bright," the old woman said, relieved. "I don't mean to be a burden on you, but is it at all possible to get a lift with you, when your friend comes? I don't really like the idea of staying here alone."

"I'm sure we can work something out," Valkyrie said. She could see Tanith in the flickering light. Her friend did not look pleased. "I'll look for a torch."

Valkyrie moved into the office, searched the two desks and then the shelves. She found a torch and clicked it on. The beam lit up the entire room.

"Found one," she called.

She heard Tanith gag, and fear shot through her. She ran out of the office. The old woman had her thin, frail hands wrapped around Tanith's throat.

Valkyrie gave a roar and the old woman cursed in a language Valkyrie had never heard before. Valkyrie was almost on top of her when the old woman's thin, spindly fist flashed out, almost taking her head off. The torch went spinning across the floor and Valkyrie went down, rolled by pure instinct, got up and didn't know what was happening. Her legs buckled slightly and she staggered, saw the old woman hurling punches down on Tanith.

Valkyrie's palm snapped against the air, and the space rippled as the old woman shot sideways, whooping as she went. Tanith sprawled across the floor, unconscious

The old woman scrambled up. By the light of the torch Valkyrie saw her black lips and vein-ridden face.

"You can't escape," the old woman said. "And why would you want to? You have a glorious destiny."

"It's not destiny," Valkyrie seethed, stepping closer. "Even if it was, I've changed it. It's not happening."

"That's why we're here," the woman explained. "To make sure it does. Darquesse, we were aimless. We were nothing. We were anger and hatred and spite. But now? Now we have purpose. Now we have a future. With you."

"If you want me to lead you, then let's start right now. I have a pair of shackles in my pocket. I want you to put them on."

The old woman smiled and shook her head. "You need to be guided further along the path," she said. "Then you will assume your mantle. Then we'll obey. Right now, you still think you're Valkyrie Cain. You still think you have friends. Like this one." The old woman knelt by Tanith, and stroked her hair. "Let me be your friend. I'll leave this body, this old decrepit thing, and I'll join with her. Such a nice form to take, with that pretty face, with everything so hard, and strong, and firm. All this muscle, and all this leather."

"Stop describing her," Valkyrie said. "It's getting weird."

The old woman lunged, but Tanith raised her arm and tripped her, and the lunge turned to a stumble. Valkyrie slid into her, flipped her to the floor, got behind her and choked. The old woman squirmed like a fish, but Valkyrie held on. She didn't want to hurt her, didn't want to cause the old woman actual harm, she just needed her to go to sleep for a while. She tightened the choke and the old woman weakened, and then her head drooped forward. Valkyrie turned her on her side, and got up.

"Oh my God," Valkyrie said numbly. "We just beat up a pensioner."

"Evil pensioner," Tanith corrected, coughing slightly as she dragged herself to her feet. "What was she babbling about? I heard her say Darquesse."

"Yeah. Yeah, she did. Just, you know, more babbling. Couldn't make sense of half of it. You OK?"

"I'm good. A bit woozy. She has a pretty good right hook, you know. For a granny."

42

THE LESSON BEGINS

"Teleporting one thousand people is not that different from teleporting one person," Gordon said as they sped down the empty motorway. "The effort, the magic, goes into the initial opening of the rift in space. How wide that rift eventually opens is somewhat immaterial."

"What rift?" Fletcher asked.

"Do you actually know how your power works?"

Fletcher couldn't look at Gordon while they were in motion, so he kept his eyes fixed on the windscreen. "Sure. I think about a place I've been, and I go there. I don't open a rift in space or anything."

"Actually, that's precisely what you're doing. Emmett Peregrine told me how he got his head around it, and I think it might help you. Uh, Fletcher, I don't want to sound like a schoolteacher or anything, but could you look at me when I'm talking to you?"

"Sorry," Fletcher said, "I can't. You make me carsick."

Ghastly frowned. "How does Gordon make you carsick?"

"Well, he keeps slipping, you know, out of the car, kind of."

"That's hardly my fault," said Gordon. "Sometimes I don't notice a turn coming up, or Ghastly switches lanes without telling me."

"Sorry about that," said Ghastly.

"It's quite all right. Fletcher, I promise I'll try harder."

Fletcher exhaled, then nodded, and turned around in his seat. "OK," he said. "Carry on."

Gordon smiled gratefully, then the Bentley went over a bump and his face disappeared into the backseat. He had to lean forward to be visible again. The whole thing made Fletcher quite queasy.

"Instead of focusing on the distance travelled," Gordon said, "think of it like this. You're not the one moving."

"I'm not?"

"You're using your power to stay totally still, and the world moves around you until you are exactly where you want to be."

"Uh..."

"It's like me, right now. I'm tethered to the Echo Stone, and the Echo Stone is moving, but *I'm* not. The world is moving around me. And occasionally through me. For you, Fletcher, existence itself rotates and pivots according to your will. I'm sure someone of your self-esteem has no problem with the notion that the universe revolves around him, am I correct?"

"I think that all the time."

Gordon smiled. "I know the feeling well. Emmett used to say that he let the world do the travelling while he stayed in the same place. He focused on where he wanted the world to stop, and that's all he did. He didn't burden himself with thoughts of distance, or how many people he was taking with him, or how big a cargo he was transporting. He saw his destination as a clear point in a whirlwind, and he let it come to him. Do you understand?"

"I... I think so."

"That's good. Understanding is the first step. Acceptance is the second. Once you've accepted this as fact, the possibilities are endless."

43

BY THE SWORD

Burgundy Dalrymple didn't live in a very nice house. It was, in China's opinion, ramshackle to the point of dilapidation. It stood alone, a bungalow on a dead road. Two windows were lit up, and even the light was sickly. The garden was a jungle of weeds and long grasses. To be fair, China couldn't see much of it in the darkness, and for that she was grateful. Squalor held no appeal.

Valkyrie called just as Skulduggery turned off the van's engine. China waited while he spoke to her. They'd obviously succeeded in securing their half of the key. Skulduggery told

Valkyrie to wait for them, and then he activated his façade and nodded to China. They got out, and approached the house.

The front door opened slightly.

"Go away!" said a man's voice from behind it.

Skulduggery and China stopped, and Skulduggery's fake face smiled. "Hello, Burgundy," he said.

"That's not me," said the man. "That's somebody else. Go away."

"Burgundy," Skulduggery said, "we just want to talk to you. One minute of your time, and we'll be gone."

"I'm not Burgundy!"

"You're Burgundy Dalrymple," China said. "Master swordsman and war hero."

The man's laugh came out as something like a bark. "War hero? No one calls me a war hero!"

"Well," China said, stepping out of the shadows so that he could see her face, "I suppose it all depends on which side of the war you were fighting on."

There was a moment of silence, then his voice cracked as he said, "You're China Sorrows."

"I am, and this is Skulduggery Pleasant. We'd like to talk to you about Remnants, if you have the time."

"I... I suppose..."

"May we come in?" Skulduggery asked.

"Well... all right. But I don't allow people to bring in weapons. Are you armed?"

"No."

"Show me. Open your jacket."

Skulduggery hesitated. "Oh," he said, "*armed*. Yes, I am armed. I'm a *little* armed. I just have a gun. In some people's hands that's *barely* a weapon."

"Take it out and leave it there."

Grumbling, Skulduggery did as he was told.

"OK," said the voice, "come in."

They stepped on to the porch. The wood was old and rotten and creaked under their weight. Skulduggery pushed the front door open. The hall which greeted them did so with dim light. The moment he stepped through, his face rippled, and withdrew from his skull. He stopped immediately, and turned to her. "Be careful," he said, his voice soft. "This house has been bound."

China felt it too upon crossing the threshold – the invisible tattoos that graced her body went dull as her magic was dampened.

"In here," the man called.

They walked slowly into the living room. It was

surprisingly big, but barely furnished. There was a dining table in the middle of the room and a few chairs around it. A few lamps. That was it. The walls, however, were decorated with all manner of fencing swords, rapiers and sabres, and unlike their dusty surroundings, these swords looked like they were lovingly kept in perfect working order.

Burgundy Dalrymple stood on the far side of the dining table. He was a little too skinny and he needed a shave and a haircut and, China imagined, a wash.

"I'm Burgundy Dalrymple," he said nervously.

"We need your help," Skulduggery told him. "We know of your history with the Remnants, and we know how much it has affected you and how you live your life."

"OK," Dalrymple said. "Go on."

"We also know that you have tracked down one half of the Receptacle key."

"I'd have tracked them both down by now," Dalrymple nodded, "but people stopped talking to me about ten or fifteen years ago, so no one would answer my, you know, my questions. Why? What do you want?"

"We want your half of the key," China said.

Dalrymple's tone was firm. "No. No. I'm keeping it so that

no one will be able to trap the Remnants ever again. I would have destroyed it already if I'd been able to, but it's pretty durable. Why do you want it?"

Skulduggery tilted his head. "You mean you don't know?"

"If I knew, would I be asking?"

"We need it to turn the machine on, Burgundy. The Remnants are loose."

Dalrymple looked at Skulduggery, and for a long moment he said nothing.

"Where," he said at last, sounding like he needed a drink of water, "where are they?"

"We need the key, Burgundy."

"I thought you wanted to study it, or something. To run tests, to find out how something like that, how it works, but... But you want to *use* the Receptacle? Why would I help you do that? This is what I've been waiting for!"

"I don't want to threaten you in your own home," Skulduggery said, "so if you'd like to step outside, I can threaten you there."

"Outside?" Dalrymple sneered. "Where magic isn't bound? Where you can throw fire at me and take the key from around my charred neck?"

"Ah, so you have it *on* you?"

Dalrymple went to the wall, and grabbed a sword. "You want it? You're welcome to take it."

"It would really be much easier if you just gave it to me."

"Come on!" Dalrymple snarled. "Let's be having you!"

"I'd really rather not," Skulduggery said.

"If you can beat me, you can take the key from my blood-soaked corpse!"

"Again, not entirely appealing."

"Take up your steel!"

Skulduggery sighed, walked to the closest wall and chose a sword with a jewel-encrusted hilt. Dalrymple walked forward, and suddenly lunged. The blades clashed, and Dalrymple began circling.

"We really don't have to do this," Skulduggery said. "I mean you no harm. None at all."

"I mean you *acres* of harm," Dalrymple growled. "Untold *quantities* of harm. I will visit a whole *continent* of harm upon you before we are through."

"You are an odd fellow."

China watched Dalrymple come in with three quick jabs. Skulduggery parried the first two and sidestepped the third, responding with a riposte that Dalrymple blocked easily. They went at it again, blades flashing and singing together.

Dalrymple kept his left hand held high behind him in a classical fencer's stance. Skulduggery kept his free hand low and out in front – far less flashy, far more cautious.

"You're good," Dalrymple said.

"You're too kind," Skulduggery responded.

"I haven't faced anyone half as good as you in a hundred years."

"That's very nice of you to say so."

"Not really. I just haven't *fought* anyone in a hundred years." Dalrymple pressed forward his attack, and Skulduggery retreated, barely keeping the slashing blade at bay. "I'm rusty," Dalrymple continued. "Out of practice. My form is all wrong."

"It looks fine to me."

"It's sloppy." Dalrymple batted Skulduggery's blade down and swiped at his head. Skulduggery jerked away and stumbled. "In my prime that would have taken your head off."

Skulduggery scrambled to his feet. "How embarrassing for you."

"There was a time in my life when swordplay was the only thing that meant anything."

"Everyone needs a hobby."

"But it was an empty time," Dalrymple said, almost sobbed. "A lonely time." Skulduggery moved in, trying to take advantage of the distraction, but couldn't get through Dalrymple's defence. "And then the Remnant came into me, and that loneliness went away." Dalrymple slashed, cutting through the sleeve of Skulduggery's jacket.

Skulduggery backed off. "But you can't remember any of it," he said.

"I don't need to remember details. It was the *feeling*. The feeling of being *whole*. Being *complete*. That's what I remember. That's what I miss. That's what I want back."

"And have you ever tried just making friends?"

Dalrymple snarled again, and stepped in quickly, his blade seeking out Skulduggery, who was doing his best to remain elusive. "You mock me."

"I don't," Skulduggery insisted, on the retreat once more.

"You laugh at me."

"I find it rude to laugh at a man with a sword."

The blades scraped together and Dalrymple flicked his wrist. Skulduggery's sword flew from his grip, and he had to dive to the floor to escape. He rolled and came up, giving himself some room.

"Burgundy," China said, taking a rapier from the wall, "would you mind awfully if I replace Skulduggery for the remainder of this duel?"

Dalrymple looked around, his eyes narrowed. "I'm not going to spare you just because I've fallen in love with you," he warned. "I know about you. I know it's not real love."

"But of course it's real," she said, flourishing the rapier. "All love is real love." She sent out a light jab that he batted away. "Otherwise it's not love, is it? Otherwise it's pointless. A waste of time and energy. And I despise wasting either."

Now it was Skulduggery's turn to watch as Dalrymple came back at China and she blocked, replied with a swipe that *he* blocked, the shrill taps of blade on blade settling into a rhythm as they moved around each other.

"You're trying to confuse me," Dalrymple said.

"I am trying no such thing. The love you're feeling is a real and genuine thing. Just because it is not reciprocated in the slightest does not lessen its worth."

"You don't love me," Dalrymple sneered.

"Isn't that what I just said?"

He neared. "You wouldn't be fighting if you knew what it was like. When your body is a vessel for a Remnant, you don't need tricks to make people fall in love with you. You don't *need* their love."

China backed away, blocking and countering. She stepped up on to a chair, and then she was on the table, and he was following her up, the clashing of their swords only getting faster. It was dangerous up there, not much room to manoeuvre, and Dalrymple's strikes were increasing in strength. China was impressed. Her wrist was already aching.

She saw Skulduggery, out of the corner of her eye, retrieve his sword and walk towards them. "Burgundy," he said, "I am a firm believer in fair fights. I really am. But we did not come here to lose. We came here to get the half of the key that you stole, and we won't be leaving without it. So I'm afraid we must cheat a little."

While Dalrymple parried China's thrust, Skulduggery poked at his leg – and Dalrymple's blade clanged off his.

China blinked, then defended, and Skulduggery tried again to injure Dalrymple. But once again, Dalrymple's sword flashed down, faster than her eye could follow, and he batted Skulduggery's attempt away and then resumed his attack on China. She would have thought it impossible if she had not been there to personally witness it.

"Cheating against you isn't easy," Skulduggery murmured.

Dalrymple jumped down from the far side of the table. China followed him to the floor while Skulduggery moved around. They closed in, their swords cutting towards Dalrymple while he defended with startling alacrity. China went left and Skulduggery went right, and still they failed to draw blood. The entire affair was becoming completely unacceptable. Any moment now, China was about to perspire.

She leaned in with a deep thrust that was parried, but she responded with a flick that almost took Dalrymple's hand off at the wrist. Now the master swordsman was on the back foot. Skulduggery went low and China went high, and then they switched, and switched again, robbing Dalrymple of a chance to anticipate their next move.

"Surrender," Skulduggery said.

Dalrymple didn't answer immediately, too busy defending. "You seem to have me beaten," he said at last.

"So it seems. But if this is true, then why are you smiling?"

"Because," Dalrymple answered, "I know something you don't know."

"And what is that?" asked Skulduggery.

"I'm not right-handed," Dalrymple replied, and threw the sword into his left hand. China cursed and fell back under his renewed onslaught, and Skulduggery cried out as a sliver of bone was cut from his arm. China lashed out desperately to keep Dalrymple away, but his sword was moving much faster than her own, and she couldn't find her balance. She fell to one hand, continuing the fight with her other while she tried to scuttle out of range.

Skulduggery reared up behind Dalrymple and Dalrymple spun, thrusting through Skulduggery's ribcage. Skulduggery froze, looking down at the blade that pierced his clothing. Then Dalrymple twisted the sword and dragged it out so that it scraped across Skulduggery's sternum, and Skulduggery howled in pain and crumpled to the ground.

China slashed her rapier at the back of Dalrymple's neck, but he dodged, whirled, and his sword crashed against hers and suddenly her hand was empty. He kicked her in the chest and she went down.

He stood over her with the tip of his blade at her throat. "There," he said, panting a little. "You are defeated. Now it is *you* who will answer *my* questions. Where are they? Where are the Remnants?"

"I don't know," she said.

The tip pressed against her skin. "Tell me or I'll kill you."

Skulduggery was still curled up on the floor, his arms wrapped around himself. China sighed. "Fine. I'll tell you. But if you switched on a television or a radio, you'd already know all this."

"I don't trust modern technology," he informed her.

"Why doesn't that surprise me? In that case, you've missed the countless stories of riots that are breaking out all across the city. All across the country."

Dalrymple's mouth hung open. "They're all out? The Remnants? All of them? That's... That's..."

"That's what you've been waiting for?"

His eyes brimmed with tears. "Yes."

"For well over a hundred years?"

He nodded quickly. "Yes."

"Then tonight is your lucky night, Burgundy. But you better hurry or else there'll be none left to join with you."

"Yes," he said, his eyes unfocused. "Yes, I... I have to go."

The tip of his sword wavered from her throat and China lashed out, the toe of her expensive boot crunching into his knee. He fell back and Skulduggery rose, grabbed Dalrymple's sword-hand and wrenched it behind him, breaking it. Dalrymple screamed and the sword dropped, and Skulduggery threw him against the wall.

"Give me your half of the key," Skulduggery said, his voice cold, devoid of humanity.

Dalrymple sobbed in pain. He tried to run for the door, but Skulduggery kicked his feet from under him. He stomped on Dalrymple's broken arm and the poor man screeched until he passed out. China stood up as Skulduggery searched him, finally finding the key on a light chain around the unconscious man's neck.

"Are you OK?" Skulduggery asked China as he examined the flat piece of gold.

"I'm fine," she replied. "How are you? He hurt you, I see."

"Just a scratch."

"Just enough to make you lose your sense of humour?"

He looked at her. "Only temporarily, I assure you. I'm right as rain now, though. We have one half of the key, Valkyrie has the other. We might actually win this, you know, even against overwhelming odds."

China shrugged. "Stranger things have happened."

44

SIEGE AT THE HIBERNIAN

kulduggery and China arrived in Drogheda, and they all got into the nice warm van. Tanith immediately told them that Valkyrie had beaten up a priest and an old woman. China laughed, and Skulduggery handed Valkyrie the half of the key he'd recovered from Dalrymple. She pressed it against the half from the church and was unable to pry them apart again.

They got on to the motorway and drove without seeing another car until they got to the slipway for Balbriggan. Two cars were stopped in the middle lane – the doors open and no one around.

"A crash?" Tanith asked as they drove slowly by. Valkyrie could see no sign of collision, and she got the uncomfortable feeling that they were being watched.

Skulduggery pressed down on the accelerator. "We don't stop," he said. "For anyone."

Neither Valkyrie or Tanith said anything.

They reached the city centre and cut through the empty streets, ignoring traffic lights. At the entrance to Trinity College, a grit-spreader was pulled in to the side of the road with its lights on and its engine running, but there was no sign of the driver. They swung around St Stephen's Green and saw a man running up to them, waving his arms frantically. Valkyrie looked away as they left him behind.

The city was dead around them, killed by cold and fear.

"Checkpoint," Skulduggery said, as his façade flowed over his skull.

Valkyrie peered out at the flashing blue lights of the Garda squad cars ahead of them. Four cops in reflective jackets waved them down.

Valkyrie and Tanith lay flat in the back. Valkyrie's heart was thumping wildly by the time the van stopped. She heard the window whir down, and a cop asking Skulduggery for his driver's licence. China asked if there was a problem. The cop stammered a little when he replied that this was just a routine checkpoint, nothing to worry about. At least his love-struck reaction to China Sorrows was a normal response. That was a good start. But when Skulduggery told him that he didn't have his licence on him, the cop ordered him to step out of the van.

"Is there a problem?" Skulduggery asked.

"Just step out of the van, sir," the cop replied.

"We weren't speeding, Guard."

"Sir," the cop said, irritation creeping into his voice, "I'm telling you to step out of the van. You can either do as I ask, or we'll pull you out and arrest you."

"There's no need for threats," Skulduggery said. Valkyrie heard the door open, and Skulduggery got out. The door closed.

"There's four of them," China whispered from the front. "One on my side. Three around Skulduggery."

There was a knock on the passenger side window. China wound it down.

"Hello, there," Valkyrie heard a cop say.

"Hello," China said back, a smile in her voice.

Valkyrie noticed Tanith moving slightly. The streetlight

glinted briefly across the steel of her sword. Valkyrie swallowed.

There was a short cry from outside, then something slammed into the side of the van at the same time as China kicked her door open. The sound of the door hitting the cop's head was unmistakable. China closed her door calmly as Skulduggery got back behind the wheel, and they sped on.

"Trouble?" Tanith asked, sitting up.

"Nothing I couldn't talk my way out of," Skulduggery replied.

Valkyrie looked out the back window at the crumpled forms of the Guards. "Were they possessed?"

"I don't think so," China said. "They didn't seem especially strong."

"All it takes is one Remnant in a position of power," Skulduggery said. "For all we know, they could have the entire police force on the lookout for us. Everyone hold on – we're going to be moving a little faster."

He pressed his foot down on the accelerator, and the van roared.

By the time they reached the Hibernian, Valkyrie was scared and depressed. She worried about her parents, and for the first time she worried about her cousins. She wondered how they were coping with what they'd learned over the past twenty-four hours. The events they'd witnessed, plus the madness breaking out all over the city, all over the country, would be enough to freak *anyone* out, let alone two highly-strung teenagers.

According to the radio, the entire country was, understandably, panicking. The authorities were inundated with reports of missing people. Some commentators were saying this was a neurological virus, others said it was a biological attack, and still others were saying, and this was Valkyrie's personal favourite, that this was God's punishment for not going to church any more. Some of the attacks reported were genuine Remnant activity, but others were clearly down to Kenspeckle's time-released thought bomb.

Whatever the cause, the effect was the same. People were staying in, locking their doors and windows and isolating themselves from their neighbours. There were reports of scientists in hazmat suits walking the streets. The country was going crazy, and the rest of the world was just waiting for the sickness to spread to them.

Skulduggery parked Ghastly's van across the road from the Hibernian and out of sight. Making sure no one was watching, they hurried over to the locked door at the rear of the cinema.

A hidden camera picked them up, and a few moments later the door clicked. They hurried inside and the moment the door closed again it locked, sliding steel bars into place and activating an alarm system that Kenspeckle himself had designed.

"Ghastly called," Kenspeckle said when he saw them. "He said they're three hours away, if they're lucky."

Skulduggery sent Tanith to check defences on the upper levels, and he took Valkyrie with him as he checked the lower ones.

"When do you think the possessed will get here?" Valkyrie asked as they walked.

"Any time now. To be honest, I'm surprised they're not here already."

"I don't like waiting," Valkyrie said. "I think too much. I think of everything that could go wrong with this dreadful plan of ours."

"Surely not *everything*."

"You are of no reassurance at all, do you know that? If you were any kind of a friend, you'd be telling me that in a few hours the Remnants will be gone and everyone will be back to normal."

"You mean if I was a true friend," Skulduggery said, "I'd take this opportunity to lie to you?"

"Pretty much, yes."

"In that case, this dreadful plan cannot fail. In a few hours, the Remnants will be trapped in the Receptacle and everyone will be back to normal. People can carry on arguing about who should be the two new Elders, I can get back to tracking down this Tesseract character, and you can continue your lessons in Necromancy while you go on another date with Fletcher, as Caelan seethes with jealousy on the sidelines."

He tested iron shutters that were sealing off an old doorway.

"You notice everything," she said.

"Not everything, but a lot."

"He told me he loves me," Valkyrie said. "Caelan."

They resumed their walk.

"You don't want a vampire loving you, Valkyrie."

"He's not a bad person."

"Because he's not a person."

"Don't give me that," she said irritably. "That's all anyone ever says. *He's an animal. He can't be trusted.* That's what *he* says, too. He calls *himself* an animal, for God's sake."

"And what do you think he is? Troubled? Misunderstood? He's a killer."

"Caelan is different from the others."

"Yes, he is."

Valkyrie frowned. "You agree with me?"

"Absolutely. The other vampires are brutal, bloodthirsty animals barely held in check by their brutal, bloodthirsty code. But Caelan? He's much worse."

She sighed and shook her head, but he continued.

"He broke the first law of being a vampire when he killed his own kind. If he can't stick to that simple rule, how safe do you think you are? Do you know why vampires are known for holding grudges? It's because once a passion for something, in that case vengeance, starts to burn, it consumes them absolutely. Vengeance, hatred, or love. They each burn as bright."

"So you're saying he'll become obsessed with me?"

"If he told you he loves you, he's *already* obsessed with you."

"If you talked to him, if you sat down and gave him a chance, you'd realise how wrong you are."

Skulduggery didn't say anything. He just looked at her, then slowly cocked his head to one side. Valkyrie looked away, aware of the blush that was rising.

"What did you do?" he asked.

"I didn't do anything. What are you talking about?"

"Loath as I am to protect your relationship with Fletcher, you *are* still with the boy, aren't you?"

"Of course."

"You're not with Caelan, then?"

She shook her head.

"And you have no *plans* to be with him?"

"He's way too old."

"That's not an answer."

"Well, I don't know what you want me to say! Do you want me to say we kissed? Because OK, we did! Once! That's all. And I said never again because I'm with Fletcher, and he agreed. There. What else do you want to know?"

Skulduggery said nothing, just kept walking. She felt the flash of righteous anger fading fast, leaving her feeling stupid and childish and really wishing she hadn't said anything.

"I see," he said at last.

"I don't have to explain myself to you," said Valkyrie. "I don't need to get your permission to kiss Caelan, or Fletcher, or anyone."

"That's right," he said quietly, "you don't. But we still have the problem of a vampire being in love with you."

"I told you, it's *not* a problem."

"You can't afford to encourage him."

She glared. "I'm not encouraging him."

"Then kissing him probably sends the wrong signal."

Valkyrie looked away, unable to argue with him there.

"And what if Fletcher finds out?" Skulduggery continued. "Are you willing to lose your boyfriend over this? Caelan may be on his best behaviour with *you*, but by now, I can assure you, he is *hating* Fletcher. A hint, a suggestion, that's all it would take to ruin things between you two."

"Caelan's not going to say anything," she said, without conviction.

Then the lights went out. Before Valkyrie could even click her fingers, the emergency generator activated.

"Power cut?" she asked. "Or...?"

"Remnants," Skulduggery said. "They're here."

They ran back to the others. Kenspeckle had a screen set up in the Medical Bay that showed multiple shots of the building's exteriors.

There were hundreds of them – men and women and even a few children, mortal and sorcerer, all of them out there in the freezing cold with black-lipped smiles on their black-veined faces. Valkyrie could see Wreath and Shudder and Ravel, and a few other people she recognised. There was movement in the crowd around the main door, and Tesseract walked forward. He looked straight up into the camera.

Valkyrie felt the fear in her gut, and the cold, cold guilt. A part of her, a despairing part, wailed and cried that they were here for her, that all this was her fault.

It wasn't, of course. The Remnants getting free had nothing to do with her, as far as she knew. If they hadn't come after her, they'd still be out there, still hurting people and taking over bodies. This way, at least, they weren't targeting mortals. For the moment.

They watched the screens as the possessed spread out, wrapping around the building like a noose on a neck.

A few of them approached the perimeter on the west side. One of them waved a stick at the air until it hit the invisible dome Kenspeckle had set up. The dome glowed blue at the point where the stick touched it, and the blue rippled outwards and gradually dissipated, like a pebble thrown into a still lake. The possessed let out a chorus of appreciation for such fine defensive work.

On the street-facing side, a sorcerer hurled a stream of energy that was soaked up into the blue without causing damage. A ball of fire exploded against it, bullets hit and dropped harmlessly, and a fist of shadows broke apart on impact. All those attacks did was send ripples of blue around the little building.

A group of the possessed broke off from the rest, started using their magic to blast away at the ground.

"They're digging under," Valkyrie said.

"They're going to have to dig deep," Kenspeckle told her. "We're not encased in a bubble, but the dome does continue down into the earth for about ten metres. It's not going to be easy for them."

"How long till they break through?" asked Tanith.

"The dome will not fail completely," Kenspeckle said, "but some gaps may start to appear. We can expect some of them to get through before the dome repairs itself."

"Don't mind that at all," Tanith shrugged. "Just don't want to get bored."

Valkyrie didn't say it, but looking down at the hundreds of murderous, black-lipped faces, she didn't think there'd be much chance of that.

"Spread out," Skulduggery said, "but not too far. We go where we're needed, but we don't go alone. Is that understood? Our aim is to defend and repel attacks until Fletcher teleports back to us. Until then, we do not rest and we do not stop. Let's go."

Under sustained attacks, gaps were appearing, and sorcerers were getting through to the building itself. There were further defences there, of course, and even more inside, but little by little, the building was breached.

Valkyrie was down in the morgue, watching helplessly as a large hole was blasted through the wall and three sorcerers jumped through.

Skulduggery ran to intercept the intruders. He pushed at the air and sent one of them back to the dome. The other two were Elementals, and knew how to meet the rush of air without losing ground. The biggest of them, an ugly man with curly black hair, slammed into Skulduggery and took him down. The other one, dressed in a suit and tie splattered with mud, went for Valkyrie.

She dropped right before he reached her, sweeping his feet from under him. He hit the floor and she gripped him with shadows, threw him spinning to the side of the morgue. The *smack* his head made against the concrete was wet and sickening.

The man with the curly hair punched Skulduggery's head, grunting as his hand broke. Skulduggery kicked him away and rolled to his feet, slid sideways to avoid a lunge from the third intruder. His hand came around, caught the guy behind the ear, sending him stumbling. Valkyrie pushed at the air, directing it at the guy's feet. His legs flew out behind him and he fell, and she ran up and volleyed his head like a football.

Skulduggery whipped an elbow into the curly-haired man's

nose. The Remnants were strong, and their sensitivity to pain was lessened, but they were still in human bodies, and human bodies had certain reactions to certain things. An elbow to the nose causes the eyes to water, which blurs the vision. A kick to the shin sends signals shooting into the brain, which in turn brings the hands down to protect the injured area. And a knee to the chin rocks the head back, which makes the brain slam into the wall of the skull, which results in blackout.

The man with the curly hair dropped like a sack of ugly potatoes.

Through the hole in the wall, Valkyrie could see the blue energy of the dome, and the possessed on the other side. She barely resisted the urge to shout, "That all you got?" The urge came from fear and the expectation of the inevitable, like when she was a kid playing hide-and-seek and she'd be consumed by the need to lunge from her hiding place as the seeker grew close and shout, "I'm here! I'm here!"

She wasn't a kid any more, and those kinds of self-destructive urges had no place in her life, especially now.

The possessed looked at her and smiled. A few of them chanted her true name. She just stood there beside Skulduggery and waited for the next lot to break through.

45

FRIGHTENING

Tanith knew the sorcerer striding through the laboratory towards her. His skin was dark as ebony, his body big and broad and his eyes burning. He had taken the sword that fitted so comfortably in his hand from a vanquished opponent on a battlefield long ago, and it had served him well ever since. He was an Adept, his name was Frightening Jones, and they had briefly dated back in the 1970s.

His sword came for her and she slipped to the side, tried to sweep her own blade along the back of his leg, but he was already pivoting. Steel clashed and Tanith backed off.

"I've missed you," he smiled.

"How've you been?" she muttered.

He shrugged, and sent the tip of his sword whistling for her throat. She dodged away.

"I'm doing all right," he said, continuing his advance. "I was just over here for a bit of business, and then, well, you know..." He tapped his head. "It's really not as bad as you think, sharing space with a Remnant. Although, to be fair, this new joining hasn't made me appreciate Irish weather to any great degree. Still looking forward to being back in Africa."

He lunged and she parried, flicked her sword to his shoulder, but he raised his blade, and her cut went wide.

"What about you?" he asked. "Anyone special in your life?"

"Oh, Frightening, you know you're the only one for me."

He laughed, and she pressed in, and now it was he who was forced to retreat. His defence was strong, the steel of his blade backed up by muscle and sinew. It flickered where it needed to flicker and his feet moved where they needed to move. He was still good. He hadn't let his skills diminish. Tanith wondered if he was still better than she was.

He blocked a cut and shuffled forward, using his shoulder to knock her sideways. She flipped backwards to avoid the swipe to her knees, parried the follow-up and avoided the next strike altogether.

"When you've quite finished dancing," China said as she strolled by.

Frightening moved round so that he could keep both of them in view. "Miss Sorrows," he said, "so good to see you again. If you wait right there, I'll get around to killing you as soon as possible."

China folded her arms. "I haven't got all day, Mr Jones."

Frightening brought his sword down on Tanith's, nearly ripping it out of her hands. He stepped up and booted her in the gut. She staggered, half bent over, and barely managed to roll away from the next assault.

"Well?" Tanith gasped to China.

China's eyebrow raised. "Well what?"

"Are you going to help me or not?"

"Nonsense, you don't need my help. You're doing fine."

Frightening feinted low, then brought the sword high. Tanith blocked, replied with three strikes in quick succession. The first two he batted aside with ease, but the third he let sail overhead as he ducked below it, bringing his blade dangerously close to her ribs. She darted away just in time.

Three more possessed sorcerers came through. China

turned to them, arms still folded, her fingers briefly touching the invisible symbols carved into her forearms. Her arms flew wide and the nearest possessed caught a wave of blue energy at point-blank range. His bones broke and his flesh ruptured even as he was sent flying backwards. The other two Remnants rounded on China, just as Frightening renewed his attack on Tanith.

Tanith stumbled as she parried and blocked, trying to regain her footing and give herself some space at the same time. An almighty swing from Frightening took the sword from her hands. Instead of retreating further, she surprised him by leaping forward.

They struggled with his sword, Tanith kicking and kneeing at his legs the whole time. She sneaked a boot around his foot and pushed into him. He went back, tripping over her, but bringing her with him. He grunted as she landed on top of him. Using her full weight, she pressed the sword down against his throat. Teeth gritted and perspiration dotting his forehead, he resisted.

Out of the corner of her eye, she saw China fling a dagger of red light into the chest of one of the possessed. He gasped and sagged, fell to his knees and keeled over. The remaining sorcerer grabbed China and slammed her against the wall.

Frightening was pushing back, the blade moving away from his throat with agonising slowness. It was all Tanith could do to watch the inevitable happen. In another few seconds, the blade would be far enough away for Frightening to start squirming beneath her. He'd throw her off, the battle would resume, and she'd more than likely die.

She thought of Ghastly, of the brief kiss she'd given him. All that time wasted. To die here and now, killed on this cold ground by a man she had cared for yet never loved, it was almost more than she could bear. She had thought she had all the time in the world to find the right moment with Ghastly. The curse of immortality, she reckoned, was procrastination.

Tanith flipped her body vertically, till she was in a handstand with both hands still on the sword. Frightening's eyes widened as her full weight bore down on him, but her balance was easily shifted. She sprang away before he could try anything tricky, snatching up her sword as he got to his feet.

China, meanwhile, was getting down and dirty with the remaining mage. They rolled across the ground, China's hair in her face. Finally, China simply grabbed the sorcerer's head and slammed it down on the concrete, once, twice. Satisfied that her opponent was no longer a threat, she got up, breathing hard and looking angry.

The pupils dissolved in Frightening's eyes, leaving them pure white and glowing. Tanith cursed, had to dive to avoid the stream of white light that burst out. She got behind a metal desk, felt the heat and heard the metal sizzle all around her. Abruptly, the light moved, and she peered out, saw Frightening closing in on China. China's forearms were pressed together, forming the sigil that erected the shield between her and Frightening's eye beams. Tanith had always thought those eye beams were among the coolest of Adept powers to have. She didn't think they were quite so cool today.

"Keep the shield up!" she shouted. "He can't sustain that level of intensity for more than a few seconds!"

"If you're bored," China shouted back, "you could always lend a hand."

"Nonsense! You're doing great!"

Frightening swivelled his head, the twin beams scorching towards her, forcing Tanith to duck back behind cover. She felt the heat die, and the brightness falter, and risked another peek to see Frightening blinking his pupils back into service.

"Now!" she called, lunging from cover.

For a few moments after using his power, Frightening was

left blind as his magic recharged. China hit him from the side and Tanith leaped, both boots crunching into his jaw. He sprawled, his sword clanging to the floor. In an instant, China was leaning over him, her hand pressing against his forehead. He screamed, then went silent, but China kept her hand on his forehead, making his body jerk. Tanith grabbed China and yanked her back.

China's elbow cracked against Tanith's cheek and Tanith held up her hands.

"Stop! Wait! What the hell was that?"

China narrowed her eyes. "You attacked me."

"No, I didn't."

"Yes, you did. You're one of them."

Tanith stared at her. "Did you see a Remnant slide down my throat? No, you bloody didn't!"

"Then why did you stop me?"

"Because you were going to kill him!"

"He was going to kill *us*, you stupid girl."

"No, China, he was going to lie there and be unconscious. Once that thing is out of him, he's a good guy again. The same goes for most of these people that you don't seem to have a problem using lethal force against."

Without taking her eyes from Tanith's, China tied her hair

back off her face. "If it's a choice between them or me, I pick me. Your little concessions of mercy are going to get you killed."

Tanith wiped blood from her lip and didn't respond.

46

ACCORDING TO PLAN

he shield held.

Its colour deepened with each impact. With each attempt to break through, it would darken, then fade, and then the attacks would begin again and the Hibernian Cinema would be covered by a blue dome of energy.

The sorcerers outside were taking turns, fifty of them each time, throwing everything they had at Kenspeckle's defences.

The defenders went where they were needed – constantly repelling attacks and forcing back intruders. It was exhausting.

Valkyrie fought her way from one side of the building to the other and back again. She was cut and bleeding and bruised and she couldn't catch her breath.

There was a crash from a corridor behind her, and she heard Tanith shout, "They're in!"

Valkyrie ran to help. Tanith was locked in a struggle with a black-lipped sorcerer, the pair of them rolling amid the debris around the massive hole in the middle of the floor. Another sorcerer was climbing up, and Valkyrie snapped her palm at the air, sending a rock hurtling into his face. The sorcerer fell back with a scream of pain, but another one took his place before the scream was even half done.

A flash of red light blinded her and she felt something hot sizzle by her cheek. She stumbled back, hands out against the air. There was a disturbance, something big coming for her. She clicked her fingers and flicked out a fireball, heard rapid cursing in response. She blinked quickly, able to see shapes now, and she saw the figure as he batted out the flames on his shirt. She gathered shadows and sent them roughly to where his head should be. His blurred form spun in mid-air and dropped.

Valkyrie squeezed her eyes shut, then opened them, vision clearing, in time to see Tanith rising off the unconscious sorcerer she'd been struggling with. Another black-lipped man climbed up into the room and Tanith met him, ducking the swipe of a knife and firing back three punches in return. The man grunted and the knife dropped. Tanith caught him with a kick that toppled him backwards into the hole.

Skulduggery ran in, fire in both his hands. He stopped in the middle of the room and sent twin streams of flame down into the hole. Valkyrie heard screams and shouts and a lot more cursing. Suddenly he doused the flames and crouched, fingers splayed out on the ground. The floor rumbled, cracked, and belched clouds of dust into the air as the tunnel caved in beneath them.

Skulduggery looked up. "Everyone OK?"

Tanith nodded. Valkyrie raised an eyebrow. "Another one of your new tricks?" she panted.

"Just the natural progression of earth manipulation. I'll have to teach it to you sometime."

"It won't hold them for long," Tanith said.

The possessed were inside the cinema and they were trying to get through into the science-magic facility. Valkyrie heard a terrified scream, and she split off from the rest. She rounded the corner to see a woman with wild, bushy hair closing in on Clarabelle. Valkyrie dived on her.

"Run!" she said to Clarabelle, and Clarabelle did.

The woman elbowed her and Valkyrie heard a crackle, just as the woman brought up a stun gun. Valkyrie dodged back, stumbled and fell backwards. She was so tired, her body so drained, that when she hit the ground it actually felt good to be lying down. Then the crazy woman jumped on her and it didn't feel so good any more.

The stun gun crackled centimetres from her neck, and Valkyrie did her best to keep it away. "You'll thank me for this later," the crazy woman said through gritted teeth.

Valkyrie braced her forearm against the lower half of the woman's face and slowly forced it back. She was running on pure adrenaline, and she was down to her last reserves. The crazy woman grinned, and Valkyrie's strength failed. A moment before the stun gun pressed into her skin, Fletcher grabbed the woman and yanked her off. They vanished and Valkyrie sank back. Slowly, and with a moan, she raised both arms up. Fletcher reappeared above her, took her hands, and pulled her to her feet.

"I'm getting pretty good at this nick of time stuff, aren't I?" he asked. She would have hit him if she wasn't so tired.

Skulduggery ran over, China and Tanith behind him. "Fletcher, did you make it to the mountains?"

"Yes, we did," Fletcher said. "We don't know where the cavern is exactly, but I can definitely teleport to the general area."

"You're the only one immune to the Remnants," China said to Skulduggery. "When we get there, we'll do our best to hold them off while you activate the machine. From this point on, you're the only one who matters."

"I got Kenspeckle to open a few doors," Ghastly said, hurrying over, "so they're all flowing into the cinema. We need them in one place, and we're not going to get a better chance than right now."

Skulduggery turned to Valkyrie. "Are you ready?"

She nodded. "I can do it."

"Fletcher, they're going to be focused on the screen, trying to get through. You need to teleport us behind them, and then be ready to teleport everyone to the MacGillycuddy's Reeks. Can you do that?"

"I can," Fletcher said. "Everybody hold hands, now."

Suddenly they were in the cinema, watching two thousand crazy people as they shouted and laughed and cursed.

"Valkyrie," Skulduggery said. "*Now.*"

She reached out, allowing the coldness of the ring to spread to her fingertips. The shadows swirled and rose like a dark mist. The noise gradually died down, as the possessed swiped at the mist, expecting an attack. When none came, they looked around, confused. Valkyrie felt the shadows drift between them, and concentrated on spreading it out further. She opened her eyes, saw them all looking at her.

"Fletcher!" Skulduggery barked.

"Everyone hang on," Fletcher said. His hand gripped Valkyrie's shoulder. The others formed a chain on the other side of her.

"I'm not the one moving," she heard him murmur. "It's the universe that revolves around me..."

Valkyrie saw it out of the corner of her eye, a sliver of blackness reaching from behind Fletcher's shoulder. Before she could warn him, the Remnant scampered up to his face and he stumbled back, trying to tear it away. He fell to one knee, but it was already in his mouth. He reared back and it was gone from sight, and his body arched in pain, then relaxed.

All around them, the possessed were laughing. Fletcher raised his head, and smiled with black lips.

Skulduggery's gun leaped into his hand, but Fletcher disappeared.

"Over here," Fletcher said.

They spun. Ghastly pushed at the air, but Fletcher was

already gone. He appeared beside Tanith, who whirled in an instant, her sword slicing through nothing but empty space.

"You can't beat me," Fletcher said from behind them.

Skulduggery fired and China hurled daggers of red light.

"How stupid are you?" Fletcher called from the stage.

"I can be everywhere and anywhere," Fletcher said from ten paces away.

"You can't stop me," Fletcher laughed from right beside them. He grabbed Valkyrie, pulling her from the others, and teleported her to the middle of the possessed sorcerers. The dark mist was already gone. The sorcerers around them started to chuckle. She glimpsed Skulduggery and the others through the gaps, but they were being ignored now that the Remnants had their prize.

"I love you," Fletcher said, holding her close. "I was pretty sure I loved you before this, but now? Now I know. I love you more than anything, Val, and please trust me. When you're joined, you'll like it."

Valkyrie punched him right across the jaw, elbowed a woman who reached for her and kicked out at a man. Someone tripped her and she fell. The people laughed, and then she felt hands grabbing her from *beneath*, and she sank into the ground. The sorcerers dived for her, but it was no use, and she shut her eyes as she was pulled down, underground.

"Hello, li'l darlin'," Billy-Ray Sanguine said in her ear.

47

STRANGE BEDFELLOWS

The rumbling stopped and Valkyrie felt the cold, hard earth all around her. It was pitch-black and the familiar fears rose in her throat. Her thumb pressed against her index finger.

"If you're plannin' on clickin' those fingers and generatin' a little flame to see by," Sanguine said, "may I suggest an alternative that will not burn up our remainin' oxygen?"

Yellow light flooded the small space that surrounded them, and Valkyrie found herself looking at her own reflection in his sunglasses. He handed her the narrow torch.

"Got this for you," he said, his perfect white teeth flashing in a smile.

"What are you doing?" she whispered.

"I ain't exactly sure on this," he replied, "but it looks to me, and I may be wrong, but it looks to me like I'm savin' your life. Yep, I... I think that's what it is."

She frowned. "You're not one of them?"

"The Remnants? Naw, they haven't got me yet. Creepy critters, ain't they?"

Valkyrie shifted a little. A half-dozen rocks were sticking painfully into her. "Why are you here?"

"Now, before you get all aggressive, let me say that I *do* remember the last time we met, and I *do* remember the promise you made me."

"I said I'd kill you."

"I *told* you I remembered, didn't I?" Sanguine said crossly. "No need to threaten me again, just because you can. Fact is, I was plannin' on leavin' you alone for a while, but a job came up, and I needed my... payment."

"How are you mixed up in this?"

"For once, I'm on the side of the angels, if those Roarhaven folk can be described as such. They hired me to help out against the creepy critters. I had a look, saw that they seemed to be goin' after *you* all the time, so I figured the best way to hurt them is to take away the thing they want.

"I admit, the thought did enter my mind to kill you, and so take you away from them on a more permanent basis, but two factors stopped me from that course of action. The first factor is that for all I know, the reason they want you so bad is to kill you, and so by killin' you myself, I'd be doin' them one hell of a favour. The second factor is that I don't want you dead just yet. I'm quite lookin' forward to all the pain and torture I know you got comin' to you."

"You're on our side?"

"That appears to be what I'm tryin' to say."

"So... you'll be fighting beside us?"

"It'll be strange, not tryin' to cut your throat all the time, but yeah."

Valkyrie pushed questions and suspicions and misgivings out of her mind. "OK, fine. We need to get into the Medical Bay to get Kenspeckle and Clarabelle, and then we have to get to the van on the other side of the street."

"In a sec."

She glared. "Let's go."

"You ain't my damn boss, Cain. For your information, whatever force field thing you guys cooked up means I have to go deeper than usual to get around it, which means I have to work harder. We'll move when we're able to move."

"You're still injured."

"Yes," he said, his mouth twisting into an ugly sneer, "I'm still injured from when you cut me with a damn *sword*. I am still unable to move with my usual efficiency. Now, if this inconveniences you, please accept my heartfelt apologies. But once again, I must let it be known that this is *your* damn fault."

The look on his face and the hate in his voice told Valkyrie to tread cautiously. He was a killer and a psychopath, and although he may have temporarily switched sides, she knew it wouldn't take a lot for him to abandon her down here.

"Bet you never thought we'd end up on the same side, huh?" he asked, a new smile crossing his features. "Bet you never thought I'd save your skin."

"What?"

"Just makin' small talk. Got to distract myself from the pain, y'know? Life has a funny way of workin' out, don't it? Take your friend, for example. The sword-lady."

"Tanith?"

"First time we met, we were tryin' to kill each other,

remember that? But every time subsequent to that there's been a kind of a *frisson* between us."

"A what?"

"*Frisson.* It's French for... To be honest I don't really know what it's French for, but I know what it means in American. A sort of electrical undercurrent of emotion."

"I know what *frisson* means, but I really don't think Tanith would share your view."

"You're a kid. You don't know the ways of menfolk and womenkind. All those threats she fires my way? That there is the mark of flirtation."

"Oh, dear God," Valkyrie said, the colour draining from her face. "You fancy Tanith."

"I don't *fancy* her, I—"

"You have a crush on Tanith. That is disgusting."

"What? Why would it be disgustin'?"

"Because you're a hired killer."

"That don't make it disgustin', just makes it... unusual. Does she talk about me?"

"Somebody shoot me."

"What does she say? I'm a formidable foe, right? Does she say anythin' in a kind of a more... wistful voice?"

"I don't want to talk about this."

"Does she ever say, 'If only he were good…'?"

"Stop your talking. Stop it right now. Stop it. She has a boyfriend."

His face fell. "Someone I know?" he asked morosely.

"He may have punched you a few times, yes."

"She's not… She's not datin' the skeleton, is she? How would that be even possible, let alone… nice? He's got no skin, or lips, or… or nothin'. And he talks. Good God, he talks and he never shuts up."

"It's not Skulduggery."

"Well then, who else could it…? It's not the ugly fella, is it? It couldn't be the ugly fella."

"Don't call him ugly."

"It *is* him! But he's all scars! I mean, I know I ain't got no eyes, but once you get past that, you got my face. And my face is all right. Better'n his. His is a mess, like he was dropped head first into a blender as a kid. Seriously? She's with him?"

"Seriously, and you're not going to break them up. Not because you won't try, but because you won't be able to. Look, are you ready yet? Can we move now?"

"I'm ready," he snapped. "But this conversation stays between us, understand? My romancin' ain't gonna work if she knows it's comin'."

"Believe me, I never want to speak to anyone about this ever again."

Sanguine took a breath and clenched his jaw, and Valkyrie clung on tight. They burrowed through the ground, the rumbling like thunder in her ears. She spat out dirt, keeping her eyes closed. Eventually she felt their trajectory shift. They were headed upwards now, but moving slower and slower with each passing second.

They broke through to light. They weren't in the Medical Bay, but they were close enough. She left him panting on the ground.

"Stay here," she said, "and catch your breath. I'll be back in a minute."

"Missin' you... already," he managed.

Valkyrie took off running. She called Kenspeckle's name, then Clarabelle's. She knew Kenspeckle wouldn't allow himself to be taken over again, but didn't know quite how far he'd go to stop that from happening. Would he hurt himself? Would he do worse?

"Kenspeckle!" she shouted. "We have to go! Clarabelle!"

Getting no answer, she ran the length of the corridor and turned into the next one. She called again for Kenspeckle, and passed yet another darkened room.

Drip.

She stopped, and turned. Slowly, she retraced her steps. She listened intently.

Drip. Drip. Drip.

Valkyrie pressed her shoulder to the wall, centimetres from the doorway.

"Hello?" she said softly. "Kenspeckle? Clarabelle?"

Drip.

"Kenspeckle. It's me. It's Valkyrie. Are you in there?"

Still no answer. Still no sound, apart from that irregular dripping.

"I'm coming in," she said, and stepped into the room. She poured her magic into a flame and it burned fiercely, throwing light across the countertops and equipment to each of the four corners. A warm, flickering light that illuminated Kenspeckle Grouse as he lay on the table, and Clarabelle, his assistant, as she crouched on top of him, a scalpel in each hand. Kenspeckle's eyes were open and unseeing, and the work Clarabelle had been doing reminded Valkyrie of her own dissection just a few days earlier. Blood covered him, and dripped to a puddle on the floor.

Clarabelle screeched, her lips black and her skin riddled with veins. She leaped off the old man's corpse and fell on to Valkyrie. They sprawled out through the door, landing in the corridor, those scalpels whipping at Valkyrie like snakes. Valkyrie seized one of Clarabelle's wrists, held the blade away from her, tried to block the other one, but it bit into her face and scraped along her cheekbone. Warm blood flowed. Valkyrie cried out, and anger coursed through her, giving her the strength to throw Clarabelle off.

She got up, grabbed a metal tray and swung it into the back of Clarabelle's head. She hit her again, and again, and wouldn't let her up. Valkyrie battered her until Clarabelle dropped to the floor and didn't move. Valkyrie threw the tray to one side and ran.

The corridors twisted and turned. Valkyrie's hand was at her face, the blood pouring through her fingers. She slowed, panting, and heard voices. She crept forward, peered round the corner. Shudder and Tesseract were heading her way, followed by several other sorcerers, including Fletcher.

"We're going to have to break her," Fletcher was saying. "You don't know her, not like I do."

"Leave Darquesse to us," Tesseract said.

"But that's it, right there, that's your problem. She's not Darquesse, not yet. She's still Valkyrie. We'll never convince her to embrace her inner mass-murderer unless we cut off the things that she clings to."

"And your suggestion?" asked Shudder.

Valkyrie ducked into a doorway as they neared.

"I'll go pick up her parents," she heard Fletcher say, and her stomach lurched. "I'll bring them back here and kill them in front of her."

"And what will this accomplish?" Tesseract asked. "Apart from making her hate us so much she never gives in? No, Valkyrie must become Darquesse willingly. We leave her family alone, for now."

Valkyrie stayed where she was, crouched in the darkness as they walked away, trying to get her breathing under control. Her hands were shaking as she took her phone from her pocket. She thumbed a button and called her reflection.

"Take my parents out of the house," she whispered.

The reflection's voice was as cold and uninterested as ever. "Why?"

"They're in danger. Fletcher's been possessed. Take them somewhere. Not to Beryl's, Fletcher knows where they live. I don't care where you take them, just get them out of the house."

"Hello, baby," said Fletcher from right behind her.

Valkyrie twisted, but he was already gone. Something hit her hand and her phone went flying. She swung a fist in an arc,

471

but didn't catch him, and then he was behind her again and his fist crunched into the back of her head. She dropped to all fours, hair in her face, stunned. He grabbed her and hauled her up, threw her over a table and teleported to the other side as she landed on the ground. He kicked her, the Remnant inside him adding to his strength. She curled up, struggling for air.

"I thought I heard you," he said. He was smiling. That cute smile she liked so much. "When I said I wanted to kill your folks, I thought I heard something, a little gasp. I knew it was you."

Valkyrie turned over, gave a moan of pain.

"I'll bring you to the others in a bit," Fletcher said, "don't you worry about that. I just thought it'd be nice if we spent a few minutes alone. I thought you might want to talk or something."

She moved quickly, pushing at the air, sending the table hurtling to the other end of the room. But not Fletcher. Fletcher wasn't there any more. She sensed him behind her, but was too slow to do anything as he grabbed her under the jaw with both hands and started dragging her across the floor.

"Knew you were fooling," he said. "I know you too well, you see. Can't bluff me, babe."

Valkyrie grabbed his wrists to ease the pressure and swung her legs up and over in a backwards somersault. Her boots caught him in the face and he let go, cursing. She was up now. She took hold of the shadows in the room and they lifted him up and slammed him to the ground. She glanced at the door, but she couldn't outrun a Teleporter and she knew it.

She aimed a kick at his head. He moved at the last second, rolled away, tried to come up, but her knee caught him under the chin. He fell back and she pressed in. If she gave him even a moment to recover, he'd teleport. She got behind him and wrapped one arm around his throat, braced it with the other, going for a choke. Fletcher reared back, but she hung on. He heaved forward, lifting her off her feet, trying to shake her loose. She tightened her hold. The Remnant might not need air to function, but the body it was using sure did. Another few moments and Fletcher would be unconscious.

He stopped trying to pry her fingers back, and instead, staggered to a chair that stood against the wall. He put one foot up on the seat. Valkyrie wriggled, did her best to throw him off balance, but didn't dare loosen the choke. Grunting, Fletcher shifted his weight forward, and slowly stood up on the chair, taking Valkyrie with him.

She screamed a thousand curses in her mind, but there was

nothing she could do, as Fletcher stood on shaky legs, and then propelled himself backwards. They fell in silence, Valkyrie shutting her eyes and waiting for the impact. She hit the ground and her head smacked off it, and stars burst behind her eyelids. She wasn't even aware that she'd lost the choke. She wasn't even aware of Fletcher getting to his feet beside her. She just lay there.

"Wow, you're tough," she heard Fletcher say. His voice sounded dim. "I'm not mad. I'm not. This is good. Darquesse is going to have to be tough, am I right?"

His image came into view. "But, wow, you nearly got me there. You nearly had me. If I didn't have all this extra strength, I'd be out cold. I think I like that, you know, my girlfriend being stronger than me. I'd never admit it – well, the old me wouldn't – but the new me is a lot more self-assured."

Valkyrie moaned, and Fletcher knelt beside her. He gently raised her head off the ground, then slammed it back down again. His hands moved over her, checking her pockets.

"You know, I fancied you the moment I saw you. I didn't want to admit it, because you were young and, you know, really annoying, but yeah, I liked you. We had something, didn't we? A connection? I liked the way you took all of this so seriously. I found that really funny. Ah, here they are." He dangled her own handcuffs over her. "I've really liked being your boyfriend, actually. I love all the fun stuff we do. But that's *nothing* compared to the fun we're going to have."

He clicked the cuff on to her right wrist, and was going for the left when someone collided with him from behind. They crashed against the chair in the dark.

Valkyrie rolled slowly on to her side. Her head hurt and she felt sick, but she brought her legs in and got them under her. In the dark around her were more crashes, the sounds of struggle. Two figures, throwing each other into walls. She took a deep breath, then another, willing herself not to throw up. Strength was returning with each moment that passed. The world was becoming clearer. She stood.

Fletcher came stumbling from the shadows. There was a snarl and he turned just as Caelan leaped at him, and they both vanished.

Valkyrie frowned, and even as she started to wonder what Caelan was doing here, a wave of dizziness nearly pitched her on to her face. She managed to stay upright and staggered out into the corridor. She slumped against the wall and stayed there, gathering her strength. She took a small key from her pocket, opened the handcuff and put both away. Warm blood trickled down her face.

Her phone was on the floor nearby. She held out her hand. She could feel the air, but it took a few seconds before she could focus enough to pull it towards her. The phone lifted into her hand, and she slipped it into her jacket, then pushed herself away from the wall. Her balance was back. Her strength was back. She was hurting, but she'd get over it.

Valkyrie found her way back to Sanguine, who raised an eyebrow as she approached, but didn't say anything. He took her underground, and they moved slowly through the earth and under the street. He was breathing hard, straining against the pain.

Finally, she heard shouting. Hands gripped her, pulling her from the ground. They were on the other side of the road, away from the Hibernian. She opened her eyes to see Ghastly dragging Sanguine to his feet, his fist pulled back, ready to punch. She called out and he looked around, puzzled.

"Our side," she coughed in Skulduggery's arms. "He's on our side."

Ghastly frowned at Sanguine and let him go. The Texan dropped to his knees, exhausted and in pain. Valkyrie heard shouting.

"They've noticed us," said Tanith.

"Everyone get to the van," Skulduggery ordered.

They ran, the Remnants behind them. Ghastly jumped in behind the wheel and they took off, tyres spinning.

"Are we going to *drive* there?" Tanith asked. "I know this thing is fast, but I don't like the idea of a five-hour car chase on icy roads. And they have Fletcher now. He could teleport them all to any one of a hundred places he's been between here and Kerry, and we'd drive right into them."

"Fletcher's distracted," Valkyrie said. "I don't know for how long. Caelan was there. He helped me. Kenspeckle's dead."

There was a moment of awful calm, that Skulduggery quickly dispelled. "We need to stay ahead of them just long enough so we can find somewhere to pull in. We'll let them overshoot, get to Kerry ahead of us, and we'll take our time, approach it right."

"It's going to be tricky," Ghastly murmured.

"It usually is."

48

PLAN FALLS APART

Valkyrie chewed on a leaf to numb the pain as Tanith stitched the cut on her face as best she could. When Tanith was finished, Valkyrie sat back and closed her eyes. After an hour of driving, they turned off the main road and bounced down narrow lanes of potholes and ice for twenty minutes, then headed north, moving perpendicular to their destination. Valkyrie kept her head down. The van was warm, but it was no comfort. After everything she'd seen and been through, she just wanted her boyfriend's arms around her. Sometimes the most comforting thing in the world was a hug.

It got dark, and Ghastly turned the headlights on. They passed three cars in two hours, and with every one they'd ready themselves for an attack. But the drivers were human, and mortal, and no threat to them.

Skulduggery asked questions. Sanguine answered them in his lazy drawl. Valkyrie didn't pay attention. She lay down in the back, her head on Tanith's lap, and fell asleep.

She woke to a conversation Skulduggery was having with Ghastly about abandoning the van and getting another. Ghastly was insisting on speed. Skulduggery was of the opinion that they should pick the first suitable vehicle they came across – there was no telling when this van would be recognised and reported.

Valkyrie dozed off again, only opening her eyes when the van pulled into an all-night petrol station. There was snow outside. Tanith took a few food orders and got out, hurried up to the bored man at the station window. Ghastly activated his façade and went to keep an eye on her, in case the Remnants had spread out this way. Valkyrie got out to stand beside Skulduggery while he filled the tank.

"I know he hid it well," Skulduggery said, "but Kenspeckle really liked me."

She surprised herself with a small smile. "No, he didn't," she said.

"No, he didn't. But he liked you."

"I don't really want to talk about this. What is there to say? I can't believe he's gone? Can't believe he's dead? Obviously, it's a shock. I don't need to *tell* anyone that."

"Sometimes it's not what you say, Valkyrie, it's just the fact that you're saying it."

She shook her head. "We don't have the time. Fight now, mourn later. That's our thing, right? If we stop and consider the implications every time something bad happens, we'd never get anything done."

"Kenspeckle was your friend."

"When all this is over, we'll see who's alive and who's dead, and then I'll cry, OK?"

He put his hand on her shoulder. "OK."

"Clarabelle's going to feel so bad when this is done with," Valkyrie said quietly, then shook her head. She had to focus. "How far are we from the Receptacle?"

"We're less than an hour from the mountain range, but we should wait until morning before approaching. Once we're there, that golden key in your pocket will guide us to where we need to go."

"Do we have a plan?"

"Plans are an invitation to disappointment."

"And yet we're probably going to need one. The Remnants are going to be all over the place to stop us from reaching the machine. Are you going to fly us in over their heads?"

"They'll be expecting that. Now that we have Sanguine on our side, we could always *burrow* right under them."

"I don't think so. These days he can't go 3 metres without needing a rest."

"So we can't go above, and we can't go under. Looks like we're going to drive in as close as we can, and just walk right in."

"The direct approach."

"The only approach we have left."

Morning was slow in coming, and failed to bring with it warmth. Valkyrie's nerves jangled beneath her skin. She noticed Tanith clenching and unclenching her fists beside her, and Ghastly had gone scarily quiet. Only China and Skulduggery seemed unperturbed by the danger they were about to walk into. Valkyrie couldn't have cared less about how Sanguine was coping.

They drove deeper into a small town, which seemed to be hibernating under all the snow. Valkyrie longed to see normal people out walking, or buying the morning paper, or even sitting at traffic lights. She didn't like this ghost town thing that had struck and spread, turning Ireland into a ghost *country*.

The van slowed suddenly, pulling in to the side of the road. Valkyrie peered over Skulduggery's shoulder. A police car lay on its side at the junction ahead of them, its lights still flashing.

"The rest of you stay here," Skulduggery said. "Valkyrie, you're with me."

They got out. She slid the door closed, and pulled the bandage away from her face. "How does it look?"

He peered at her. "It's healing. The swelling has gone. It's a nasty scar, but with everything Tanith applied to the wound, it should disappear in a day or so."

She glanced back at the van, and her voice lowered. "You don't trust them."

"Not entirely," he admitted.

"You think one of them's possessed?"

"We have no way of knowing until they reveal themselves. You're to stick with me, OK? Do not allow yourself to be caught alone with any of them."

She nodded. Skulduggery held his gloved hand out in front as they approached the car, turning the ice to steam, allowing them a firm grip on the road. Valkyrie wished she could have done that while she was slipping and sliding all over Drogheda.

They reached the junction. Two cops lay on the far side of the car. Valkyrie went to one, Skulduggery to the other. She hunkered down, felt for a pulse.

"This one's alive," she said.

"This one isn't," Skulduggery replied. "But I don't think the Remnants are out this far any more. I'd say they're panicking, keeping everyone back."

"So they're content to just sit around and wait for us to show up?"

"Why not? They know we have to go to them eventually. They probably have a few scouts flying around, checking the perimeter. We'll have to be very careful from here on out."

They turned, and retraced their steps. Sanguine walked towards them.

"Get back in the van," Skulduggery said.

"We may," Sanguine responded, his words slurring like he was drunk, "have a bit of a problem."

And then he collapsed. A stream of red light hit Skulduggery and blasted him back, all the way to the junction, where he hit the overturned police car and flipped over it. Valkyrie jumped sideways. She could see Ghastly, lying on the road beneath the open door of the van, and then China, strolling towards her with a beautiful, black-lipped smile.

Valkyrie raised her hand, but China flicked a dagger of red light into her. It hit her jacket and it was like she'd stuck her fingers into an electrical socket. She jerked back and fell to her knees.

"It's time to come with me," China said. "You've impressed all of us, but really, you didn't need to. You're Darquesse. That's all we needed to know."

China crouched over her, and took the golden key from Valkyrie's jacket, and put it in her own pocket. "I don't think this is going to be much use to you, to be perfectly honest."

Someone moved around the van. Valkyrie's vision cleared, just as Tanith collided with China from behind. They slipped on the ice and went down, but Tanith instantly sprang to her feet. China kicked out, catching her in the leg and knocking her back, then came up and tapped her forearms and flung them wide. Tanith dodged the wave of blue energy and got in close, her fist smacking against China's cheek. Tanith's hands blurred. A punch caught China in the ribs. She staggered back, gasping for breath, but managed to block the kick that followed. She tried to give herself some room, but Tanith was already closing in.

China knocked her knuckles together, and the tattoos glowed briefly red. She swung a punch that missed, but the next one caught Tanith in the chest. Tanith went sprawling, and slid across the ground.

Valkyrie glimpsed the glowing symbol on China's right palm a moment before she seized Tanith's wrist. Tanith screamed in abject agony, kicking out by pure instinct. Her boot crunched into China's ribcage. China grunted and released her hold, and Tanith scrambled up and charged.

She went low, her shoulder against China's stomach while her arms wrapped around her legs. She lifted China and then slammed her to the ground, falling on top of her. With her left arm, China held Tanith close, not giving her the room she'd need to throw damaging attacks. Tanith was concentrating on keeping China's right hand, with that glowing symbol, away from her.

Feeling returned to Valkyrie's legs, and she started to get up. Her brain struggled to sort itself out.

Tanith shoved China away and they parted, coming up on their feet at the same time. Tanith was the first to strike, but China parried the blow and chopped at Tanith's bicep. Tanith back-peddled, her right arm hanging uselessly, and China stepped in quickly and caught her with a solid haymaker to the jaw. Tanith spun and fell to her knees.

Sanguine leaped at China, wrapping an arm around her

throat. They stumbled back, but instead of trying to break the choke, China's hand went to her belly. Blue energy crackled through her, throwing Sanguine off. He dropped to the pavement, and China turned her attention back to Tanith. She activated the symbols on both of her palms, then stepped up to clamp her hands on either side of Tanith's head. Tanith arched her back and screamed.

Valkyrie pushed at the air, but her focus was off, and all she could do was stir up a breeze that played with China's hair. China looked at her and let go of Tanith, who collapsed beneath her. Valkyrie's legs gave out and she fell. She saw a Remnant flitting down towards Tanith, but China held out her hand.

"No," she commanded. "Leave her. She annoys me. Take the scarred one."

The Remnant hovered as if reluctant, then darted for Ghastly. China turned back to Valkyrie. "Come now," she said. "Your disciples are waiting."

49

FOLLOWING THE KEY

Tanith raised her head, and watched China and Ghastly drive off in the van, taking Valkyrie with them. Tanith's head was buzzing and every joint was sore.

"Is someone gonna help me up?" Sanguine asked as he lay spreadeagled on the pavement. Tanith ignored him. Skulduggery came over, pulled her to her feet, and a wave of dizziness overtook her. She stumbled back against a lamp post.

"They have Val," she muttered, waiting for the world to stop spinning. "Why didn't China just kill her? Why do they want to keep her alive?"

"Valkyrie is Darquesse," Skulduggery said.

"What?"

"It's a long story, one that we're going to help her make sure never comes true. Our only chance is the Receptacle. Are you OK? Can you fight?"

"Always." Tanith pushed herself away from the wall, managing to stand by herself. "But China has the key. Can you activate the machine without it?"

"Hello?" said Sanguine. "Anyone hear me?"

"According to Gordon we *need* the key," Skulduggery said. "We have to get it back."

"So we fight our way through all the possessed to China, and then fight our way back to the Receptacle? I like a good scrap as much as the next girl, Skulduggery, but we'd never make it. We need another plan."

"We don't *have* another plan. The Remnants are in place right *now*. We don't have time to mess about trying to hotwire a machine that none of us have ever *seen* before."

Sanguine grunted. "Fine. Don't help me up. See if I care. I'll just lie here an' freeze to death."

Tanith spun to him. "Will you shut up?"

Sanguine smiled. "You are finally succumbing to my charms, ain't ya?"

"Unless you have something constructive to add," Skulduggery said, anger biting the edges of his words, "then I agree with Tanith. Shut. Up."

"Oh, but I *do* have somethin' constructive to add. Sword-lady, help me up now an' I'll solve all your problems an' woes, I swear on my dear dead momma, may she rest in pieces."

Tanith stalked over to him, grabbed his outstretched hand, and twisted his wrist until he leaped up, howling.

"There," she said. "Happy?"

The Texan scowled at her. "We got to work on our communication skills, honey bunny."

"This constructive thing you were going to add to our conversation," Skulduggery said. "Now would be a good time to share it."

There was a sound, like a car backfiring in the distance. Sanguine frowned, and his hand went to his shoulder. When he took it away, it was covered in blood. "Hey," he said, surprised. "I think I been shot."

Tanith looked past him, and saw a man running towards them, his left arm in a sling, his right holding a gun. He was firing as he came.

"That guy shot me!" Sanguine exclaimed.

The man's aim wasn't improving, but the closer he got, the closer the bullets whined. Tanith ducked behind Skulduggery as he held up a hand, creating a solid wall of air. Sanguine took a deep breath, and the ground swallowed him.

"Remnant?" Tanith asked.

"Dalrymple," Skulduggery replied.

The man, Dalrymple, threw the gun away and took a sword from his belt, yelling a battle-cry. A hand emerged from the ground, snagged his foot, and Dalrymple sprawled onto the road. Sanguine rose up behind him, kicking the sword from his hand. Dalrymple lunged, but Sanguine caught him with a knee to the gut, then grabbed his ear. Dalrymple cried out, and Sanguine dragged him over to the pavement. He dumped him at Skulduggery's feet, then turned his full attention to clutching his injured shoulder.

"This really hurts," he muttered. "I hope we're gonna kill this guy. We *are* gonna kill him, right?"

"Please," Dalrymple sobbed. "Let me close to them. I'm sorry I shot at you. You were just in my way. I thought you were going to stop me."

Skulduggery turned his head, looking behind them. Tanith followed his gaze. The possessed would have been preparing to stop anyone from reaching the Receptacle – so that probably meant that the place where they gathered was directly outside the chamber. She looked at Skulduggery and knew he was thinking the same thing.

"Leave the weapons here," Skulduggery said. "We won't stop you."

Sanguine looked up. "What? We're lettin' him go?"

"This has nothing to do with you, Sanguine."

"I'm the one he shot!"

"Dalrymple, go. Now."

Dalrymple looked up, tears in his eyes, like he was waiting for Skulduggery to change his mind. When nothing more was said, he scrambled up, and sprinted past them.

"I don't believe you guys," Sanguine said, shaking his head. "I bet if he'd shot *you*, you wouldn't be nearly so forgivin'."

Tanith looked at him. "How stupid are you?"

Sanguine looked offended. "Not very."

"Think about it, moron. None of us know where the Receptacle is, do we? None of us know where the Remnants are. They could be anywhere. It's a big mountain range."

"It ain't *that* big."

"He's going to lead us right where we need to go. And you notice he's on foot? So he knows a short cut."

"And... we're gonna follow him?"

"Do you need me to explain it to you slower?"

"Hey, enough with the attitude, OK? I been shot, an' my insides are still all twisted up, and I'm sufferin' from blood loss. But I ain't no moron. Fact is, both of *you* are the morons. You're plannin' on followin' him to the creepy critters an' the machine that'll save us all, but you can't start it, can ya? What're you plannin' on doin', lookin' at it awhile? Remarkin' on how pretty an' shiny it is? Call that a plan?"

"Do you have a better idea?" Skulduggery asked.

"Course I do. I'm from Texas. We all got better ideas in Texas. My idea is to follow that fool who shot me, get into the cavern where the giant Soul Catcher is kept, and turn it the hell *on*, usin' this key I picked from the pocket of Miss China Sorrows." Sanguine held up the golden key, and tossed it to Skulduggery. "Now tell me – what do y'all think of *that* particular plan?"

They kept at a safe distance, but they needn't have bothered. Dalrymple was so intent on getting to his precious Remnants that he didn't even glance back once. Sanguine spent most of the time complaining about his arm. He was chewing on a leaf to numb the pain, but it was obvious, just by looking at him, that he was getting weaker with each step. Halfway there, Skulduggery slowed down to help him traverse the rocky terrain. Sanguine was too tired to question the sudden change of heart, but Tanith knew that Skulduggery must have one last job for him to do before he fell by the wayside.

"Hold on," Skulduggery said at last, as they watched Dalrymple disappear from sight. The golden key was glowing. He moved it around, and the glow strengthened. "This way. Tanith, check on Dalrymple."

He half-carried Sanguine up an incline to their right, and Tanith jogged to where she had last seen Dalrymple. She crouched as she approached an outcrop, and peered over it. Below her, in a wide-open space of grasses and gorse bush, were two thousand possessed people. She saw Dalrymple running towards them, then ducked down before anyone saw her. Keeping low, she hurried back, and rejoined Skulduggery just as he sat Sanguine down next to a sheer wall of rock.

"I'm feelin' distinctly woozy," Sanguine mumbled.

"It looks like they're all there," Tanith told Skulduggery. "And I mean, all of them. There's an *army* down there. Is this the cavern? Where's the door?"

"I think this *is* the door," Skulduggery replied. "Notice how sharp the angles are on this section? See? Less weathered. Less beaten down by the elements."

"So... what? What does that mean?"

"They're resistant to damage. And the door to the cavern would have to be *very* resistant to damage."

"Hey," she said, nudging Sanguine with her foot, "can you take us inside?"

"Let him rest," Skulduggery told her. "We're going to need him soon enough. I'm sure we can get in here by ourselves."

"So how do we open it? Is there a magic word or something?"

"I hope not. I'm assuming this key will activate the machine *and* open the door, but..."

"But where's the keyhole?"

"Indeed."

He tapped the key against the rock wall. Nothing happened. She pressed her hand flat against it, the way she'd open any locked door. Still nothing.

"Are you sure this is the door?" Tanith asked. "I can't see any join, or hinge, or anything like that. How does it open? Does it swing, or rise, or sink, or what? If we knew that, we could work our way back from there."

Skulduggery examined the rock anew. "It wouldn't be easy

to open, but at the same time it should be straightforward. Anyone who needs to access the Receptacle ought to be able to do so, once they have the key."

"So maybe it's a combination of both," Tanith said. "A magic word spoken by whoever's holding the key."

"It's possible, but that doesn't exactly help us. Any one word in any language, magical or mortal, could unlock it."

"Well, you're the detective. You figure it out."

Skulduggery sighed, and considered the rock wall again. "Open," he said loudly. "*Oscail. Oscailte amach.* Enter. *Mellon.* Open Sesame. Remnant. Soul Catcher. Receptacle. Danger."

"Wow," Tanith breathed. "We could be here a while."

Sanguine looked up from his seated position beside Skulduggery. "There's somethin' written on it," he said, slurring his words. "The key. Look."

Skulduggery turned it over and Tanith stepped up, but all she could see was flat gold. "I can't see anything," she said.

"I can," Skulduggery murmured. He tilted the key till it caught the light. "It's faint, but it's there."

She peered closer. "You sure it's not just your imagination playing tricks?"

"When my imagination plays tricks," Skulduggery answered, "they're a lot more elaborate."

"I swear, I can't see anything."

"That's because you're lookin' with your eyes," Sanguine said, his head drooping. "Me an' the skeleton, we ain't *got* eyes."

"It says *erode*," Skulduggery said.

Tanith looked at the rock wall. "Nothing's happening."

Skulduggery thought for a moment, then said, "*Creim*," and the wall started to rumble.

Tanith looked at him. "It worked. It's working. What did you say?"

"*Creim*," he repeated. "It means *erode* in Irish."

Relief swept through her and she smiled, and the rock exploded into a cloud of dust that stung her eyes and got into her mouth. Tanith stumbled away, coughing and spluttering. The dust was in her hair and in her clothes. Her vision finally cleared and she saw Skulduggery, standing there in a dust-free air bubble.

"Oh," he said, noticing the state she was in. "Sorry."

The cloud parted for him as he walked through it. Tanith scowled and followed, helping Sanguine up and entering the newly-formed cave mouth.

"Maybe you should put your arm around me," Sanguine said. "I'm feelin' faint."

"If you faint, you fall," Tanith responded.

Torches flared in brackets as they passed. The tunnel went on for twenty metres, then opened out into a cavern. Skulduggery stood just ahead, waiting for them to catch up.

"Well?" Tanith asked. "Is it there?"

He didn't answer. He didn't have to.

A globe, like a small glass moon, 100 metres high and 100 metres wide, sat in a cradle of metal and wooden struts, lashed together with rope and chains. The architects, the engineers, whoever had built this, had used the rocky outcrops to border the machine, to supply its foundation. The cavern itself seemed to be an extension of the massive device, designed to accentuate the size and shape, giving the Receptacle an air of something that had always been here, a natural formation of magic and old science, deep within the mountain.

"Cool," Tanith said.

She left Sanguine leaning against the wall, and joined Skulduggery as he hurried to what looked like a control centre. There were dials and gauges and levers, and a narrow rectangular slot. Without wasting time on ceremony, Skulduggery slipped the key into the slot. Immediately, a gauge came to life. Skulduggery grabbed a lever and pulled it down sharply.

And nothing happened.

"Well," Tanith heard Sanguine say, "that's kinda disappointin'."

"No," Skulduggery said, "look. It's moving."

Tanith could see it now. The globe was beginning to rotate – very, very slowly. It creaked as it did so.

"It hasn't been used in over a century," Skulduggery said. "It needs some time to warm up. In order for the Remnants to be dragged into it, we've got to make sure that the possessed stay close by."

"An' just how," Sanguine asked, "are you plannin' on doin' *that*?"

Skulduggery looked at him, and his head tilted.

Sanguine's mouth turned down. "Aw, hell," he muttered.

50

MACGILLYCUDDY'S REEKS

Her surroundings were quite beautiful – a snow-covered mountain, layers of mist rising from the valleys, a pale blue sky. They had passed a lake on the way here, and the roads were narrow and winding, occasionally edged with low stone walls. Altogether very pretty, with the effect only ruined by the two thousand black-veined people waiting for her when she was pulled out of the van.

China marched her to a small hill in the middle of the

clearing, all the Remnants gathered round in their hijacked bodies. China removed the shackles from Valkyrie's wrists. Anton Shudder and Tesseract joined them on the hill. The crowd was silent.

"Valkyrie Cain," Tesseract said, "I am very glad I didn't kill you. What a mistake that would have been. I would have robbed us of our saviour."

"Let me go," Valkyrie said. "If I'm your saviour, then do as I command. Let me go."

"You're not our saviour. Not yet. But with a little help from us, you soon will be."

"I don't know what you expect me to say. Do you think I'm just going to agree to all this? I'm not going to hurt innocent people."

"If we torture you enough," said Tesseract, "you'll do anything we tell you to."

Valkyrie said nothing.

"I'm the one who saw you. I saw you through the eyes of Finbar Wrong, laying waste to the world. That's all we want. We want a dead world, where we are free, where we don't have to hide in flesh suits. You give us that world. From the moment I saw you I knew we had to help, to guide you on your path. Now, I am not so sure I was right."

"So you're going to let me go?"

There was a ripple of laughter in the crowd.

"No," Tesseract said. "You see, we have been talking, all of us, and we wonder if we are taking the correct approach. It was China who thought of it, actually."

China smiled. "We're friends, aren't we, Valkyrie? That's what you said. And because we're friends, because I know you so well, I can see that it would take a lot to make you hurt the people you love."

"I'm not Darquesse," Valkyrie blurted. "I've changed all that. That future doesn't happen any more."

"How can you be sure?" asked China.

"I've sealed my name."

"Ah, I see. So you think the only reason you kill everyone is because someone is forcing you to, yes?"

"Of course. Why else would I do it?"

"Because you want to, perhaps? Because something happens, something so awful that it drives you to the edge, and the only way out you can see is if everybody dies?"

"That's insane."

"All kinds of people want to kill the world, Valkyrie."

"Not me."

"Not yet." China laughed. "But I agree with you. I don't

think you have it in you. So I came up with an alternative. What if, Valkyrie, what you say is true? What if you *would* never do this? What if, in fact, it isn't even you?"

"What?"

"I think Darquesse is like *us*, you see. I think Darquesse has a Remnant inside her."

Valkyrie shrank back. "No."

"I think in order for our messiah to come out, one of us is going to have to bond with you."

"No."

"And we already have a volunteer," China said with a smile.

Fletcher appeared at China's side. "I love you," he said to Valkyrie. "And now I'm going to *be* you."

Hands grabbed her and she struggled against them, but there were too many. Her head was pulled back and there were fingers in her mouth. She bit down and tasted blood, heard a howl of pain, but her jaws were forced apart and she saw it, the Remnant, darting from Fletcher's mouth as he dropped to the ground, unconscious.

The Remnant latched on to her face and it was cold. The hands released her and Valkyrie staggered back, lost her footing. She fell, rolled down the small hill, all the while trying to pull the darkness away from her. She felt it slither down into her throat. Her hands clutched at her chest as the Remnant dissipated within her. Tendrils of cold slithered through her body and pierced her brain. Something burst within her mind and the fear went away, and Darquesse stood.

The others were watching her expectantly, eyes filled with hope and hunger, mouths twisted in smiles.

Ghastly was the first to step forward. "My Lady?" he asked, voice shaking. When Ghastly had been Ghastly, before the Remnant shared his being, he had been a good man. Darquesse remembered their first meeting, when he had told her that magic wasn't a game, and that she should walk away and leave this behind her. He had said those words for her own good, but of course she hadn't listened. This was a path she had always been meant to walk.

Destiny? She didn't believe in it. But she had seen into the future and they had seen herself burn the world. And *that*, she believed in.

She took her eyes off the people around her and looked at the world. The mountains and the snow, and the rocks and the sky. She tasted the air. Why would she want to destroy all this? What was it that could drive her to annihilate an entire planet? And what would she do, once everyone and everything was dead? Who would there be to talk to?

Darquesse smiled at the questions she found herself asking. No doubt, when the time came, she would fully understand why she was killing everything. When the time came, she was sure it would all make perfect sense.

"Lady Darquesse," someone said, barging through the crowd to throw himself at her feet. His left arm was in a sling. "I am yours to command. You have given me purpose. You have given me a reason to exist. What is your will?"

He looked up at her, tears in his eyes.

She kicked him under the chin, marvelling at her strength. His jaw splintered instantly, but her boot continued upwards and his head came apart around it. Some important piece of him, possibly his brain, shot into the sky like a football. His body crumpled and she laughed and turned to the others. The shock over what she had just done made some of them step back, but there were plenty of others who were laughing along with her, and there were a few who actually applauded. She despised them all.

She leaped for the nearest one, a sorcerer she had once spoken to in the old Sanctuary. Her fingers closed around his throat and she tore out his windpipe. The woman beside him clapped, and Darquesse put her fist through the woman's chest, then flung the body behind her.

The laughter was dying. No one was cheering any more.

Darquesse swept through them, their screams like a lullaby, making her smile. As she moved, she could sense the Remnant inside her. She could sense its presence and its confusion. This was not how it was meant to be. It had slithered its way inside and opened her up, allowed Darquesse to surface. But they had not, as the Remnant had expected, become one pure being. They were still two separate entities, and she felt its fear and it brought a chuckle to her lips.

Her soul was sealed, Nye had seen to that. It was hers, and hers alone. All the Remnant had managed to do was break down some walls between Valkyrie Cain and the source of her magic. It may have tainted something along the way, Darquesse couldn't be entirely sure. Not that it mattered. It was Darquesse who was in control here.

The Remnant wanted to get out. It was trying to bring itself back together and crawl out of her, but Darquesse wouldn't allow it. She kept it where it was, isolating it, draining its malevolence to add to the magic that was pumping through her body.

The sorcerers were attacking her now, trying to subdue her, trying to save themselves. She used the air to fling three of them upwards, then sent three spears of shadows after them.

Hands seized her from behind, trying to choke her. She poured darkness through her skin into his, and the man shrieked and fell back, his hands melting away to stumps. A stream of energy sizzled to her and she caught it in her palm, countered its effects without even knowing how she was doing it, and threw it back. The stream hit its owner, and its owner split apart in a fine red mist.

She crushed the skull of a handsome man and tossed him away from her. His body spiralled over the angry crowd. Things were not going as they had planned.

Darquesse clicked her fingers and flame enveloped her. Her skin and hair and clothes all burned, fiercely and brightly, but the fire didn't damage her. People scrambled to get away. She held out a hand and fire leaped at them. They rolled and writhed and screamed. She laughed. A man tried to run. Tesseract caught him by the throat.

"You run from your saviour, you ungrateful wretch?"

"She's killing us," the man gasped.

"This is what we call warming up." Tesseract shoved him back. "Darquesse, please accept my apologies. Kill as many as you like. When you are ready to begin the decimation of the world, please know that we will be ready to serve, to help in any way."

Darquesse used the fire to kill the man who had run, then let the flame go out and stalked towards Tesseract, wondering how long he would stay faithful once she started pulling out his spine. But then the ground started to crack, and Skulduggery Pleasant and Tanith Low burst up in a shower of dirt and rock. Billy-Ray Sanguine collapsed behind them and didn't move.

"Valkyrie," Skulduggery said, "stop this."

Darquesse looked at him, then looked at Tanith. Tanith looked scared, and shocked, and upset, and worried. She held her sword like she was ready to use it on anyone who got close. Darquesse could see her own reflection in the blade. A pretty girl with a scar in her cheek, sixteen years old and dark-haired. Her pale face splattered with other people's blood. Her eyes, dark-ringed. Is this what they all saw, she wondered, or did they see something else? Something magnificent and terrible? Something monstrous?

"Valkyrie," Skulduggery said. She looked back at him. "You're not yourself. Do you understand me? You're confused. You are Valkyrie Cain. You are not Darquesse."

"You cannot change who she is," Tesseract said from behind him.

"Shut up," Skulduggery said without looking around. "Valkyrie. Listen to my voice. I'm your friend. I'm your partner. I promised you I'd help you with this and I intend to. You don't want this to happen, I know you don't."

A man lunged at Tanith and Darquesse gestured, took his head off with a shadow.

"Val," Tanith said, her voice shaking. "Please. It's me. It's us. You don't want to hurt anyone. Come back to us."

"I could kill you," Darquesse said. She didn't have to talk loudly to be heard. "I could reach out, take hold of your face and squeeze, turn your head to mush. In your last few seconds of life, what would you think of me? Would you still love me? What about you, Skulduggery? I could kill you just as easily."

"You're not going to kill me, Valkyrie."

"Valkyrie is gone."

"No, she's not," Skulduggery said. "I'm talking to her."

Darquesse shook her head. "You don't understand."

"I understand perfectly. Darquesse isn't a separate entity. She isn't another person. She's you. If you make the wrong choices, if you stop loving the people who love you, if you allow the world to twist and turn and change you, then yes, the future we've seen will come to pass. But if you fight, and if you kick, and struggle, and refuse to give in to the apathy, or the anger, or the hopelessness, then you'll change the future, and you'll walk your own path. And I'll be right there beside you, Valkyrie. I'll always be beside you."

She felt the Remnant inside her, its anguish, and she grew tired of playing with it. It had come into her so eagerly, impatient to share her being and help her fulfil the fate that the psychics had foreseen. But now it understood that there would be no sharing. The Remnant's presence was merely offering her a peek at what was to come – but she would get there on her own. She didn't need any help.

It squirmed and fought and its screams filled her head, and when she was done enjoying it all, she flooded her body with heat, and the heat burned away the cold that the Remnant had brought. She purged it from her body, and purged it from her mind, and then it was gone. And with it, for the moment, went the bad thoughts and the emptiness.

Valkyrie's legs folded beneath her and Skulduggery darted forward to keep her from falling. "Thanks," she mumbled, as the crowd surged around her.

"No problem," Skulduggery said softly, then pressed his gun into her temple and said loudly, "Any of you take even one more step and Valkyrie dies."

51

THE RECEPTACLE

The crowd froze. Tesseract stared.

"You're bluffing," he said.

"Try us," Tanith told him, her sword flashing to Valkyrie's throat, where it lay cold against her skin. "You're not going to kill her," Tesseract said. "Put the weapons down."

Skulduggery thumbed back the hammer of his gun. "Valkyrie would rather die, here and now, than allow another one of you to possess her and drive her to become the monster that kills the world. We'd be doing her a favour, she knows we would."

Wreath came up beside Tesseract, smiling. "Don't be ridiculous. She's your friend. She's your partner. She's an honest, decent, innocent girl with her whole life ahead of her. You're not going to kill her in cold blood."

"Ghastly," Skulduggery called. "Are you here?"

The crowd parted, and Ghastly made his way forward.

"You've known me a long time," Skulduggery said. "Do you think I'd be willing to kill Valkyrie to save the world?"

Ghastly's fist clenched, and he looked at Tesseract. "He'll do it," he said.

"I agree," said China, gliding easily through the throng of people. "To be perfectly honest, I'm surprised he hasn't pulled the trigger already."

Wreath's lip curled in a snarl. "Then we'll take her from him."

"I don't like your chances," Skulduggery said. "There are some among you who could probably take down either myself or Tanith before we could act. But both of us? You don't have a hope. We're giving you ten seconds to vacate the people you've possessed."

"I'm not going back to prison," Ghastly said. "If you're going to kill Valkyrie, then go ahead. We might not get our dead world, but anything is better than going back to that room."

"We're not telling you to," Tanith said. "Vacate those people and leave. Neither side is going to win here today, so we're calling it a draw. Try your luck again tomorrow, and tomorrow we'll kick the hell out of you."

"You expect us to give you back these people?" China asked. "I think not. I rather like this body and this mind, and all the magic that comes with them."

"Those of us who are inhabiting the forms of sorcerers are *weapons* now," said Tesseract. "We're not going to relinquish these weapons so you can use them against us the next time we meet."

"I'm afraid you don't have a choice," Skulduggery said. "Those ten seconds start now."

Tesseract glared at him with hatred in his eyes, and then he looked at Valkyrie. "Your friends are prepared to kill you, Darquesse. They fear you. As well they should."

"Five seconds," Skulduggery said.

"This isn't over," Tesseract said.

He pried his mask away from his face and opened his mouth wide, as all around him his companions did the same. The Remnant squirmed out and flitted to the sky, and Tesseract collapsed, unconscious, the mask snapping back into place. All around Valkyrie, Remnants crawled out of the mouths of their vessels to emerge as a cloud of writhing blackness that filled the air with angry shrieks.

Valkyrie looked up at Skulduggery. "The Receptacle," she whispered.

"Don't worry, Val," Tanith said. "We already found it. See that little cave over there? That's the entrance." And even as she spoke, the ground started to rumble.

The Remnants' movements grew erratic, as the first of them felt the pull. Three of them suddenly whipped out of the cloud, yanked by an invisible hand to the mountain, their screeches turning from anger to terror. More followed, in greater numbers, forming a continuous stream of howling darkness.

The Remnant that had vacated Tesseract's body dived down, clinging on to the collar of the assassin's coat, fighting the pull. It dragged itself towards his masked face, stopping only when Skulduggery went to stand over it.

"The moment you inhabit that man," Skulduggery said, speaking loudly to be heard over the shrieking and the rumbling, "I'll kill him and you'll be destroyed. Do you think I'm bluffing?"

Tanith lowered her sword from Valkyrie's neck, and Valkyrie started to breathe again. The stream ended, disappearing into the mouth of the cavern. The Remnant clinging defiantly on to Tesseract was the last one. And then it too let go.

But instead of allowing itself to be pulled into the mountain, it veered off and lunged at Valkyrie. Tanith shoved her out of the way and the Remnant collided with her instead. Tanith went rolling down the embankment, and Valkyrie and Skulduggery leaped down after her. Tanith tried to pull the Remnant from her, but it was no use. Her throat bulged, and she stopped gagging.

Immediately, she spun on to her back, her boot striking Skulduggery's leg with a sharp crack of breaking bone. He yelled in pain and Tanith was up and jumping, spinning in mid-air to deliver another kick to his ribs. Skulduggery stumbled and went down.

Tanith reached for Valkyrie, who stepped back and slapped the hand away, struggling to adjust to Tanith as an enemy. Tanith had no such qualms. Her elbow smacked into Valkyrie's jaw and Valkyrie sprawled in the gorse brush. She got up and blocked a kick that drove her back, tried to respond with one of her own, but Tanith just laughed.

The air rippled and Tanith hurtled off her feet.

"Run!" Skulduggery shouted as he tried to get up.

Valkyrie sprinted for the cavern. The Receptacle was still active, she could hear the rumble and feel the ground tremble beneath her boots. If she could lure Tanith into the cavern, the machine would rip the Remnant out of her, but she didn't have much time. It was already slowing down. She glanced back to see Tanith flipping over Skulduggery's head, landing to scoop something off the ground. Skulduggery's gun.

Valkyrie turned to run back. Tanith fired twice and Skulduggery jerked, stumbling on his bad leg. He went down and Tanith threw the gun away, then looked up to grin at Valkyrie.

Cursing, Valkyrie resumed her run to the cavern. Tanith was behind her and gaining fast, and Valkyrie realised just how much her friend had been holding back during their time training together. Tanith was always stronger, faster and better, but she had never made it too obvious. There were occasions when Valkyrie had even fancied that they were becoming equals. Now, with the effortless way Tanith was closing the distance between them, Valkyrie could see what a self-deluding fool she'd been.

She reached the cavern before Tanith caught up to her. The deep roar from the Receptacle was almost deafening, dust falling from the rock ceiling. The orb in the machine was alive with swirling blackness. Valkyrie turned, panting, as Tanith staggered in behind her. The grin was gone, replaced with a strained determination. The Remnant inside her must have been screaming in pain.

"Let her go!" Valkyrie shouted.

Tanith kept coming, lurching with each step. Valkyrie pushed at the air, just hard enough to hurt and maybe loosen the Remnant's hold, but Tanith sprang, catching her by surprise. Valkyrie fell back, whipping the shadows to cover her retreat, but Tanith cartwheeled on one hand and ran to the wall, running up and disappearing behind a jagged outcrop.

Valkyrie kept stepping back, searching for a place to stand that wouldn't leave her vulnerable. She saw movement out of the corner of her eye as Tanith dropped behind her, but she was too slow to do anything about it. Tanith wrapped an arm around her throat, going for a sleeper hold. Panic flashed in Valkyrie's mind. Her hands moved of their own accord, snapping flat against the air, the way she used to do at home to boost herself up to her windowsill. This time, she shot backwards, hearing Tanith's surprised yell as they both went sprawling.

She expected Tanith to already be on her feet by the time

she looked up, but the effect of the machine was becoming more noticeable. Tanith's lips were black, and the veins were spreading as she dragged herself up off the ground.

Valkyrie ran at her, intent on piling on the pressure until the Remnant couldn't take any more. Tanith blocked the first punch and dodged the second, but Valkyrie kicked at her shin and connected with the third. She followed it with a side kick, shooting it out like Tanith herself had taught her. Tanith doubled over and Valkyrie pulled her head down to meet her knee. Tanith snapped back on impact and staggered away, tripping over her own feet and falling in the dust.

"Leave her," Valkyrie demanded.

Tanith laughed, and spat blood. "You're going to have to kill me, Val."

Valkyrie went to move forward, but she could tell Tanith was trying to draw her in. Instead, she grasped a trail of shadows and flicked it. Tanith dived and rolled, the shadows missing her completely. She kicked out, sweeping Valkyrie's legs from under her. Valkyrie hit the ground, felt Tanith's hands on her, and then her jacket was yanked off. Tanith hauled her up and threw her against the wall. A fist flew at her face and suns exploded before her eyes. Another one came in low, swooping into her side. Without the protection of her jacket her lungs turned sharp and painful and she knew a couple of ribs were broken.

Her eyes were blurred with tears and she couldn't see what she was doing, but she knew roughly where Tanith was, so she launched her head forward. She felt the impact and heard Tanith's howl of pain. She wiped her eyes, saw Tanith holding her nose. She shuffled forward with a kick that would have felled anyone without Tanith's abdominal muscles. As it was, all the kick did was to give her a little more room.

Tanith grimaced suddenly, and gasped, and for a moment the veins went away and Valkyrie knew it was her friend looking at her through tortured eyes. Then the eyes turned narrow as the Remnant regained control.

Valkyrie stepped up with a punch that jarred her whole body and sent Tanith to the ground. "Fight it!" she screamed. "Tanith, fight it!"

Tanith rolled over. She tried to get up, then collapsed.

"Force it out of you!" Valkyrie called. "Do it now!"

The Receptacle was starting to slow down. They only had a few more seconds before it deactivated. Valkyrie grabbed Tanith's ankles, started dragging her closer to the spinning orb. Tanith kicked and struggled, but she was weakening. Valkyrie dropped the ankles and bent over her, slipping her hands under Tanith's arms and pulling her up. Grunting with the effort, she shoved Tanith the last few metres to the machine. Tanith grabbed on to an outcrop to keep herself upright and stood there, gasping.

"It's over," Valkyrie said. She didn't have to shout any more because the rumbling was dying down. "Please. Leave Tanith alone. You've lost, OK? You're not going to win this so please leave her. Rejoin the others."

"Now why..." Tanith managed to say, "would I want to do that?"

"Because you've lost!"

"No, Val... I'll only have lost if I get stuck back in that room."

Valkyrie stalked up. Tanith raised a hand to stop her, but Valkyrie pushed it down, and her fingers closed around Tanith's throat. "If I have to choke you out of there, I will."

Tanith's black lips parted in a weak laugh that Valkyrie cut off by squeezing.

The rumbling was now nothing but a low, rhythmic throb. The orb was spinning on nothing but its own momentum, and that was slowing with every turn. Valkyrie squeezed tighter, and Tanith's free hand tapped uselessly at her.

"Get out of there!" Valkyrie screamed.

The orb stopped spinning, and the rumbling stopped, and the Receptacle deactivated.

"No," Valkyrie whispered.

Tanith smiled, grabbed Valkyrie's t-shirt and pulled her closer, and her elbow cracked against Valkyrie's head. The next thing Valkyrie was aware of was a gunshot. She was on the ground – she couldn't remember falling – and she was watching Tanith run up a wall of rock and vanish into the darkness.

Skulduggery limped over, keeping his gun-hand trained on where Tanith had last been.

"Are you OK?" he asked.

"No," Valkyrie whispered.

52

NEW YEAR'S EVE

Ireland was under quarantine, all flights in and out of the country cancelled. There were no boats or ferries, not even the fishermen could leave port. Europe was on high alert, even now that a cure had been found for the so-called Insanity Virus. The scientists had a technical name for it, but because they didn't have a clue how it started, no one bothered with them.

A small group of researchers had stumbled on to the cure, and they were getting all the attention and all of the praise. They had saved the country from a bizarre and mysterious new pathogen which had baffled experts from around the world. The virus had struck, receded, and was now eradicated.

Some thought it had been a terrorist attack. Others blamed secret government experiments, which drew much mirth from government representatives. People had been hurt, property had been damaged, and memories had been wiped. The number of dead, it was reported, was much lower than it could have been, for which everyone should have been thankful. But there would be no big parties or celebrations this New Year's Eve. After the last few days, it seemed like the whole of Ireland just wanted to lay low.

Valkyrie wasn't feeling especially thankful either. It was still freezing cold, still harsh and unforgiving, and Roarhaven was the last place she wanted to be tonight. She wanted to be back at home, where she'd been spending most of the last few days, keeping an eye on her parents.

Skulduggery had arranged for a squad of Cleavers to provide protection, in case Tanith decided to pay Haggard a visit, but Valkyrie was still worried, and in no mood to watch other people play politics.

Roarhaven Sanctuary was a mass of corridors that spiralled inwards to its centre. It was smaller than the old Sanctuary in Dublin, and less concerned with charm or, indeed, heat.

Heavy doors led off into rooms of varying sizes and functions. Many of the corridors were swamped in darkness, and others too dimly lit to be of any real use.

They arrived at the centre room. Skulduggery pushed the doors open and Valkyrie and Ghastly entered after him. Ravel nodded to them, but didn't break off his conversation with Geoffrey Scrutinous and Philomena Random. Valkyrie saw many people she recognised from the first meeting before Christmas. They were quiet, and looked tired.

The Necromancers stood off to one side, talking among themselves. To their right the Torment stood alone. The mood was sombre. Eyes were cast down. Gazes were not met. The atmosphere hung heavy with shame and regret and guilt.

Corrival Deuce was one of the dead. Who had killed him was unknown, and virtually impossible to establish, but it had sent all their plans and schemes into a spiral. Valkyrie hadn't known him for long, but she recognised the loss as much as anyone. He had been their great hope, a leader strong enough to convince the international community that Ireland could stand on its own, without interference from others. And now that hope was gone.

Gradually, the conversation died down. Ravel cleared his throat. "I suppose we should start, then. Welcome, all of you.

We've been through a lot in the last week, and I am immensely glad to see so many of you here tonight. We have lost friends and family, we have seen the whole country plunged into a nightmare we can only hope it will recover from – but of course, we don't have the luxury of time in which to lick our wounds and grieve for the departed.

"We have a state of emergency. According to a trusted source in the German Sanctuary, in those few days when we were compromised, the international community, headed by the American Council, was about to swoop in and save the day. While it could be seen as reassuring to have such good friends around the world, the unfortunate fact of the matter is that if they did swoop in, they would never swoop out again."

"Which means we need to consolidate our power as soon as possible," Scrutinous said, "and *that* means choosing a new Council of Elders."

"A vote," said Shakra. "Now. Tonight. We need to show them we're strong and decisive in the wake of what happened."

"Erskine," Skulduggery said, "I think the obvious thing would be to have you as the Grand Mage."

Ravel frowned. "What?"

"I agree with Skulduggery," Ghastly said. "You know how the game works. In fact, I'd say the internationals would actually find you *better* to work with than Corrival. You were his right-hand man for years – you share some of his views, but you aren't nearly as extreme."

Ravel rubbed his forehead wearily. "And does it matter at all that I have absolutely no interest at all in doing this job?"

"Not really," Skulduggery said. "Desperate times, desperate measures."

"A vote," said Scrutinous. "All those in favour."

Ayes filled the room.

Ravel sighed. "Fine. And in that spirit of desperation, Skulduggery can be my first Elder."

Skulduggery shook his head. "Not a chance."

"And how come you get to pass on the job offer and I don't?"

"Because I'm me."

"I have a suggestion," said the Torment. Everyone looked at him. "We have already given you the Roarhaven facility to use as your new Sanctuary, which you have gratefully accepted. However, some of the citizens of our fair town have voiced misgivings. They feel that our good will has been taken advantage of."

"Go on," Ravel said, suspicion in his voice.

"It is our opinion that the Council of Elders should be comprised of three mages of firmly different sensibilities. For too long, the members of the Council have all thought the same way, held the same view, and clung on to the same prejudices. If Erskine Ravel is indeed elected Grand Mage, it is my feeling that the first of his Elders should be Madam Mist."

Ravel actually recoiled at the suggestion. "But... Madam Mist is a Child of the Spider."

"As am I," the Torment said. "You would dismiss us all because of this?"

"No, of course not, it's just... Children of the Spider have always been reclusive. Even more so than the Necromancers."

The Torment nodded like a wise old man. "And it is time we changed our ways. Madam Mist would not only be a representative of the people of Roarhaven – and you would need their support for this Sanctuary to succeed – but she would also be a voice for the few, and the marginalised."

"Everyone gets heard in the Sanctuary," Ravel countered.

"And Madame Mist will ensure that valued tradition continues," the Torment said. "Unfortunately, this is not open to discussion. If our request is denied, we will be forced to withdraw all assistance – this very building included."

"You're holding us to ransom," Flaring said. "There's no way we'd ever agree to that."

"Excuse us for a moment," Skulduggery said, drawing stares from everyone in the room. He walked to the side, followed by Ravel and Ghastly and Valkyrie.

"You can't be serious," Ravel whispered. "You can't seriously expect me to work beside Mist."

"It's what they've been planning all along," Skulduggery replied. "When they offered us this building, we knew there was going to be a hitch."

"Mist is more than a hitch," said Ravel.

"Your Council is going to need her in order to survive here."

"If they planned this," Valkyrie said, "then we're just going along with their plan. How is that a good idea? This is the Torment we're talking about."

Skulduggery shook his head. "Their plan was for Mist to be an Elder alongside Erskine, with Corrival as Grand Mage. But that isn't the case any more. Now Erskine is the Grand Mage, and so whatever schemes they've come up with are going to have to change."

"Then we need another Elder who's on our side," Ghastly said. "To make sure Mist is kept in line."

"Yes, we do," Skulduggery nodded. "Which is why it should be you."

Ghastly's eyes widened. "Have you lost your mind?"

"Why not? You're liked, you're well-respected, and everyone knows about your bravery on the battlefield. This could be your chance to make a real difference."

"I'm not a politician," Ghastly said. "I'm a tailor."

"You can still make my suits in your spare time, but we're really going to need you to do this."

Ravel nodded solemnly. "Destiny is calling, my friend."

"That's not destiny, that's you. And if it's bravery on the battlefield you're after, why not ask Anton, or Vex, or any one of the Dead Men? There were more than just you, me and Skulduggery in our little group, if you remember."

"Anton Shudder scares people, and Dexter Vex is halfway around the world, living the life of an adventurer."

"Ghastly, think about what this will mean," Skulduggery said. "As Elder, you could track down Tanith, capture her without harming her, and authorise a team of experts to figure out how to get rid of the Remnant inside her. Who else is going to take the time to do that? Who else is going to care enough?"

Ghastly closed his eyes. "Fine."

"Well?" the Torment asked as they rejoined the others. "Have you reached a decision?"

"Yes, I have," Ravel said. "I will need to meet with Madame Mist to discuss a wide range of matters, but it would be an honour to have her beside me, providing no one has any objection to my own nominee, Ghastly Bespoke. No? No objections? Excellent. In that case, we have a new Council of Elders. I think applause is due."

They started to clap, and Valkyrie joined in. She waited until they were on their way out, when she was alone with Skulduggery, before speaking again. "Is it possible?" she asked. "To help Tanith?"

"No," he said. "From what we know of Remnants, it's permanently bonded to her. There's no helping her, not any more."

"So you lied to Ghastly."

"Ghastly knows," Skulduggery said, his voice sad. "He just doesn't want to believe it."

Fletcher was waiting outside. When Skulduggery left them, Fletcher gave Valkyrie a pair of sunglasses.

She frowned. "Where are we going?"

"Australia," he smiled, and took her hand. In an instant they were standing in a park on a sunny Sydney morning, obscenely bright despite the sunglasses, and the heat hit her like a fist.

"Woah," she breathed.

She turned, saw couples and families strolling in the sun. She saw the edge of the Opera House, half-hidden by tall trees, and she turned again and saw the city.

"Thought you might appreciate the change," Fletcher said, slipping on his own pair of sunglasses.

Valkyrie took off her jacket and sat on the grass, then lay back, smiling broadly despite everything that had happened. "I should get you to bring me places like this more often," she said. "Pack a pair of shorts, a bikini... I'd be set."

Fletcher sat down beside her. "And how'd you explain a tan to your folks in the middle of winter?"

"I'm sure I'd find a way."

"So why don't you?" he asked.

"Why don't I what?"

"Get me to take you to places like this more often?"

"I don't know. I should. I suppose I'm always busy."

"Well," he said with a laugh, "it's either that or you'd rather spend your time with Skulduggery than me."

"You know that's not true."

"Really?"

"It's partly true," she admitted.

Fletcher nodded. "I don't blame you, actually. He didn't try to hurt you like I did."

Her smile dropped. "That wasn't your fault."

"It still happened."

"And you can't remember any of it."

"Does that mean I don't get to feel guilty?"

"We all feel guilty, Fletch."

He looked at her, and she looked away. To her right, a bright green bird, some kind of parrot, was feasting on a discarded sandwich. Valkyrie watched it until it had eaten its fill, and then it hopped closer. She stayed very still. The bird hopped on to her folded jacket. It was so close she could sit up and touch it, but she didn't move.

Fletcher looked at the bird and smiled. "This is what I love about Australia. If we were in Dublin or London, this would be a dull old pigeon, and we'd be shooing it away. But here, everything's brighter, more colourful. More fun. I should take you down to the Gold Coast. Take you surfing."

"Wait till I'm better at manipulating water," Valkyrie replied. "Then I'll surf."

"But that takes the fun out of it."

The bird hopped on to her leg, and she laughed. It travelled north, and stood on her belly, its head twitching as it surveyed its surroundings.

Fletcher grinned. "You've made a friend."

"It's waiting for me to give it some food. I haven't got any food, birdie. Look, it's completely ignoring me. If it perches on my face, I swear to God..."

"Give me a smile," Fletcher said, moving his phone up slowly. He took three pictures, and on the third the parrot or cockatoo or whatever it was looked around, and Fletcher nodded. "That's a good one," he said. "That's one you can never show your family."

The bird flapped its wings. Valkyrie yelped and turned her face to the side as it lifted off, and when she looked back, it was sitting on Fletcher's head. She burst out laughing and rolled away, fumbling with her own phone before the opportunity was gone. Laughing so much her hand was shaking, she took a half-dozen pictures of an increasingly horrified Fletcher.

"Please don't poo," he muttered.

The bird flapped its wings and he yelled as it leaped from his head and dropped down on the other side of him. Immediately, his hands went to his hair, fixing and straightening where the bird had flattened. Then he lunged, trying to grab the phone from Valkyrie's hand, but she held on to it and curled up into a ball, laughing too hard to form words. Finally, he gave up, and lay back.

"Please don't show that picture to anyone," he said.

She slipped the phone into her pocket and lay against him. "No promises."

Fletcher put his arm round her. "We should do this more often. You need a break, Val. A holiday. When was the last time you had a holiday? I bet it was years ago, wasn't it? You need a week away from everything. A week where people aren't trying to kill you, where you're warm and happy and safe."

She kissed his cheek. "You're always looking out for me, aren't you? That's why I love you."

She felt his body stiffen. "You love me?"

Her smile faded. "Pretend I didn't say that." Fletcher sat up to look at her, but she closed her eyes. "It's a beautiful day, and it was a nice moment. Don't spoil it."

"OK," he said. He hesitated, then lay back down. "Sure."

They lay there, on the grass, in the sun.

"So when do you want to go back?"

"Let's give it a half-hour," she said. "I'm just getting warm."

*　　*　　*

They stayed an hour, and then teleported back to Ireland. The cold came in at Valkyrie from all sides, and she groaned as she handed Fletcher back the sunglasses. She called Skulduggery to pick her up, and as the sun went down, they arrived at the Necromancer Temple.

53

TENEBRAE

elancholia led them to the High Priest's private meeting room. She looked tired, and thin, and didn't even take the time to glare at Valkyrie like she usually did.

"The High Priest will be with you shortly," she mumbled. She swayed slightly, like she might faint, but regained her composure and left them in the room.

"She looks sick," Valkyrie said. Skulduggery nodded, but didn't comment.

The meeting room was a circular chamber with a domed

ceiling, lit by dozens of candles. Valkyrie sat at the round table and waited. Fifteen minutes later, High Priest Tenebrae walked in, and she stood. She was so used to seeing him flanked by Craven and Quiver, that meeting him alone was a little jarring. It was like he'd turned up without his clothes on.

"Detective Pleasant," Tenebrae said, "Miss Cain, what can I do for you? We're all very busy here, dealing with the fallout from the Remnant attacks."

"You weren't at the Sanctuary meeting," Skulduggery said.

"I felt my time was better spent in an environment where I wasn't despised. From what I hear, however, you all seem to have managed without me. Ravel and Bespoke and Mist – strange bedfellows. But I must ask why you are here. I am, as I have said, very busy."

Skulduggery's lunge was so sudden that Valkyrie jumped back in shock. He shoved Tenebrae against the wall.

Flustered, the High Priest tried to break the hold. "What the hell do you think you're doing?"

Skulduggery pointed his gun into Tenebrae's face. "Where's the Remnant?"

Tenebrae froze. "The Remnants are trapped. You said so yourself."

"I mean *your* Remnant. The one you had trapped in your

own little Soul Catcher. The one who inhabited Kenspeckle Grouse, who tortured Tanith Low. Where is *that* Remnant?"

"I... I assume it's with all the others..."

"Five months ago, Solomon Wreath took possession of the Soul Catcher with that particular Remnant inside. We were assured it would be returned to the Midnight Hotel. Anton Shudder said that never happened."

"There's obviously been a mistake..."

"Finbar Wrong can't remember much, but he can remember Wreath turning up with the Soul Catcher a few days before all this started."

"You're saying Wreath released the Remnant on purpose? To what end? To inhabit this Finbar Wrong person?"

Skulduggery stepped closer. "I'm saying you ordered him to."

"Preposterous. This man is a Sensitive, isn't he? Why would I order such a thing?"

"Maybe because you wanted a glimpse into the future."

"In which case," said Tenebrae, "I could have merely paid a Sensitive to do so."

"Not if there was something in that future you wanted to keep secret."

"Detective Pleasant, you're accusing me without one single shred of proof that I had anything to do with this."

"Where's Wreath?" Skulduggery asked.

"I'm afraid I don't know."

"He's in hiding?"

"I told you, I don't know. We haven't seen him since the Remnant attack. I fear he may have been killed."

"Which would be very convenient for you."

"Quite the contrary. If Cleric Wreath were here, I'm sure he could explain why he didn't return the Remnant to the Midnight Hotel as per my instructions. I neither like nor appreciate being accused of something I did not do. And if you're going to shoot me, then shoot me. Otherwise, put down the gun and stop this ridiculous posturing."

"I should shoot you. I should kill you."

"Cold-blooded murder? In front of your protégée?"

"It wouldn't be murder. It would be a justifiable execution."

Tenebrae's eyes flickered to Valkyrie. "And are you prepared to let him? If he kills me, it all changes for you. You'll be banished from the Necromancer Order. You'll never be able to fulfil your destiny. You'll never become the Death Bringer—"

Skulduggery smacked the gun against Tenebrae's head. "Stop calling her that."

"Why?" Tenebrae snarled, his hand rising to his forehead. "Because you don't want to hear it? Because it offends your delicate sensibilities? If she is who Cleric Wreath thinks she is, she has a chance to save the world."

"From what, exactly? You've never been too clear on the *threat*, have you? What does the Death Bringer save us from?"

Blood was trickling through Tenebrae's fingers. "These are matters I will not speak about to outsiders."

"Then you'll tell Valkyrie?"

"When she's ready to hear it."

"And when will that be? When it's too late for her to turn back?"

"Detective Pleasant, are you worried that Valkyrie will slip from your influence? I would never have guessed you'd be so insecure."

"This has nothing to do with me."

"Which presumably means that this is all to do with her, am I correct? And yet you haven't once allowed her to speak for herself this entire conversation."

"I enjoy listening," Valkyrie said.

Tenebrae's smile was not particularly good-humoured. "You're not usually so shy, Valkyrie. When you're on your own, you talk an extraordinary amount, don't you? You have opinions on everything. But when Detective Pleasant is here, you seem content to let him do all the talking for you. Have you noticed this?"

"Can't say I have," Valkyrie said.

"But now that I've pointed it out, I assure you that you're going to. He's afraid, you see. He's terrified that you'll turn out to be the next Lord Vile. Isn't that true, Detective?"

Skulduggery's voice lowered. "Valkyrie's path is her own."

"And if she does, in fact, turn out to be the next Lord Vile? What then? Will you still be so philosophical? Or will you hunt her down and kill her?"

"If it comes to that," Skulduggery said, putting his gun away, "you'll be dead long before you get to see if you're right."

Tenebrae took his hand away from his forehead, and looked at the blood. "Just so you know, I will be making a formal complaint about you to the Sanctuary. Not that they'll take any notice. Two of your best friends on the Council of Elders, Detective – this couldn't have worked out better for you if you'd planned the whole thing."

The mood in the car on the drive back was sombre.

"What are you thinking about?" Skulduggery asked.

She shook her head. "I don't know. Everything. My

thoughts can't seem to settle. Too much to think about. Have you heard anything about Clarabelle?"

"No," he said. "No I haven't."

"We shouldn't have allowed her to return to the Hibernian alone. We should have realised she'd find Kenspeckle's body."

"Valkyrie, we were organising the teleportation of two thousand people – most of whom were still unconscious. We didn't have time to consider each and every one of them."

"We let her go, Skulduggery. We didn't even think about what she'd find. Do you think she's figured out what she did?"

"She won't remember it, but..." He sighed. "The evidence is there. We made a mistake."

"And now Clarabelle has run off."

"If she wants to be alone, we should respect that. She's lost someone who meant the world to her. She needs time to grieve. How are you coping?"

"I'm grand."

"Have you mourned? Fight now, mourn later. Like you said, that's our thing. And now is the time to mourn."

"I don't know. I don't know how to feel or how to, to process it, you know? Kenspeckle reminded me of my granddad. Grumpy and grouchy and not approving of the people I hung out with. I felt safe with him. Every time he was around I knew that whatever happened, he could fix me. He'd shuffle in, complain, make me feel guilty about getting into another fight. Then he'd insult you, make me laugh, and fix me. And right before he left he'd say something really nice, to make sure I'd know he cared."

"You're going to miss him."

She looked out the window. "Please don't make me cry."

"Of course," Skulduggery said. "I'm sorry."

She didn't say anything, and they drove on in silence until another name drifted, unwelcome, into her thoughts. "Scapegrace," she muttered.

Skulduggery turned his head to her. "What about him?"

"He's still locked in Kenspeckle's examination room. They both are."

"And?"

"Well, we should probably let them out?"

"So they can make more trouble for us?"

"We can't just leave them there. They're looking for a cure, and Kenspeckle said it might be possible. We ought to let them out so they can find someone else to help them."

"Like who?"

"How about Nye? This'd be right up his alley."

"We don't want anything to do with Doctor Nye."

"And we won't *have* anything to do with him. We'll give them his name, let them find him. We can't leave them locked up in that room, Skulduggery. You know we can't. Just stop by the Hibernian. I'll be two minutes."

He grumbled about it a little more, but fifteen minutes later, Valkyrie was hurrying from the Bentley into the Hibernian. The place was a mess. The walls were scorched and rubble littered the walkways. The screen was off, but a hole had been blown through the wall, and she climbed in. Lights flickered in the corridors. Her footsteps were loud. Suddenly, coming in alone didn't seem like such a great idea. What if a Remnant had stayed behind?

She reached the examination room, but the transparent door stood open.

"They said they—"

Valkyrie shrieked and leaped away, spinning in mid-air to face her attacker. She landed and stumbled, and all the while Caelan watched her with a raised eyebrow.

"My God!" she gasped. "Don't do that!"

"Don't do what?"

"Don't sneak up on me!"

"I wasn't sneaking."

"You nearly gave me a heart attack!"

"I wasn't sneaking. I was walking."

"You should wear a bell round your neck!"

"Are you finished hyperventilating?"

"No!" Valkyrie shouted, then felt stupid. "What? What do you want?"

"I was just going to say, before you started screaming, that I released them. The two zombies. They said they were friends of yours."

"They said that?"

"I suspect they may have been lying, but the taller one would not shut up, so I opened the door and asked them to leave me alone. I hope you don't mind."

She forced herself to calm down. "No. No, I don't mind. I came to let them out anyway, so..."

"The crisis is over, I take it?"

"Yes. You didn't hear the details?"

"I'm a vampire without a pack. Nobody tells me anything."

"Ah," said Valkyrie. "Right. Yes, the crisis is over. And now that, you know, you're here, I suppose I should thank you for arriving when you did."

"You were in danger. I had to save you."

She nodded, and smiled. Out of gratitude, she knew she should have just let that one go – but then she found herself saying, "Well, thank you for *helping* me. *Saving* me is a bit... strong."

"Have you seen him since? The boy?"

"You mean Fletcher. Yes, of course I have."

"Even after everything he did?"

"That wasn't him – that was the Remnant."

"If what happened to him had happened to me, I would never have hurt you."

"It couldn't happen to you," Valkyrie said, "you're a vampire. Remnants can't possess the dead."

"Is that how you see me? As a dead thing?"

"No," she admitted.

"How do you see me?"

"As a friend."

"Nothing more?"

He touched her arm and she smiled, but moved away. "Caelan, I don't want you to think that this is going somewhere. You've been a really good friend to me, you've really come through, but I am firmly and absolutely with Fletcher. And even if I wasn't, I still don't think it'd be a good idea."

"Love is rarely a good idea."

"You don't love me."

"Yes, I do."

"Please, stop saying that."

"What will it take for you to love me?"

"I can't love a vampire."

"Because we're monsters? Because when the sun goes down, we change? You realise, of course, that the sun went down a few hours ago."

Valkyrie's eyes widened, and she immediately backed away. "What are you doing?"

"Don't worry," he smiled, "I'm not going to change." He took a syringe from his pocket. "Dusk used this, remember? It's a mixture of wolfsbane and hemlock and various other herbs. He'd inject it a few times a night, and it'd stop him changing. I've spent the last few days searching for it. The old man had manufactured more. Dozens of vials of it, for whatever reason."

"Kenspeckle hated vampires," Valkyrie said softly.

"I took every last one of the vials. I didn't think he'd mind, now that he's dead. I read his notes too, so I know how to make my own." Caelan's eyes closed. "I can feel it. It wants to get out. It doesn't understand why it can't." He looked at Valkyrie. "I don't have to be the monster. For you... For you, I can be normal. I can be human."

"If this is how you're going to live, you have to do it for yourself, not for me."

He smiled again. "You're my reward."

"No, Caelan, I'm not."

"Not yet, maybe. I have to prove myself. I'm willing to do that."

"Listen," said Valkyrie, "I'm trying to be as clear about this as I possibly can. I don't want to be with you."

"I can hear how fast your heart beats every time you look at me."

"Well," she muttered, "that's hardly fair."

"You are a strange girl, Valkyrie Cain."

"And I've got a Skeleton Detective waiting for me outside."

"You'd better get back to him, then. I'll see you soon."

Valkyrie thought he might step closer, try to kiss her, but instead, he just smiled. She walked away, and tried to ignore the fact that she was disappointed.

She didn't tell Skulduggery about Caelan. She got in the Bentley, told him the zombies had already escaped, and they drove back to Haggard.

"It's not over," said Valkyrie.

"What isn't?"

"This whole Darquesse business. I didn't stop it, did I?"

Skulduggery hesitated. "It doesn't look like it, no."

"No one else remembers what they did when they were possessed, but I do. I remember more and more all the time. The Remnant wasn't controlling me, it just... opened a door. Those people who died. I did that." She took a breath, and let it out slowly. "Don't worry. I'm not going to start crying or anything. If I had been in control, it wouldn't have happened. Obviously, I wasn't in control."

"I'm glad you realise that."

"But now we have proof, right? That there is something in me capable of doing everything we saw in that vision. So what are we going to do about it?"

"What do you suggest?"

Valkyrie looked straight ahead, at the road. "You could kill me."

"I have no intention of killing you, Valkyrie. Something turns you. Something triggers the change from the Valkyrie Cain we all know and tolerate to Darquesse, evil witch-queen of Dublin."

"It's going to be something tragic, isn't it?" she said. "Something awful happens to me or to someone I love, and I go nuts and seek revenge on the whole world."

"That's a possibility."

"Any idea what this awful, tragic event might be?"

"I don't know. But whatever it is, I'll be looking out for it, and so will you. When it comes, we'll be ready."

He dropped her off at the pier, and she gave him a wave and watched him drive away. She took out her phone as she hurried to her house, making sure the reflection was still out at a neighbour's party.

According to the message it had left her, it was standing in the corner not talking to anyone. The party itself was a complete flop, with no one being in the mood to make merry. Valkyrie, however, managed a smile at the thought of walking through her own front door for once, and letting the reflection be the one to climb up to the window.

She felt bad about the Cleavers, forced to keep watch out here in the freezing cold. Their van was parked on the far side of the road, with the engine off so as not to arouse suspicion. She had never engaged a Cleaver in conversation, had never even heard one speak, not really, but she approached the van anyway. She could sneak them out a couple of coffees if they needed warming up, and possibly give them some straws so they wouldn't even have to take their helmets off. She didn't know if they even drank coffee. She doubted it.

The front of the van was empty, so Valkyrie rapped lightly on the side door. The windows were darkened. When there was no sound from inside, she frowned. There were three Cleavers stationed here – one stayed with the van at all times, and the other two took regular patrols around the area. She gripped the handle. To her surprise it wasn't locked. She slid the door open. Three Cleavers lay dead inside.

She turned and ran to her house. She slipped on the road and fell, rolled, lunged up and kept running. She jumped the low wall around her front garden, landing in the shadows, staying out of the light that shone from the living room window. The fire was roaring and the TV was on.

Valkyrie saw her mum and dad chatting, and her knees went weak with relief. But they were talking to someone, a woman in jeans and a heavy sweatshirt. Valkyrie didn't recognise her until she turned her head to laugh. Valkyrie ran into the house and burst through into the living room. They all looked round, surprised at the dramatic entrance.

"Hi, Stephanie," Tanith said.

54

ENEMIES

"Heat," Valkyrie's mum said. "Heat!"

Her dad got up, hurried out into the hall. She heard him close the front door to stop the draught, but couldn't take her eyes off Tanith. "What are you doing here?"

"My car broke down," Tanith smiled. "I remember you said you lived here, so I thought I'd stay somewhere warm until my lift arrived. Are you OK? You look like you're in shock."

Her dad came back in. "Born in a barn, were you? I

swear to you, Tanith, I don't know where she gets it from."

Tanith laughed. "Don't worry, Des, she's exactly the same in school. I may only be a substitute teacher, but I've been around long enough to know that Stephanie swans in and out of class expecting doors to close all by themselves."

They all chuckled, except for Valkyrie.

"Tanith," Valkyrie's mum said, "were you caught up in this Insanity Virus thing? Wasn't it awful?"

"Oh, Melissa, it was. My neighbour got it, actually. He went nuts. Didn't hurt anyone, thank God, but it was so scary. Just like the reports on TV. He's fine now, though."

"It was an attack," Valkyrie's dad said. "Something like this just doesn't happen in nature. I bet you that whoever did this was using Ireland as a testing ground. It'll be America next, you wait and see. Or London."

His wife shook her head. "Some people are saying now it was hallucinogenic drugs pumped into the water supply. They're even saying it started out as a prank. A *prank*!"

"I'm sure you're right," Tanith said, nodding. "But it was terrifying. I stayed home the entire time – there was no way I was setting foot outside."

"Wise woman."

"Oh, excuse me," Tanith said, taking out her phone and reading the screen. "My lift is here."

"That was quick."

"That's the good thing about boyfriends – they come when you call. I'm not too sure how to get back to my car, though. It was on *one* of these roads..."

"Oh, I'm sure Steph won't mind walking you back."

"No problem," Valkyrie said. "You ready to go now? Let's go now."

Tanith stood up, and smiled again. "So eager to get a teacher out of her house. Des, Melissa, thank you so much for your hospitality. Hopefully I'll see you at the next parent-teacher meeting."

While her parents said their goodbyes, Valkyrie ushered Tanith out of the house.

"If you're going to set me on fire," Tanith said quietly, "you might want to wait until we're around the corner."

Valkyrie glanced back. Her dad was on the front step watching them go. After another few moments of letting the heat out, he closed the door.

Immediately, she stepped away from Tanith. "Why are you here?"

Tanith kept walking, forcing Valkyrie to keep up. "We're friends, Val. I just wanted to drop in, say hi."

"Ghastly's an Elder. He's getting everyone to figure out a way to help you."

She smiled. "Why would you think I need help? Look at me – don't I seem happy to you?"

"You're a Remnant."

They were around the corner now, out of sight and heading down to the pier.

"And we Remnants are happy creatures," Tanith said. "So Ghastly's an Elder, is he? Well, I'm glad. I wouldn't have liked to see him spend the rest of his life in that little shop, never making any new friends. Maybe now he'll meet a nice girl, settle down..."

"He loves you."

"He *is* a sweetheart."

Valkyrie stopped walking. "What do you want, Tanith?"

Tanith turned to her. "I'm here to tell you that I'm not going to kill your folks. That's what you're worried about, isn't it? Well, you don't have to be. I had a perfect opportunity to kill them, right there, and I didn't. The fact is, I'm going to leave your family alone."

"Why?"

"I've been a few people these past few days. I've been Finbar, Shudder, Tesseract. I have to say, though, and I'm not being biased, that I prefer being me. I prefer being Tanith. I'm just *prettier*, you know? And I smell nicer.

"But when I was Finbar, I saw that vision of you, in the future, and I got so excited. I started thinking of all the different ways we could help. First we were worshipping you, then we tried possessing you, and that didn't work. Have you talked to any psychics lately? They're still having dreams about Darquesse, did you know that? Whatever you did, Val, it didn't change anything. You sealed your name, but that just means you decide to kill the world all on your own, with nobody controlling you. It means you kill your own parents, of your own free will.

"So now you see why I don't want any harm to come to your folks. I want you to get there naturally – I want things to happen as they're meant to happen. And that means your parents stay alive and stay healthy, right up until the moment you kill them."

"And what are you going to do?" Valkyrie asked. "You're just going to sit around and watch?"

"I'm not the sitting around type now, am I? I'll be getting into all sorts of trouble, don't you fret. I'll be guiding you, nudging you. Every so often I'll give you the occasional push, just to keep life interesting, to make sure you're not straying too far from your path."

"I will never become Darquesse."

"You already did, Val, for three minutes, and it was beautiful. And I understand it now, why she turned on my brothers and sisters. Darquesse is indiscriminate about who she kills. She is a true, pure force of destruction. The next time she comes out, I don't plan to be anywhere nearby."

"I'll die first," Valkyrie said. "I'll kill myself."

"No," said Tanith, "you won't."

"I'd rather die than hurt my family."

"But you won't kill yourself. You don't have it in you."

"You don't know what I have in me."

"But we're all going to find out." Tanith smiled. "How is *my* family, by the way? My *other* family?"

"The Remnants are trapped and locked away. We're finding somewhere new to keep them. You'll never find them."

"Maybe I will, maybe I won't. But that's all yet to come, isn't it? We have all that to look forward to. For the right now, though, for the here and now, the most we can do is enjoy the time we have left." She held out her arms. "Hug?"

Valkyrie stayed where she was, and eventually Tanith dropped her arms.

"You really need to lighten up, you know that? I've lightened up completely, now that I'm sharing this mind. Now all I want to do is have fun."

"Tanith," Valkyrie said, "please. We're your friends. *I'm* your friend. I love you like a sister."

"And I love you, Val. I really and honestly do. Back when I was me, alone in here, without the Remnant, you were my favourite person in the whole world. I would have died for you. And now that the Remnant's here with me, I love you even more. Now I'd kill for you."

Valkyrie couldn't help it. Tears came. "I know you don't want to hurt anyone."

"No," Tanith smiled gently, "I really, really do."

"I want my friend back. I want my sister back. I don't want you to be the enemy."

"Oh, Val, in a few weeks, you're probably going to have a *proper* sister, a *real* sister. Then you won't need me any more. And I'll be OK. I'm good at making friends. Speaking of which, would you like to meet my new boyfriend?"

The wall beside her cracked and crumbled, and Billy-Ray Sanguine stepped through. Valkyrie moved back instinctively, but he barely paid her any attention. Tanith turned to him and they kissed, and Valkyrie's insides went cold. That act, the simple act of a kiss, was more powerful than any violent demonstration. Tanith was gone now. She was lost.

"Don't look so upset," Sanguine said, and Valkyrie realised he was grinning at her. "I'll look after her."

"Thanks, sweetie," Tanith said, resting her head on his shoulder. "Will you be all right to get us out of here?"

"So long as you have some more of that painkiller, honey bunny."

Tanith dipped into her pocket, came out with a leaf that Sanguine put into his mouth and chewed. "OK," he said. "I'm ready."

Valkyrie watched them step back against the wall. Thousands of tiny fractures spread outwards behind them. Sanguine went first, the wall sucking him in.

"We'll come after you," she said.

"I know you will," said Tanith. "What are friends for? Oh, and Val? Happy New Year."

The wall swallowed her, too, and Valkyrie was alone.

55

THE RETURN

esseract couldn't understand what all the fuss was about – it really wasn't that cold. Russia was cold. Parts of Siberia were especially cold. Ireland, during the winter, was practically tropical.

He was looking forward to going home. He'd spent far too long here, had been delayed time and time again. But now his return journey was close. All he needed to do was take care of one last piece of business, and then he could put Ireland behind him.

He had been watching the Torment for days, but the old man

never allowed himself to be caught outside alone. Syc and Portia were always with him, and occasionally Madame Mist joined them for a stroll through the streets of Roarhaven. Tesseract wasn't keen to take them all on again, so he watched and waited.

He knew there was an underground tunnel leading from somewhere in the town to the Sanctuary. Twice now the Torment had exited the Sanctuary without re-entering. Tesseract returned to his trailer, where he examined plans of the town and read back over its history. An underground tunnel was not mentioned in any of his research.

He took a different approach, focusing instead on the Torment's known associates. Like many of Roarhaven's citizens, the Torment hadn't been born in the town. He had retreated there, no longer prepared to tolerate the mortal civilisation that showed no sign of stopping its global spread. Roarhaven was a town of prejudice and bigotry, of bitter sorcerers and magical malcontents. The Torment, and later on the other Children of the Spider, found a home there that welcomed them and their views.

Beneath his mask, Tesseract smiled. He found a mention of Vaurien Scapegrace in a story from the Torment's past. Scapegrace had once been a citizen here, before he'd been kicked out. He'd even owned a tavern for a few years.

Tesseract put the files away, and chose a new mask from the wall. This one had rivets over the brow and a long slit at the mouth. The needles sank into the puckered wounds around his face as he left his trailer. He walked for fifteen minutes before he reached the edge of the town.

Using the night as cover, he stole through the streets, moving so silently even those he crept behind didn't hear him. The tavern was dark, the door locked. He forced a window at the back and climbed through. He found a trapdoor behind one of the bars, and followed the steps down into living quarters. The lamps were on, but no one was there. Tesseract waited.

A little under three hours later, he heard a low rumble coming from the bedroom, the sound of a wall sliding apart. He didn't move. The wall slid shut again, and now he could hear shuffling footsteps moving into the small living room. Music began to play. He knew the group, it was The Carpenters, but he wasn't sure of the name of the song. 'There's a Kind of Hush' perhaps. The last song the Torment would ever hear. Tesseract hoped he liked it.

He moved silently to the living room, but when he stepped in, it was empty.

"I don't wish to alarm you," Skulduggery said from behind him, "but I have a gun pointed at your head."

Tesseract spun, flailing one arm, and managed to knock Skulduggery's hand to one side just as he fired. He batted at the gun-hand again, sent the revolver flying, and Skulduggery caught him with a right hook that almost sent him to the carpet.

"If you would just give yourself up," Skulduggery said as he kicked him, "you'd make this a lot easier on me."

Tesseract caught the second kick in the crook of his arm, and immediately Skulduggery sprang into the air, twisting from Tesseract's grip. He tried to push at the air, but Tesseract lunged, barrelling into him, forcing him back. Tesseract got an elbow in his ear for his trouble, and he fought a wave of dizziness that threatened to topple him. The skeleton snapped out two punches to the head, then sent a sneaky one to the ribs. Tesseract felt something pop, and he growled.

Skulduggery swayed away from one punch and blocked the next, but couldn't stop the third. Tesseract grabbed him and pulled his head down to meet his knee, then hooked two fingers into his left eye socket and stepped back, swinging him around the room. Skulduggery hit the couch and went over. Tesseract picked him up and slammed him head first into the wall. He did it twice more, until he was sure the detective was dazed, and then he dropped him.

He heard the rumble of the parting wall, and left the living room. The Torment emerged from the bedroom, looked up and his old eyes widened for a moment.

"I see," he said. "There's no point in arguing with you, is there?"

"None," Tesseract admitted. "You tried to kill me, and you didn't pay me. I can't have that."

"I should have cut your throat."

"You should have."

Tesseract pressed his hand against the Torment's forehead and splintered his skull. The old man's body dropped, and Tesseract stepped over it. He could hear Skulduggery, on his feet again, no doubt with his gun back in his hand. Tesseract hurried into the bedroom and ran through the gap in the wall, into the tunnel beyond. A few moments later, he heard Skulduggery sprinting after him.

The tunnel was long and dark. It began to incline, the darkness giving way to an indistinct grey that became a door. Tesseract ran through into one of the Sanctuary's broad corridors. His natural inclination was to stick to the shadows, but the corridors ahead were brighter, and that meant they led to the exit. He ran on.

A bullet tugged at his coat at the same time as he heard the shot, and he dodged right, bursting into a room. He ignored the sorcerer inside and went straight for the opposite door.

He found himself in another room, filled with boxes and unopened crates. He grabbed a crowbar and stepped to one side. Skulduggery ran in and Tesseract swung for his legs. Skulduggery did a flip and crashed down. The crowbar hit him again and he grunted, and Tesseract helped him to his feet with a kick to the ribs. The crowbar cracked against Skulduggery's cheek, making him reel back.

"I haven't been paid to kill you," Tesseract said. "Lie down and don't get up. You don't have to die tonight."

Skulduggery clicked his fingers and a fireball sparked off in his hand. Tesseract hurled the crowbar. It struck the skeleton between the eye sockets and he went down.

The light in the room flickered, and Tesseract frowned. Shadows moved along the walls, in the corners, across the floor. He looked around, looked for whoever was doing this. The shadows whipped at him like a giant claw, its talons ripping deep into his back. Tesseract spun in almost a full circle, and for a moment he thought he might stay on his feet. But no, his legs collapsed from under him and he fell.

He'd once known a man who said that life hinged on the moment, that everything changed in the blink of an eye.

Tesseract knew the truth of that as well as anybody. It was in those moments that he struck, after all, snatching people's lives away. He'd always known that it was only a matter of time before one of those moments worked against him. The shadows had torn right through his body. He fancied he could feel his organs shutting down, one by one.

The room was quiet. The sorcerer in the other room, the one he'd passed, had obviously fled. Tesseract doubted there were any others working through the night. This Sanctuary wasn't fully active, after all. It would take a few weeks for that.

He watched Skulduggery pick up his gun, and stand. It took him a moment to see Tesseract, lying there in a pool of his own blood. The detective's head tilted. He was puzzled. Then he looked up, at something behind Tesseract.

Tesseract heard footsteps, but couldn't move his head. All he could do was watch Skulduggery as he backed away.

"No," Skulduggery said.

Skulduggery fired three times. The footsteps didn't even slow down.

Now Tesseract could see someone stepping into the edge of his vision. A shadow flicked the gun from Skulduggery's hand. The detective went to push at the air, but another shadow batted his arm down. Skulduggery charged, and the figure in black watched him come, and then the shadows swooped in.

They slid beneath Skulduggery's clothes – Tesseract could see them curl and writhe within him. They were in his very skeleton, wrapping around his bones, and Skulduggery screamed in agony as he was lifted off his feet. Darkness slipped from his open jaws to his eye sockets, leaked from his sleeves to between the buttons of his shirt. His body was rigid while the darkness investigated every part of him, and still he screamed.

The figure observed him without moving, letting the shadows do all the work. And then it was over. Skulduggery fell to the ground as the shadows retracted, melting back into the black armour their master wore.

"You can't be here," Skulduggery said. "You died. You're dead."

The figure must have said something in response, but Tesseract didn't hear.

"This is insane," Skulduggery said. He put all his strength into getting to his hands and knees. "You can't be here. This is... You can't be here."

The man in the black armour walked slowly around the detective, who was shaking his head, like he was willing this not to be true. "You're dead. You're not real. You're dead."

The figure stopped walking, and Skulduggery looked up at him, like he was listening. Tesseract thought he could hear the faintest of whispers, and then Skulduggery roared in anger, and leaped up. His fist struck the figure and there was an explosion of darkness, a wave of shadows that filled the room, and then it was gone.

Tesseract blinked, his vision returning. Skulduggery was on the floor, on his knees with his head down. The figure in black was gone.

Tesseract grimaced as he rolled on to his side. Moving slowly, he got to his feet. He could no longer feel the pain in his back. His legs were going numb. He was aware of all the blood he was losing, but he didn't dwell on any of it. Instead, he pointed himself at the door, and walked. Each step was a battle.

"Stop," said Skulduggery, from behind him.

Tesseract stopped. He didn't turn. He didn't have to. From the angle of the voice, he knew that Skulduggery was standing, and most likely the gun was back in his hand.

"Who was that?" Tesseract asked.

"No one."

"The gaping wound in my back tells a different story. I recognised the armour. It's the same armour Baron Vengeous wore three years ago, isn't it? But that wasn't Baron Vengeous."

"You're under arrest."

Beneath his mask, Tesseract smiled. "I'm dead, Detective. I have a few minutes left, if I'm lucky. He killed me most effectively, did he not? I would at least like to know his name. Did he give it?"

"He did."

"And what name did he give?"

For a moment, Skulduggery didn't answer. Then, "He said he was Lord Vile."

Tesseract gritted his teeth, and turned halfway, so he could see the Skeleton Detective. Skulduggery stood with his gun held down by his side. "And where is he now? Did you strike him down with one mighty blow?"

"He's gone. I don't know where he is. I hit him and he... vanished."

"What did he say to you?"

"What does it matter?"

"I'd really like to know."

Skulduggery shook his head. Tesseract waited, feeling those precious seconds slip by him so, so slowly. When Skulduggery spoke again, his voice was surprisingly empty.

"He said he came back for her."

"For Valkyrie?"

"He's building his strength. When he's strong enough, he'll kill her. He said he'll kill the Death Bringer, then all the Necromancers."

"And why did he choose to tell *you*? What connection do you have to him?"

Skulduggery didn't answer. He emptied his gun of spent shells.

"I know about you," Tesseract continued. "I make a file on everyone I am likely to go up against. I know about you, and I know there is no recorded instance of you and Lord Vile ever meeting."

"That's right," Skulduggery said. He slipped a fresh bullet into a chamber.

"You never fought him. Never faced him. When he arrived, you were gone. Why did you choose *then* to leave, I wonder? Did you know what was coming?"

"You think you know about me," Skulduggery said. "But you don't." Another bullet into the chamber.

"You're scared of him, aren't you, Detective? I know fear. I've felt it often enough, and I've inflicted it. You're terrified of him, so much so that you ran when you realised he was coming. Are you going to run this time, I wonder?"

Skulduggery clicked the chamber back into place. "No running. Not any more. I'm going to stand and fight."

"So what is your connection? Why do you fear him? What power does he have over you?"

Skulduggery raised the gun and thumbed back the hammer.

Slowly, Tesseract brought his hands up to the straps around his head, his numb fingers clumsily unbuckling the mask. Finally, it came free, and he let if fall, felt the air on his ravaged face. It felt so good. He felt like laughing.

"A dying man's last request," he said. "Answer me this. You were killed, yet you came back. Do you know how it happened? Do you know who would be powerful enough to hold back death, *true* death? Was it Necromancy that brought you back, Skulduggery? Was it Lord Vile?"

Skulduggery's gloved finger tightened on the trigger, but before the gun fired Tesseract's legs gave way beneath him once again. He stumbled to the wall, hit it with his shoulder and slid down to the floor. There was no pain, which was nice, because he could feel the rot spreading over his head. When he looked up, Skulduggery was putting his gun away.

"Not going to kill me?" he asked.

"Waste of a bullet."

"I realise I have no right to ask this, but would you help me outside? It's almost dawn, and I would like to feel the sun on my face."

Skulduggery tilted his head slightly. Then he came forward, stooped to wrap Tesseract's left arm around his neck, and straightened up, lifting Tesseract out of a pool of his own blood.

"The problem with living so long," Tesseract said, as Skulduggery walked him to the door, "is that we get used to it. We watch the mortals age and wither and die around us, watch the world change and decay... but no matter the hardship or the pain or the sorrow we suffer, we choose to continue living. Out of sheer habit, I think."

"You're quite chatty now that I've got to know you," Skulduggery said.

"I have a cat, you know. Back home."

"I know. You had cat hair on your lapel the day you killed Davina Marr."

"You don't miss much, do you? She doesn't have a name. She is just Cat. She curls up on my chest whenever I sit down, and goes to sleep. I hope she doesn't miss me. I'm going to miss her."

They emerged into the cold air of the morning. Dawn had yet to break. Skulduggery found a bench and he let Tesseract sit, facing the stagnant lake, and beyond it, the horizon. Then he sat beside him.

"Is there anything you regret?" Skulduggery asked.

"I regret being mortally wounded just a few minutes ago."

"Understandable."

"Apart from that, no. I lived. I killed. My life is my own."

The rot was seeping through Tesseract's body. He turned his hand over, but it was probably a good thing he couldn't see much in this dim light. He felt the flesh bubble, like he was being boiled from the inside out. It was an effort to look up again.

"What about you?" he asked, his words not much more than a mumble. "Regrets?"

"Many," Skulduggery said.

Tesseract's breath rattled in his chest. "That's the good thing about living. You get to make up for past mistakes."

"Or make brand-new ones."

Tesseract tried to smile, but didn't have the strength for it. His head dipped, and Skulduggery reached out to steady him. The sun cracked the horizon, split it with light that spilled through the sky in streaks of orange and deep red.